HBJ ALGEBRA 1
REVISED EDITION

Arthur F. Coxford

Joseph N. Payne

Harcourt Brace Jovanovich, Publishers

Orlando   San Diego   Chicago   Dallas

ABOUT THE AUTHORS

ARTHUR F. COXFORD
Professor of Mathematics Education
University of Michigan
Ann Arbor, Michigan

JOSEPH N. PAYNE
Professor of Mathematics Education
University of Michigan
Ann Arbor, Michigan

EDITORIAL ADVISORS

Thomas Day
Mathematics Department Chairman
Farmington High School
Farmington, Connecticut

Mrs. Billy Dooley
Formerly Mathematics Teacher
Central High School
Columbia
Tennesssee

Mrs. Alice Mitchell
Mathematics Supervisor
Campbell Union High School District
San Jose, California

Donald Nutter
Chairperson, Department of Mathematics
Firestone High School
Akron, Ohio

Richard J. Wyllie
Chairperson, Department of Mathematics
Community High School District 99
South High School
Downers Grove, Illinois

August J. Zarcone
Mathematics Instructor
College of DuPage
Glen Ellyn, Illinois

The contributions of **Brother Neal Golden, S.C.,** who wrote the
Computer Applications, are gratefully acknowledged.

ISBN 0–15–353800–7

Printed in the United States of America

Contents

UNIT II   GRAPHING AND APPLICATIONS

UNIT IV   QUADRATIC EQUATIONS AND APPLICATIONS

PHOTO CREDITS

KEY: *t* top; *c* center; *b* bottom

pages 13, Monkmeyer; 25, National Park Service; 34, News Bureau, University of Pennsylvania; 35 *(t)*, HBJ Photo; *(c)*, HBJ Photo; *(b)*, American Telephone and Telegraph; 92 *(t)*, AGA Corporation; *(b)*, AGA Corporation; 93; Joe Barnell, Shostal; 138, HBJ Photo; 168 *(t)*, Schwinn; *(b)*, L. Druskis, Taurus; 201, L.L.T. Rhodes, Taurus; 202, Tom McHugh, Photo Researchers; 216, The Regina Company; 231, Freda Leinwand, Monkmeyer; 262, Clifford Hausner, Leo deWys; 263, David Forbert, Shostal; 294, NASA; 295, Chester Higgins, Jr., Photo Researchers; 325, HBJ Photo; 360, Ray Ellis, Photo Researchers; 361, Michal Heron, Monkmeyer; 399, H. Armstrong Roberts; 406, Focus on Sports; 446, NASA; 447, Randa Bishop, Contact; 459, John Colwell, Grant Heilman; 478, H. Armstrong Roberts; 482, Mimi Forsyth, Monkmeyer; 483, L.L.T Rhodes, Taurus; 508, H. Armstrong Roberts; 510 *(t)*, Stockphotos; *(b)* Tom Tracy; 521, Culver Pictures; 529, Focus on Sports.

CHAPTER **1** **Uses of Algebra**

1-1 Algebraic Expressions

The table below shows you how to find a person's distance in kilometers from the center of a storm by counting the number of seconds between a flash of lightning and the sound of thunder.

Number of Seconds	Distance in Kilometers from the Storm's Center
1	0.33 × 1, or 0.33
2	0.33 × 2, or 0.66
3	0.33 × 3, or 0.99
4	0.33 × 4, or 1.32
t	**0.33 × t**

The expression,

$$0.33 \times t$$

is an *algebraic expression.* In the expression, the letter, t, is a **variable.** It represents the time in seconds. An **algebraic expression** contains at least one variable.

An expression such as $0.33 \times t$ can also be written as

$$\textbf{0.33} \cdot \textbf{\textit{t}} \quad \text{or} \quad \textbf{0.33(\textit{t})} \quad \text{or} \quad \textbf{0.33\textit{t}.}$$

Each expression means "0.33 times the value of t."

EXAMPLE 1 Give the meaning of each expression.

    a. $10m$ **b.** $\dfrac{4}{x}$ **c.** $a + b$ **d.** $r - 18$

Solutions: **a.** $10m$ means **10 times** m, or the **product of 10 and** m, or **10 multiplied by** m.

    b. $\dfrac{4}{x}$ means **4 divided by** x or the **quotient of 4 and** x.

    c. $a + b$ means the **sum of** a **and** b, or b **added to** a.

    d. $r - 18$ means the **difference of** r **and 18**, or **18 subtracted from** r.

You can write an algebraic expression for a word description.

EXAMPLE 2 Write an algebraic expression for each word description.

    a. The sum of the principal, p, and the interest, i

    b. The cost of r stamps at 20¢ each

    c. The cost per liter if p liters of gasoline cost $2.05

Solutions: **a.** $p + i$ **b.** **20 · r**, or **20r** cents   **c.** **2.05 ÷ p**, or $\dfrac{2.05}{p}$ dollars

Expressions such as

$$18\tfrac{1}{2} + 16\tfrac{3}{4} \qquad 210 - 47 \qquad 18.6 \times 9.05 \qquad 21 \div \tfrac{1}{3}$$

are *numerical expressions*. They do not contain a variable. A **numerical expression** contains at least one of the operations of addition, subtraction, multiplication, and division. To find the value of a numerical expression when it contains parentheses, **do the work inside parentheses first.**

EXAMPLE 3 Find the value of each of the following.

 a. $(2 \cdot 5) + 6$

 b. $18 - (12 \div 2)$

Solutions: **a.** $(2 \cdot 5) + 6 = 10 + 6$

 $= 16$

 b. $18 - (12 \div 2) = 18 - 6$

 $= 12$

CLASSROOM EXERCISES

With each algebraic expression in Exercises 1–6, match the letter of the corresponding phrase in a–f that gives its meaning.

1. $4n$

2. $\dfrac{n}{4}$

3. $n - 4$

4. $n + 4$

5. $4 - n$

6. $\dfrac{4}{n}$

 a. n divided by 4

 b. 4 subtracted from n

 c. n subtracted from 4

 d. n multiplied by 4

 e. 4 divided by n

 f. 4 added to n

Find the value of each of the following.

7. $(8 \cdot 2) + 18$

8. $16 - (25 \div 5)$

9. $(5 \div 5) + 6$

10. $5 \cdot (10 - 6)$

WRITTEN EXERCISES

A Give the meaning of each of the following.

1. $q - 5$

2. $5 + q$

3. $5 - q$

4. $q + 5$

5. $5q$

6. $5 \div q$

7. $q \div 5$

8. $\dfrac{q}{5}$

9. rs

10. $\dfrac{r}{s}$

11. $s - 4$

12. $b - a$

13. $16s$

14. $t + n$

15. $n \div t$

Write an algebraic expression for each word description.

16. The sum of the restaurant bill, b, and the tip, t

17. The sum of the down payment, d, and the mortgage loan, l

18. The amount borrowed, a, added to the finance charge, c

19. The net income, i, added to the total deductions, d

20. The amount of tax withheld, w, subtracted from the total tax owed, t

21. The total number of days absent, a, subtracted from 180

22. The number of hours of darkness, d, subtracted from 24

23. The amount spent, s, subtracted from $150

24. The cost of 2 tickets at d dollars per ticket

25. The cost of renting a boat for h hours at $4.50 per hour

26. The cost of g gallons of gasoline at $1.55 per gallon

27. The cost of 3 pounds of bananas at c cents per pound

28. The number of books you can buy for $25 if each book costs d dollars

29. The number of times at bat, t, divided by 24, the number of hits

30. The number of kilometers driven, k, divided by 80, the average speed in kilometers per hour

31. The total weekly earnings, s, divided by 40, the total number of hours worked per week

Find the value of each of the following.

32. $(12 - 8) + 3$
33. $15 + (18 - 7)$
34. $40 - (1 + 10)$
35. $(20 - 9) - 2$

36. $(16 + 23) \div 3$
37. $4 + (64 \div 4)$
38. $21 - (80 \div 16)$
39. $4 - (20 \div 5)$

40. $18 - (0 \cdot 150)$
41. $0 \cdot (360 \div 12)$
42. $(7 \cdot 15) + (3 \cdot 15)$

43. $(18 \cdot 6) - (10 \cdot 6)$
44. $(41 + 9) \div (75 \div 15)$
45. $(80 \div 10) \div (21 - 13)$

B

46. $36 - (12 \cdot \frac{1}{3}) - 1$
47. $24 - (4 \div \frac{1}{2})$
48. $28 + (0 \div 4) - (10 \div 2)$

Give the meaning of each of the following.

49. $\dfrac{a + b}{5}$
50. $\dfrac{a - b}{5}$
51. $9(a - b)$
52. $9(b - a)$

_____ **REVIEW CAPSULE FOR SECTION 1–2** _____

Write in lowest terms.

1. $\dfrac{8}{12}$
2. $\dfrac{9}{36}$
3. $\dfrac{18}{54}$
4. $\dfrac{45}{60}$
5. $\dfrac{12}{18}$
6. $\dfrac{84}{96}$

Multiply. Write your answers in lowest terms.

7. $\dfrac{1}{2} \times \dfrac{1}{3}$
8. $\dfrac{1}{4} \times \dfrac{4}{5}$
9. $\dfrac{2}{3} \times \dfrac{2}{5}$
10. $\dfrac{3}{8} \times 7$
11. $\dfrac{5}{6} \times 3\dfrac{1}{5}$

Perform the indicated operations.

12. $8.35 + 0.62$
13. $23.92 + 0.8 + 0.45$
14. $9.6 + 12.07 + 15 + 23.967$

15. 6×0.9
16. 0.8×6.7
17. 0.072×42.6
18. 10×19.06

19. 29×2.9
20. 1.6×0.04
21. 82.7×0.79
22. 18.8×100

23. $0.966 \div 7$
24. $4.34 \div 0.7$
25. $25.9 \div 0.74$
26. $144 \div 3.2$

1-2 Evaluating Expressions

In Section 1-1, parentheses were used to help you in **evaluating** (finding the value of) an expression.

Two students evaluated this expression which has no parentheses.

$$2 \cdot 6 + 4 \cdot 5$$

First Student

$2 \cdot 6 = 12$

$12 + 4 = 16$

$16 \cdot 5 = 80$ ⟵ **The answer is incorrect.**

Second Student

$2 \cdot 6 = 12$

$4 \cdot 5 = 20$

$12 + 20 = 32$ ⟵ **Correct answer**

Only one answer can be correct. The first student did not apply the rules for order of operations. Mathematicians agreed to follow these rules so that expressions such as $2 \cdot 6 + 4 \cdot 5$ will have *exactly one value.*

Rules

Order of Operations
1 Do all multiplications and divisions in order from left to right.
2 Do all additions and subtractions in order from left to right.

Problem	Procedure	Computation
$4 \cdot 7 + 9$	Multiply 4 and 7. Then add 9.	$4 \cdot 7 + 9 = 28 + 9$ $= 37$
$2 + 5 \cdot 6$	Multiply 5 and 6. Then add 2.	$2 + 5 \cdot 6 = 2 + 30$ $= 32$
$18 - 2 \cdot 5$	Multiply 2 and 5. Then subtract this from 18.	$18 - 2 \cdot 5 = 18 - 10$ $= 8$
$16 + 10 \div 2$	Divide 10 by 2. Then add 16.	$16 + 10 \div 2 = 16 + 5$ $= 21$

Parentheses, ( ), and brackets, [ ], are called **grouping symbols.** A fraction bar is also a grouping symbol.

Rules

Rules for Grouping Symbols
1 Perform the operations within parentheses, or in the numerators or denominators.
2 When parentheses have been removed, or where there are no parentheses, follow the rules for order of operations.

Problem	Procedure	Computation
$3(5+6)$	Add 5 and 6. Then multiply by 3.	$3(5+6) = 3 \cdot 11$ $= 33$
$(2 \cdot 4) - 7$	Multiply 2 and 4. Then subtract 7.	$(2 \cdot 4) - 7 = 8 - 7$ $= 1$
$3 \cdot \dfrac{7-5}{6 \div 2}$	Subtract 5 from 7. Divide 6 by 2. Multiply by 3.	$3 \cdot \dfrac{7-5}{6 \div 2} = 3 \cdot \dfrac{2}{3}$ $= 2$

REMEMBER: $3(5+6)$ means $3 \cdot (5+6)$.

When an expression contains more than one grouping symbol, perform the operations within the innermost grouping symbols first. Then work towards the outermost grouping symbols.

EXAMPLE 1 Evaluate: $3 + [5 + 2(8 \div 4)]$

Solution: $3 + [5 + 2(8 \div 4)] = 3 + [5 + 2(2)]$ ⟵ **Next, evaluate 2(2).**
$$= 3 + [5 + 4]$$
$$= 3 + 9 = 12$$

You follow the same rules when evaluating algebraic expressions.

EXAMPLE 2 Evaluate $\dfrac{x-y}{4}$ for $x = 19$ and $y = 10$.

Solution: Replace x with 19 and y with 10.
$$\frac{x-y}{4} = \frac{19-10}{4}$$
$$= \frac{9}{4}, \text{ or } 2\frac{1}{4}$$

CLASSROOM EXERCISES

Evaluate.

1. $2 \cdot 3 + 4$ **2.** $4 + 2 \cdot 5$ **3.** $2 \cdot 7 + 2 \cdot 8$ **4.** $2(5+1)$

5. $2 \cdot (5+6)$ **6.** $28 - 3 \cdot 7$ **7.** $15 - 2 \div 2$ **8.** $15 - (2 \div 2)$

9. $10[4 + (7-1)5]$ **10.** $75 - 6[6(8-6)]$ **11.** $36 - [1 + (4 \div 4)3]$

12. Evaluate $30 - 2w$ for $w = 10$.   **13.** Evaluate $\dfrac{2m-n}{5}$ for $m = 8$ and $n = 3$.

14. Evaluate $\dfrac{2(a-3)}{5}$ for $a = 21$.   **15.** Evaluate $\dfrac{4(1-y)}{3}$ for $y = \dfrac{1}{4}$.

WRITTEN EXERCISES

A   Evaluate. Follow the rules for order of operations and for the use of grouping symbols. Express answers in lowest terms.

1. $7 \cdot 9 + 6$
2. $8 + 3 \cdot 7$
3. $6 \cdot (3 + 11)$
4. $(6 + 3) \cdot 3$
5. $4 + (2 \cdot 7)$
6. $(4 + 2) \cdot 7$
7. $8 \cdot 7 + 9 \div 9$
8. $3 \cdot 7 + 4$
9. $5 \cdot 7 - 12$
10. $15 - 6 \div 2$
11. $18 - 1 \cdot 6$
12. $30 - 7 \cdot 0$
13. $0 + 7\frac{1}{2} \cdot 0$
14. $62 \cdot 4 - 3$
15. $6 + 89 \cdot 2$
16. $89 \cdot (2 + 6)$
17. $5(2 \cdot 10)$
18. $(5 \cdot 2) \cdot 10$
19. $6 \cdot (15 \cdot 4)$
20. $(6 \cdot 15) \cdot 4$
21. $7(1 + 8) \div 9$
22. $\dfrac{15 - 4}{3}$
23. $\dfrac{6}{12 - 5}$
24. $\dfrac{8 - 3}{5 - 2}$
25. $\dfrac{6 - 2 \cdot 1}{9}$
26. $\dfrac{4}{2 \cdot 7 + 5}$
27. $\dfrac{13 - 2 \cdot 6}{5 + 2 \cdot 3}$
28. $\dfrac{4(3 - 1)}{8}$
29. $\dfrac{6}{2(7 + 1)}$
30. $\dfrac{2(7 - 3)}{3(4 + 5)}$
31. $2[3 + 2 \times (10 - 3)]$
32. $3[15 - (5 + 3)]$
33. $8[29 - (14 - 5)]$
34. $4[24 \div (6 + 2)]$
35. $4[(24 \div 6) + 2]$
36. $2[(11 \cdot 8) \div 4]$
37. $2[11 \cdot (8 \div 4)]$
38. $8 \div [16 - 2(3 + 4)]$
39. $8 \div [(16 - 2)3 + 4]$

Evaluate for the given values of the variables.

40. $50 + 2w$, for $w = 20$
41. $100 + 3y$, for $y = 10$
42. $100 - 5q$, for $q = 8$
43. $2p + 2s$, for $p = 4$ and $s = 5$
44. $2(a + b)$, for $a = 4$ and $b = 5$
45. $2a + b$, for $a = 7$ and $b = 5$
46. $\dfrac{8}{x - y}$, for $x = 10$ and $y = 6$
47. $\dfrac{3r}{2s}$, for $r = 10$ and $s = 15$
48. $\frac{3}{4}c + \frac{5}{7}d$, for $c = 12$ and $d = 14$
49. $\frac{5}{6}m - \frac{2}{9}r$, for $m = 12$ and $r = 9$
50. $2.3g + 0.7f$, for $g = 4$ and $f = 8$
51. $3.7a - 2.1b$, for $a = 4.8$ and $b = 3.7$
52. $5r - 9.2s$, for $r = 2.8$ and $s = 0.6$
53. $8.5s - 0.6t$, for $s = 5$ and $t = 0.5$

B
54. $\dfrac{2(t - 1)}{t}$, for $t = 11$
55. $\dfrac{a + 2b}{5}$, for $a = 10$ and $b = 2$
56. $\dfrac{m + m + m}{3m}$, for $m = 0.1$
57. $\dfrac{m \cdot m \cdot m}{m}$, for $m = 1.5$
58. $\frac{3}{8}a + \frac{5}{6}b - \frac{3}{5}c$, for $a = \frac{1}{3}$, $b = \frac{8}{15}$, and $c = \frac{2}{3}$

Insert parentheses so that the result of the indicated operations will be the given answer.

59. $1 + 9 \cdot 2 + 7$ Answer: 90
60. $3 + 3 + 3 \cdot 3$ Answer: 21

Insert parentheses so that the result of the indicated operations will be the given answer.

61. $2 \cdot 5 + 7 + 9$ Answer: 42   **62.** $56 \div 6 - 2 \cdot 1$ Answer: 14

63. $2 \cdot 12 \div 2 + 6$ Answer: 3   **64.** $34 + 2 \div 2 + 10$ Answer: 3

APPLICATIONS: Using Algebraic Expressions

C   Write an algebraic expression to represent each word description.

65. The cost of a service call for a plumber who charges a base fee of $25 plus $11 per hour for t hours

66. The total cost of p pounds of potatoes at 69¢ per pound and r pounds of chicken at 89¢ per pound

67. The amount in a savings account if the balance in the account is $475 and $15 is withdrawn per week for w weeks

68. The amount in a checking account after x weeks if the present balance is $315 and $20 is added per week

---

Puzzle

Look for a pattern in a–d below.

a. $25 \times 25 = 625$ **b.** $75 \times 75 = 5625$ **c.** $45 \times 45 = 2025$ **d.** $95 \times 95 = 9025$

Without using paper and pencil, find the value of each expression.

1. 35×35 **2.** 55×55 **3.** 65×65 **4.** 85×85

REVIEW CAPSULE FOR SECTION 1–3

Write a decimal for each per cent.

1. 8%   **2.** 2%   **3.** 12%   **4.** 128%   **5.** $4\frac{1}{2}\%$ **6.** 0.5%

Place the decimal point in each product.

7. $0.23 \times 43.4 = 9982$ **8.** $0.74 \times 39.5 = 29230$ **9.** $0.56 \times 3.84 = 21504$

Multiply.

10. 0.1×0.1 **11.** 2.5×2.5 **12.** $\frac{1}{3} \times \frac{1}{3}$ **13.** $\frac{5}{8} \times \frac{5}{8} \times \frac{5}{8}$

Add or subtract as indicated. Write your answer in lowest terms

14. $\frac{5}{9} + \frac{3}{9}$ **15.** $\frac{5}{8} + \frac{7}{8}$ **16.** $\frac{7}{8} + \frac{3}{4}$ **17.** $\frac{3}{4} + \frac{5}{7}$

18. $6\frac{1}{3} + \frac{1}{6}$ **19.** $7\frac{3}{5} + 2\frac{7}{10}$ **20.** $4\frac{1}{2} + 8\frac{1}{4}$ **21.** $12\frac{2}{5} + 4\frac{1}{8}$

22. $\frac{5}{6} - \frac{3}{5}$ **23.** $\frac{3}{4} - \frac{1}{5}$ **24.** $\frac{5}{8} - \frac{1}{3}$ **25.** $\frac{8}{9} - \frac{3}{7}$

26. $12\frac{1}{6} - 7\frac{5}{12}$ **27.** $6\frac{5}{8} - 2\frac{1}{6}$ **28.** $5\frac{3}{16} - 2\frac{5}{6}$ **29.** $3\frac{1}{8} - 2\frac{7}{10}$

30. $5\frac{2}{3} - 1\frac{1}{4}$ **31.** $3\frac{7}{8} - 2\frac{2}{3}$ **32.** $14 - 9\frac{2}{3}$ **33.** $6 - 3\frac{1}{12}$

1–3 Formulas and Replacement Sets

You can use this **formula** to find the amount of tax, T, on a purchase of p dollars in a state that has a 4% sales tax.

$$T = 0.04p$$

To find T, you replace p in the formula with the amount of a purchase.

In the formula, the letter p is a **variable**. It represents any number from a given **set** or collection of numbers called the **replacement set**.

NOTE: Any letter may be used to represent a variable.

EXAMPLE 1 Use the formula $T = 0.04p$ to find T when the replacement set for p is {$15, $31.50, $42.75}.

Solutions:

Replace p with 15.	Replace p with 31.50.	Replace p with 42.75.
$T = 0.04p$	$T = 0.04p$	$T = 0.04p$
$T = 0.04(15)$	$T = 0.04(31.50)$	$T = 0.04(42.75)$
$T = 0.60$	$T = 1.26$	$T = 1.71$
Tax: **$0.60**	Tax: **$1.26**	Tax: **$1.71**

The formula for the area of the square at the right can be written in two ways. In the formula, the variable s represents the length of a side of the square.

$$A = s \cdot s \quad \text{or} \quad A = s^2$$

In $A = s^2$, the **exponent, 2**, shows that the **base, s**, is taken as a factor two times.

(Recall that since $35 = 7 \cdot 5$, 7 and 5 are *factors* of 35. Similarly, 35 and 1 are also *factors of 35* because $35 \cdot 1 = 35$.)

The following table illustrates the meaning of exponents.

Expression	Read	Exponent	Base	Meaning
3^2	3 squared	2	3	$3 \cdot 3$, or **9**
5^3	5 to the third power	3	5	$5 \cdot 5 \cdot 5$, or **125**
$\left(\dfrac{1}{6}\right)^4$	$\dfrac{1}{6}$ to the fourth power	4	$\dfrac{1}{6}$	$\dfrac{1}{6} \cdot \dfrac{1}{6} \cdot \dfrac{1}{6} \cdot \dfrac{1}{6}$, or $\dfrac{1}{1296}$
2^5	2 to the fifth power	5	2	$2 \cdot 2 \cdot 2 \cdot 2 \cdot 2$, or **32**
a^1	a to the first power	1	a	a
y^4	y to the fourth power	4	y	$y \cdot y \cdot y \cdot y$

EXAMPLE 2 Use the formula $A = s^2$ to find A when the replacement set for s is $\{10, 2\frac{1}{2}\}$.

Solutions: Replace s with 10.

$A = s^2$

$A = (10)^2$

$A = 10 \cdot 10$, or **100**

Replace s with $2\frac{1}{2}$.

$A = s^2$

$A = (2\frac{1}{2})^2$, or $\left(\dfrac{5}{2}\right)^2$

$A = \dfrac{5}{2} \cdot \dfrac{5}{2} = \dfrac{25}{4}$, or $6\frac{1}{4}$

NOTE: Area is measured in square units, such as square inches (in²), square feet (ft²), square centimeters (cm²), square meters (m²), and so on.

CLASSROOM EXERCISES

1. Use $T = 0.03p$ to find T when the replacement set for p is $\{\$18, \$24, \$40\}$.

Find each value.

2. 6^2 3. 4^3 4. 1^6 5. $(\frac{1}{5})^2$ 6. $(\frac{2}{3})^3$ 7. $(\frac{1}{2})^4$

8. The formula for the perimeter of a square is $P = 4s$. Find P when the replacement set for s is $\{\frac{1}{2}, 2, 9\}$.

Find R for each formula. The replacement set for t is $\{0, \frac{1}{4}, 3\}$.

9. $R = 2t$ 10. $R = t^2 + 1$ 11. $R = \dfrac{16t}{2}$ 12. $R = \dfrac{t+1}{3}$

WRITTEN EXERCISES

A   Find T for each formula below. The replacement set for p is $\{\$20, \$50, \$100\}$.

1. $T = 0.04p$ 2. $T = 0.03p$ 3. $T = 0.05p$ 4. $T = 0.075p$

Find B for each formula. The replacement set for t is $\{1, 2, 3\}$.

5. $B = 4t$ 6. $B = t^2$ 7. $B = t - 1$ 8. $B = 2t - 1$

9. $B = 5 + t^2$ 10. $B = t + 2$ 11. $B = \dfrac{t}{3}$ 12. $B = \dfrac{t+1}{3}$

Find Q for each formula. The replacement set for n is $\{8, 10, 12\}$.

13. $Q = 2n$ 14. $Q = 2n - 1$ 15. $Q = 2n + 2$ 16. $Q = 3n$

17. $Q = n + \frac{1}{2}$ 18. $Q = 2n - \frac{1}{2}$ 19. $Q = \frac{n}{2} + 7$ 20. $Q = 5(n - 3)$

21. $Q = \dfrac{3+n}{2}$ 22. $Q = 3n(5 + n)$ 23. $Q = n^3$ 24. $Q = \dfrac{n}{3} + \dfrac{2}{3}n$

Evaluate.

25. 2^5 26. $(\frac{5}{9})^2$ 27. $(0.1)^2$ 28. $(0.01)^2$ 29. $(1.2)^2$

30. $(1.5)^2$ 31. $(0.04)^2$ 32. $(\frac{3}{5})^3$ 33. $(0.04)^3$ 34. $(\frac{3}{4})^3$

35. $(\frac{2}{3})^4$ 36. $(1.1)^2$ 37. $(1.02)^2$ 38. 1^{25} 39. 10^5

In Exercises 40–43, use the formula $A = s^2$ to find A for each replacement set for s.

40. $\{10, 25, 50\}$ **41.** $\{\frac{1}{2}, \frac{1}{10}, \frac{3}{10}\}$ **42.** $\{1.2, 1.04, 0.05\}$ **43.** $\{0.15, 0.25, 1.43\}$

44. Find V in the formula $V = s^3$. The replacement set for s is $\{\frac{1}{3}, 0.5, 8\}$.

45. The formula $K = \dfrac{m}{1000}$ gives the number of kilometers in m meters. Find K if the replacement set for m is $\{\frac{1}{2}, 1, 100, 1000, 10{,}000\}$.

46. The formula $C = \frac{5}{9}(F - 32)$ relates the number of degrees on the Fahrenheit scale, F, to the corresponding number of degrees on the Celsius scale, C. Find C if the replacement set for F is $\{32, 68, 98.8, 212\}$.

47. The formula $S = 180(n - 2)$ gives the sum of the measures of the angles of a polygon of n sides. Find S when the replacement set for n is $\{3, 4, 5, 6\}$.

B   If the replacement set for n is $\{0, 1, 2, 3\}$, which expressions represent even numbers only?

48. $3n$ **49.** $2n$ **50.** $2n + 1$ **51.** $3n + 1$ **52.** n^2

If the replacement set for t is $\{\frac{1}{2}, 0.25, 1\}$, give the least number represented by each algebraic expression.

53. t **54.** $2(t + 3)$ **55.** $2 - t$ **56.** $t - t$ **57.** $t \div 4$

58. t^2 **59.** $t \cdot t \cdot t$ **60.** $\dfrac{t}{2}$ **61.** $\dfrac{1 - t}{4}$ **62.** $\dfrac{t^3}{8}$

Puzzle

Name all the whole numbers 1–12, using six 6's, operation symbols, and parentheses only.

The first one is done below.

$$(6 + 6 + 6) \div (6 + 6 + 6) = 1$$

REVIEW CAPSULE FOR SECTION 1-4

Round each decimal to the nearest tenth.

1. 0.93 **2.** 1.09 **3.** 37.45 **4.** 0.507 **5.** 100.98

Divide. Round your answer to the nearest thousandth.

6. $1.92 \div 280$ **7.** $4.59 \div 2.4$ **8.** $250 \div 0.75$ **9.** $1.09 \div 784$

Multiply. Express answers in lowest terms.

10. 3500×1.24 **11.** 6000×1.36 **12.** $72{,}000 \times 1.09$ **13.** $100{,}000 \times 1.84$

14. $\frac{5}{6} \times \frac{3}{5} \times \frac{10}{12}$ **15.** $1\frac{1}{2} \times 4\frac{3}{10} \times 8$ **16.** $6\frac{4}{5} \times 17\frac{1}{8} \times \frac{1}{2}$

1–4 Using Formulas

Formulas use variables to show how quantities are related. To use a formula, you replace the known variables with given values (replacement set) in order to find the unknown variable.

EXAMPLE 1 The amount of money (A) in Ellen's savings account is given by the formula

$$A = P(1 + 0.06t).$$

In the formula, P is the **principal** (amount deposited) and t is the time in years that the principal has been in the account. Find A when $P = \$3500$ and $t = 4$ years.

Solution: $A = P(1 + 0.06t)$ ←——— **Write the formula.**

$A = 3500(1 + 0.06 \cdot 4)$ ←——— **Replace P with 3500 and t with 4.**

$A = 3500(1 + 0.24)$

$A = 3500(1.24)$

$A = 4340$ The amount, A, in the account is **$4340**.

You can use a formula to find unit price. **Unit price** is the cost per gram, per ounce, and so on.

To find the unit price, U, of an item, divide the total price, P, by the number of units, n. That is,

$$U = P \div n \quad \text{or} \quad U = \frac{P}{n}.$$

EXAMPLE 2 A 305–gram can of soup costs 79¢. A 539–gram can of the same brand costs $1.09. Which is the better buy?

Solution: Find the unit price for each size. Round each unit price to the nearest tenth of a cent. Then compare the prices.

305-gram can: $U = \dfrac{P}{n}$ ←——— **P = 0.79** **n = 305**   539-gram can: $U = \dfrac{P}{n}$ ←——— **P = 1.09** **n = 539**

$U = \dfrac{0.79}{305}$ $U = \dfrac{1.09}{539}$

$U = 0.003$ ←——— **0.3¢ per gram** $U = 0.002$ ←——— **0.2¢ per gram**

Since the **539–gram can** costs less per gram, it is the better buy.

Formulas can also be used to find the perimeter, area, and volume of geometric figures.

EXAMPLE 3 The volume, V, of this refrigerator car can be found by using the formula $V = lwh$. Find V when $l = 60$ feet, $w = 10\frac{1}{2}$ feet and $h = 12$ feet.

Solution: $V = lwh$ ⟵ **Replace l with 60, w with $10\frac{1}{2}$, and h with 12.**

$V = 60 \cdot 10\frac{1}{2} \cdot 12$

$V = 60 \cdot \dfrac{21}{2} \cdot 12$

$V = 7560$

The volume is **7560 cubic feet.**

NOTE: Other cubic units of measure are cubic inches (in³), cubic yards (yd³), cubic centimeters (cm³), cubic meters (m³), and so on.

CLASSROOM EXERCISES

1. Use the formula $A = P(1 + 0.06t)$ to find A when $P = \$2500$ and $t = 2$ years.
2. Use the formula in Exercise 1 to find A when $P = \$8000$ and $t = 3\frac{1}{4}$ years.
3. Use the formula $U = P \div n$ to find U when $P = \$1.09$ and $n = 24$ ounces. Round your answer to the nearest tenth of a cent.
4. Use the formula $V = lwh$ to find V when $l = 10.5$ meters, $w = 4$ meters, and $h = 8.4$ meters.

WRITTEN EXERCISES

A   In Exercises 1–6, use the formula $A = P(1 + 0.06t)$ to find A.

1. $P = \$1500$; $t = 5$ years
2. $P = \$780$; $t = 3$ years
3. $P = \$1000$; $t = 1$ year
4. $P = \$1060$; $t = 1$ year
5. $P = \$1123.50$; $t = 1$ year
6. $P = \$1120$; $t = 1$ year

In Exercises 7–12, use the unit price formula, $U = P \div n$, to find U for each value of P and n. Round each answer to the nearest tenth of a cent.

	Product	Price (P)	Size (n)	Unit Price (U)
7.	Tuna	\$1.92	280 grams	?
8.	String beans	\$1.99	46 ounces	?
9.	Detergent	\$4.59	2.4 liters	?
10.	Paper towels	\$0.75	250 sheets	?
11.	Toothpaste	\$0.99	8 ounces	?
12.	Mayonnaise	\$1.09	784 grams	?

In Exercises 13–16, use the formula $U = P \div n$ to determine the better buy. In each expression, assume that the items compared are the same brand.

13. A 473–milliliter bottle of vinegar for 43¢ or a 946–milliliter bottle for 75¢

14. A 2–pound bag of flour for 61¢ or a 5–pound bag for $1.11

15. A 16–ounce container of cottage cheese for $0.96 or a 24–ounce container for $1.38

16. A 50–gram jar of mustard for $1.09 or a 110–gram jar for $2.09

In Exercises 17–24, use the formula $V = lwh$ to find V for each value of l, w, and h.

17. $l = 4$ in, $w = 2\frac{1}{2}$ in, $h = 6$ in

18. $l = 5\frac{1}{3}$ in, $w = 3\frac{1}{2}$ in, $h = 9$ in

19. $l = 18$ cm, $w = 5$ cm, $h = 24$ cm

20. $l = 9.1$ cm, $w = 6.5$ cm, $h = 8$ cm

21. $l = 5\frac{1}{3}$ ft, $w = 3\frac{1}{2}$ ft, $h = 27$ ft

22. $l = 8\frac{1}{2}$ yd, $w = 5$ yd, $h = 12\frac{1}{3}$ yd

23. $l = 1.5$ m, $w = 0.8$ m, $h = 3$ m

24. $l = 7.6$ cm, $w = 4.5$ cm, $h = 9$ cm

In Exercises 25–30, use the formula

$$A = \tfrac{1}{2}h(b + c)$$

to find the area of each trapezoid. Refer to the trapezoid at the right. (In a trapezoid, the bases are parallel.)

25. $h = 10$, $b = 15$, $c = 8$

26. $h = 2$, $b = 12$, $c = 5$

27. $h = 3$, $b = 4$, $c = 6$

28. $h = 5$, $b = 3$, $c = 2$

29. $h = 2$, $b = \frac{3}{4}$, $c = \frac{1}{4}$

30. $h = 4$, $b = \frac{1}{4}$, $c = \frac{1}{2}$

In Exercises 31–36, use the formula

$$p = 100\left(\frac{g - s}{g}\right)$$

to find the per cent of discount, p, on a purchase. In the formula, g represents the original price and s represents the sale price.

SALE!
10%–33⅓% OFF

31. Original price: $40; sale price: $36

32. Original price: $25; sale price: $20

33. Original price: $96; sale price: $64

34. Original price: $96; sale price: $72

35. Original price: $100; sale price: $70

36. Original price: $48.96; sale price: $42.84

B In Exercises 37–40, use the formula

$$A = P(1 + 0.075t)$$

to find A for each value of P and t. (HINT: Remember to express t in years.)

37. $P = \$3000$; $t = 6$ months

38. $P = \$6500$; $t = 4$ months

39. $P = \$10,000$; $t = 3$ years 9 months

40. $P = \$1000$; $t = 8$ months

The formula for the area of a circle with radius r is $A = \pi r^2$.

The formula for the circumference of a circle with radius r is $C = 2\pi r$.

Use these formulas in Exercises 41–44 to find the circumference and area of each circle with the given radius. Express your answers in terms of π.

$A = \pi r^2$
$C = 2\pi r$

Example: $r = 10$ **Answers:** $C = 20\pi$; $A = 100\pi$

41. $r = 20$ **42.** $r = 9$ **43.** $r = 40$ **44.** $r = 4.2$

In Exercises 45–48, find the circumference and area of each circle with the given radius. Use 3.14 as an approximation for π.

45. $r = 10$ **46.** $r = 50$ **47.** $r = 100$ **48.** $r = 5.6$

Complete the table. Then write the formula. Exercise 49 is begun for you.

49. Tickets to a baseball game cost $3 each.

a.

n: number of tickets	1	2	3	4	5
C: cost of n tickets	$3	$6	$9	?	?

b. **Cost $= 3 \cdot$ Number of Tickets, or $C =$? $\cdot n$.**

50. The amount of profit the Jones family can expect to make from selling their house is the difference between the amount offered for the house and $35,000, the amount they paid.

a.

a: amount offered	$60,000	$63,000	$65,000	$68,000
P: profit	$25,000	?	?	?

b. **Profit = Amount offered $-$ $35,000, or $P =$? $-$?**

51. To estimate the number of bricks needed for a wall, a bricklayer multiplies the area of the wall by 7.

a.

A: area in square feet	40	80	160	320
d: number of bricks	?	?	?	?

b. **Bricks needed $= 7 \cdot$ Area, or $d =$?**

52. The time in hours that it takes to travel d kilometers at an average rate of 86 kilometers per hour equals d divided by 86.

a.

d: distance in kilometers	774	1548	3096	6192
t: time in hours	?	?	?	?

b. **Time = Distance $\div$ 86, or ? $=$? $\div$?**

53. At the XYZ Tool Company, weekly earnings equal $340 plus $12.75 for each hour of overtime.

a.

h: hours of overtime	1	2	3	4	5
E: weekly earnings	?	?	?	?	?

b. Weekly earnings = __?__ + $12.75h, or E = __?__

C

54. The total cost of a purchase in a state that has a 5% sales tax is the cost of the purchase plus the tax.

a.

c: cost of purchase	$5	$10	$15	$20	$25
0.05c: tax	?	?	?	?	?
T: total cost	?	?	?	?	?

b. Total cost = __?__ + __?__, or T = __?__

55. When driving on dry pavement, a driver should stay 5.5 meters (one car length) distant from the car ahead for each 16 kilometers per hour of speed.

a.

r: rate in kilometers per hour	32	48	64	72	80
F: following distance	?	?	?	?	?

b. Following distance = __?__ $\cdot \left(\dfrac{\text{rate}}{16} \right)$, or F = __?__

REVIEW CAPSULE FOR SECTION 1–5

Evaluate each expression for the given value of the variable. *(Pages 5–8)*

1. $3(x + 4) - 2$ when $x = 2$ **2.** $14 - 2(y - 5)$ when $y = 7$

3. $4(k - 5) + 5$ when $k = 5$ **4.** $12 + 4(t + 1)$ when $t = 9$

5. $2r + (r - 7)$ when $r = 12.5$ **6.** $21t - 8$ when $t = 0.5$

In Exercises 7–11, find Q for each formula. The replacement set for n is $\{0, 2, 4, 6, 8\}$. *(Pages 9–11)*

7. $Q = 4n + 1$ **8.** $Q = 7n + 3$ **9.** $Q = 100n + 1$

10. $Q = \dfrac{4n + 6}{4n + 3}$ **11.** $Q = \dfrac{8n + 12}{2}$ **12.** $Q = \dfrac{2n + 1}{2n + 1}$

Consumer Applications
Yearly Driving Costs

Knowing the real cost for operating and maintaining a car may help the consumer save money and energy. To find the **yearly cost per mile**, use this formula.

$$\text{Cost per Mile} = \left(\begin{array}{c}\text{Total Fixed} \\ \text{Costs}\end{array} + \begin{array}{c}\text{Total Variable} \\ \text{Costs}\end{array} + \begin{array}{c}\text{Total Other} \\ \text{Costs}\end{array}\right) \div \begin{array}{c}\text{Total Miles} \\ \text{Driven}\end{array}$$

EXAMPLE Samantha drives her car 24,000 miles per year. She listed the costs for operating her car last year. Compute the cost per mile.

	YEARLY TOTALS	
FIXED COSTS		
1. Depreciation	$2100	
2. Insurance	$ 700	
3. License, registration, taxes	$ 250	
4. Finance charges	$ 875	
5. **TOTAL FIXED COSTS**	$3925	← Line 1 + Line 2 + Line 3 + Line 4
VARIABLE COSTS		
6. Gas and oil per mile	$0.08	
7. Number of miles driven	24,000	
8. Cost per year	$1920	← Line 6 × Line 7
9. Maintenance	$ 325	
10. Tires (average yearly cost)	$ 40	
11. **TOTAL VARIABLE COSTS**	$2285	← Line 8 + Line 9 + Line 10
12. **OTHER COSTS** (car wash, tolls, parking fees, etc.)	$ 240	
13. **TOTAL YEARLY DRIVING COSTS**	$6450	← Line 5 + Line 11 + Line 12
14. **COST PER MILE**	$0.26875	← Line 13 ÷ Line 7

Thus, the cost per mile is **26.9¢.** ← **Rounded to the nearest tenth of a cent.**

EXERCISES

In Exercises 1–4, find the cost per mile to the nearest tenth of a cent.

	Total Fixed Costs	Total Variable Costs	Other Costs	Total Mileage	Total Yearly Driving Costs	Cost Per Mile
1.	$3416	$1825	$450	20,000	?	?
2.	$4650	$1975	$320.50	18,000	?	?
3.	$3829	$2120.50	$218.75	21,000	?	?
4.	$3118	$1865.70	$455.60	24,000	?	?

1-5 Sentences and Solution Sets

This table shows four different *mathematical sentences*.

Sentence	Read
$5 + 2 = 7$	Five plus two **equals** 7.
$8 > 5$	Eight **is greater than** five.
$15 + 6 < 25$	Fifteen plus six **is less than** twenty-five.
$17 \neq 4$	Seventeen **is not equal to** 4.

A mathematical sentence that contains the symbol "$=$" is an **equation.**

A sentence which contains a variable such as $3t - 5 = 22$, or any formula is also an equation. Such an equation is neither true nor false until you choose numbers to replace the variables. Equations that contain variables are **open sentences.**

When you find all the values for the variables that make a sentence true, you have found the *solution set.*

For example, when $t = 9$, $3t - 5 = 22$ is a true sentence. Thus, the solution set is $\{9\}$.

Definition

> The **solution set** of an open sentence is the set of numbers that makes the sentence true.

EXAMPLE 1 Find the solution set of $40 = 2n + 10$. The replacement set is $\{5, 10, 15\}$.

Solutions:

Replace n with 5.	Replace n with 10.	Replace n with 15.
$40 = 2n + 10$	$40 = 2n + 10$	$40 = 2n + 10$
$40 = 2(5) + 10$	$40 = 2(10) + 10$	$40 = 2(15) + 10$
$40 = 10 + 10$	$40 = 20 + 10$	$40 = 30 + 10$
$40 = 20$ **False**	$40 = 30$ **False**	$40 = 40$ **True**

Since 15 makes $40 = 2n + 10$ true, the solution set is $\{\textbf{15}\}$.

A mathematical sentence that uses $>$, $<$, or $\neq$ is an *inequality.*

Symbol	Meaning	Symbol	Meaning
$>$	is greater than	$<$	is less than

Symbol	Meaning
$\neq$	is not equal to

An inequality that contains a variable is also an open sentence.

EXAMPLE 2 Find the solution set of $x + 2 > 4$ where the replacement set is $\{2, 4, 6\}$.

Solutions:
Replace x with 2.	Replace x with 4.	Replace x with 6.
$x + 2 > 4$	$x + 2 > 4$	$x + 2 > 4$
$2 + 2 > 4$	$4 + 2 > 4$	$6 + 2 > 4$
$4 > 4$ **False**	$6 > 4$ **True**	$8 > 4$ **True**

Since 4 and 6 make $x + 2 > 4$ true, the solution set is $\{4, 6\}$.

When no number in the replacement set makes an open sentence true, the solution set is the **empty set**, or the **null set**. The symbol for the empty set is ϕ.

CLASSROOM EXERCISES

Classify each sentence as true, *T,* or false, *F.* When a sentence is false, tell why it is false.

1. $5 \cdot \frac{3}{8} = \frac{8}{3} \cdot 5$
2. $812 + 91 = 91 + 812$
3. $0 \cdot 491 < 0 \cdot 512$
4. $597 - 0 = 597 + 0$
5. $(\frac{1}{5} + \frac{1}{3}) + \frac{5}{12} > \frac{1}{5} + (\frac{1}{3} + \frac{7}{12})$
6. $12\frac{1}{2} \cdot 1 = \frac{25}{2}$

Find the solution set of each sentence. The replacement set is $\{3, 5, 7, 9, 11\}$.

7. $x + 5 = 10$
8. $x + 5 > 10$
9. $x + 5 \neq 10$
10. $x + 2x = 3x$

WRITTEN EXERCISES

A Classify each sentence as true, *T,* or false, *F.* When a sentence is false, tell why it is false.

1. $3 + 4 = 4 + 3$
2. $4 \cdot 3 = 3 \cdot 4$
3. $3 + (3 + 10) = (3 + 5) + 10$
4. $(4 + \frac{1}{5}) + \frac{4}{5} > 4 + (\frac{1}{5} + \frac{4}{5})$
5. $(2 \cdot 3) \cdot 5 < 2 \cdot (3 \cdot 6)$
6. $18 + 96 = 95 + 18$
7. $632 + 49 = 49 + 632$
8. $0 \cdot 632 > 632$
9. $0 + 632 = 632$
10. $1 \cdot 3\frac{1}{2} = 3\frac{1}{2}$
11. $12 + 44 < 43 + 12$
12. $27 \cdot 9 > 9 \cdot 26$

Find the solution set for each sentence. The replacement set is $\{2, 4, 6, 8, 10\}$.

13. $x + 2 = 10$
14. $x + 2 < 10$
15. $x + 2 > 10$
16. $n \neq 3 + 5$
17. $a + 2 = 2 + a$
18. $3x > 15$
19. $w + w = 8$
20. $t = 8$
21. $x \neq 2 + x$
22. $w + 5 = 7$
23. $2x < 8$
24. $x < 2$

Find the solution set. The replacement set is {0, 1, 2, 3, 4, 5}.

25. $x + 3 < 15$ **26.** $x + 2 < 10$ **27.** $10 + x = 15$

28. $10 + x > 30$ **29.** $x + 3 = x + 4$ **30.** $x + 1 < 5$

31. $3x > 9$ **32.** $x + 5 \neq 6$ **33.** $25 < 2x + 3x$

Find the solution set. The replacement set is {0, 5, 10, 15, 20}.

34. $30 = 2l + 30$ **35.** $4l + 70 = 150$ **36.** $50 = 5w$

37. $6.2 + x > 9.8$ **38.** $2y - 10 < 15$ **39.** $2a - a \neq 5$

40. $2m \cdot m = 0$ **41.** $\dfrac{a^2}{5} = 45$ **42.** $\dfrac{1}{2}x = 40$

Find the solution set for each sentence. The replacement set is {1, 2, 3, 4, 5, 6}.

43. $\dfrac{x}{2} = 1$ **44.** $x^2 = 25$ **45.** $x = x^2$ **46.** $\dfrac{x}{10} < 1$

47. $x < 5 - 2$ **48.** $3x > \dfrac{x^2}{4}$ **49.** $x^2 > 10$ **50.** $\dfrac{6}{x} > 3$

C

In Exercises 51–61, the replacement set for x and y is the set of whole numbers. Tell whether each sentence is true, T, or false, F, for all whole numbers. If the sentence is false, give an example that shows it is false.

51. $x + y = y + x$ **52.** $(x + y) + x = x + (y + x)$

53. $x^2 > x + x$ **54.** $x^3 > x^2$ **55.** $1 \cdot x = x$ **56.** $0 + y = y$

57. $x + y$ names one and only one whole number.

58. xy names one and only one whole number.

59. There is a whole number a such that $xa = 0$.

60. There is a whole number a such that $x + a = x$.

61. There is a whole number a such that $xa = 1$.

62. Is Exercise 53 true or false when the replacement set for x is the set of fractions? Give a reason for your answer.

63. Is Exercise 54 true or false when the replacement set for x is the set of decimals? Give a reason for your answer.

——— **Review** ———

Write an algebraic expression for each word description. *(Section 1–1)*

1. The cost of 3 records at d dollars per record.

2. The number of miles, m, divided by 15, the number of gallons.

Evaluate. *(Section 1–2)*

3. $4 \cdot 5 + 2$ **4.** $15 - 1 \cdot 8$ **5.** $\dfrac{3(8 - 5)}{4(2 + 8)}$ **6.** $12 \div [24 - 3(1 + 6)]$

Evaluate for the given values of the variables. *(Section 1-2)*

7. $80 - 8m$, for $m = 10$ **8.** $(2a + b)$ for $a = 3$, $b = 5$

Find A for each formula. The replacement set for m is $\{\frac{1}{2}, 4, 6\}$. *(Section 1-3)*

9. $A = 8 \cdot m + 6$ **10.** $A = \dfrac{2m + 4}{2}$ **11.** $A = m^3$ **12.** $A = 12(m + 2)$

Use the formula $A = \frac{1}{2}h(b + c)$ to find A. *(Section 1-4)*

13. $h = 10$, $b = 12$, $c = 15$ **14.** $h = 0.6$, $b = 0.03$, $c = 0.11$ **15.** $h = \frac{2}{3}$, $b = \frac{1}{3}$, $c = \frac{2}{3}$

Find the solution set. The replacement set is $\{1, 2, 3, 4, 5\}$. *(Section 1-5)*

16. $x + 7 < 10$ **17.** $x - 3 \neq 1$ **18.** $\dfrac{x}{2} > 1$ **19.** $x^2 < 9$

CALCULATOR APPLICATIONS

Evaluating Expressions and Formulas

To evaluate expressions and formulas with a calculator, follow the rules for order of operations. It may be necessary to use the memory keys, $\boxed{\text{M+}}$ and $\boxed{\text{MR}}$.

EXAMPLE   **a.** Use $C = \frac{5}{9}(F - 32)$ to find C when $F = 104$.

           b. Evaluate: $9.35 - 4.062 \cdot 2.1 + 6.9$

SOLUTIONS

     a. First perform the operation in the parentheses.

     $1\ 0\ 4\ \boxed{-}\ 3\ 2\ \boxed{\times}\ 5\ \boxed{\div}\ 9\ \boxed{=}$ $\boxed{\qquad\qquad 40.}$

     b. Multiply first and store the product in the memory.

     $4\ .\ 0\ 6\ 2\ \boxed{\times}\ 2\ .\ 1\ \boxed{=}\ \boxed{\text{M+}}\ 9\ .\ 3\ 5\ \boxed{-}\ \boxed{\text{MR}}\ \boxed{+}\ 6\ .\ 9\ \boxed{=}$ $\boxed{\qquad 7.7198}$

EXERCISES

Use the formula $C = \frac{5}{9}(F - 32)$ to find C for each value of F.

1. $F = 68$ **2.** $F = 95$ **3.** $F = 212$ **4.** $F = 77$ **5.** $F = 98.6$ **6.** $F = 113$

Evaluate each expression.

7. $6.04 + 2.72 \cdot 0.953 - 1.24$ **8.** $17.257 - 8.044 - 2.3 \cdot 3.64$

9. $2.76 - 0.894 + 15.25 \div 1.90625$ **10.** $0.026 \div 0.25 + 170 \div 1.6$

———— REVIEW CAPSULE FOR SECTION 1-6 ————

Complete.

1. $\dfrac{1}{4} = \dfrac{?}{8}$ **2.** $\dfrac{5}{?} = \dfrac{10}{12}$ **3.** $\dfrac{3}{8} = \dfrac{?}{40}$ **4.** $\dfrac{1}{14} = \dfrac{5}{?}$

5. $3\dfrac{3}{4} = \dfrac{?}{4}$ **6.** $5\dfrac{3}{8} = \dfrac{?}{8}$ **7.** $8\dfrac{4}{9} = \dfrac{?}{9}$ **8.** $7\dfrac{5}{6} = \dfrac{?}{6}$

1-6 Rational Numbers

Some sets of numbers can be represented by listing their **elements** or **members**. The three dots mean that the numbers continue on indefinitely.

Counting or natural numbers: $N = \{1, 2, 3, 4, \cdots\}$

Whole numbers: $W = \{0, 1, 2, 3, \cdots\}$

The set of **integers** consists of the set of whole numbers and their **opposites**. The opposite of a positive integer is a **negative integer**. The opposite of a negative integer is a **positive integer**. For example, $^-2$ (read "negative 2") is the opposite of 2, and 3 is the opposite of $^-3$. The integer **0 is its own opposite**.

Integers: $I = \{\cdots\, ^-4, \, ^-3, \, ^-2, \, ^-1, \, 0, \, 1, \, 2, \, 3, \, 4, \cdots\}$

Since every number in the set of natural numbers is also a member of the set of integers, the set of natural numbers is a **subset** of the set of integers. The symbol $\subset$ means "is a subset of." Here are some subset relationships.

$$N \subset W \qquad W \subset I \qquad \{0\} \subset W \qquad \{^-6\} \subset I \qquad W \subset W$$

NOTE: **Every set is a subset of itself.**

Not all points on the number line represent integers. Numbers such as $^-1\frac{2}{3}$, $\frac{^-1}{3}$, $\frac{3}{2}$, $2\frac{5}{6}$, and so on, are **rational numbers**.

Definition

> A **rational number** is a number that can be expressed in the form $\frac{a}{b}$, where a is an integer and b is a natural number.

Examples of rational numbers are given in the table below. Note that there are many ways of writing the same rational number:

Rational Number	Expressed as $\frac{a}{b}$	Some Other Names
4	$\frac{4}{1}$	$\frac{8}{2}, \frac{16}{4}, \frac{100}{25}, \cdots$
0	$\frac{0}{1}$	$\frac{0}{2}, \frac{0}{3}, \frac{0}{500}, \cdots$
0.73	$\frac{73}{100}$	$\frac{365}{500}, \frac{1460}{2000}, \frac{2190}{3000}, \cdots$
$^-5\frac{3}{4}$	$\frac{^-23}{4}$	$\frac{^-46}{8}, \frac{^-69}{12}, ^-5\frac{6}{8}, \cdots$

> The **set of rational numbers,** _Q_, is made up of the positive rational numbers, the negative rational numbers, and zero.

Positive and negative rational numbers are used in various ways. One way is to show amounts above or below zero.

	Statement	Number
Temperature	32° above 0	32
	10° below 0	⁻10
Elevation	150 meters above sea level	150
	100 meters below sea level	⁻100

Positive and negative rational numbers can also be used to show both the amount and direction of change.

	Statement	Number
Football	Gain of 10 yards	10
	Loss of 3 yards	⁻3
Money	Deposit of $30.75	30.75
	Withdrawal of $25	⁻25

CLASSROOM EXERCISES

Use the words _natural number, whole number, integer,_ or _rational number_ to classify each number. More than one answer may be possible.

1. 0   **2.** ⁻5   **3.** $\frac{2}{5}$ **4.** $1\frac{1}{8}$ **5.** $\frac{-4}{5}$ **6.** ⁻1

Write each number in the form $\frac{a}{b}$.

7. 0   **8.** 1   **9.** $16\frac{2}{3}$ **10.** ⁻0.25   **11.** ⁻5.2   **12.** 15.9

WRITTEN EXERCISES

A Classify each sentence as true, _T,_ or false, _F._ When a sentence is false, tell why it is false.

1. $\frac{1}{3}$ is a natural number.   **2.** $\frac{-1}{3}$ is an integer.

3. $12\frac{5}{6}$ is a rational number.   **4.** 6.5 is a rational number.

5. The opposite of 5 is ⁻5.   **6.** Every counting number is an integer.

7. Every integer is a rational number.

8. There is at least one whole number that is not a natural number.

9. The number 0 is neither positive nor negative.

10. The set of whole numbers is made up of the set of positive integers and 0.

11. The set of rational numbers is made up of the negative integers, the positive integers, and zero.

12. The set of counting numbers is a subset of the rational numbers.

Write each rational number in the form $\frac{a}{b}$, where a is an integer and b is a natural number.

13. 0.4   14. 0.75   15. 0.37   16. 0.24   17. $^-6\frac{1}{3}$ 18. $8\frac{2}{5}$

19. $3\frac{3}{4}$ 20. $^-6\frac{8}{9}$ 21. 67.25   22. $^-0.01$ 23. 0   24. $^-100$

Represent each of the following by a positive or negative rational number.

25. A temperature 6° above zero

26. A temperature 3° below zero

27. An elevation of 462 meters below sea level

28. An elevation of 6070 meters above sea level

29. A deposit of $525 in a saving account

30. A deposit of $76.20 in a checking account

31. A withdrawal of $155 from a savings account

32. A loss of 7 yards on a football play

33. A gain of 12 yards on a football play

34. A velocity forward of 60 kilometers per hour

35. A velocity backward of 15 kilometers per hour

36. A stock loss of $\frac{1}{4}$ of a point   37. A jump upward of $4\frac{1}{2}$ feet

38. A stock gain of $3\frac{1}{8}$ points   39. A fall of 6 meters

40. A climb of 2000 feet   41. A descent of 1 kilometer

42. A drop in temperature of 2°   43. Growth of $2\frac{3}{4}$ inches

44. A weight gain of $2\frac{1}{2}$ pounds   45. A weight loss of 31 pounds

46. A paycheck deduction of $3.15   47. An income tax refund of $73.20

48. A team penalty of 15 yards   49. A debt of $250

50. A temperature rise of 5.7°   51. A fall in temperature of 3.5°

52. A profit of $750   53. A loss of $315

54. A salary increase of $2.50 per hour   55. A submarine dive of 500 feet

B   Classify each statement as true, T, or false, F. When a statement is false, tell why it is false.

56. N ⊂ W   57. I ⊂ W   58. N ⊂ I   59. W ⊂ N   60. N ⊂ N

61. Q ⊂ I   62. N ⊂ Q   63. Q ⊂ W   64. Q ⊂ Q   65. {0} ⊂ N

Divide. Carry the division to five decimal places.

1. $2 \div 3$ **2.** $3 \div 11$ **3.** $2 \div 9$ **4.** $7 \div 12$ **5.** $1 \div 6$

Complete. Write a decimal for each fraction or mixed number.

6. $\dfrac{3}{5} = \dfrac{?}{100} = 0.6$ **7.** $\dfrac{7}{10} = \dfrac{?}{100} = \underline{\ ?\ }$ **8.** $\dfrac{19}{20} = \dfrac{?}{100} = 0.95$

9. $\dfrac{23}{50} = \dfrac{46}{?} = \underline{\ ?\ }$ **10.** $\dfrac{18}{25} = \dfrac{72}{?} = \underline{\ ?\ }$ **11.** $\dfrac{21}{4} = \dfrac{?}{100} = \underline{\ ?\ }$

12. $7\dfrac{1}{2} = 7 + 0.5 = \underline{\ ?\ }$ **13.** $9\dfrac{3}{4} = 9 + \underline{\ ?\ } = 9.75$ **14.** $8\dfrac{1}{5} = 8 + \underline{\ ?\ } = \underline{\ ?\ }$

1-7   Real Numbers

Any rational number such as $\frac{1}{3}$ and $\frac{2}{11}$ can be represented by an infinite repeating decimal.

$$\frac{1}{3} = 0.333 \cdots = 0.\overline{3} \qquad\qquad \frac{2}{11} = 0.1818 \cdots = 0.\overline{18}$$

The bar indicates the digits that repeat.

Rational numbers such as 0.75 and 1.4 are **terminating decimals.** However, they can be written as infinite repeating decimals.

$$\frac{3}{4} = 0.75 = 0.75000 \cdots \qquad\qquad 1\frac{2}{5} = \frac{7}{5} = 1.4 = 1.4000 \cdots$$

Zero is the digit that repeats.

Irrational numbers can be represented by **infinite nonrepeating decimals.** This means that no matter how many digits are used in the decimal representation of an irrational number, the sequence of digits **never** repeats. Here are some examples of irrational numbers.

    $1.4142135 \cdots$ $2.2360679 \cdots$ $3.4641016 \cdots$ $3.14114111411114 \cdots$

Irrational numbers may be positive or negative. For example, $^{-}1.4142135 \cdots$ is a negative irrational number. The number $1.4142135 \cdots$ can be written another way. That is,

    $1.4142135 \cdots = \sqrt{2}$ ←——— **Read: "the square root of 2."**

Taking the square root of a number is the inverse of squaring. For example,

$$\sqrt{16} = 4 \qquad \text{because} \qquad 4^2 = 4 \cdot 4 = 16.$$
$$\sqrt{225} = 15 \qquad \text{because} \qquad 15^2 = 15 \cdot 15 = 225.$$

For an irrational number such as $\sqrt{2}$, there is no positive integer whose square is 2. That is, there is no positive integer n, such that $n \cdot n = 2$.

> For any positive integer n, $\sqrt{n}$ is either a positive integer (rational number) or an irrational number.

EXAMPLE 1 Tell whether n is rational or irrational. Give a reason for your answer.

	$\sqrt{n}$	Rational or Irrational	Reason
a.	$\sqrt{81}$	Rational	$\sqrt{81} = 9$ and 9 is a rational number.
b.	$\sqrt{13}$	Irrational	There is no positive integer n such that $n \cdot n = 13$.
c.	$\sqrt{7}$	Irrational	There is no positive integer n such that $n \cdot n = 7$.

Recall that any rational number can be represented in the form $\frac{a}{b}$, where a is an integer and b is a natural number. Irrational numbers *cannot* be represented in this way. Together, the set of rational numbers, Q, and the set of irrational numbers, Ir, form the set of real numbers.

> The set of rational numbers, Q, and the set of irrational numbers, Ir, make up the set of **real numbers, R.**

Every point on the number line can be associated with a real number.

A number associated with a point on the number line is called the **coordinate** of the point.

EXAMPLE 2 Name the coordinates of A, B, C, and D.

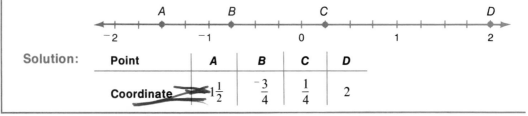

Solution:

Point	A	B	C	D
Coordinate	$-1\frac{1}{2}$	$-\frac{3}{4}$	$\frac{1}{4}$	2

Every real number can also be associated with a point on the number line.

You will learn a geometric method of locating an irrational number on the number line when you study the Pythagorean Theorem on page 439.

However, you can use the Table of Square Roots on page 541 to find approximate values for some irrational numbers.

EXAMPLE 3 Use the Table of Square Roots to find an approximate value for $\sqrt{10}$.

Solution: ① Find "10" in the No.–column.
② Look directly to the right under the Square Root–column.

Number	Square	Square Root
10	100	3.162

3.162

Thus, $\sqrt{10} \approx 3.162$ ⟵ $\approx$ **means "is approximately equal to."**

Rounded to the nearest tenth, $3.162 = 3.2$. Thus, on a number line, $\sqrt{10}$ is close to 3.2.

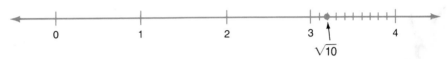

CLASSROOM EXERCISES

Identify each number as rational, Q, or irrational, Ir. Give a reason for each answer.

1. $\sqrt{5}$ **2.** $\sqrt{49}$ **3.** $\sqrt{21}$ **4.** $\sqrt{18}$ **5.** $\sqrt{144}$ **6.** $\sqrt{51}$

Name the sets to which each number belongs. More than one answer may be possible.

7. $\sqrt{1}$ **8.** $\sqrt{2}$ **9.** $0.\overline{3}$ **10.** $\sqrt{\dfrac{9}{16}}$ **11.** $^-1.5$ **12.** $\sqrt{5}$

Use the Table of Square Roots on page 541 to find an approximate value for each number.

13. $\sqrt{19}$ **14.** $\sqrt{97}$ **15.** $\sqrt{101}$ **16.** $\sqrt{63}$ **17.** $\sqrt{149}$ **18.** $\sqrt{135}$

WRITTEN EXERCISES

A Write a decimal for each fraction or mixed number. Use a bar to indicate the repeating, nonzero digits.

1. $\dfrac{2}{3}$ **2.** $\dfrac{5}{9}$ **3.** $\dfrac{16}{3}$ **4.** $2\dfrac{1}{2}$ **5.** $7\dfrac{3}{16}$ **6.** $\dfrac{8}{25}$

7. $1\dfrac{3}{8}$ **8.** $4\dfrac{1}{12}$ **9.** $\dfrac{3}{20}$ **10.** $\dfrac{^-6}{7}$ **11.** $\dfrac{^-3}{11}$ **12.** $\dfrac{5}{13}$

Identify each number as rational, Q, or irrational, Ir. Give a reason for each answer.

13. $\sqrt{7}$ **14.** $\sqrt{64}$ **15.** $\sqrt{11}$ **16.** $\sqrt{17}$ **17.** $\sqrt{625}$ **18.** $\sqrt{19}$

19. $\sqrt{83}$ **20.** $\sqrt{\dfrac{25}{9}}$ **21.** $\sqrt{\dfrac{36}{16}}$ **22.** $\sqrt{53}$ **23.** $\sqrt{100}$ **24.** $\sqrt{13}$

Copy this table. Then use a *check mark* (✔) to indicate the sets to which each number belongs. The first one is done for you.

		Integers	Rational Numbers	Irrational Numbers	Real Numbers
25.	-3.5		✔		✔
26.	$\frac{5}{6}$				
27.	$\sqrt{3}$				
28.	$0.\overline{524}$				
29.	$3.4641016\cdots$				
30.	$\frac{81}{3}$				
31.	$\sqrt{121}$				
32.	$1.\overline{26}$				
33.	$\frac{3}{5}$				
34.	$-2\frac{5}{6}$				

Give the coordinate of the point named by each letter.

35.

36.

37.

Use the Table of Square Roots on page 541 to find an approximate value for each number.

38. $\sqrt{39}$ **39.** $\sqrt{18}$ **40.** $\sqrt{136}$ **41.** $\sqrt{110}$ **42.** $\sqrt{55}$

43. $\sqrt{17}$ **44.** $\sqrt{40}$ **45.** $\sqrt{80}$ **46.** $\sqrt{139}$ **47.** $\sqrt{76}$

48. Use your answer to Exercise 39 to graph the approximate position of $\sqrt{18}$ on a number line.

49. Use your answer to Exercise 43 to graph the approximate position of $\sqrt{17}$ on a number line.

50. Use your answer to Exercise 44 to graph the approximate position of $\sqrt{40}$ on a number line.

51. Use your answer to Exercise 47 to graph the approximate position of $\sqrt{76}$ on a number line.

B Replace *n* with the smallest possible whole number to make a true statement.

52. $6 < \sqrt{39} < n$ **53.** $7 < \sqrt{63} < n$ **54.** $3 < \sqrt{12} < n$

55. $15 < \sqrt{229} < n$ **56.** $11 < \sqrt{140} < n$ **57.** $8 < \sqrt{76} < n$

Replace *x* with the largest possible number to make a true statement.

58. $x < \sqrt{223} < 15$ **59.** $x < \sqrt{442} < 22$ **60.** $x < \sqrt{189} < 14$

61. $x < \sqrt{627} < 26$ **62.** $x < \sqrt{171} < 14$ **63.** $x < \sqrt{1588} < 40$

The number π is an irrational number. It is the quotient of the circumference of a circle divided by the length of a diameter. To six decimal places,
$$\pi = 3.141592.$$

In Exercises 64–67, four approximations to π computed by ancient mathematicians are given. Divide to find the value of each approximation to six decimal places.

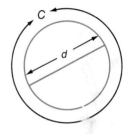

64. Archimedes (240 B.C.): $\pi = \frac{223}{71}$ **65.** Ptolemy (A.D. 150): $\pi = \frac{377}{120}$

66. Tsu Ch'ung–chik (A.D. 480): $\pi = \frac{355}{113}$ **67.** Bhāshara (A.D. 1150): $\pi = \frac{3927}{1250}$

68. Which of the approximations in Exercises 64–67 is closest to $\pi = 3.141592$?

Replace each __?__ with ⊂ or ⊄. (⊄ means "is not a subset of.")

69. I __?__ W **70.** Q __?__ R **71.** N __?__ Q **72.** R __?__ Q **73.** W __?__ N

74. I __?__ Q **75.** N __?__ W **76.** Q __?__ Ir **77.** I __?__ R **78.** Ir __?__ R

Choose from the box at the right the word or words that complete each statement. More than one answer may be possible.

| natural |
| whole |
| rational |
| irrational |
| real |

79. Every __?__ number is a real number.

80. Every rational number is a __?__ number.

81. Every irrational number is a __?__ number.

82. Every natural number is a __?__ number.

Puzzle

In Roman numerals, I stands for 1, and VII stands for 7. Therefore, $\frac{1}{7}$ can be written as $\frac{I}{VII}$ in Roman numerals.

Using straight lines for each digit, make $\frac{I}{VII}$ equal in value to 1 by changing the position of one line only.

1–8 Postulates For Real Numbers

The table illustrates four *postulates* that are true for all real numbers a and b. **Postulates** are statements that are accepted as true.

Name	In Symbols	Example
Commutative postulate for addition	$a + b = b + a$	$\frac{6}{7} + \frac{1}{2} = \frac{1}{2} + \frac{6}{7}$
Commutative postulate for multiplication	$a \cdot b = b \cdot a$	$\frac{6}{7} \cdot \frac{1}{2} = \frac{1}{2} \cdot \frac{6}{7}$
Identity postulate for addition	$a + 0 = 0 + a = a$	$3.5 + 0 = 0 + 3.5 = 3.5$
Identity postulate for multiplication	$a \cdot 1 = 1 \cdot a = a$	$1 \cdot \sqrt{2} = \sqrt{2} \cdot 1 = \sqrt{2}$

EXAMPLE 1 Use the postulates in the table to find a value of the variable that makes each equation true. Name the postulate that gives the reason for each answer.

a. $172 \cdot \frac{9}{7} = \frac{9}{7} \cdot x$ **b.** $15 + 0.3 = t + 15$ **c.** $\frac{3}{2} \cdot s = \frac{3}{2}$ **d.** $3 + z = 3$

Equation	Solution	Reason
a. $172 \cdot \frac{9}{7} = \frac{9}{7} \cdot x$	$x = 172$	Commutative postulate for multiplication
b. $15 + 0.3 = t + 15$	$t = 0.3$	Commutative postulate for addition
c. $\frac{3}{2} \cdot s = \frac{3}{2}$	$s = 1$	Identity postulate for multiplication
d. $3 + z = 3$	$z = 0$	Identity postulate for addition

The **Associative Postulates for addition and multiplication** allow you to regroup numbers. Remember that a, b, and c represent real numbers.

Name	In Symbols	Example
Associative postulate for addition	$a + (b + c) = (a + b) + c$	$7 + (5 + 8.1) = (7 + 5) + 8.1$
Associative postulate for multiplication	$a(bc) = (ab)c$	$7(5 \cdot 8.1) = (7 \cdot 5)8.1$

The **Distributive Postulate (multiplication over addition)** shows how to write a product as a sum.

Name	In Symbols	Example
Distributive postulate	$a(b + c) = ab + ac$	$9\left(3 + \frac{2}{3}\right) = 9 \cdot 3 + 9 \cdot \frac{2}{3}$

The postulates for real numbers can be used to evaluate expressions. Recall that to evaluate an expression means to find its value.

EXAMPLE 2   Evaluate: **a.** $10(45 \cdot 6)$ **b.** $5\left(2 + \frac{1}{5}\right)$

Solutions: **a.** Use the associative postulate.

$$10(45 \cdot 6) = (10 \cdot 45)6 \longleftarrow \textbf{By the associative postulate}$$
$$= 450 \cdot 6$$
$$= \textbf{2700}$$

b. Use the distributive postulate.

$$5\left(2 + \frac{1}{5}\right) = 5(2) + 5\left(\frac{1}{5}\right)$$
$$= 10 + 1$$
$$= \textbf{11}$$

The distributive postulate can also be expressed in this form.

$$(a + b)c = ac + bc$$

EXAMPLE 3   Use the distributive postulate to find $(45)8$.

Solution: First write 45 as $40 + 5$.

$$45(8) = (40 + 5)8$$
$$= 40 \cdot 8 + 5 \cdot 8 \longleftarrow \textbf{By the distributive postulate}$$
$$= 320 + 40$$
$$= \textbf{360}$$

You already know that the sum of two real numbers is a real number and that the product of two real numbers is a real number. The following two postulates state this. Recall that

the symbol $\in$ means "is an element of."

For example,

$\sqrt{5} \in$ R means that $\sqrt{5}$ is an element of the set of real numbers.

Name	In Symbols	Examples
Closure postulate for addition	$(a + b) \in$ **R**	$0.05 + 1.65 = 1.70$ $\frac{3}{5} + \frac{1}{10} = \frac{7}{10}$
Closure postulate for multiplication	$(a \cdot b) \in$ **R**	$0.05 \cdot 1.65 = 0.0825$ $\frac{3}{5} \cdot \frac{1}{10} = \frac{3}{50}$

CLASSROOM EXERCISES

Name the postulate illustrated by each sentence.

1. $5 \cdot (20 + 3) = (5 \cdot 20) + (5 \cdot 3)$

2. $17 + 3\frac{1}{2} = 3\frac{1}{2} + 17$

3. $5\frac{1}{2} \cdot 6\frac{1}{2} = 6\frac{1}{2} \cdot 5\frac{1}{2}$

4. $4 + (2 + \frac{1}{2}) = (4 + 2) + \frac{1}{2}$

5. $0 + 62.9 = 62.9$

6. $3 \cdot (2 \cdot \frac{1}{2}) = (3 \cdot 2) \cdot \frac{1}{2}$

7. $0.\overline{9} \cdot 1 = 0.\overline{9}$

8. $(98)12 = 90 \cdot 12 + 8 \cdot 12$

9. $x + \sqrt{5} = \sqrt{5} + x$

10. $r \cdot \frac{1}{5} \cdot s = \frac{1}{5}rs$

11. $(0.5)(290)$ is a real number.

12. $16.8 + 7.2$ is a real number.

WRITTEN EXERCISES

A   Name the postulate illustrated by each sentence.

1. $6 + 8 = 8 + 6$

2. $(10 \cdot 5) \cdot 4 = 10 \cdot (5 \cdot 4)$

3. $3(10) = (10)3$

4. $8(2 + \frac{1}{2}) = (8 \cdot 2) + (8 \cdot \frac{1}{2})$

5. $(6 \cdot 0)5 = 6(0 \cdot 5)$

6. $(1 + 3) + (6 \cdot 7) = (3 + 1) + (6 \cdot 7)$

7. $(6 \cdot 3) + (8 \cdot 2) = (8 \cdot 2) + (6 \cdot 3)$

8. $(6 + 0) + \frac{2}{3} = 6 + \frac{2}{3}$

9. $(6 + \frac{1}{3}) + (\frac{4}{3} \cdot 2) = (\frac{1}{3} + 6) + (\frac{4}{3} \cdot 2)$

10. $6 \cdot 1 = 6$

11. $8(\frac{1}{2} + 3) = (8 \cdot \frac{1}{2}) + (8 \cdot 3)$

12. $(3 \cdot 4) + (3 \cdot 5) = 3 \cdot (4 + 5)$

13. $\frac{2}{3} + \frac{1}{2}$ is a real number.

14. $7 \cdot \frac{1}{49}$ is a real number.

Use the postulates for real numbers to find a value of the variable that makes each equation true. Name the postulate that gives the reason for your choice.

15. $12 \cdot \frac{4}{5} = \frac{4}{5} \cdot n$

16. $6(2 + x) = (6 \cdot 2) + (6 \cdot 1)$

17. $5 + 10 = a + 5$

18. $\frac{1}{6} \cdot (\frac{1}{5} \cdot \frac{1}{4}) = (c \cdot \frac{1}{5}) \cdot \frac{1}{4}$

19. $\frac{2}{3} + a = \frac{2}{3}$

20. $9 + (3 + 1) = (b + 3) + 1$

Evaluate each expression.

21. $(2 + 29) + 1$

22. $(18 + 6) + 14$

23. $(5365 + 1150) + 1850$

24. $(879 + 13) + 21$

25. $0.3(8 \cdot 10)$

26. $\frac{1}{5}(3 \cdot 100)$

27. $2(5 \cdot 19)$

28. $25(4 \cdot 12)$

29. $250(4 \cdot 12)$

30. $125(8 \cdot 65)$

31. $4(26 \cdot 25)$

32. $0.5(362 \cdot 2)$

33. $3 \cdot (10 + 6)$

34. $3 \cdot (20 + 9)$

35. $2 \cdot (9 + \frac{1}{2})$

36. $8 \cdot (200 + 6)$

37. $20 \cdot (40 + 7)$

38. $\frac{3}{4} \cdot (3000 + 8)$

39. $10(4) + 10(6)$

40. $3(15) + 3(9)$

41. $8(3) + 8(4)$

42. $6(0) + 6(1)$

43. $67(8) + 67(2)$

44. $86(97) + 86(3)$

45. $3(21)$

46. $\frac{1}{4}(102)$

47. $11(205)$

48. $9(1009)$

49. $5(86)$

50. $9(1200)$

51. $5(52)$

52. $6(4\frac{2}{3})$

Name the postulate that gives the reason for each step.

53. $8 \cdot (5 \cdot 6) = (8 \cdot 5) \cdot 6$ __?__
$\qquad = 6 \cdot (8 \cdot 5)$ __?__

54. $(3 \cdot 2) + (3 \cdot 7) = 3 \cdot (2 + 7)$ __?__
$\qquad\qquad\qquad = 3 \cdot (7 + 2)$ __?__

55. $a \cdot (b + c) = (ab) + (ac)$ __?__
$\qquad\qquad = (ba) + (ca)$ __?__

56. $(b + c) \cdot a = a \cdot (b + c)$ __?__
$\qquad\qquad = (a \cdot b) + (a \cdot c)$ __?__
$\qquad\qquad = (b \cdot a) + (c \cdot a)$ __?__

57. A frame is $(3 + x)$ units long and 5 units wide.

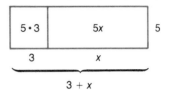

$$\text{Area} = 5(3 + x) = 15 + \underline{\ ?\ }$$

Find the area inside the frame when the replacement set for x is $\{7, 19, 265\}$.

58. A frame is $(4 + x)$ units long and 6 units wide.

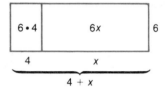

$$\text{Area} = 6(4 + x) = \underline{\ ?\ } + \underline{\ ?\ }$$

Find the area inside the frame when the replacement set for x is $\{1.5, 6.2, 9.8\}$.

In Exercises 59–62, evaluate each expression.

59. $5 - (4 - 1)$ and $(5 - 4) - 1$

60. $30 - (10 - 6)$ and $(30 - 10) - 6$

61. $25 - (11 - 2)$ and $(25 - 11) - 2$

62. $2832 - (2762 - 13)$ and $(2832 - 2762) - 13$

B

63. Does the associative postulate hold for subtraction? (Refer to Exercises 59–62.)

64. Does the commutative postulate hold for subtraction? Give an example to explain your answer.

65. Does the commutative postulate hold for division? Give an example to explain your answer.

C Classify each sentence as true, *T*, or false, *F*. If a statement is false, give an example to show why it is false.

66. Division is distributive with respect to division.

67. Division is distributive with respect to multiplication.

68. Division is distributive with respect to subtraction.

69. Subtraction is distributive with respect to addition.

70. Addition is distributive with respect to addition.

71. Subtraction is distributive with respect to subtraction.

72. Multiplication is distributive with respect to subtraction.

BASIC: COMPUTER PROGRAMMING STATEMENTS

The first electronic computer was completed in 1945 at the University of Pennsylvania. Named ENIAC ("Electrical Numerical Integrator and Computer"), it weighed almost 30 tons and filled the entire basement of a building.

Today, schools, businesses, and homes have microcomputers that sit on desk tops. The most common language for microcomputers is called BASIC (Beginners' All-Purpose Symbolic Instruction Code), which was created at Dartmouth College in 1965.

In BASIC, the following symbols are used for arithmetic operations.

Operation	BASIC Symbol
Addition	+
Subtraction	−
Multiplication	*
Division	/
Raising to a power	↑ or ∧

With regard to order of operations in BASIC, raising to a power is done first. Then follow the rules given on pages 5 and 6.

EXAMPLE 1   Find the value of $12 + 9 * 8 - 4 \uparrow 2 / 8$.

Solution: First raise to the power.

$$12 + 9 * 8 - 4 \uparrow 2 / 8 = 12 + 9 * 8 - 16 / 8 \quad \longleftarrow \text{ Now multiply and divide.}$$
$$= 12 + 72 - 2 \quad \longleftarrow \text{ Add and subtract.}$$
$$= 82$$

Unlike algebra, the multiplication symbol "*" must always be shown in BASIC. For example, $(5 + 3)2$ would *not* be correct in BASIC. It must be written as $(5 + 3) * 2$.

When writing an algebraic formula in BASIC, you do not use raised exponents or fractions. Note that in BASIC a variable is a capital letter. A formula in BASIC is a LET statement. However, the word LET is unnecessary in some forms of BASIC.

Algebraic Formula	Formula in BASIC
$y = 2x$	LET Y = 2 * X
$k = (a - 7)(b + 3)$	LET K = (A - 7) * (B + 3)
$m = \dfrac{a + b}{c - d}$	LET M = (A + B)/(C - D)
$z = x^2 + 2x - 3$	LET Z = X↑2 + 2*X - 3

To use the computer to solve a problem, the computer is given instructions in a step-by-step form called a **computer program**. Any computer program has four phases.

1. **Input:** A program and data are entered into the machine from a keyboard, a tape, or a diskette. Some computers also accept input from punched cards.

2. **Storage:** Anything entered into a computer goes into **memory**.

Picture part of the computer's memory as "boxes," where each box is named by a letter and each box can hold a number. For example,

A	B	C	$\cdots$	X	Y	Z

LET X = 10

puts a 10 in location X. Once numbers are in memory, they can be added, subtracted, multiplied and so on. Another way to put a number in memory is the INPUT command. For example,

INPUT X

takes a number typed on the keyboard and stores it in location X.

3. **Processing:** When told to RUN ("execute") a program, a computer does what the program tells it to do. It computes values and can make decisions based on these values.

4. **Output:** The results of a program are usually typed on a printer or shown on a television screen ("cathode ray tube" or "CRT"). Computers can also put answers on tapes or diskettes. To see the number stored in a location, you use the PRINT command.

The following example illustrates the use of LET, INPUT, and PRINT statements in a program.

Problem: *Write a program which accepts a baseball player's times at bat and number of hits, and prints the batting average. Use the following formula.*

Batting Average = Number of Hits ÷ Times at Bat

Program:
```
10  PRINT "HOW MANY TIMES AT BAT";
20  INPUT B                              ⟵——— B = Times at Bat
30  PRINT "HOW MANY HITS";
40  INPUT H                              ⟵——— H = Number of Hits
50  LET A = H / B                        ⟵——— Formula in BASIC
60  PRINT "BATTING AVERAGE = ";A
70  END
```

Statement 70 END tells the computer that there are no more lines in the program.

As shown in this program, the statements are numbered in multiples of 10. This allows you to insert additional statements later. To distinguish zero from the letter "O," some systems use the symbol Ø for zero.

EXERCISES

A Find the value of each of the following BASIC formulas.

1. $(5 - 1) * 10$
2. $9 * 2 \uparrow 2$
3. $8.5 * 2/4$
4. $(2 - 10) * 2/4$
5. $(5 - 19)/7 * 3$
6. $((7.2 + 0.9) * 2)/3$

Write each formula as a BASIC LET statement.

7. $y = 3x - 5$
8. $p = 2(l + w)$
9. $z = -6x$
10. $r = 5(4s - k)$
11. $t = (r + s)(x - 8)$
12. $y = 2x^2 - 3x + 6$
13. $k = \dfrac{mn}{c + 2}$
14. $s = \dfrac{x - a}{3y}$
15. $r = -7 + \dfrac{b}{c - d}$

Write a BASIC program for each problem.

16. Given the number of wins and losses of a team, compute and print the winning percentage.

$$\frac{\text{Winning}}{\text{Percentage}} = \frac{\text{Number}}{\text{of Wins}} \div \frac{\text{Games}}{\text{Played}} \times 100$$

17. Given the number of hours worked and the rate per hour, compute and print a worker's weekly pay.

$$\frac{\text{Amount}}{\text{Earned}} = \frac{\text{Amount}}{\text{per Hour}} \times \frac{\text{Number}}{\text{of Hours}}$$

18. Given the number of miles a car has traveled and the number of gallons used, compute and print the average miles per gallon for the car.

$$\frac{\text{Miles}}{\text{per Gallon}} = \frac{\text{Number}}{\text{of Miles}} \div \frac{\text{Number}}{\text{of Gallons}}$$

19. Given the number of sides of a polygon, compute and print the sum of the measures of the angles of the polygon.

$$\frac{\text{Sum of}}{\text{Measures}} = 180 \times \frac{\text{Number}}{\text{of Sides}} - 360$$

Review

Represent each of the following by a positive or negative rational number. *(Section 1–6)*

1. A weight loss of $12\frac{1}{2}$ pounds

2. A fare increase of $1.25

Classify each statement as true or false. When a statement is false tell why it is false. *(Section 1–6)*

3. $I \subset I$ **4.** $Q \subset N$ **5.** $\{0\} \subset W$ **6.** $W \subset Q$ **7.** $N \subset I$

Identify each number as rational or irrational. Give a reason for each answer. *(Section 1–7)*

8. $\sqrt{16}$ **9.** $\sqrt{33}$ **10.** $\sqrt{\frac{9}{36}}$ **11.** $\sqrt{\frac{100}{49}}$ **12.** $\sqrt{18}$ **13.** $\sqrt{50}$

Replace *n* with the smallest possible whole number to make a true statement. *(Section 1–7)*

14. $13 < \sqrt{175} < n$ **15.** $5 < \sqrt{30} < n$ **16.** $12 < \sqrt{150} < n$

Name the postulate illustrated by each sentence. *(Section 1–8)*

17. $5(9) = (9)5$ **18.** $7 + (8 + 6) = (8 + 6) + 7$ **19.** $4(2) + 4(9) = 4(2 + 9)$

Evaluate each expression. *(Section 1–8)*

20. $7 + (2 + 10)$ **21.** $0.4(8 \cdot 6)$ **22.** $\frac{2}{3}(75 + 9)$

Chapter Summary

IMPORTANT TERMS

Algebraic expression (p. 2)
Associative postulate (p. 30)
Base (p. 9)
Closure postulate (p. 31)
Commutative postulate (p. 30)
Coordinate (p. 26)
Distributive postulate (p. 30)
Element (p. 22)
Empty set (p. 19)
Equation (p. 18)
Evaluating expressions (p. 5)
Exponent (p. 9)
Formula (p. 9)
Grouping symbols (p. 5)
Identity postulate (p. 30)
Inequality (p. 18)

Infinite nonrepeating
  decimal (p. 25)
Integer (p. 22)
Irrational number (p. 25)
Natural number (p. 22)
Numerical expression (p. 3)
Open sentence (p. 18)
Opposite (p. 22)
Postulate (p. 30)
Rational number (p. 22)
Real number (p. 26)
Replacement set (p. 9)
Solution set (p. 18)
Subset (p. 22)
Variable (p. 2)
Whole number (p. 22)

1. **Order of Operations**

    [1] Do all multiplications and divisions in order from left to right.

    [2] Do all additions and subtractions in order from left to right.

2. **Rules for Grouping Symbols**

    [1] Perform the operations within parentheses, or in the numerators or denominators, first.

    [2] When the parentheses have been removed, or where there are no parentheses, follow the rules for order of operations.

3. When an expression contains more than one grouping symbol, perform the operations within the innermost grouping symbols first. Then work towards the outermost grouping symbols.

4. To use a formula, you replace the known variables with given values (replacement set) in order to find the unknown variables.

5. The symbol for the empty set is ϕ.

6. For any positive integer n, $\sqrt{n}$ is either a positive integer (rational number) or an irrational number.

7. Every point on the number line can be associated with a real number. Every real number can be associated with a point on the number line.

8. The number π is an irrational number.

9. The symbol $\in$ means "is an element of."

—— Chapter Objectives and Review ——

Objective: *To write algebraic expressions for word descriptions (Section 1–1)*

Write an algebraic expression for each word description.

1. The cost of 5 tickets at x dollars per ticket.
2. The sum of the sale price, s, and the sales tax, t.
3. The amount, a, spent on tires, divided by 4.
4. The price of long–distance calls, d, subtracted from the total telephone bill, P.

Objective: *To evaluate numerical expressions involving parentheses (Section 1–1)*

Find the value of each numerical expression.

5. $(9 + 16) \div 5$
6. $8 + (2 \times 12)$
7. $40 \div (10 - 2)$
8. $18 - (3 \div 3)$
9. $(4 + 7) \times (60 \div 12)$
10. $(3 - 3) \cdot (14 \div 2)$

Objective: *To evaluate algebraic expressions using the rules for order of operations and grouping symbols (Section 1–2)*

11. $7 + 90 \div 10$
12. $38 \cdot (7 - 3)$
13. $\dfrac{18 \div 2}{3 \cdot 7 + 6}$

14. $\dfrac{7(8-4)}{2(10-8)}$ **15.** $4[8 + 6 \times (4 + 2)]$ **16.** $11 \div [(14 - 3) \div 1]$

Evaluate for the given values of the variables.

17. $(18 + 7)w$, for $w = 3$ **18.** $6a - 9b$, for $a = 6$ and $b = 4$

19. $\dfrac{2r}{5m}$, for $r = 20$ and $m = 4$ **20.** $3t - 6.1f$, for $t = 10.2$ and $f = 3.9$

Objective: *To evaluate formulas using replacement sets (Section 1–3)*

Find R for each formula. The replacement set for b is $\{3, 5, 7\}$.

21. $R = 0.07b$ **22.** $R = 2b^2 + 5$ **23.** $R = \dfrac{b + 5}{2}$

Objective: *To evaluate numerical expressions involving exponents (Section 1–3)*

24. 2^4 **25.** $\left(\dfrac{3}{8}\right)^2$ **26.** $(0.12)^2$ **27.** 1^{42}

Objective: *To use formulas to solve word problems (Section 1–4)*

28. Use the formula $V = lwh$ to find V when $l = 3\frac{1}{2}$ feet, $w = 2$ feet, and $h = 4\frac{1}{2}$ feet.

Objective: *To find the solution set of a sentence using a given replacement set (Section 1–5)*

Find the solution set for each sentence. The replacement set is $\{0, 3, 6, 9, 12\}$.

29. $x + 6 = 9$ **30.** $4m + 3 > 15$ **31.** $39 < 2y + y$

Objective: *To identify elements which belong to the set of natural numbers, the set of rational numbers (Section 1–6)*

Classify each sentence as true, *T,* or false, *F.* When a sentence is false, tell why it is false.

32. The number 0 is a natural number.

33. Every natural number is also an integer.

34. The set of whole numbers is a subset of the set of integers.

35. The opposite of ⁻7 is 7.

36. 3.8 is an integer.

37. $2\frac{1}{5}$ is a rational number.

38. ⁻0.07 can be written in the form $\dfrac{a}{b}$.

Objective: *To use positive and negative rational numbers to represent word statements (Section 1–6)*

Represent each of the following by a positive or negative rational number.

39. A loss of 3 yards on a football play   **40.** A stock gain of $1\frac{3}{8}$ points

41. A rise in temperature of $10°$ **42.** A paycheck deduction of \$14.25

Objective: *To identify irrational numbers and real numbers (Section 1–7)*

Indicate the set or sets to which each number belongs. Use I = {Integers}, Q = {Rational Numbers}, Ir = {Irrational Numbers}, and R = {Real Numbers}.

43. $\sqrt{81}$ **44.** $^-1.3$ **45.** $\sqrt{7}$ **46.** $1.\overline{37}$

47. $\frac{2}{11}$ **48.** $^-2\frac{1}{2}$ **49.** $8.3769138\cdots$ **50.** $\frac{64}{4}$

Objective: *To identify the coordinates of points on the real number line (Section 1–7)*

Give the coordinate of the point named by each letter.

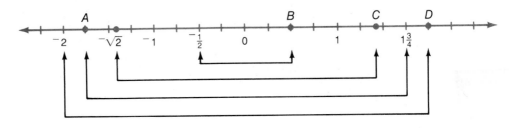

51. *A*   **52.** *B*   **53.** *C*   **54.** *D*

Objective: *To approximate values of irrational numbers using the Table of Square Roots (Section 1–7)*

Use the Table of Square Roots on page 541 to find an approximate value for each number.

55. $\sqrt{7}$ **56.** $\sqrt{60}$ **57.** $\sqrt{113}$ **58.** $\sqrt{12}$

Objective: *To identify the postulates for the addition and multiplication of real numbers (Section 1–8)*

Name the postulate illustrated by each sentence.

59. $7 + 3 = 3 + 7$ **60.** $121 \cdot 1 = 121$ **61.** $7 \cdot (10 \cdot 3) = (7 \cdot 10) \cdot 3$

Objective: *To use the postulates for real numbers (Section 1–8)*

Use the postulates for real numbers to find a value of the variable that makes each equation true. Name the postulate that gives the reason for your choice.

62. $9(x + 5) = (9 \cdot 2) + (9 \cdot 5)$ **63.** $\frac{3}{5} \cdot (\frac{1}{8} \cdot \frac{5}{9}) = (\frac{3}{5} \cdot t) \cdot \frac{5}{9}$

Evaluate each expression.

64. $21 \cdot (68 + 32)$ **65.** $\frac{5}{24} + (3\frac{1}{8} + 2\frac{2}{3})$

Chapter Test

Write an algebraic expression for each word description.

1. The total coupon value, v, subtracted from the weekly food bill, b.

2. The sum of a $1500 loan and the total interest, t.

3. The cost of y record albums at $7.55 per album.

Find the value of each numerical expression.

4. $(3 + 14) \cdot 8$

5. $(70 \div 10) + (8 - 3)$

6. $\dfrac{9(19 - 15)}{33 + 11 + 7}$

7. $2[8 \cdot (11 - 2) \div 36]$

Evaluate for the given values of the variables.

8. $17p - 3b$, for $p = 8$ and $b = 11$

9. $\frac{1}{2}a + \frac{3}{4}c$, for $a = 16$ and $c = 4.8$

10. Use the formula $M = 2x^2 - 3.1$ to find M when the replacement set for x is $\{2, 2.1\}$.

11. Use the formula $A = \frac{1}{2}h(b + c)$ to find the area of a trapezoid when $b = 6.8$ meters, $c = 3.2$ meters, and $h = 7$ meters.

Find the solution set for each sentence.
The replacement set is $\{0, 1, 2\}$.

12. $w + 11 = 13$

13. $r + 3 \neq r + 7$

14. $9t > t + 7$

Classify each sentence as true, T, or false, F. When a sentence is false, tell why it is false.

15. $\frac{9}{5}$ is a rational number

16. 0.3 is a natural number.

17. The opposite of 2 is $\frac{1}{2}$.

18. Every integer is also a rational number.

19. Write the positive or negative rational number which represents a bank withdrawal of $105.10.

Indicate the set or sets to which each number belongs. Use $I = \{\text{Integers}\}$, $Q = \{\text{Rational Numbers}\}$, $\text{Ir} = \{\text{Irrational Numbers}\}$, and $R = \{\text{Real Numbers}\}$.

20. $\sqrt{21}$

21. $^-\sqrt{144}$

22. $\sqrt{\dfrac{25}{121}}$

23. $^-1.0363987 \cdots$

24. Find the value of t in the following equation: $15(11 + 4) = (15 \cdot t) + (15 \cdot 4)$. Then name the postulate that gives the reason for your choice.

25. Evaluate: $73(47) + 73(53)$.

Additional Practice

Skills

Find the value of each of the following. *(Sections 1–1, 1–2)*

1. $(7 \cdot 2) - 4$

2. $6 + (49 \div 7)$

3. $(11 + 7) \div 3$

4. $(24 \div 2) \div (8 - 4)$

5. $\dfrac{11 - 9}{7 \cdot 3}$

6. $\dfrac{4(6 - 2)}{6 - 6 \div 3}$

7. $\dfrac{4 \cdot 4 - 7}{7 + 10 \cdot 2}$

8. $4[(5 - 2) \div 3]$

Find B for each formula. The replacement set for n is $\{4, 5, 6\}$. *(Section 1–3)*

9. $B = 3n - 1$

10. $B = 8(n - 2)$

11. $B = n^2 + 3$

12. $B = n^3$

Find the solution set for each sentence. The replacement set is $\{1, 3, 5, 7, 9\}$. *(Section 1–5)*

13. $x + 3 = 12$

14. $x \neq 6 + 1$

15. $10 + x > 14$

16. $9x < 7$

Write each rational number in the form $\dfrac{a}{b}$, where a is an integer and b is a natural number. *(Section 1–6)*

17. 0.3

18. $^-0.25$

19. $2\frac{1}{3}$

20. $^-6\frac{1}{6}$

21. $^-38$

22. 7.37

Identify each number as rational, Q, or irrational, Ir. Give a reason for each answer. *(Section 1–7)*

23. $\sqrt{5}$

24. $\sqrt{81}$

25. $\sqrt{100}$

26. $\sqrt{\dfrac{49}{4}}$

27. $\sqrt{52}$

28. $\sqrt{12}$

Use the Table of Square Roots on page 541 to find an approximate value for each number. *(Section 1–7)*

29. $\sqrt{41}$

30. $\sqrt{23}$

31. $\sqrt{111}$

32. $\sqrt{54}$

33. $\sqrt{75}$

34. $\sqrt{32}$

Name the postulate illustrated by each sentence. *(Section 1–8)*

35. $\frac{1}{3} + 0 = \frac{1}{3}$

36. $2 \cdot (5 \cdot 7) = (2 \cdot 5) \cdot 7$

37. $11 + 4 = 4 + 11$

Applications

For Exercises 38 and 39 write an algebraic expression to represent each word description. *(Section 1–2)*

38. The cost of t gallons of gasoline at $1.15 per gallon.

39. The total cost of p tickets at $12 per ticket and $7 for a program.

40. Use the formula $V = lwh$ to find the volume, V, of a rectangular garden pool where $l = 6$ meters, $w = 4$ meters, and $h = \frac{1}{2}$ meter. *(Section 1–4)*

41. Use the formula $A = \frac{1}{2}h(b + c)$ to find the area, A, of a car window where $h = 18$ inches, $b = 13$ inches, and $c = 17$ inches. *(Section 1–4)*

CHAPTER 2 Operations with Real Numbers

2-1 Positive and Negative Numbers

On the number line below, 3 and ⁻3 are on *opposite sides* of 0, and 3 and ⁻3 are the *same distance* from 0.

Hence, ⁻3 and 3 are **opposites**. That is,

3 is the opposite of ⁻3.
⁻3 is the opposite of 3.

These statements can be expressed in symbols by using a dash, −, to represent "the opposite of."

$$3 = -\,(^-3)$$
$$^-3 = -\,3$$

Since $^-3 = -3$, we will use the symbol for "the opposite of" to indicate a negative number. Thus, -3 can be read as "negative 3." It may be more appropriate to say "the opposite of" for the dash, −, in certain instances. Examples are shown in this table.

Example	Read	Meaning
$-(5)$	The opposite of 5.	-5
$-(-6)$	The opposite of negative 6.	6
$-(2)$	The opposite of 2.	-2
$-(-8\frac{1}{2})$	The opposite of negative $8\frac{1}{2}$.	$8\frac{1}{2}$
$-(-9.3)$	The opposite of negative 9.3.	9.3

Note that the number zero is its own opposite. That is,

$$0 = -0, \quad \text{and} \quad -0 = 0.$$

EXAMPLE 1 Write without parentheses.

 a. $-(-5)$ **b.** $-(9.6 - 3.2)$

Solutions: **a.** $-(-5) = 5$ ⟵──── **Think: The opposite of negative 5 is 5.**

 b. $-\overline{(9.6 - 3.2)} = -\overline{(6.4)}$ ⟵ **Think: The opposite of 6.4 is negative 6.4.**

   $= -6.4$

You can use the idea of opposites to solve equations.

EXAMPLE 2 Solve: $-x = 7$

 Solution: $-x = 7$ ⟵──── **Think: The opposite of some number is 7.**

   $x = -7$ Thus, the solution is -7.

You can use a number line to compare positive and negative numbers.

For any two real numbers, the smaller is to the left of the larger on the number line.

EXAMPLE 3 Use > or < to compare the numbers. Refer to the number line above.

a. $3 \underline{\ ?\ } -9$ b. $-11\frac{1}{2} \underline{\ ?\ } -7$ c. $0.5 \underline{\ ?\ } 0$

Solutions: a. $3 > -9$ ⟵——— **3 is to the right of −9**

b. $-11\frac{1}{2} < -7$ ⟵——— **−11½ is to the left of −7.**

c. $0.5 > 0$ ⟵——— **0.5 is to the right of 0.**

CLASSROOM EXERCISES

Write the opposite of each number.

1. 2   2. −1   3. −7.8   4. 0   5. $7\frac{1}{3}$ 6. $-\frac{5}{6}$

Write without parentheses.

7. $-(-\frac{1}{7})$ 8. $-(t)$ 9. $-(\pi \cdot 0)$ 10. $-(9.1 + 6.7)$

Solve for q.

11. $-q = 6$ 12. $-q = -6$ 13. $q = -(-6)$ 14. $-q = -(-6)$

Use > or < to compare the numbers.

15. $0 \underline{\ ?\ } -1$ 16. $-0.5 \underline{\ ?\ } -3$ 17. $-5 \underline{\ ?\ } -6$ 18. $-12 \underline{\ ?\ } -11\frac{3}{4}$

WRITTEN EXERCISES

A   Write the opposite of each number.

1. 6   2. −7   3. 9   4. $-\sqrt{3}$ 5. $-6\frac{1}{2}$ 6. 0

7. 9.02   8. −6.33   9. $-\frac{2}{3}$ 10. 5   11. −9.001   12. $-\pi$

Write without parentheses.

13. $-(5)$ 14. $-(-9)$ 15. $-(3.14)$ 16. $-(-3.14)$ 17. $-\frac{5}{6}$

18. $-(-5)$ 19. $-(9)$ 20. $-(-0.9)$ 21. $-(0.9)$ 22. $-(-0)$

23. $-(3.6 - 2.4)'$ 24. $-(16 + 0)$ 25. $-(71 \cdot 0)$ 26. $-(\frac{1}{2} \cdot \frac{3}{4})$ 27. $-(33 \div 11)$

28. $-(t)$ 29. $-(-t)$ 30. $-(r \cdot 0)$ 31. $-(-m)$ 32. $-(-\pi)$

Solve.

33. $-x = 9$ 34. $-m = -6$ 35. $-x = 0$ 36. $-y = 6\frac{1}{2}$

37. $-y = 3.25$ 38. $-x = -\pi$ 39. $-a = -\frac{3}{4}$ 40. $-a = 1$

Operations with Real Numbers   **45**

Use < and > to compare the numbers. Draw a number line if necessary.

41. -5 _?_ 5 **42.** -15 _?_ -5 **43.** -8 _?_ 0.2 **44.** -12 _?_ -15

45. 7 _?_ 5 **46.** -15 _?_ -20 **47.** 0 _?_ -9 **48.** 0 _?_ -8.6

49. $6\frac{2}{3}$ _?_ -6 **50.** 6.2 _?_ 6.3 **51.** -7.4 _?_ -7.5 **52.** $-8\frac{2}{5}$ _?_ $-8\frac{1}{5}$

53. $-(-6)$ _?_ 0 **54.** 0 _?_ $-(-5)$ **55.** $-(-\pi)$ _?_ 3 **56.** $-(-\sqrt{3})$ _?_ 3

57. $-\sqrt{2}$ _?_ 2 **58.** $-(-\sqrt{3})$ _?_ $(-\sqrt{2})$ **59.** $\sqrt{6}$ _?_ $-(-\sqrt{7})$ **60.** $-(-3)$ _?_ 0

APPLICATIONS: Using Opposites

B   Use algebraic symbols to represent each sentence.
The first one is done for you.

In Words	In Symbols

61. Depositing $27 in a checking account is the opposite of withdrawing $27. $27 = -(-27)$

62. The opposite of taking an elevator down 6 floors is taking an elevator up 6 floors.   _?_

63. A fall of 20° in temperature is the opposite of a rise of 20°.   _?_

64. An altitude of 400 meters above sea level is the opposite of a depth of 400 meters below sea level.   _?_

65. The opposite of owing $200 is having $200 in savings.   _?_

66. A weight gain of $3\frac{1}{2}$ pounds is the opposite of a weight loss of $3\frac{1}{2}$ pounds.   _?_

67. An investment loss of $1\frac{1}{4}$ per share is the opposite of an investment gain of $1\frac{1}{4}$ per share.

68. The opposite of a profit of $2000 is a loss of $2000.   _?_

69. The opposite of a loss of 500 meters in altitude is a gain in altitude of 500 meters.   _?_

70. A decrease in speed of 6.5 kilometers per hour is the opposite of an increase in speed of 6.5 kilometers per hour.   _?_

71. The opposite of growing $2\frac{3}{4}$ inches is shrinking $2\frac{3}{4}$ inches.   _?_

72. If a is a positive real number, is $-a$ positive or negative?

73. If $-a$ is a positive real number, is a positive or negative?

74. If $-a$ is a negative real number, is a positive or negative?

75. If a is a positive real number, is $-(-a)$ positive or negative?

76. If a is a negative real number, is $-(-a)$ positive or negative?

C   Solve for the variable.

77. $-(-x) = 4$ **78.** $-(-y) = 6$ **79.** $-x = 0$ **80.** $-x < 0$

81. $-x > 0$ **82.** $-t > 4$ **83.** $-t < 4$ **84.** $-r > -6$

2–2 Additive Inverses and Absolute Value

You can use a number line to show the following.

The sum of a number and its opposite is 0.

Arrows pointing to the right represent positive numbers. Arrows pointing to the left represent negative numbers.

Example	On the Number Line	Sum
a. $5 + (-5)$ Think: A gain of 5 followed by a loss of 5	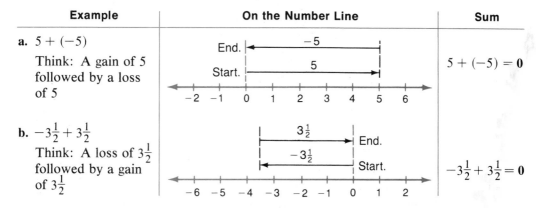	$5 + (-5) = 0$
b. $-3\frac{1}{2} + 3\frac{1}{2}$ Think: A loss of $3\frac{1}{2}$ followed by a gain of $3\frac{1}{2}$		$-3\frac{1}{2} + 3\frac{1}{2} = 0$

The Additive Inverse Postulate summarizes this property of real numbers.

Postulate

> **Additive Inverse Postulate**
>
> For any real number a, there is one and only one real number, $-a$, such that
> $$a + (-a) = 0.$$

Numbers that are opposites, such as 3 and -3, are **additive inverses of** each other because their sum is 0.

The number 0 is its own additive inverse.

Additive inverses are the same distance from 0 on the number line.

You use *absolute value notation* when you want to indicate distance, but not direction, from 0. The symbol for absolute value is $|\ |$.

Definition

> The **absolute value** of a real number x is the distance of x from 0. It is written $|x|$.

When $x = 0$, $|x| = 0$. For all other real numbers, $|x|$ is a positive real number.

Example	Meaning	Solution
$|-5|$	Distance of -5 from 0	$|-5| = 5$
$|8|$	Distance of 8 from 0	$|8| = 8$
$|-3\frac{1}{2}|$	Distance of $-3\frac{1}{2}$ from 0	$|-3\frac{1}{2}| = 3\frac{1}{2}$
$|0|$	Distance of 0 from 0	$|0| = 0$

Since $|x|$ is a positive real number for all real numbers x except 0, $-|x|$ is a negative real number.

EXAMPLE 1 Evaluate: **a.** $-\left|-\frac{2}{3}\right|$ **b.** $-(|-5| + |-1|)$

Solutions: **a.** $\left|-\frac{2}{3}\right| = \frac{2}{3}$ ⟵——— By the definition of absolute value

So $-\left|-\frac{2}{3}\right| = -\frac{2}{3}$.

b. $(|-5| + |-1|) = (5 + 1) = 6$ ⟵——— By definition

So $-(|-5| + |-1|) = -6$.

To compare expressions such as $|-8|$ and $-|-10|$, first *evaluate each expression. Then compare the results.*

EXAMPLE 2 Use $>$ or $<$ to compare the numbers.

a. $|-8|$ _?_ $|-10|$ **b.** $-|-8|$ _?_ $-|-10|$

Solutions: **a.** $|-8| = 8$; $|-10| = 10$; **b.** $-|-8| = -8$; $-|-10| = -10$;
and $8 < 10$ and $-8 > -10$
Thus, $|-8| < |-10|$. Thus, $-|-8| > -|-10|$.

CLASSROOM EXERCISES

Write the additive inverse of each real number.

1. 6.5 2. -9 3. $-m$ 4. $-(-9)$ 5. $-(-0)$ 6. $-(-t)$

Evaluate.

7. $|7|$ 8. $|-15|$ 9. $-|7|$ 10. $-|-15|$ 11. $|-(-3)|$ 12. $-|-(-\frac{1}{2})|$

Use $>$ or $<$ to compare the numbers.

13. $|10|$ _?_ $|-12|$ 14. $-|-\frac{1}{2}|$ _?_ $|\frac{1}{3}|$ 15. $|0|$ _?_ $-|-1.5|$ 16. $-|-7.3|$ _?_ $-|8.4|$

WRITTEN EXERCISES

A   Write the additive inverse of each number.

1. 6   **2.** -7 **3.** $-3\frac{1}{5}$ **4.** 9   **5.** -6.8

6. 7.09   **7.** $-\pi$ **8.** $\sqrt{7}$ **9.** $-\sqrt{2}$ **10.** $\sqrt{10}$

11. $-(-5)$ **12.** $-(5)$ **13.** $-(-4)$ **14.** $-(-6.7)$ **15.** $-(-0.9)$

Complete.

16. $9 + \underline{\ ?\ } = 0$ **17.** $-12 + \underline{\ ?\ } = 0$ **18.** $-8.6 + \underline{\ ?\ } = 0$ **19.** $15\frac{1}{2} + \underline{\ ?\ } = 0$

20. $8 + (-8) = \underline{\ ?\ }$ **21.** $-\frac{1}{4} + \frac{1}{4} = \underline{\ ?\ }$ **22.** $m + \underline{\ ?\ } = 0$ **23.** $-r + \underline{\ ?\ } = 0$

24. $y + (-y) = \underline{\ ?\ }$ **25.** $\underline{\ ?\ } + a = 0$ **26.** $-(-t) + \underline{\ ?\ } = 0$ **27.** $\underline{\ ?\ } + -(-x) = 0$

Evaluate.

28. $|6|$ **29.** $|-6|$ **30.** $|-3\frac{1}{2}|$ **31.** $|-\pi|$ **32.** $|-19.5|$ **33.** $|15|$

34. $|-18.5|$ **35.** $|0|$ **36.** $|-16|$ **37.** $|-100|$ **38.** $|695|$ **39.** $|-462|$

40. $|-72.5|$ **41.** $|22{,}000|$ **42.** $|37.75|$ **43.** $|-7.25|$ **44.** $|-\sqrt{21}|$ **45.** $|\sqrt{5}|$

46. $|86.75|$ **47.** $|-7.6|$ **48.** $|-\sqrt{7}|$ **49.** $|\sqrt{7}|$ **50.** $-|19|$ **51.** $-|-19|$

52. $|3| + |15|$ **53.** $|-3| + |-9|$ **54.** $|23| + |-18|$ **55.** $|-1| + |14|$

56. $|6| + |-8|$ **57.** $|-4| + |8|$ **58.** $|-9| + |9|$ **59.** $|9| + |-12|$

60. $|0| + |0|$ **61.** $|\frac{1}{2}| + |\frac{2}{3}|$ **62.** $|0.2| + |-0.37|$ **63.** $|-235| + |16|$

64. $-|3| + |3|$ **65.** $-|\frac{1}{2}| + |\frac{1}{2}|$ **66.** $|3.1| - |3.1|$ **67.** $|x| - |x|$

Use $>$, $=$, or $<$ to compare the numbers.

68. $|0.23| \underline{\ ?\ } |-3.7|$ **69.** $|-6| \underline{\ ?\ } |6|$ **70.** $|-\frac{1}{2}| \underline{\ ?\ } |\frac{1}{3}|$ **71.** $|0.02| \underline{\ ?\ } |-0.001|$

72. $|0| \underline{\ ?\ } |-1|$ **73.** $|-\frac{1}{6}| \underline{\ ?\ } |\frac{1}{7}|$ **74.** $|-1| \underline{\ ?\ } |1|$ **75.** $|0| \underline{\ ?\ } -|0|$

76. $|-3| \underline{\ ?\ } |-\frac{1}{4}|$ **77.** $|-3| \underline{\ ?\ } |4|$ **78.** $|-2| \underline{\ ?\ } |-2|$ **79.** $|-5| \underline{\ ?\ } |-5|$

Classify each equation as true, *T*, or false, *F*. When an equation is false, tell why it is false.

80. $|8| = 8$ **81.** $|-231| = 231$ **82.** $|-663| = |663|$ **83.** $|9| = 9$

84. $|-235| > |235|$ **85.** $|-35| > |35|$ **86.** $|-27| < |17|$ **87.** $|17.9| < |-17.9|$

88. $|-0.01| < |-0.001|$ **89.** $|-\frac{1}{3}| < \frac{1}{4}$ **90.** $\frac{2}{3} < |-\frac{3}{4}|$ **91.** $|\frac{1}{8}| > -\frac{1}{7}$

B   Solve.

92. $x = |-2|$ **93.** $|-7| = a$ **94.** $b = -|9|$ **95.** $-|-2\frac{2}{3}| = y$

96. $|q| = 0$ **97.** $|y| = 4$ **98.** $|x| = |-1|$ **99.** $-|x| + |-2| = 0$

Complete each statement by writing $<$, $>$, or $=$.

100. If $x > 0$, then $|x| \underline{\ ?\ } 0$.   **101.** If $x < 0$, then $|x| \underline{\ ?\ } 0$.

Classify each statement as true, *T*, or false, *F*. When a statement is false, tell why it is false.

102. If x is any real number, then $|x| = x$.

103. If y is any real number, then $|y| = |-y|$.

104. If x and y are real numbers and $x < y$, then $|x| < |y|$.

105. If x is any real number, then $-(-x) = x$.

CALCULATOR APPLICATIONS

Powers and Patterns

The power key, x^y or y^x , on a scientific calculator simplifies the process of evaluating an expression that contains an exponent. If your calculator does not have a power key, you simply multiply. In either case, the answer may be too large for your calculator to express.

EXAMPLE Find 8^n for $n = 1, 2, 3, \cdots, 8$. Study the last digit of each product to see if you can discover a pattern. Predict the last digit for 8^9.

SOLUTION $8^1 = 8$

$8^2 = 8$ x^y 2 $=$ 64

$8^3 = 8$ x^y 3 $=$ 512

$8^4 = 8$ x^y 4 $=$ 4096

$8^5 = 8$ x^y 5 $=$ 32768

$8^6 = 8$ x^y 6 $=$ 262144

$8^7 = 8$ x^y 7 $=$ 2097152

$8^8 = 8$ x^y 8 $=$ 16777216

Pattern of the last digits: 8, 4, 2, 6, 8, 4, 2, 6. Thus, the last digit for 8^9 is **8.**

EXERCISES

Predict the last digit for each of the following.

1. 8^{12} **2.** 8^{16} **3.** 8^{100} **4.** 8^{101} **5.** 6^{100} **6.** 2^{27} **7.** 2^{50} **8.** 2^{99}

REVIEW CAPSULE FOR SECTION 2-3

Add.

1. $76 + 39$

2. $703 + 527$

3. $456 + 72 + 4998 + 39$

4. $0.44 + 0.32$

5. $15.72 + 4.95$

6. $12.19 + 2.5 + 14.306 + 27$

Add. Write your answers in lowest terms.

7. $\frac{3}{6} + \frac{1}{6}$

8. $8 + \frac{3}{5}$

9. $\frac{7}{8} + \frac{3}{4}$

10. $\frac{1}{6} + \frac{1}{8}$

11. $12\frac{5}{8} + \frac{7}{8}$

12. $3\frac{2}{3} + \frac{5}{6}$

13. $7\frac{3}{5} + 9\frac{7}{10}$

14. $6\frac{5}{8} + 9\frac{1}{3}$

2-3 Addition of Real Numbers

You know that the sum of two positive numbers is a positive number. You can use a number line to show the following.

The sum of two negative numbers is a negative number.

Example	On the Number Line	Sum
a. $-3 + (-4)$ Think: A loss of 3 followed by a loss of 4	End. ←—-4—←—-3—⊣ Start. $-8\ -7\ -6\ -5\ -4\ -3\ -2\ -1\ \ 0\ \ 1$	$-3 + (-4) = -7$
b. $-2.5 + (-1.5)$ Think: A loss of 2.5 followed by a loss of 1.5	End. ←—-1.5—←—-2.5—⊣ Start. $-8\ -7\ -6\ -5\ -4\ -3\ -2\ -1\ \ 0\ \ 1$	$-2.5 + (-1.5) = -4$

You can use this procedure to find the sum of two positive numbers or of two negative numbers.

> **Procedure:**
>
> To add two positive numbers or two negative numbers:
>
> 1. Determine whether the sum is positive or negative.
>   - **a.** The sum of two positive numbers is positive.
>   - **b.** The sum of two negative numbers is negative.
> 2. Add the absolute values of the numbers.

EXAMPLE 1 Add: $-6 + (-9)$

Solution: Follow the steps of the procedure.

1. $-6 + (-9) = -(\underline{\ ?\ })$ ◄——— **The sum is negative.**
2. $\qquad\qquad = -(6 + 9)$
   $\qquad\qquad = -15$ ◄——— $|-6| = 6;\ |-9| = 9$

The procedure for adding negative numbers can be stated as a *theorem*. A **theorem** is a statement that can be proved from postulates and definitions.

Theorem 2-1

> **Sum of Two Negative Numbers**
>
> The sum of two negative numbers is the opposite of the sum of their absolute values.
>
> **If $x < 0$ and $y < 0$, then $x + y = -(|x| + |y|)$.**

You can also use a number line to find the sum of a positive and a negative number.

Example	On the Number Line	Sum
a. $5 + (-3)$ Think: A gain of 5 followed by a loss of 3.		$5 + (-3) = 2$
b. $-7 + 4$ Think: A loss of 7 followed by a gain of 4.		$-7 + 4 = -3$

Follow this procedure to find the sum of a positive and a negative number.

Procedure

> To find the sum of a positive and a negative number:
>
> $\boxed{1}$ Determine whether the sum is positive or negative.
>
> **a.** The sum is positive when the positive number has the greater absolute value.
>
> **b.** The sum is negative when the negative number has the greater absolute value.
>
> $\boxed{2}$ Subtract the lesser absolute value from the greater absolute value.

EXAMPLE 2   Add: $8 + (-10)$

Solution: Follow the steps of the procedure.

$\boxed{1}$ $8 + (-10) = -(\underline{\ ?\ })$ ◄────── **Since $|-10| > |8|$, the sum is negative.**

$\boxed{2}$ $ = -(10 - 8)$ ◄────── $(|-10| - |8|)$

$ = -2$

Sometimes the positive number has the greater absolute value.

EXAMPLE 3   Add: $20 + (-8)$

Solution: $\boxed{1}$ $20 + (-8) = (\underline{\ ?\ })$

$\boxed{2}$ $ = (20 - 8)$ ◄────── **Since $|20| > |-8|$, the sum is positive.**

$ = 12$ ◄────── $(|20| - |8|)$

The procedure can be stated as a theorem.

Theorem 2-2	**Sum of a Positive and a Negative Number**

The sum of a positive number, x, and a negative number, y, is the difference of their absolute values. The sum is positive when x is farther from 0 and negative when y is farther from 0. That is,

$$x + y = (|x| - |y|) \text{ when } |x| > |y|;$$
$$x + y = -(|y| - |x|) \text{ when } |y| > |x|.$$

CLASSROOM EXERCISES

In Exercises 1–8, state whether each sum will be positive or negative.

1. $7 + (-15)$ **2.** $(-6) + (-4)$ **3.** $8 + (-9)$ **4.** $(-16) + 26$

5. $19 + 8$ **6.** $(-\frac{2}{3}) + (-\frac{1}{8})$ **7.** $(1\frac{1}{2}) + (-1\frac{1}{4})$ **8.** $-9.8 + 10.1$

Add.

9. $-6 + (-9)$ **10.** $-12 + (-13)$ **11.** $-\frac{1}{2} + (-\frac{1}{2})$ **12.** $-2.3 + (-4.7)$

13. $-3 + 4$ **14.** $-9 + 5$ **15.** $9 + (-5)$ **16.** $-12 + 18$

17. $-4.6 + (-2.7)$ **18.** $0.9 + (-9.4)$ **19.** $-3\frac{2}{3} + 4\frac{1}{2}$ **20.** $-\frac{4}{5} + (-\frac{1}{4})$

21. $-40 + 15$ **22.** $-8 + (-17)$ **23.** $(-9) + 22$ **24.** $-30 + (-11)$

WRITTEN EXERCISES

A   Add.

1. $-3 + 6$ **2.** $3 + 6$ **3.** $(-3) + (-6)$

4. $3 + (-6)$ **5.** $9 + (-6)$ **6.** $(-9) + 6$

7. $2 + (-5)$ **8.** $(-7) + (-2)$ **9.** $(-4) + (-9)$

10. $7 + 5$ **11.** $(-3) + 7$ **12.** $(-10) + (-3)$

13. $6 + (-2)$ **14.** $(-9) + (-6)$ **15.** $8 + (-3)$

16. $6 + 2$ **17.** $(-10) + (-4)$ **18.** $-8 + 3$

19. $9 + 0$ **20.** $0 + 9$ **21.** $(-9) + 8$

22. $7 + (-3)$ **23.** $8 + (-7)$ **24.** $(-3) + (-7)$

25. $9 + 6$ **26.** $(-6) + 3$ **27.** $5 + (-6)$

28. $(-3) + 7$ **29.** $(-9) + 0$ **30.** $0 + (-9)$

31. $2\frac{3}{4} + (-1\frac{1}{2})$ **32.** $(-\frac{3}{5}) + (-\frac{2}{3})$ **33.** $7 + 4\frac{1}{2}$

34. $-9\frac{1}{3} + 6\frac{3}{4}$ **35.** $(-6\frac{5}{12}) + 8\frac{1}{6}$ **36.** $8.6 + (-3.7)$

37. $(-4.5) + 2.4$ **38.** $8.0 + (-3.2)$ **39.** $(-6.0) + (-7.2)$

40. $8.2 + 6.4$ **41.** $1.3 + (-0.7)$ **42.** $2.4 + (-4.5)$

43. $(-3.7) + 8.6$ **44.** $(-4.0) + 0.7$ **45.** $(-1.6) + (-6.0)$

APPLICATIONS: **Using Addition**

In Exercises 46–53:

a. Use positive and negative numbers to represent each word description.

b. Find the sum.

46. An elevator on the 21st floor goes down 8 floors. Then it goes up 4 floors and the door opens. On what floor is the elevator now?

47. On three successive plays, a football team lost 4 yards, gained 5 yards, and gained 7 yards. What was the team's net gain in the three plays?

48. The temperature at 9 A.M. was 3°C. At noon, the temperature had risen 7°. By 5 P.M., it had fallen 4°, and by midnight, it had fallen another 6°. What was the midnight temperature?

49. The stock of HCJ Corporation opened in the morning at $52 per share. Two hours later, it lost $4. By closing time, it gained $2. What was its value at closing?

50. A plane was flying at an altitude of 12,000 meters. Then it dropped 3000 meters and rose 780 meters. What was the plane's new altitude?

51. Joann has $250 in her checking account. She wrote checks for $75 and $40 and made a deposit of $110. What was her new balance?

52. A submarine is cruising at a depth of 40 meters below the ocean's surface. The submarine then descends 15 meters and rises 18 meters. What is the submarine's new depth?

53. A company's loss during its first year of operation was $15,890. During its second and third years, it had profits of $5750 and $30,765. Find the net profit or loss over the three years.

B   Add.

54. $[5 + (-8)] + (-2)$

55. $[5 + (-7)] + (-8)$

56. $[-8 + 9] + [7 + (-5)]$

57. $[7 + 4] + [(-9) + 8]$

58. $-12 + [37 + (-18)]$

59. $2 + [37 + (-22)]$

Find the real number that can replace the variable to make a true sentence.

60. $y + 5 = 17$

61. $q + 9 = 21$

62. $n = -8 + 22$

63. $-11 + 10 = n$

64. $6 + y = -2$

65. $10 + t = 1$

66. $a + (-7) = -17$

67. $u + (-3) = -5$

68. $7 + c = 0$

69. $z + (-1\frac{2}{5}) = 0$

70. $-14 + u = 42$

71. $-18 + r = 20$

Evaluate each expression when $x = -10$, $y = 8$ and $q = -15$.

72. $x + y$

73. $x + q$

74. $y + q$

75. $y + y$

76. $q + q$

77. $x + y + q$

78. $x + x + x$

79. $q + q + x$

C

80. The following gives the steps for the proof of the following statement.

$$-14 + 8 = -6$$

Give the reasons for Steps 2, 3, and 4.

Statements	Reasons
1. $-14 + 8 = [-6 + (-8)] + 8$	1. Theorem 2–1
2. $\quad = -6 + [(-8) + 8]$	2. __?__
3. $\quad = -6 + \quad 0$	3. __?__
4. $\quad = -6$	4. __?__

81. Give the reasons for Steps 2, 3, and 4 in the following proof that $-11 + 17 = 6$.

Statements	Reasons
1. $-11 + 17 = -11 + (11 + 6)$	1. Renaming 17 as $11 + 6$
2. $\quad = (-11 + 11) + 6$	2. __?__
3. $\quad = \quad 0 \quad + 6$	3. __?__
4. $\quad = 6$	4. __?__

82. To prove that $-4 + (-3) = -(4 + 3)$, you must show that $-4 + (-3)$ is the opposite of $(4 + 3)$, or that the sum of $-4 + (-3)$ and $(4 + 3)$ is 0. Give the reason why each statement in the following proof is true.

Statements	Reasons
1. $[-4 + (-3)] + (4 + 3) = -4 + [(-3) + 4] + 3$	1. __?__
2. $\quad = -4 + [4 + (-3)] + 3$	2. __?__
3. $\quad = (-4 + 4) + [(-3) + 3]$	3. __?__
4. $\quad = \quad 0 \quad + \quad 0$	4. __?__
5. $\quad = 0$	5. __?__

83. Once you know that the sum is 0, you know that $-4 + (-3)$ and $(4 + 3)$ are inverses. What part of the additive inverse postulate tells you that if $-4 + (-3)$ is the opposite of $(4 + 3)$, then $-4 + (-3)$ must be the same number as $-(4 + 3)$? Hence, $-4 + (-3) = -(4 + 3)$ is true.

Prove each of the following.

84. $-9 + (-15) = -24$ **85.** $-9 + 7 = -2$ **86.** $-9 + 17 = 8$

———— **REVIEW CAPSULE FOR SECTION 2–4** ————

Subtract.

1. $66 - 45$ 2. $65 - 48$ 3. $603 - 245$ 4. $724 - 596$

5. $6.2 - 0.8$ 6. $12.3 - 8.5$ 7. $10.47 - 3.64$ 8. $14 - 10.7$

Subtract. Write your answers in lowest terms.

9. $\frac{9}{10} - \frac{2}{10}$ 10. $15 - \frac{5}{8}$ 11. $\frac{3}{12} - \frac{1}{4}$ 12. $\frac{3}{5} - \frac{1}{2}$

13. $3\frac{1}{6} - \frac{2}{3}$ 14. $6\frac{1}{2} - 3\frac{7}{8}$ 15. $3\frac{1}{8} - 2\frac{5}{6}$ 16. $13\frac{5}{8} - 6\frac{11}{12}$

2-4 Subtraction of Real Numbers

Note that the answers to each pair of the following problems are the same.

Subtraction: $10 - 3 = 7$ **Addition:** $10 + (-3) = 7$

Subtraction: $17 - 6.1 = 10.9$ **Addition:** $17 + (-6.1) = 10.9$

Subtraction: $\dfrac{3}{5} - \dfrac{1}{5} = \dfrac{2}{5}$ **Addition:** $\dfrac{3}{5} + \left(-\dfrac{1}{5}\right) = \dfrac{2}{5}$

Thus,

$$10 - 3 = 10 + (-3)$$ ⟵   **NOTE: 3 and −3 are opposites.**

$$17 - 6.1 = 17 + (-16.1)$$ ⟵   **NOTE: 6.1 and −6.1 are opposites.**

$$\frac{3}{5} - \frac{1}{5} = \frac{3}{5} + \left(-\frac{1}{5}\right)$$ ⟵   **NOTE: $\frac{3}{5}$ and $-\frac{3}{5}$ are opposites.**

This suggests that subtraction can be defined in terms of addition.

Definition

> **Subtraction of Real Numbers**
>
> To subtract a real number b from a real number a, add *the opposite of b* to a. That is,
>
> $$a - b = a + (-b)$$

EXAMPLE 1   Subtract: $3 - 7$

Solution: Write the subtraction problem as an addition problem.

$$3 - 7 = 3 + (-7)$$ ⟵   **Add the opposite of 7.**

$$= -4$$

You can use addition to check your answers.

EXAMPLE 2   Subtract: $-5.1 - (-8.2)$

Solution: $-5.1 - (-8.2) = -5.1 + 8.2$ ⟵   **The opposite of (−8.2) is 8.2.**

$$= 3.1$$

Check: Does $3.1 + (-8.2) = -5.1$?   Yes ✔

To find the amount of change, **subtract the first value from the final value.**

EXAMPLE 3   The temperature was $-3°$ C. It is now $9°$ C. How much did the temperature change?

Solution: Subtract -3 (first value) *from* 9 (final value).

$$9 - (-3) = 9 + 3$$

$$= 12 \qquad \text{The temperature changed } 12°.$$

CLASSROOM EXERCISES

Write an addition problem for each subtraction problem.

1. $6 - 3$ **2.** $0 - 9$ **3.** $-10 - 5$ **4.** $-9 - 15$

5. $-5 - (-2)$ **6.** $-5 - (-10)$ **7.** $8 - (-4)$ **8.** $20 - (-7)$

Subtract.

9. $16 - (-7)$ **10.** $14 - (-8)$ **11.** $-9 - (-4)$ **12.** $-18 - (-5)$

13. $-1.5 - 6.9$ **14.** $-0.9 - (-0.1)$ **15.** $\frac{3}{4} - \frac{1}{2}$ **16.** $-\frac{1}{3} - (-\frac{2}{3})$

WRITTEN EXERCISES

A   Write an addition problem for each subtraction problem.

1. $3 - 6$ **2.** $0 - 7$ **3.** $5 - (-9)$ **4.** $8 - (-3)$

5. $0 - (-2)$ **6.** $0 - (-6)$ **7.** $-5 - (-5)$ **8.** $-3 - (-7)$

9. $-2 - 8$ **10.** $-5 - (6)$ **11.** $-3 - (-9)$ **12.** $0 - (-8)$

13. $-2\frac{1}{2} - (-\frac{1}{2})$ **14.** $-5.4 - (-2.6)$ **15.** $2.9 - 3.8$ **16.** $-6 - 2\frac{3}{4}$

Subtract.

17. $5 - 11$ **18.** $6 - 8$ **19.** $-4 - 5$ **20.** $-5 - 1$

21. $-6 - 2$ **22.** $-6 - 4$ **23.** $4 - (-6)$ **24.** $-6 - (-4)$

25. $-4 - 6$ **26.** $-8 - 3$ **27.** $-4 - 8$ **28.** $-8 - 4$

29. $16 - (-15)$ **30.** $24 - (-12)$ **31.** $15 - 15$

32. $9 - 9$ **33.** $-9 - 10$ **34.** $-10 - 10$

35. $-2.4 - 9.4$ **36.** $-54 - 14$ **37.** $-7.8 - 0$

38. $0 - 7.8$ **39.** $\frac{1}{2} - (-\frac{1}{2})$ **40.** $\frac{5}{3} - (-\frac{2}{3})$

41. $-54 - (-14)$ **42.** $-64 - (-74)$ **43.** $12.3 - 6.7$

44. $6.7 - 12.3$ **45.** $12.3 - (-6.7)$ **46.** $6.7 - (-12.3)$

47. $-12.3 - (-19)$ **48.** $-6.7 - (12.3)$ **49.** $-6.7 - (-12.3)$

50. $-12.3 - (-6.7)$ **51.** $-\frac{1}{2} - (-\frac{1}{2})$ **52.** $-\frac{3}{4} - (-\frac{3}{4})$

APPLICATIONS: Using Subtraction

53. The temperature six hours ago was $-1°C$. It is now $11°C$. How much did the temperature change in the last six hours?

54. The actual temperature is $20°F$. The wind chill temperature is $-15°$. How much colder than the actual temperature is the wind chill?

55. A dolphin is swimming at a depth of 2 meters below the surface of a pool. It leaps to a height of 1 meter above the surface. Find the difference in height.

56. The greatest recorded temperature change in one day in North America took place in Montana. The change was from $7°C$ to $-49°C$. Find the amount of change.

57. The lowest temperature ever recorded in West Virginia was −37°F. The lowest temperature recorded in Wyoming was −63°F. Find the difference between the two temperatures.

58. The highest point in Texas, Guadalupe Peak, is 2667 meters above sea level. The greatest known depth of the Atlantic Ocean (in the Puerto Rico trench) is 8648 meters below sea level. Find the difference between the points.

B Subtract.

59. $(2 - 10) - 3$

60. $2 - (10 - 3)$

61. $(3 - 7) - (2 - 9)$

62. $(5 - 2) - (-4 - 8)$

63. $12 - (8 - 7)$

64. $(-4 - 9) - 3$

65. $-\frac{2}{3} - \frac{1}{12} - (-\frac{1}{4})$

66. $-1.8 - 0.12 - 0.36$

67. $16 - 32 - 15 + 14$

Evaluate when $x = 12$, $y = -6$, and $q = -4$.

68. $y - x$

69. $x - y$

70. $y - q$

71. $q - y$

72. $x - y - y$

73. $y - q - q$

74. $q - y - y$

75. $q - q$

76. $x + y + q$

77. $y + y + q$

78. $q + q + x$

79. $x + x + y + q$

C Classify each of the following as true, T, or false, F. When an equation is false, tell why it is false. The replacement set is the set of real numbers.

80. $-6 + (-2) = 4$

81. $-\frac{2}{3} - (-\frac{2}{3}) = \frac{1}{3}$

82. $-4 - (-2) = 2 - (-4)$

83. $0 = 0.24 - (-0.24)$

84. $8 - (-8) = 0$

85. $6 - 2 = 6 + (-2)$

86. $|8 - 2| = |2 - 8|$

87. $|8 - 2| = |8| - |2|$

88. $|2 - 8| = |2| - |8|$

89. $-3 + (-3) = -6$

90. $a - b = a + (-b)$

91. $|a - b| = |b - a|$

_____ Review _____

Write without parentheses. (Section 2–1)

1. $-(-1.5)$

2. $-(600)$

3. $-(16 + 21)$

4. $-(9.2 - 5.6)$

Use algebraic symbols to represent each sentence. (Section 2–1)

5. The opposite of losing 3 games is winning 3 games.

6. A rise of 15° in temperature is the opposite of a fall of 15°.

Evaluate. (Section 2–2)

7. $|5| + |13|$

8. $|-\sqrt{13}|$

9. $|4| + |-3|$

10. $-|1.6| + |1.6|$

Solve. (Section 2–2)

11. $x = |-6|$

12. $m = -|8|$

13. $|y| = 9$

14. $|a| = |-3|$

Add or subtract as indicated. (Sections 2–3 and 2–4)

15. $-5 + 2$

16. $7 + (-12)$

17. $[5 + 4] + [(-7) + 3]$

18. $(4 + 10) - 5$

19. $-2.3 - 0.16 - 0.05$

20. $10 - 26 - 8 + 16$

Consumer Applications: **Investing**

When you buy shares of **stock** in a corporation, you become part owner of the corporation. Stock prices are listed each day in the business section of the newspaper. The prices are **quoted** (listed) in **eighths of a dollar.**

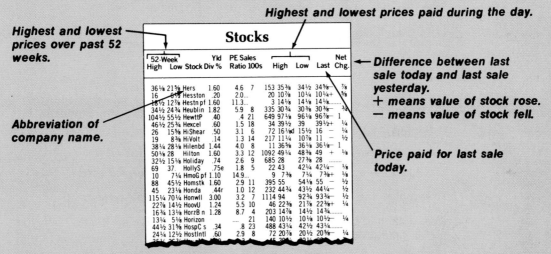

Highest and lowest prices over past 52 weeks.

Abbreviation of company name.

Highest and lowest prices paid during the day.

Difference between last sale today and last sale yesterday.
+ means value of stock rose.
— means value of stock fell.

Price paid for last sale today.

To find the amount of **profit** or **loss** on a stock sale, use this formula.

$$\text{Profit (Loss)} = \frac{\text{Amount Received}}{\text{for Stock}} - \frac{\text{Total Cost}}{\text{of Stock}}$$

EXAMPLE   Bill Aikens bought 200 shares of stock at $40\frac{5}{8}$. The stockbroker charged $90.85 for a commission. A few months later, Bill sold the stock at $38\frac{7}{8}$. The broker charged $85.60 at that time. How much was Bill's profit or loss?

Solution:
- ☐1 Cost of stock: $200 \times \$40.625 + \$90.85 = \$8215.85$ ◄——— $\$40\frac{5}{8} = \$40.625$
- ☐2 Amount received: $200 \times \$38.875 - \$85.60 = \$7689.40$ ◄— $\$38\frac{7}{8} = \$38.875$
- ☐3 Profit (Loss) = $\$7689.40 - \$8215.85 = -\$526.45$

Thus, Bill lost **$526.45** on the transaction.

EXERCISES

Find the amount of profit or loss on each transaction.

	Number of Shares	Buying Price	Broker's Commission	Selling Price	Broker's Commission	Profit (Loss)
1.	100	$36\frac{3}{8}$	$ 40.00	$38\frac{1}{8}$	$ 42.00	?
2.	200	$42\frac{7}{8}$	$ 90.50	$49\frac{5}{8}$	$ 92.80	?
3.	300	$26\frac{1}{8}$	$ 73.40	$20\frac{7}{8}$	$ 60.90	?
4.	1000	$31\frac{7}{8}$	$322.60	$27\frac{3}{8}$	$278.20	?

2–5 Combining Like Terms

A **term** is a real number, a variable, or the product of real numbers and variables. Each of these is a *term*.

$$3x^2 \qquad \frac{1}{2}xy^3 \qquad \frac{4}{5}x^2 \qquad 7mn \qquad \frac{a}{2b}$$

$3x^2$ and $\frac{4}{5}x^2$ are *like terms*. **Like terms** have the same variables. In like terms, corresponding variables have the same exponents.

Terms	Like Terms	Reason
$3z$ and $5z$	Yes	Same variable, z, with same exponent, 1
$2y^2$ and $-3x^2$	No	Different variables
$3m^2n$ and $5mn$	No	Different exponents for m
9 and $4y$	No	The number, 9, has no variable

To **combine like terms** means to **add or subtract the like terms.**

To add or subtract like terms, you apply the distributive postulate. Then you add or subtract the numerical coefficients.

Term	Numerical Coefficient
$-7y$	-7
$16m^2n^2$	16
$1 \cdot q$ or q	1

Note carefully the last expression in the table.

$$q = 1 \cdot q = 1q$$

Similarly,

$$-q = -1 \cdot q = -1q$$

EXAMPLE 1 Combine like terms: $8x + x$

Solution: $8x + x = 8x + 1x$

$\qquad\qquad = (8 + 1)x$ ◄——— **By the distributive postulate**

$\qquad\qquad = 9x$

To subtract like terms, first write the subtraction as addition. Then proceed as in Example 1.

EXAMPLE 2 Combine like terms: $-3m - 7m$

Solution: $-3m - 7m = -3m + (-7m)$

$\qquad\qquad\qquad = [-3 + (-7)]m$ ◄——— **By the distributive postulate**

$\qquad\qquad\qquad = -10m$

When you combine like terms, you are **simplifying an algebraic expression.**

EXAMPLE 3 Simplify: $5t + 3r + 9t - 10r - 8$

Solution: $5t + 3r + 9t - 10r - 8 = (5t + 9t) + (3r - 10r) - 8$ ← By the commutative and associative postulates

$$= \quad 14t \quad + \quad (-7r) \quad - 8$$

$$= \mathbf{14t - 7r - 8}$$

When you simplify an algebraic expression, the original expression and the simplified expression are equivalent. **Equivalent algebraic expressions** name the same number for all real–number replacements of the variable.

> **Substitution Principle**
>
> If two expressions are equivalent, you can always replace one with the other in a given expression.

CLASSROOM EXERCISES

Identify each pair of terms as *like terms* or *unlike terms*. Give a reason for each answer.

1. $2x$ and $3x$
2. $9m$ and $6r$
3. $\frac{1}{2}y$ and $2y^2$
4. $-6m$ and $8m^2$
5. $4xy$ and $7xy$
6. $3a$ and $-11a$

State the numerical coefficient of each term.

7. $2a$
8. $-\frac{1}{2}x^2$
9. $-0.05t$
10. $\frac{2}{3}r^3$
11. t
12. y

Combine like terms.

13. $2x + 3x$
14. $8y + y$
15. $7m - 3m$
16. $-9x - x$

WRITTEN EXERCISES

A Identify each pair of terms as *like terms* or *unlike terms*. Give a reason for each answer.

1. $4x, 7x$
2. $8y, 4m$
3. $9, 7y$
4. $6a, -8$
5. $x^2, 4x$
6. $-7y, 2.5y$
7. $-15m, 18n$
8. $8r, -r$
9. $4t, -8t$
10. $0.4xy^2, 0.1xy^2$
11. $3x^4, 5x^4$
12. $3a^2b, 5ab^2$

Combine like terms.

13. $8x + 2x$
14. $7y + 13y$
15. $15m + 6.2m$
16. $5a^2 + 7a^2$
17. $8mn + 6mn$
18. $3ab + 11ab$

19. $9x + x$ **20.** $15y + y$ **21.** $4m^2 + m^2$

22. $3ab + ab$ **23.** $m + 19m$ **24.** $a + 9a$

25. $4y + (-12y)$ **26.** $m + (-16m)$ **27.** $-4.1y + (-2.3y)$

28. $-0.4x + (-0.6x)$ **29.** $-16t + (-t)$ **30.** $(-15x) + (-1x)$

31. $7m - 6m$ **32.** $9t - 3t$ **33.** $12x - 9x$

34. $8a - 5a$ **35.** $4x - 1x$ **36.** $9m - 1m$

37. $-3a - 4a$ **38.** $-7b - 5b$ **39.** $-5m - (-8m)$

40. $-3t - (-2t)$ **41.** $-6r - (-1r)$ **42.** $-30q - (-1q)$

Simplify.

43. $3a + 2a + 4$ **44.** $8x + 3x + 9$ **45.** $15y + 6y + 3$

46. $4m + 7m - 5$ **47.** $6 + 2x + 4x$ **48.** $15 + 9y - 4y$

49. $5x + 7x - 6y$ **50.** $4y - y + 8$ **51.** $5x - x - 15$

52. $4a - b - 7b$ **53.** $2m + 7m - 8m$ **54.** $4a + 7a - 9a$

55. $7x - x + 3y + 57$ **56.** $12x - 3y + x + 2y$ **57.** $15xy - 2xy - 7xy + x$

58. $8rt + 3rt + t - 3t$ **59.** $4\frac{1}{2}xy + 7\frac{1}{3}xy + 2\frac{1}{4}xy$ **60.** $19m - m - 3n + 2n$

61. $4.75r + 1.62r + r$ **62.** $2.7m - 1.9m + m$ **63.** $4.87 + 6.52q + q$

APPLICATIONS: Using Like Terms

B   Find the sum of the areas of each group of figures.

64. Rectangle: $A = $ (length $\cdot$ width)   **65.** Parallelogram: $A = $ (base $\cdot$ height)

66. Triangle: $A = \frac{1}{2}$(base $\cdot$ height)   **67.** Rectangle: $A = $ (length $\cdot$ width)

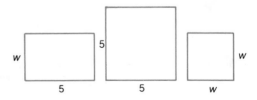

Classify each statement as true, *T*, or false, *F*. When a statement is false, give a numerical example to show why. This is called a **counterexample**.

68. $8x + x = 8x$ **69.** $3m + m = m^2$ **70.** $8 + 3x = 11x$

71. $8m - 2m + 5m = 11$ **72.** $m + m + m = m^3$ **73.** $4ab + a = 5ab$

Classify each statement as true, *T*, or false, *F*. When a statement is false, give a numerical example to show why it is false.

74. $4(a + b) + 7(a + b) = 11(a + b)$

75. $2(m - n) + 7(m - n) = 9(m - n)$

76. $4x + x^2 = 5x^3$

77. $5x^2 + 2x^2 + 9x^2 = 21x^2$

In Exercises 78–81, write a formula for the area of each shaded region. Simplify the result. Use the formulas for the area of a rectangle and of a triangle (see Exercises 64 and 66 on page 62).

78.

79.

80.

81.

Simplify.

82. $3 \cdot 5a - 7 \cdot 3b - 3 \cdot 2a + 2 \cdot 9b$

83. $\frac{5}{8}c - \frac{1}{4}d - \frac{3}{7}c + \frac{3}{5}d$

84. $7x - 3y + 2z - x + 4y + 6z$

85. $2c - 1\frac{1}{2}d + 1\frac{1}{4}c - 2\frac{3}{4}c$

86. $5x - y + 3 \cdot 5z - 1\frac{1}{6}z + 2\frac{1}{2}x + 3\frac{1}{4}y$

87. $5(x - y) + 7(x - y) - 8(x - y)$

88. $3(x + 7y) - 5(x + 7y) + 9(x + 7y)$

89. $-5(2x + 8y) + 9(2x + 8y) - 5(2x + 8y)$

90. $6(x^2 + y^2) + 7(x^2 + y^2)$

91. $9(x^2 - y^2) - 3(x^2 - y^2)$

92. $3(a + b) + (a + b) + 9(a + b)$

93. $-5(a - b) - (a - b) + 8(a - b)$

Ⓒ Complete.

94. $ax + bx = (\underline{\ ?\ } + \underline{\ ?\ })x$

95. $mx - my = (\underline{\ ?\ } - \underline{\ ?\ })m$

96. $cr - dr = (\underline{\ ?\ } - \underline{\ ?\ })r$

97. $7r + 6r = (\underline{\ ?\ } + \underline{\ ?\ })r$

98. $a(x + y) + b(x + y) = (\underline{\ ?\ } + \underline{\ ?\ })(x + y)$

99. $c(x + y) - d(x + y) = (\underline{\ ?\ } - \underline{\ ?\ })(x + y)$

———————— **REVIEW CAPSULE FOR SECTION 2-6** ————————

Multiply.

1. 54×9

2. 84×27

3. 703×428

4. 505×901

5. 0.7×0.8

6. 5.6×8.2

7. 4.059×1000

8. 0.056×34.9

Multiply. Write your answers in lowest terms.

9. $\frac{1}{4} \times \frac{4}{5}$

10. $\frac{2}{3} \times \frac{2}{5}$

11. $\frac{3}{8} \times 7$

12. $4\frac{3}{10} \times 8\frac{5}{16}$

2–6 Multiplication of Real Numbers

You already know that the product of two positive numbers is positive. You also know that the *product of a real number and zero is zero.* This is called the *Zero Multiplication Theorem.*

Theorem 2–3

> **Zero Multiplication Theorem**
>
> For any real number a, $a \cdot 0 = 0 \cdot a = 0.$

In Table 1, the first factor, 4, stays the same. The second factor decreases by 1 at each step.

If the pattern continues, what are the missing products?

$4 \cdot 4 = 16$	$4 \cdot (-1) = -4$
$4 \cdot 3 = 12$	$4 \cdot (-2) = -8$
$4 \cdot 2 = 8$	$4 \cdot (-3) = \underline{\ ?\ }$
$4 \cdot 1 = 4$	$4 \cdot (-4) = \underline{\ ?\ }$
$4 \cdot 0 = 0$	

Table 1

The table suggests Theorem 2–4.

Theorem 2–4

> **Negative Product Theorem**
>
> The product of two real numbers is negative when one number is positive and the other is negative. That is, for $a < 0$ and $b > 0$,
> $$a \cdot b = -(|a| \cdot |b|).$$

Example 1 applies the Negative Product theorem.

EXAMPLE 1   Multiply: $-21 \cdot 9.2$

   Solution: $-21 \cdot 9.2 = -(\ ?\ )$ ⟵ **The product is negative.**

$= -193.2$

Since multiplication of real numbers is commutative, you also know that the following is true.

$$4 \cdot (-2) = -2 \cdot 4 = -8$$

In Table 2 at the top of page 65, the first factor, (-4), stays the same. The second factor decreases by 1 at each step.

If the pattern continues, what are the missing products?

$$-4 \cdot 3 = -12 \qquad \qquad -4 \cdot (-1) = 4$$
$$-4 \cdot 2 = -8 \qquad \qquad -4 \cdot (-2) = 8$$
$$-4 \cdot 1 = -4 \qquad \qquad -4 \cdot (-3) = ?$$
$$-4 \cdot 0 = 0 \qquad \qquad -4 \cdot (-4) = ?$$

Table 2

Table 2 suggests Theorem 2–5.

Theorem 2–5

> **Positive Product Theorem**
>
> The product of two real numbers is positive when both numbers are positive or when both numbers are negative. That is, for $a < 0$ and $b < 0$, or for $a > 0$ and $b > 0$,
> $$a \cdot b = |a| \cdot |b|.$$

Example 2 applies Theorem 2–5 in finding a product.

EXAMPLE 2 Multiply: $-18 \cdot \left(-\dfrac{2}{3}\right)$

Solution: $-18 \cdot \left(-\dfrac{2}{3}\right) = (\ ?\ ) \longleftarrow$ **The product is positive.**

$= 12 \longleftarrow \overset{6}{\cancel{18}} \dfrac{2}{\cancel{3}} = 6 \cdot 2 = 12$

CLASSROOM EXERCISES

In Exercises 1–8, state whether each product is positive or negative.

1. $4 \cdot (-6)$ **2.** $-3 \cdot 9$ **3.** $-8 \cdot (-9)$ **4.** $-6 \cdot (-1)$

5. $-9 \cdot 7$ **6.** $12 \cdot (-\frac{1}{6})$ **7.** $(-18)(-3.7)$ **8.** $200(-8.4)$

Multiply.

9. $7 \cdot (-8)$ **10.** $13.6 \cdot 0$ **11.** $(-9)(-8)$ **12.** $(-\frac{1}{5})(15)$

13. $\frac{4}{5} \cdot 25$ **14.** $(-1)(-1)$ **15.** $(-80)(0)$ **16.** $(-1.5)(100)$

WRITTEN EXERCISES

A   Multiply.

1. $6 \times (-3)$ **2.** -5×2 **3.** $2 \times (-5)$ **4.** -2×5

5. $5(-2)$ **6.** $2(5)$ **7.** $7(0)$ **8.** $(-4)0$

9. $-4 \cdot 3$ **10.** $4 \cdot (-3)$ **11.** $-\frac{3}{4} \cdot \frac{2}{3}$ **12.** $\frac{1}{8} \cdot (-\frac{5}{6})$

13. $(-2)(-5)$ **14.** $(-5)(-2)$ **15.** $(-3)(5)$ **16.** $(-4)(7)$

17. $(-4)(-3)$ **18.** $4(-7)$ **19.** $(-2.5)(-0.1)$ **20.** $(-\frac{1}{8})(-\frac{5}{6})$

21. $(-5)(-5)$ **22.** $6 \cdot 3$ **23.** $-6 \cdot 3$ **24.** $-3 \cdot 6$

25. $8 \cdot (-\frac{1}{4})$ **26.** $12 \cdot 6$ **27.** $12 \cdot (-6)$ **28.** $-12 \cdot 6$

29. $(-1)(5)$ **30.** $8(-2.5)$ **31.** $\frac{2}{3}(-12)$ **32.** $3.8(-10)$

33. $-62(100)$ **34.** $-17(28)$ **35.** $2\frac{1}{5}(-\frac{3}{5})$ **36.** $33(-\frac{1}{3})$

37. $8.1(0)$ **38.** $-5(2.4)$ **39.** $-7.2(\frac{1}{4})$ **40.** $-6(-3)$

41. $-4(-5)$ **42.** $4(-5)$ **43.** $-4(5)$ **44.** $4(5)$

45. $0(-2)$ **46.** $-2(-9)$ **47.** $7(-1)$ **48.** $-48(-10)$

49. $-1 \cdot (-1)$ **50.** $-\frac{2}{3} \cdot (-\frac{3}{2})$ **51.** $-0.5 \cdot (-12)$ **52.** $-1.1 \cdot 3.4$

53. $(1)(-1)(1)$ **54.** $2(-4)(5)$ **55.** $(-5)(6)(2)$ **56.** $(2)(3)(-1)$

B

57. $\frac{1}{2}(-8)(5)$ **58.** $(-0.1)(10)(10)$ **59.** $(-0.1)(0.1)(0.1)$ **60.** $\frac{1}{2}(-\frac{1}{2})(\frac{1}{2})$

61. $(-2\frac{1}{2})(\frac{2}{5})(1)$ **62.** $(4)(0)(-9)$ **63.** $(3\frac{1}{2})(\frac{1}{2})(-2)$ **64.** $(4\frac{1}{5})(5)(-6)$

65. $(\frac{2}{3})(\frac{2}{3})(\frac{2}{3})$ **66.** $(\frac{7}{5})(-\frac{7}{5})(2)$ **67.** $(\frac{8}{7})(-1)(\frac{7}{8})$ **68** $(10)(-\frac{1}{100})(2)$

69. $5(4)(-2)$ **70.** $-5(4)(-2)$ **71.** $-6(-5)(-4)$ **72.** $5(-4)(-2)$

73. $6(-4)(-5)$ **74.** $-8(-1)(2)$ **75.** $3(0)(-5)$ **76.** $5(-6)(-4)$

77. $-2(-2)(-2)$ **78.** $(-3)^2$ **79.** $(-4)^2$ **80.** $(5)^2$

81. $(-1)^2$ **82.** $(1)^2$ **83.** $(-1)^3$ **84.** $(-1)^4$

In Exercises 85–94, replace the __?__ with $<$, $=$, or $>$, to make true statements.

85. $2(-3)$ __?__ $-3(2)$ 　　　　**86.** $-6(-1)$ __?__ $-1(6)$

87. $-0.34(-6)$ __?__ $-0.17(-3)$ 　**88.** $-\frac{3}{2}(\frac{1}{2})$ __?__ $-\frac{1}{2}(\frac{3}{2})$

89. $-6(0)$ __?__ $0(6)$ 　　　　　**90.** $|4 \cdot 5|$ __?__ $|4| \cdot |5|$

91. $|-0.34 \cdot -2|$ __?__ $|-0.34| \cdot |-2|$ 　**92.** $|0 \cdot 1|$ __?__ $|0| \cdot |1|$

93- $|0.2 \cdot 0.1|$ __?__ $|-0.2| \cdot |0.1|$ 　**94.** $|\frac{2}{3} \cdot \frac{1}{2}|$ __?__ $|\frac{2}{3}| \cdot |\frac{1}{2}|$

In Exercises 95–110, evaluate each expression for $x = -3$, $y = -2$, and $p = 0$.

95. $2x$ 　　　**96.** $3y$ 　　　**97.** $-2x$ 　　　**98.** $-7y$

99. px 　　　**100.** xy 　　　**101.** $3xy$ 　　　**102.** $5pxy$

103. $3x + y$ 　**104.** $2x + p$ 　**105.** $2y + p$ 　**106.** $4x + 7y$

107. x^2 　　　**108.** y^3 　　　**109.** px^2 　　　**110.** x^2y^2

For each equation in Exercises 111–114, state whether the solution is positive, negative, or equal to zero.

111. $5x = -15$ 　**112.** $-3x = 15$ 　**113.** $-9x = -27$ 　**114.** $3x = 0$

The **Multiplication Property for Equations** states that if you multiply both sides of an equation by the same nonzero number, you obtain an equivalent equation. You can use this and other postulates to prove that $3(-4) = -12$ and to prove that $(-3)(-4) = 12$.

Complete the steps in each proof by supplying the missing reason or reasons.

115. Prove: $3(-4) = -12$

Statements	Reasons
1. $4 + (-4) = 0$	1. Additive inverse postulate
2. $3[4 + (-4)] = 3 \cdot 0$	2. Multiplication property for equations
3. $3[4 + (-4)] = 0$	3. ___?___
4. $3 \cdot 4 + 3(-4) = 0$	4. ___?___
5. Hence, $3 \cdot 4$ and $3(-4)$ are additive inverses.	5. Additive inverse postulate
6. $3(-4) = -(3 \cdot 4)$, or -12	6. Additive inverse postulate

116. Prove: $(-3)(-4) = 12$

Statements	Reasons
1. $4 + (-4) = 0$	1. ___?___
2. $-3[4 + (-4)] = -3 \cdot 0$	2. Multiplication property for equations
3. $-3 \cdot 4 + (-3)(-4) = 0$	3. ___?___
4. $-12 + (-3)(-4) = 0$	4. ___?___
5. Hence, -12 and $(-3)(-4)$ are additive inverses.	5. ___?___
6. $(-3)(-4) = 12$	6. ___?___

_____ **REVIEW CAPSULE FOR SECTION 2-7** _____

Divide.

1. $95 \div 19$ **2.** $5913 \div 73$ **3.** $3780 \div 756$ **4.** $4606 \div 658$

5. $5.4 \div 6$ **6.** $5.82 \div 0.6$ **7.** $59.4 \div 1000$ **8.** $4.76 \div 0.068$

Divide. Write your answers in lowest terms.

9. $\frac{1}{9} \div \frac{1}{3}$ **10.** $\frac{7}{8} \div 4\frac{2}{3}$ **11.** $23 \div \frac{1}{4}$ **12.** $8\frac{3}{5} \div 9\frac{1}{2}$

13. $15 \div \frac{9}{10}$ **14.** $12\frac{5}{8} \div 10\frac{5}{6}$ **15.** $6\frac{1}{2} \div 6\frac{1}{2}$ **16.** $3\frac{3}{4} \div 2\frac{7}{10}$

Round each number to the nearest tenth.

17. 1.59 **18.** 0.42 **19.** 0.005 **20.** 21.35 **21.** 157.99

22. 7.03 **23.** 14.49 **24.** 76.13 **25.** 1.006 **26.** 0.019

2-7 Division of Real Numbers

Since division and multiplication are related, you can use multiplication to find the pattern for dividing positive and negative numbers.

Multiplication	Division
Since $5 \times 3 = 15$,	$15 \div 3 = 5$, and $15 \div 5 = 3$.
Since $-5 \times 3 = -15$,	$-15 \div 3 = -5$, and $-15 \div -5 = 3$.
Since $5 \times -3 = -15$,	$-15 \div 5 = -3$, and $-15 \div -3 = 5$.

Thus, the pattern for dividing positive and negative numbers is the same as the pattern for multiplying them.

Division of Real Numbers

1. The quotient of two positive numbers is **positive**.
2. The quotient of two negative numbers is **positive**.
3. The quotient of a negative number and a positive number or of a positive number and a negative number is **negative**.

EXAMPLE 1 Tell whether the quotient is positive or negative.

    a. $-18 \div -6$ **b.** $16 \div -4$ **c.** $-20 \div 5$

Solutions: **a. Positive** ⟵——— **By Rule 2**

           b. Negative ⟵——— **By Rule 3**

           c. Negative ⟵——— **By Rule 3**

Any two numbers whose product is 1 are called **reciprocals** or **multiplicative inverses** of each other. Thus,

$$3 \text{ and } \frac{1}{3} \text{ are reciprocals because } 3 \cdot \frac{1}{3} = 1;$$

$$-\frac{5}{8} \text{ and } \left(-\frac{8}{5}\right) \text{ are reciprocals because } -\frac{5}{8} \cdot \left(-\frac{8}{5}\right) = 1;$$

$$\frac{1}{6} \text{ and } 6 \text{ are reciprocals because } \frac{1}{6} \cdot 6 = 1.$$

Postulate

Multiplicative Inverse Postulate

For any real number a, $a \neq 0$, there exists one and only one real number $\frac{1}{a}$, such that $a \cdot \frac{1}{a} = 1$.

You can also divide by multiplying by the reciprocal of the divisor.

EXAMPLE 2 Divide: **a.** $24 \div (-6)$ **b.** $-24 \div (-\frac{5}{6})$

Reciprocals

Solutions: **a.** $24 \div (-6) = 24 \cdot -\frac{1}{6}$ **b.** $-24 \div -\frac{5}{6} = -24 \cdot -\frac{6}{5}$

$$= -4$$

$$= \frac{144}{5}, \text{ or } 24\frac{4}{5}$$

Recall that the quotient of zero and any number (except zero) is zero. **Division by zero is not defined.**

Finding an *arithmetic mean* (or *average*) involves finding a quotient. The **arithmetic mean** of a set of numbers, scores, and so on, is the sum of the elements in the set divided by the number of elements.

EXAMPLE 3 A city's low temperatures for one week are shown below. Find the mean low temperature for the week. Round your answer to the nearest tenth.

S	M	T	W	T	F	S
$-2.5°C$	$-3.8°C$	$4.2°C$	$2.9°C$	$-2.8°C$	$-1.4°C$	$-3.2°C$

Solution: ① Add the negative temperatures.
$$-2.5 + (-3.8) + (-2.8) + (-1.4) + (-3.2) = -13.7$$
② Add the positive temperatures: $4.2 + 2.9 = 7.1$
③ Find the sum of the positive and negative temperatures. Then divide by 7, the number of temperatures.
$$\text{Mean} = \frac{-13.7 + 7.1}{7} = \frac{-6.6}{7} \approx -0.9$$

The mean low temperature is about **$-0.9°C$**.

CLASSROOM EXERCISES

Tell whether the quotient is positive or negative.

1. $30 \div (-5)$ **2.** $-110 \div 2$ **3.** $-9 \div (-\frac{1}{3})$ **4.** $80 \div 16$

Write the reciprocal of each number.

5. 7 **6.** $\frac{1}{8}$ **7.** $-\frac{2}{3}$ **8.** -1 **9.** 0 **10.** $2\frac{1}{4}$

Divide.

11. $9 \div 9$ **12.** $9 \div (-9)$ **13.** $-9 \div 9$ **14.** $-9 \div (-9)$ **15.** $-9 \div (-\frac{1}{9})$

WRITTEN EXERCISES

A   Tell whether the quotient is positive or negative.

1. $-6 \div 2$ **2.** $-6 \div (-2)$ **3.** $6 \div (-2)$ **4.** $6 \div 2$

Divide.

5. $-20 \div 5$ **6.** $-20 \div (-5)$ **7.** $20 \div 5$ **8.** $20 \div (-5)$

9. $0 \div 5$ **10.** $0 \div (-5)$ **11.** $100 \div (-2)$ **12.** $-600 \div 5$

13. $-9 \div 9$ **14.** $6 \div 6$ **15.** $4 \div (-4)$ **16.** $-91 \div 7$

17. $48 \div (-8)$ **18.** $-56 \div (-1)$ **19.** $-12 \div \frac{1}{3}$ **20.** $(-3) \div (\frac{1}{2})$

21. $0 \div (-24)$ **22.** $\frac{-5}{8} \div \frac{3}{2}$ **23.** $\frac{-3}{7} \div (\frac{-8}{21})$ **24.** $-7.5 \div (-5)$

25. $-2.56 \div (-0.8)$ **26.** $\frac{7}{10} \div 14$ **27.** $12 \div (\frac{-2}{3})$ **28.** $\frac{-3241}{10}$

29. $\frac{785}{-100}$ **30.** $\frac{-3.2}{-1000}$ **31.** $-6\frac{2}{3} \div 3\frac{3}{4}$ **32.** $(-1\frac{1}{2}) \div (-4\frac{1}{2})$

APPLICATIONS: Using Positive and Negative Numbers

33. The Union Filter Corporation reported the following profit, shown as a positive amount, and loss, shown as a negative amount, for the last six months of a year. Find the average profit or loss for the 6 months.

July	August	September	October	November	December
$55,800	$12,500	−$10,900	−$7,700	$16,700	−$20,800

34. A town's low temperatures for one week are recorded below. Find the mean low temperature for the week. Round your answer to the nearest tenth.

S	M	T	W	T	F	S
−1.1°	−0.6°	0.3°	−1.2°	−2.3°	−0.7°	−0.4°

35. The table below shows the early arrivals, recorded as +, and the late arrivals, recorded as −, of a commuter train service for one week. Find the average number of minutes the train was early or late for the 5 working days. Round your answer to the nearest tenth of a minute.

M	T	W	T	F
+0.8	−1.5	−0.9	−2.6	On time

36. At the end of a year, the national inflation rate was 9.8%. The table below shows the change in rate for each of the first seven months of the following year. Find the average change for these seven months.

J	F	M	A	M	J	J
−0.3%	−0.2%	+0.8%	+1.2%	−0.6%	+0.5%	+1.4%

37. The following table shows the change (in feet per second) in the average speed of a moving car over a five–minute interval. Find the mean change in the average speed between 9:01 and 9:06.

Time Interval	9:01–9:02	9:02–9:03	9:03–9:04	9:04–9:05	9:05–9:06
Change in Speed	+1.4	−0.4	+0.3	−0.1	+0.8

38. The following table shows the amount of gain and loss in the price of a stock over a five-day period. Find the average change over the five days.

M	T	W	T	F
$-1\frac{1}{4}$	$+\frac{3}{4}$	$-\frac{7}{8}$	$+\frac{1}{4}$	$-\frac{5}{8}$

B Simplify.

39. $(3)(-5) \div \left(\frac{-24}{8}\right)$

40. $(-3)(-4)\left(-\left(\frac{-9}{-3}\right)\right)$

41. $\dfrac{(-51) \div (-17)}{-\left(3 \div \frac{-1}{3}\right)}$

42. $\dfrac{(-4 \div 2) \div [(-3)(-4)(-2)]}{-6 \div (-8) \div (-2)}$

43. $\dfrac{(-1)^2 - (-2)^3 + (-3)^2 - (-4)^2}{(-5)^2 - (-3)^2 + (-1)^3 - (-2)^2}$

44. $\dfrac{-100 - [12(-8+3)]}{3^2 + 4^2 + [-11(-5)]}$

45. $\dfrac{[9^2 - (-3)(-7)] \div [40 \div (-2)]}{[(-3)^2 - 2^2] \div (3^2 - 2^2)}$

In Exercises 49–57, evaluate each expression for $x = -10$, $y = -15$, and $q = 0$.

46. $\dfrac{x+y}{-5}$

47. $\dfrac{x-y}{-5}$

48. $\dfrac{y+q}{15}$

49. $\dfrac{2x+q}{4}$

50. $\dfrac{3y}{5}$

51. $\dfrac{x^2+y}{-5}$

52. $\dfrac{x^2+y^2}{x}$

53. $\dfrac{y^2+q^2}{x}$

54. $\dfrac{x^2y^2q^2}{x}$

REVIEW CAPSULE FOR SECTION 2-8

Write a fraction for each mixed number.

1. $6\frac{1}{2}$ **2.** $7\frac{3}{4}$ **3.** $-6\frac{1}{4}$ **4.** $-9\frac{3}{4}$ **5.** $1\frac{1}{10}$ **6.** $-3\frac{5}{8}$

Multiply. Write your answer in lowest terms.

7. $\frac{2}{3} \cdot \frac{9}{4}$ **8.** $6\frac{1}{2} \cdot (-4)$ **9.** $\left(-5\frac{1}{2}\right)\left(-8\frac{1}{4}\right)$ **10.** $\left(-3\frac{1}{2}\right)\left(8\frac{1}{2}\right)$

Complete.

11. $-6 + 6 = \underline{\ ?\ }$ **12.** $4\frac{1}{3} + \left(-4\frac{1}{3}\right) = \underline{\ ?\ }$ **13.** $1.5 + \underline{\ ?\ } = 0$ **14.** $-\frac{2}{3} + \underline{\ ?\ } = 0$

15. $9 \cdot \frac{1}{9} = \underline{\ ?\ }$ **16.** $-\frac{3}{5} \cdot \left(-\frac{5}{3}\right) = \underline{\ ?\ }$ **17.** $\underline{\ ?\ } \cdot \left(-\frac{1}{12}\right) = 1$ **18.** $\left(-\frac{3}{4}\right) \cdot \underline{\ ?\ } = 1$

2-8 Preparing to Solve Equations

The rules for addition, subtraction, multiplication, and division of real numbers are useful in evaluating algebraic expressions.

EXAMPLE 1   Evaluate $y^2 - xy + 3$ for $y = -2$ and $x = 3$.

Solution: $y^2 - xy + 3 = (-2)(-2) - (3)(-2) + 3$ ← Replace y with -2 and x with 3.

$= 4 - (-6) + 3$ ← $4 - (-6) = 4 + 6$

$= 4 + 6 + 3$

$= 13$

Examples 2, 3, and 4 will help you to sharpen the skills needed to solve equations.

Example 2 shows you how to find the product of a real number and an algebraic term having a numerical coefficient.

EXAMPLE 2   Multiply: **a.** $-\dfrac{1}{2} \cdot 2x$ **b.** $-\dfrac{3}{4} \cdot \left(-\dfrac{4}{3}x\right)$

Solutions: Use the associative postulate to group the real numbers.

a. The product will be negative.

$-\dfrac{1}{2} \cdot 2x = -\left(\dfrac{1}{2} \cdot 2\right)x$ ← By the associative postulate

$= -1 \cdot x$

$= -x$

b. The product will be positive.

$-\dfrac{3}{4} \cdot \left(-\dfrac{4}{3}x\right) = \left(\dfrac{\overset{1}{\cancel{3}}}{\cancel{4}} \cdot \dfrac{\overset{1}{\cancel{4}}}{\cancel{3}}\right)x$

$= 1 \cdot x$

$= x$

In Example 3, you use the fact that the product of a real number and its reciprocal (multiplicative inverse) is 1.

EXAMPLE 3   By what number would you multiply each expression to obtain y? Show that your answer is correct.

a. $-\dfrac{1}{4}y$ **b.** $-y$ ← $-y = -1 \cdot y$

Solutions: Multiply by the reciprocal of the numerical coefficient.

a. Reciprocal of $-\dfrac{1}{4}$: -4

$-4 \cdot \left(-\dfrac{1}{4}y\right) = \left[-4 \cdot \left(-\dfrac{1}{4}\right)\right] \cdot y$

$= 1 \cdot y$

$= y$

b. Reciprocal of -1: -1

$-1 \cdot (-1 \cdot y) = \left(-1 \cdot (-1)\right) \cdot y$

$= 1 \cdot y$

$= y$

In Example 4, you use the Additive Inverse postulate which states that the sum of a real number and its opposite (additive inverse) is zero.

EXAMPLE 4 What number would you add to each expression to obtain x?
Show that your answer is correct.

    a. $x + 9$ **b.** $x + (-6)$

Solutions: Add the opposite of the real numbers.

    a. Opposite of 9: -9 **b.** Opposite of -6: **6**

$$x + 9 + (-9) = x + [9 + (-9)] \qquad x + (-6) + 6 = x + (-6 + 6)$$
$$= x + 0 \qquad\qquad\qquad\qquad = x + 0$$
$$= x \qquad\qquad\qquad\qquad\quad = x$$

CLASSROOM EXERCISES

Evaluate each expression for $x = -6$, $y = -4$, and $q = 6$.

1. $x + y$ **2.** $y + q$ **3.** $x - y$ **4.** $y - q$ **5.** x^2

6. $x \div y$ **7.** $q - x$ **8.** y^2 **9.** $q^2 - xy$ **10.** $y^2 - qx$

By what number would you multiply each expression to obtain t?

11. $-4t$ **12.** $\frac{7}{4}t$ **13.** $-\frac{2}{3}t$ **14.** $-1 \cdot t$ **15.** t

What number would you add to obtain z?

16. $z + 7$ **17.** $z + (-9)$ **18.** $-9 + z$ **19.** $z + (-1)$ **20.** $\frac{3}{5} + z$

WRITTEN EXERCISES

A Evaluate each expression for $x = -15$, $y = -10$, and $q = 0$.

1. $x + y$ **2.** $y + q$ **3.** $2x$ **4.** $3y$ **5.** xy

6. qy **7.** x^2 **8.** y^2 **9.** $x^2 + y^2$ **10.** $q^2 + y^2$

11. q^3 **12.** $x^2 + q^2$ **13.** $q \cdot x \cdot y$ **14.** x^2y **15.** $y - x$

16. $x - y$ **17.** $x - y + q$ **18.** $q - y$ **19.** $q - x$ **20.** $y^2 - x$

21. $\dfrac{x}{y}$ **22.** $\dfrac{y}{x}$ **23.** $\dfrac{q}{x}$ **24.** $\dfrac{q}{y}$ **25.** $\dfrac{x}{x}$

Multiply.

26. $\frac{1}{3} \cdot 3y$ **27.** $\frac{1}{4} \cdot 4y$ **28.** $-\frac{1}{5} \cdot 5y$ **29.** $-\frac{1}{6} \cdot 6y$ **30.** $\frac{2}{3} \cdot \frac{3}{2} y$

31. $-\frac{2}{5} \cdot \frac{5}{2} y$ **32.** $-\frac{5}{7} \cdot \frac{7}{5} y$ **33.** $-\frac{5}{7} \cdot 7a$ **34.** $\frac{3}{5} \cdot (-5a)$ **35.** $-1 \cdot (-1a)$

36. $\frac{2}{3} \cdot (-3y)$ **37.** $\frac{5}{6} \cdot (-18b)$ **38.** $-1 \cdot \frac{4}{5} c$ **39.** $\frac{3}{8} \cdot (-q)$ **40.** $\frac{1}{2}(8x)$

41. $-\frac{1}{2}(8x)$ **42.** $\frac{1}{2}(-8x)$ **43.** $-\frac{3}{5}(25p)$ **44.** $\frac{3}{5}(-25p)$ **45.** $-\frac{3}{5}(-25p)$

By what number would you multiply each expression to obtain y? In Exercises 46–55, show that your answer is correct.

46. $\frac{3}{5}y$ **47.** $\frac{9}{7}y$ **48.** $-7y$ **49.** $-8y$ **50.** $-\frac{1}{2}y$

51. $-\frac{1}{5}y$ **52.** $-\frac{2}{3}y$ **53.** $-\frac{2}{5}y$ **54.** $-\frac{9}{10}y$ **55.** $-\frac{3}{8}y$

56. $-1y$ **57.** $-y$ **58.** y **59.** $1y$ **60.** $2\frac{1}{2}y$

61. $3\frac{1}{4}y$ **62.** $-7\frac{1}{4}y$ **63.** $-8\frac{1}{2}y$ **64.** $\frac{y}{2}$ **65.** $-\frac{y}{10}$

What number would you add to each expression to obtain x? In Exercises 66–73 and Exercises 82–89, show that your answer is correct.

66. $x + 10$ **67.** $x + 1$ **68.** $x + (-5)$ **69.** $x + (-9)$

70. $x + (-10)$ **71.** $x + (-4)$ **72.** $-6 + x$ **73.** $-12 + x$

74. $16 + x$ **75.** $21 + x$ **76.** $x + (12 - 4)$ **77.** $x + (-9 + 3)$

78. $(-12 + 5) + x$ **79.** $(-3 - 1) + x$ **80.** $(-9 - 17) + x$ **81.** $x + (8 - 13)$

B   **Example:** $x - 1 = x + (-1)$ Opposite of (-1): 1 Therefore, add **1**.

82. $x - 7$ **83.** $x - 15$ **84.** $x - 2$ **85.** $x - 23$

86. $x - 19$ **87.** $x - \frac{1}{5}$ **88.** $x - (-1)$ **89.** $x - (-2)$

Evaluate each expression for $x = -20$, $y = -10$, and $q = -1$.

90. $2x + 3y$ **91.** $2x - y$ **92.** $x - 2y$ **93.** $2x + 3q$

94. $q - 2y$ **95.** $q - 3x$ **96.** $3xy$ **97.** $-5q^2x^2y$

98. $\dfrac{3x + y}{q}$ **99.** $\dfrac{y - x}{x}$ **100.** $\dfrac{2x + 3y}{-y}$ **101.** $\dfrac{3x - 7y}{qy}$

——— Review ———

Simplify. *(Section 2–5)*

1. $5 + 2a + 6a$ **2.** $1.7x - x - 3.2x$ **3.** $\frac{3}{4}x - \frac{1}{3}y - \frac{1}{2}x + \frac{2}{5}y$

Multiply. *(Section 2–6)*

4. $(-3)(-6)$ **5.** $\frac{3}{4}\left(-\frac{3}{4}\right)$ **6.** $(-0.2)(0.2)(0.2)$ **7.** $(-5)^2$

Divide. *(Section 2–7)*

8. $0 \div 7$ **9.** $-16 \div \frac{1}{4}$ **10.** $-9.8 \div (-7)$ **11.** $20 \div \left(-2\frac{3}{10}\right)$

By what number would you multiply each expression or what number would you add to each expression to obtain x? *(Section 2–8)*

12. $21 + x$ **13.** $-\frac{1}{3}x$ **14.** $13x$ **15.** $x + (12 - 8)$

BASIC: FORMULAS IN PROGRAMS

The program for the following problem uses REM (short for "remark") statements. REM statements are used to add explanatory comments to a program. The computer ignores REM statements when executing a program. They are intended for the people who read the program.

Problem: *Write a program which, given the total price of a purchase, p, and the number of units, n, computes and prints the unit price of each item. (See page 12.)*

```
100 REM   P = TOTAL PRICE
110 REM   N = NUMBER OF UNITS
120 REM   U = UNIT PRICE OF AN ITEM
130 REM
140 PRINT "WHAT IS THE TOTAL PRICE";
150 INPUT P
160 PRINT "HOW MANY UNITS";
170 INPUT N
180 LET U = P / N
190 PRINT "THE UNIT PRICE = $"; U
200 PRINT "ANY MORE CALCULATIONS (1 = YES, 0 = NO)";
210 INPUT Z
220 IF Z = 1 THEN 140
230 END
```

Analysis: Here is an explanation of the program above.

Statement 130: This is a "blank" remark separating the comments from the actual program which follows. REM statements may appear anywhere in a program.

Statements 140–150: When the computer comes to a PRINT statement, it displays the message in quotation marks on the screen or on a printer. The purpose of statement 140 is to "prompt" the person running the program to enter the appropriate number. Statement 150 causes the computer to print a question mark (?) and then wait for a number to be entered from the keyboard. When the user has typed a number and pressed the ENTER or RETURN key (depending on the machine), the computer stores the value entered as variable P.

Statements 160–170: These statements repeat the work of statements 140–150, but for the variable N (number of units).

Statement 180: Now that all values needed for the calculation have been entered, the LET statement gives the formula for computing the unit price. (See page 12.) In a LET statement the left side of the "=" sign must be only a variable. The right side, however, may contain any legitimate algebraic expression.

Statement 190: The computer will print the value of U it computed in statement 180. Notice that the last U in statement 190 is outside the quotation marks. This causes the *value* of the variable U to be printed rather than the letter "U."

Statements 200–230: Statement 200 asks the user if there is more data to be entered and gives a code for answering the question. Statement 210 accepts the "1" or "0" the person types and calls this value "Z". Then, in statement 220, the computer checks the value of Z. If Z = 1, there is more data to be entered and the computer is sent back to statement 140 to repeat the steps of the program. If Z is not 1, the computer ignores "THEN 140" in statement 220 and instead moves to 230 END. At this point the computer will stop executing the program. It then prints "READY", or a similar code word or symbol, and waits for further instructions.

EXERCISES

A   Run the program on page 75 for the following values.

1. $p = \$1.09$; $n = 24$ **2.** $p = \$1.99$; $n = 46$ **3.** $p = \$0.99$; $n = 9$

4. $p = \$3.10$; $n = 15$ **5.** $p = \$0.85$; $n = 50$ **6.** $p = \$1.59$; $n = 36$

7. $p = \$1.88$; $n = 25$ **8.** $p = \$4.51$; $n = 18$ **9.** $p = \$2.85$; $n = 19$

B   Write a BASIC program for each problem.

10. Given the length of a side, s, of a square, use the formula
$$A = s^2$$
to compute and print the area. (See page 9.)

11. Given the length, width, and height of a refrigerator car, use the formula
$$V = lwh$$
to compute and print the volume. (See page 13.)

12. Given the height and the lengths of the bases a and b of a trapezoid, use the formula
$$A = \tfrac{1}{2}(a + b)h$$
to compute and print the area. (See page 14.)

13. Compute and print the average of two given real numbers x and y. (See page 69.)

14. Given the length of a side of a square, use the formula
$$P = 4s$$
to compute and print the perimeter of the square. (See page 10.)

15. Given the length of the radius of a circle, use the formula
$$C = 2\pi r$$
to compute and print the circumference of the circle. Use $\pi = 3.14$. (See page 15.)

Chapter Summary

IMPORTANT TERMS

Absolute value (p. 47)
Additive inverse (p. 47)
Arithmetic mean (p. 69)
Equivalent expressions (p. 61)
Like terms (p. 60)
Multiplicative inverse (p. 68)

Numerical coefficient (p. 60)
Opposites (p. 44)
Reciprocals (p. 68)
Subtraction (p. 56)
Term (p. 60)
Theorem (p. 51)

IMPORTANT IDEAS

1. For any two real numbers, the smaller is to the left of the larger on the number line.

2. **Additive Inverse Postulate:** For any real number a, there is one and only one real number, $-a$, such that $a + (-a) = 0$.

3. **Procedure for adding two numbers having like signs**

    $\boxed{1}$ Determine whether the sum is positive or negative.

    a. The sum of two positive numbers is positive.

    b. The sum of two negative numbers is negative.

    $\boxed{2}$ Add the absolute values of the numbers.

4. **Sum of Two Negative Numbers:** The sum of two negative numbers is the opposite of the sum of their absolute values.

    If $x < 0$ and $y < 0$, then $x + y = -(|x| + |y|)$.

5. **Procedure for finding the sum of a positive and negative number**

    $\boxed{1}$ Determine whether the sum is positive or negative.

    a. The sum is positive when the positive number has the greater absolute value.

    b. The sum is negative when the negative number has the greater absolute value.

    $\boxed{2}$ Subtract the lesser absolute value from the greater absolute value.

6. **Sum of a Positive and a Negative Number:** The sum of a positive number, x, and a negative number, y, is the difference of their absolute values. The sum is positive when x is farther from 0 and negative when y is farther from 0. That is,

    $$x + y = (|x| - |y|) \text{ when } |x| > |y|$$
    $$x + y = -(|y| - |x|) \text{ when } |y| > |x|.$$

7. **Substitution Principle:** If two expressions are equivalent, you can always replace one with the other in a given expression.

8. **Zero Multiplication Theorem:** For any real number a, $a \cdot 0 = 0 \cdot a = 0$.

9. **Negative Product Theorem:** The product of two real numbers is negative when one number is positive and the other number is negative. That is, for $a < 0$ and $b > 0$, $a \cdot b = -(|a| \cdot |b|)$.

10. **Positive Product Theorem:** The product of two real numbers is positive when both numbers are positive or when both numbers are negative. That is, for $a < 0$ and $b < 0$, or for $a > 0$ and $b > 0$, $a \cdot b = |a| \cdot |b|$.

11. **Rules for Division of Real Numbers**

    $\boxed{1}$ The quotient of two positive numbers is positive.

    $\boxed{2}$ The quotient of two negative numbers is positive.

    $\boxed{3}$ The quotient of a negative number and a positive number, or of a positive number and a negative number, is negative.

12. **Multiplicative Inverse Postulate:** For any real number a, $a \neq 0$, there exists one and only one real number $\frac{1}{a}$, such that $a \cdot \frac{1}{a} = 1$.

13. **Division by zero is not defined.**

_____ Chapter Objectives and Review _____

Objective: *To write the opposite of a real number (Section 2–1)*

Write the opposite of each number.

1. 2   2. -11 3. $-\sqrt{5}$ 4. 14.3   5. $-6\frac{1}{2}$ 6. $-\pi$

Write without parentheses.

7. $-(-3.72)$ 8. $-(83.0)$ 9. $-(9.3 + 7.4)$ 10. $-(t)$

Solve for x.

11. $-x = 7$ 12. $x = -(-8)$ 13. $-x = -\pi$ 14. $-x = 6\frac{2}{3}$

Objective: *To compare positive and negative numbers using > or < (Section 2–1)*

Use > or < to compare the numbers.

15. -14 __?__ 10   16. 6 __?__ -2 17. $-\sqrt{3}$ __?__ 1   18. $-(-4)$ __?__ 0

Objective: *To identify the additive inverse of a real number (Section 2–2)*

Write the additive inverse of each number.

19. -18 20. 37   21. $-\sqrt{7}$ 22. $-(-2.31)$ 23. $\frac{1}{3}$ 24. $-(-2\frac{1}{8})$

Complete.

25. $7 + $ __?__ $= 0$ 26. $-3.2 + $ __?__ $= 0$ 27. __?__ $+ (-a) = 0$ 28. $-4\frac{1}{2} + 4\frac{1}{2} = $ __?__

Objective: *To use absolute value notation (Section 2–2)*

Evaluate.

29. $|42{,}000|$ 30. $|-3| + |11|$ 31. $|236| + |-20|$ 32. $|4.21| - |2.33|$

Use >, =, or < to compare the numbers.

33. $|0|$ __?__ $|-3|$ **34.** $|-5|$ __?__ $|5|$ **35.** $|-0.32|$ __?__ $|0.75|$ **36.** $|-\frac{3}{5}|$ __?__ $|-\frac{1}{2}|$

Objective: *To add real numbers (Section 2–3)*

Add.

37. $7 + 8$ **38.** $(-11) + 4$ **39.** $0 + (-1\frac{1}{2})$ **40.** $(-1.3) + (-2.5)$

Use positive and negative numbers to represent each word description. Then find the sum.

41. The temperature at 7 P.M. was 5°C. By 5 A.M. it had dropped 7°. What was the temperature at 5 A.M.?

42. A plane was 12,500 meters high. It rose 725 meters and then dropped 785 meters. What was its new altitude?

Objective: *To subtract real numbers (Section 2–4)*

Subtract.

43. $14 - 20$ **44.** $-5 - 8$ **45.** $\frac{3}{10} - (\frac{-1}{10})$ **46.** $-6.8 - (-8.1)$

47. The actual temperature is 25°F. The wind chill temperature is −12°F. How much colder than the actual temperature is the wind chill temperature?

48. The actual temperature is 18°F. The wind chill temperature is −9°F. How much colder than the actual temperature is the wind chill temperature?

Objective: *To combine like terms (Section 2–5)*

Combine like terms.

49. $3g + 11g$ **50.** $9m - 17m$ **51.** $-26rt - (-2rt)$ **52.** $16ab + (-5ab)$

Simplify.

53. $6x + 9x + 11$ **54.** $15y - 3y - 4$ **55.** $31n + 6mn - 2n$ **56.** $42x - 36 + 75x$

Objective: *To multiply real numbers (Section 2–6)*

Multiply.

57. $(-6)(4)$ **58.** $(-19)(-1)(2)$ **59.** $(0.2)(-3.1)$ **60.** $-1\frac{1}{2} \cdot (-\frac{2}{3})$

Objective: *To divide real numbers (Section 2–7)*

Divide.

61. $-14 \div 14$ **62.** $117 \div (-9)$ **63.** $(-\frac{2}{3}) \div (-\frac{1}{2})$ **64.** $\frac{-7.38}{-100}$

65. The following table shows the amount of gain and loss in the price of a stock over a five–day period. Find the average change over the five days.

M	T	W	T	F
$-\frac{1}{8}$	$+\frac{7}{8}$	$-\frac{13}{4}$	$+\frac{1}{4}$	$-\frac{5}{8}$

Objective: *To practice the skills needed to solve equations (Section 2–8)*

Evaluate each expression for $x = 7$, $y = -9$ and $z = \frac{1}{2}$.

66. $x + z$ **67.** $y^2 + xz$ **68.** $(x - y)z$ **69.** $xy - x^2$ **70.** $y^2 + y$

Multiply.

71. $\frac{1}{3} \cdot (-3m)$ **72.** $-7 \cdot \frac{4}{7}t$ **73.** $-\frac{4}{9} \cdot (-81x)$ **74.** $-\frac{3}{4} \cdot 16p$ **75.** $\frac{1}{2} \cdot (-14x^2)$

By what number would you multiply each expression to obtain y?

76. $16y$ **77.** $-\frac{1}{9}y$ **78.** $2\frac{1}{3}y$ **79.** $-7\frac{3}{4}y$ **80.** $\frac{-y}{11}$

What number would you add to each expression to obtain x?

81. $x + 11$ **82.** $x - 8$ **83.** $-4 + x$ **84.** $15 + x$ **85.** $(-1 + 6) + x$

———— Chapter Test ————

1. Write the additive inverse of $-(-19)$.   **2.** Solve for k when $-k = -(-10)$.

Evaluate.

3. $-(-617.25)$ **4.** $|-(-1.2)|$ **5.** $|-102|$ **6.** $-|-\pi|$

Use $>$, $=$, or $<$ to compare the numbers.

7. -19 __?__ -14 **8.** 0.15 __?__ -0.13 **9.** $|-9|$ __?__ $|9|$ **10.** $-|21|$ __?__ $|50|$

Perform the indicated operations.

11. $(-4) + 11$ **12.** $(-6.3) + (-1.9)$ **13.** $-3 - (-12)$

14. $\left(-\frac{2}{3}\right)\left(-\frac{11}{2}\right) - 1$ **15.** $15 \div \left(-\frac{5}{6}\right)$ **16.** $(-3.2) \div (-1.6)$

17. Myra has $175 in her checking account. She wrote a check for $169 and made a deposit of $215. What was her new balance?

18. The temperature was 14°C at noon. By 4 P.M. it had dropped to -2°C. How much did the temperature change during that time?

Combine like terms.

19. $24gt - (-3gt) + 7$ **20.** $4\frac{1}{2}cd - \frac{1}{2}c + \frac{1}{2}cd - 3$

21. A town's low temperatures for one week are recorded below. Find the mean low temperature for the week.

S	M	T	W	T	F	S
$-1.3°$	$-0.5°$	$0.3°$	$-1.1°$	$-2.1°$	$-0.7°$	$0.5°$

22. Evaluate $t + mn$ for $t = 19$, $m = 7$, and $n = -1$.

23. Multiply: $\left(-\frac{14}{15}\right)\left(-\frac{105}{7}r\right)$

24. By what number would you multiply $-\frac{8}{9}y$ to obtain y?

25. What number would you add to $(-11 - 15) + x$ to obtain x?

Additional Practice

Skills

Write without parentheses. *(Section 2-1)*

1. $-(4)$ **2.** $-(-4)$ **3.** $-(3.1 - 0.1)$ **4.** $-(34 \div 17)$ **5.** $-(-x)$

Solve. *(Section 2-1)*

6. $-x = 5$ **7.** $-m = 0$ **8.** $-a = -\frac{1}{3}$ **9.** $-y = \pi$ **10.** $-t = 3.72$

Use $<$ or $>$ to compare the numbers. *(Sections 2-1, 2-2)*

11. $-4 \underline{\quad?\quad} 8$ **12.** $-9 \underline{\quad?\quad} -11$ **13.** $0 \underline{\quad?\quad} -6$ **14.** $-(-\sqrt{2}) \underline{\quad?\quad} \sqrt{5}$

15. $|-4| \underline{\quad?\quad} |6|$ **16.** $|-\frac{1}{2}| \underline{\quad?\quad} |-\frac{1}{4}|$ **17.** $|0.15| \underline{\quad?\quad} |-0.9|$ **18.** $|-3| \underline{\quad?\quad} |0|$

Evaluate. *(Section 2-2)*

19. $|3| + |-11|$ **20.** $|-\sqrt{3}| - |\sqrt{3}|$ **21.** $|7.8| - |-0.3|$ **22.** $|t| - |-t|$

Complete. *(Section 2-2)*

23. $9 + (-9) = \underline{\quad?\quad}$ **24.** $-12 + \underline{\quad?\quad} = 0$ **25.** $1.3 + \underline{\quad?\quad} = 0$ **26.** $\underline{\quad?\quad} - (-m) = 0$

Perform the indicated operations. *(Sections 2-3, 2-4, 2-6, 2-7)*

27. $8 + (-11)$ **28.** $(-14) + (-5)$ **29.** $8.4 + (-0.2)$ **30.** $(-5\frac{1}{3}) + 8\frac{5}{6}$

31. $13 - 13$ **32.** $\frac{8}{3} - (-\frac{1}{3})$ **33.** $-2 - (-7)$ **34.** $4.8 - (-1.2)$

35. $3\frac{1}{5}(-\frac{1}{8})$ **36.** $-1.3 \cdot 4.2$ **37.** $(-9)(7)(-2)$ **38.** $(-10)^2$

39. $14 \div (-2)$ **40.** $-54 \div (-\frac{9}{10})$ **41.** $-7.2 \div 3.6$ **42.** $\frac{-2.4}{100}$

Simplify. *(Section 2-5)*

43. $-7r - (-4r)$ **44.** $2.3n - 1.9n + 6$ **45.** $3bc + 9bc - 7b$

46. $-18t - t$ **47.** $24x - (-x)$ **48.** $13b + (-b)$

49. $6s - (-5s) + 10$ **50.** $-4q + (-9q) + 6r$ **51.** $4.3p - 6.2p - 7$

52. $14x - 5y - (-7x) + 6y$ **53.** $12a + 13a - (-2b) + b$ **54.** $24c - 16d - (-4d) + 6c$

Evaluate each expression for $x = 9$, $y = -3$, and $z = 0$. *(Section 2-8)*

55. zy **56.** y^2 **57.** $x^2 + y^2$ **58.** $x - y$ **59.** $x \cdot y \cdot z$

Multiply. *(Section 2-8)*

60. $\frac{1}{4}(12x)$ **61.** $-1(-3x)$ **62.** $\frac{3}{8}(-16y)$ **63.** $(-g)(-3)$ **64.** $\frac{5}{2}(-\frac{2}{5}a)$

By what number would you multiply each expression to obtain y?
(Section 2-8)

65. $\frac{2}{3}y$ **66.** $\frac{8}{5}y$ **67.** $-3y$ **68.** $-\frac{1}{2}y$ **69.** $-3\frac{1}{3}y$

What number would you add to each expression to obtain x? *(Section 2–8)*

70. $x + 6$ **71.** $x + (-3)$ **72.** $x + (3 - 1)$ **73.** $-11 + x$ **74.** $14 + x$

Applications

In Exercises 75 and 76, use algebraic symbols to represent each sentence. *(Section 2–1).*

75. The opposite of a profit of $500 is a loss of $500.

76. A fall of 10° in temperature is the opposite of a rise of 10°.

77. On four successive plays, a football team lost 4 yards, lost 2 yards, gained 5 yards, and gained 3 yards. What was the team's net gain? *(Section 2–3)*

78. The stock of Hitec, Inc. cost $48 per share at 10 A.M. By noon it had gained $3, but went down $5 by closing. What was its value at closing? *(Section 2–3)*

79. The actual temperature is 15°F. The wind chill temperature is −20°F. How much colder than the actual temperature is the wind chill temperature? *(Section 2–4)*

80. The lowest temperature ever recorded in Nebraska was −47°F. The lowest temperature ever recorded in Nevada was −50°F. Find the difference between the two temperatures. *(Section 2–4)*

In Exercises 81 and 82, find the sum of the areas of each pair of figures. *(Section 2–5)*

81. Rectangle: $A = \text{length} \cdot \text{width}$

82. Triangle: $A = \frac{1}{2} (\text{base} \cdot \text{height})$

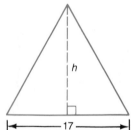

83. The table below shows a corporation's profit (+) and loss (−) over a six month period. Find the average profit or loss over the six months. *(Section 2–7)*

January	February	March	April	May	June
−$28,500	−$18,300	−$7,700	$12,500	$14,300	$22,900

84. The estimated highway MPG (miles per gallon) of a certain car is 35. On seven trips with this car, the driver calculated the difference between the actual MPG and the estimate (see the table below). Find the average difference for the seven trips. *(Section 2–7)*

Trips	A	B	C	D	E	F	G
Difference	+2	−5	−6	+5	+7	−1	+3

CHAPTER **3** # Solving Equations

3–1 Addition Property for Equations

Recall that an equation is a mathematical sentence that uses "=".

To solve equations, think of a balance. To keep the balance level, *whatever is added or subtracted from one side must be added or subtracted from the other.*

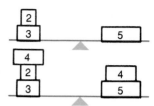

Property for Equations

Addition Property for Equations

Adding the same number to each side of an equation results in an equivalent equation.

Equivalent equations have the same solutions for the same replacement set. To solve an equation, you get the variable with a numerical coefficient of 1 alone on one side of the equation.

EXAMPLE 1 Solve and check: $y + 21 = 8$

Solution: **Think:** What must be added to $y + 21$ to get y?

$$y + 21 = 8 \qquad \longleftarrow \quad \textbf{Add (−21) to each side.}$$

$$y + \underline{21 + (-21)} = \underline{8 + (-21)} \quad \longleftarrow \quad \textbf{Solve for } y.$$

$$y + \quad 0 \quad = \quad -13 \qquad \longleftarrow \quad \textbf{\textit{y} is alone.}$$

$$y = -13$$

Check: Replace y with -13 in the original equation.

$$y + 21 = 8$$
$$-13 + 21 \overset{?}{=} 8$$
$$8 \overset{?}{=} 8 \quad \text{Yes} \; \checkmark \qquad \text{The solution is } \mathbf{-13}.$$

Always check your work by showing that the solution of the final equivalent equation also satisfies the original equation.

EXAMPLE 2 Solve and check: $x - 3\frac{1}{2} = 8$

Solution: Write $x - 3\frac{1}{2} = 8$ as $x + (-3\frac{1}{2}) = 8$.

Think: What must be added to $x + (-3\frac{1}{2})$ to get x?

$$x + (-3\tfrac{1}{2}) = 8 \qquad \longleftarrow \quad \textbf{Add } 3\tfrac{1}{2} \textbf{ to each side.}$$

$$x + (-3\tfrac{1}{2} \pm 3\tfrac{1}{2}) = 8 + 3\tfrac{1}{2} \quad \longleftarrow \quad \textbf{Solve for x.}$$

$$x + \quad 0 \quad = 11\tfrac{1}{2}$$

$$x = 11\tfrac{1}{2} \qquad \longleftarrow \quad \textbf{x is alone.}$$

Check: $x - 3\frac{1}{2} = 8$ ← ──── **Replace x with 11$\frac{1}{2}$.**

$11\frac{1}{2} - 3\frac{1}{2} \overset{?}{=} 8$

$8 \overset{?}{=} 8$ Yes ✔ The solution is **11$\frac{1}{2}$.**

Unless otherwise stated, the replacement set for the variables in equations is the set of real numbers.

CLASSROOM EXERCISES

In each of Exercises 1–8, what number would you add to each side of the equation in order to get x?

1. $x + 2 = 11$

2. $6 + x = 13$

3. $x - 9 = 15$

4. $x - 5.2 = 8$

5. $x - 6 = 14$

6. $4.5 = 2.1 + x$

7. $x - (-9) = 8$

8. $x - (-1.6) = 4$

Solve and check each equation.

9. $x + 6 = 8$

10. $y + 9 = 41$

11. $t - 11 = 13$

12. $r - 25 = 63$

13. $18 = a + 5$

14. $-11 = 3 + q$

15. $x - (-1) = 52$

16. $-13 = t - (-8)$

WRITTEN EXERCISES

A   Solve and check each equation.

1. $x + 7 = 13$

2. $m + 3\frac{1}{2} = 7$

3. $8 + n = 5$

4. $11.2 + t = 3.7$

5. $y - 6 = 14$

6. $x - 6\frac{1}{4} = 12\frac{1}{2}$

7. $y - 4 = 13$

8. $3 + y = 17$

9. $5.4 + n = -0.6$

10. $-4 + y = 13$

11. $-3 + y = -12$

12. $5 = 28 + n$

13. $25 = x + 6$

14. $2 + x = -1$

15. $0.2 + t = 1.3$

16. $-1.5 + r = 9.6$

17. $-8 + z = 30$

18. $v - (-5) = 10$

19. $m - (-3) = 1$

20. $r - (-9) = -19$

21. $-8 + t = -13$

22. $-12 + z = 1$

23. $-15 + a = 0$

24. $q - (-7) = 4\frac{1}{2}$

25. $r - (-4.6) = 8.1$

26. $s + 4.5 = 7.9$

27. $z - 1.6 = 2$

28. $y + 9.4 = 15$

29. $a + 4.22 = 7$

30. $3.35 + x = 5$

31. $8.91 + x = 11.09$

32. $-11.5 + r = 0$

33. $z - \frac{1}{4} = 1\frac{3}{4}$

34. $t + \frac{3}{5} = \frac{9}{10}$

35. $\frac{1}{4} = \frac{3}{4} + c$

36. $b + 1\frac{1}{2} = 2\frac{1}{8}$

37. $1 + r = 7\frac{1}{2}$

38. $\frac{7}{8} = q + \frac{3}{8}$

39. $y + 5 = 8\frac{1}{4}$

40. $6\frac{2}{3} = c + 4$

B

41. If $s + 9 = 11$, find the value of $7s$.

42. If $t + 8 = 11$, find the value of $\frac{1}{3}t$.

43. If $r - 1.5 = 3.5$, find the value of $r + 1$.

44. If $t - 6 = 21$, find the value of $\frac{1}{9}t$.

45. If $z - 1\frac{1}{4} = 5\frac{1}{2}$, find the value of $4z - 18$.

46. If $r - \frac{1}{5} = \frac{1}{4}$, find the value of $5r$.

47. If $2.8 + m = 3.7$, find the value of $1 - m$.

48. If $0.2 + p = 9$, find the value of $7p$.

C   Solve and check.

49. $|x| - 1 = 3$

50. $-1 + |t| = 0$

51. $6 + |n| = 6$

52. $|s| + 9 = 18$

Multiply. *(Pages 72–74)*

1. $\frac{1}{6}(6y)$ **2.** $-\frac{1}{5}(5t)$ **3.** $\frac{1}{3}(-3q)$ **4.** $-\frac{1}{8}(-8t)$ **5.** $-\frac{1}{12}(-12n)$

Write the reciprocal (multiplicative inverse) of each number. *(Pages 68–71)*

6. $\frac{2}{3}$ **7.** $\frac{5}{8}$ **8.** $-\frac{1}{2}$ **9.** $-\frac{3}{4}$ **10.** -9 **11.** 7

By what number would you multiply each expression to obtain t?
(Pages 72–74)

12. $2t$ **13.** $8t$ **14.** $-\frac{3}{4}t$ **15.** $-\frac{1}{4}t$ **16.** $\frac{5}{6}t$ **17.** $-t$

3-2 Multiplication Property for Equations

You can also obtain equivalent equations by multiplying each side of an equation by the same number (not zero).

$$5x = 35 \quad \text{is equivalent to} \quad \tfrac{1}{5}\cdot 5x = \tfrac{1}{5}\cdot 35, \quad \text{or} \quad x = 7.$$

$$\tfrac{2}{3}z = 6 \quad \text{is equivalent to} \quad \tfrac{3}{2}\cdot\tfrac{2}{3}z = \tfrac{3}{2}\cdot 6, \quad \text{or} \quad z = 9.$$

The examples suggest this property.

Property
for
Equations

> **Multiplication Property for Equations**
>
> **Multiplying each side of an equation by the same *nonzero* number results in an equivalent equation.**

Recall that to solve an equation, you try to get the variable with a numerical coefficient of 1 alone on one side of the equation.

EXAMPLE 1 Solve and check: $2x = 12$

Solution: **Think:** By what number must $2x$ be multiplied in order to get x?

$$2x = 12 \quad \longleftarrow \text{ Multiply each side by } \tfrac{1}{2}.$$

$$\tfrac{1}{2}\cdot 2x = \tfrac{1}{2}\cdot 12 \quad \longleftarrow \text{ Solve for x.}$$

$$\left(\tfrac{1}{2}\cdot 2\right)x = 6$$

$$x = 6 \quad \longleftarrow \text{ x is alone.}$$

Check: $2x = 12 \quad \longleftarrow \text{ Replace x with 6.}$

$$2(6) \overset{?}{=} 12$$

$$12 \overset{?}{=} 12 \quad \text{Yes } \checkmark \qquad \text{The solution is 6.}$$

The number or numbers that satisfy an equation are also called the **solution set** of the equation. Thus, in Example 1, the solution set is $\{6\}$.

EXAMPLE 2   Solve and check: $-\frac{3}{4}y = 15$

Solution: **Think:** By what number must $-\frac{3}{4}y$ be multiplied in order to get y?

$$-\frac{3}{4}y = 15 \quad \longleftarrow \quad \textbf{Multiply each side by } -\frac{4}{3}.$$

$$-\frac{4}{3} \cdot \left(-\frac{3}{4}y\right) = -\frac{4}{3} \cdot 15$$

$$\left[-\frac{4}{3} \cdot \left(-\frac{3}{4}\right)\right] \cdot y = -\frac{4}{3} \cdot 15 \quad \longleftarrow \quad \left[-\frac{4}{3} \cdot \left(-\frac{3}{4}\right)\right] \cdot y = 1 \cdot y = y$$

$$y = -20 \quad \longleftarrow \quad \textbf{The left side is } y, \textbf{ or } 1 \cdot y.$$

Check: $$-\frac{3}{4}y = 15 \quad \longleftarrow \quad \textbf{Replace } y \textbf{ with } (-20).$$

$$-\frac{3}{4} \cdot (-20) \overset{?}{=} 15$$

$$15 \overset{?}{=} 15 \quad \text{Yes} \quad \text{✔} \qquad \textbf{Solution set: } \{-20\}$$

An expression such as $\frac{t}{4}$ means the same as $\frac{1}{4} \cdot t$. Thus, the numerical coefficient of $\frac{t}{4}$ is $\frac{1}{4}$.

EXAMPLE 3   Solve and check: $\frac{t}{4} = -9$

Solution: **Think:** By what number must $\frac{t}{4}$ be multiplied in order to get t?

$$\frac{t}{4} = -9 \quad \longleftarrow \quad \textbf{Multiply each side by 4.}$$

$$4 \cdot \frac{t}{4} = 4 \cdot (-9) \quad \longleftarrow \quad \frac{t}{4} = \frac{1}{4} \cdot t$$

$$\left(4 \cdot \frac{1}{4}\right) \cdot t = -36$$

$$t = -36 \quad \longleftarrow \quad \textbf{The left side is } t, \textbf{ or } 1 \cdot t.$$

Check: $$\frac{t}{4} = -9 \quad \longleftarrow \quad \textbf{Replace } t \textbf{ with } -36.$$

$$\frac{-36}{4} \overset{?}{=} -9$$

$$-9 \overset{?}{=} -9 \quad \text{Yes} \quad \text{✔} \qquad \textbf{Solution set: } \{-36\}$$

REMEMBER: Always use the original equation to check your answers. Then write the solution set.

CLASSROOM EXERCISES

In each of Exercises 1–8, by what number would you multiply each side of the equation in order to get t alone on one side of the equation?

1. $3t = 9$
2. $12t = 1.2$
3. $-\frac{4}{5}t = 6$
4. $\frac{2}{3}t = 20$
5. $\frac{t}{5} = 30$
6. $-\frac{t}{27} = 1$
7. $-t = 8$
8. $2.1 = -t$

Solve and check each equation.

9. $3x = 21$
10. $-8x = 148$
11. $\frac{1}{2}y = 8$
12. $\frac{2}{3}q = 10$
13. $\frac{z}{6} = 10$
14. $\frac{t}{5} = 0$
15. $-\frac{4}{5}t = 16$
16. $-\frac{3}{8}q = 12$

WRITTEN EXERCISES

A   Solve and check each equation.

1. $2x = 8$
2. $15y = 50$
3. $-12b = 24$
4. $13t = -52$
5. $\frac{1}{4}x = 7$
6. $-\frac{1}{2}y = 4$
7. $-2.3s = 4.6$
8. $2.1x = 105$
9. $\frac{n}{3} = 2$
10. $\frac{y}{0.5} = 1$
11. $\frac{2}{3}n = 12$
12. $\frac{5}{6}n = 15$
13. $-9 = \frac{5}{4}v$
14. $12 = -\frac{3}{2}n$
15. $-\frac{1}{4}x = 0$
16. $5y = 0$
17. $\frac{t}{7} = -\frac{7}{2}$
18. $-\frac{30}{9} = \frac{5n}{3}$
19. $-y = 6$
20. $0 = -t$
21. $-r = \frac{1}{4}$
22. $-\frac{1}{8} = -x$
23. $-\frac{1}{8} = 4n$
24. $\frac{1}{2}y = 0$
25. $-0.25t = 8$
26. $-0.1x = -8$
27. $\frac{2}{3} = 5t$
28. $-1 = \frac{3}{4}t$
29. $\frac{y}{6} = \frac{2}{3}$
30. $\frac{n}{2.4} = 0.2$
31. $\frac{c}{0.01} = 0.75$
32. $\frac{t}{1.4} = 1$
33. $-\frac{2}{3}n = 1\frac{1}{9}$
34. $1.2x = -1.44$
35. $-\frac{2}{9}x = -\frac{4}{3}$
36. $\frac{4}{5} = -\frac{2}{15}u$
37. $-\frac{y}{2} = 1\frac{1}{4}$
38. $-\frac{a}{3} = 1\frac{2}{3}$
39. $\frac{y}{3} = \frac{5}{9}$
40. $-\frac{c}{100} = 0.75$

B   Complete.

41. If $2a + b = 10$, then $4a + 2b = $ __?__
42. If $3r + s = 5$, then $9r + 3s = $ __?__
43. If $q + 4p = 20$, then $5q + 20p = $ __?__
44. If $2x + 3 = 15$, then $8x + 12 = $ __?__
45. If $6y + 5z = 21$, then $-(6y + 5z) = $ __?__
46. If $2w + z = 7$, then $-(2w + z) = $ __?__
47. If $9p = 111$, then $3p = $ __?__
48. If $8u = 124$, then $2u = $ __?__
49. If $2x = 88$, then $\frac{1}{4}x = $ __?__
50. If $5t = 120$, then $\frac{1}{2}t = $ __?__

C   Classify each sentence as true, *T*, or false, *F*. When a sentence is false, tell why it is false.

51. For all real numbers x, $x + 2 = 3$.
52. For all real numbers x, $2x + 3x = 5x$.
53. For all real numbers x, $x + x = 1$.
54. For all real numbers, $\frac{x}{2} = \frac{1}{2}x$.

3-3 Using the Equation Properties

The cost in dollars of taking students on a two-day skiing trip is given by

$$C = 210 + 35n.$$

If you know that the cost, C, is \$1890, you can solve the resulting equation to find n, the number of students who went on the trip.

To solve such an equation, use the addition property for equations first. Then use the multiplication property.

EXAMPLE 1   Solve and check: $3x + 8 = 23$

Solution:
$$3x + 8 = 23 \qquad \longleftarrow \quad \textbf{Add } (-8) \textbf{ to each side.}$$
$$3x + 8 + (-8) = 23 + (-8)$$
$$3x = 15 \qquad \longleftarrow \quad \textbf{Multiply each side by } \tfrac{1}{3}.$$
$$\frac{1}{3} \cdot 3x = \frac{1}{3} \cdot 15 \qquad \longleftarrow \quad \tfrac{1}{3} \cdot 3x = \left(\tfrac{1}{3} \cdot 3\right)x = 1 \cdot x$$
$$x = 5$$

Check:
$$3x + 8 = 23 \qquad \longleftarrow \quad \textbf{Replace } x \textbf{ with 5.}$$
$$3 \cdot 5 + 8 \overset{?}{=} 23$$
$$15 + 8 \overset{?}{=} 23$$
$$23 \overset{?}{=} 23 \quad \text{Yes} \ \text{✓} \qquad \textbf{Solution set: } \{5\}$$

Always check your answer in the original equation.

EXAMPLE 2   Solve and check: $-7 + \dfrac{3n}{5} = 14$

Solution:
$$-7 + \frac{3n}{5} = 14 \longleftarrow \quad \textbf{Add 7 to each side.}$$
$$7 + (-7) + \frac{3n}{5} = 7 + 14$$
$$\frac{3n}{5} = 21 \longleftarrow \quad \textbf{Since } \frac{3n}{5} = \frac{3}{5}n, \textbf{ multiply}$$
$$\textbf{each side by } \frac{5}{3}.$$
$$\frac{5}{3} \cdot \frac{3}{5}n = \frac{5}{3} \cdot 21$$
$$n = 35$$

Check:
$$-7 + \frac{3n}{5} = 14 \quad \longleftarrow \quad \textbf{Replace } n \textbf{ with 35.}$$
$$-7 + \frac{3(35)}{5} \overset{?}{=} 14$$
$$-7 + 21 \overset{?}{=} 14$$
$$14 \overset{?}{=} 14 \quad \text{Yes} \ \text{✓} \qquad \textbf{Solution set: } \{35\}$$

CLASSROOM EXERCISES

What number would you add to each side of the equation to get the term with the variable alone on one side?

1. $4n + 7 = 19$
2. $20 + 1.2x = 0$
3. $8x - 5 = 11$
4. $3t - 7 = 8$
5. $-12 + r = 10$
6. $13 = 6x - 17$
7. $10 - 7x = 3$
8. $6\frac{1}{2} - 5x = 11\frac{1}{2}$

Solve and check each equation.

9. $2x + 4 = 8$
10. $3x - 1 = 8$
11. $5 + 6t = 17$
12. $10 = -3x - 5$

WRITTEN EXERCISES

A   Solve and check each equation.

1. $5n + 3 = 33$
2. $2n + 3 = 7$
3. $5n - 3 = 17$
4. $5x - 9 = -19$
5. $3t + 17 = 5$
6. $4a + 17 = 53$
7. $2n + 5 = 17$
8. $3n + 17 = 4$
9. $3n - 4 = 17$
10. $3n - 17 = 4$
11. $2a + 15 = 3$
12. $6a + 1 = 37$
13. $8a - 7 = 41$
14. $9a - 1 = 80$
15. $2b + 3 = 21$
16. $4v + 27 = 3$
17. $5 - 3a = 32$
18. $5 - 2y = 15$
19. $7 = 6x + 19$
20. $8 = 5t + 33$
21. $4 = 30 - 6t$
22. $-5 = 32 - 3b$
23. $5x + 37 = 17$
24. $\frac{2}{3}t + 5 = 23$
25. $9a - 8 = 73$
26. $15 - \frac{5}{4}v = 23$
27. $\frac{1}{2}y + 11 = 5$
28. $8n + 22 = 70$
29. $1.2t + 3.4 = -1.0$
30. $-0.6n + 11 = 17$
31. $2.1 = 4.3 - 1.1w$
32. $7.0 = 2.2 - 0.8n$
33. $0 = 0.6n - 3.6$
34. $0 = \frac{7}{10}n - 35$
35. $\frac{5}{6}n + 34 = 9$
36. $\frac{6}{8}n + 12 = 84$
37. $\frac{9}{10}x - 17 = 19$
38. $\frac{16}{15}x + 78 = 14$
39. $\frac{3}{4}x - 3 = 18$
40. $\frac{7}{8}t - 8 = 34$
41. $\frac{2}{3}t - 13 = 57$
42. $\frac{5}{12}t - 12 = 48$
43. $28 = \frac{17}{32}n - 23$
44. $6 = 26 + \frac{2}{5}n$
45. $15 = \frac{3}{10}n - 15$
46. $18 = -\frac{9}{32}n - 26$
47. $53 + \frac{3}{5}x = 26$
48. $49 + \frac{3}{5}x = 16$

B

49. $32{,}856 + 49x = 41{,}284$
50. $-683 + 33t = -485$
51. $0.6z + 0.06 = 0.006$

C   In Exercises 52–55, give the reason for each step of the proof. In the proofs, all variables represent real numbers.

52. Prove: $(a + b) + (-b) = a$

Statements	Reasons
1. $(a + b) + (-b) =$ $\quad a + [b + (-b)]$	1. __?__
2. $(a + b) + (-b) = a + 0$	2. __?__
3. $(a + b) + (-b) = a$	3. __?__

53. Prove: $-(-a) = a$

Statements	Reasons
1. $a + (-a) = 0$	1. __?__
2. $-a + a = 0$	2. __?__
3. $-a + [-(-a)] = 0$	3. __?__
4. $-(-a) = a$	4. __?__

54. Prove: $(-a) + (-b) = -(a + b)$

Statements	Reasons
1. $[-a + (-b)] + [a + b] =$ $-a + (-b + a) + b$	1. ___?___
2. $-a + (-b + a) + b =$ $-a + [a + (-b)] + b$	2. ___?___
3. $-a + [a + (-b)] + b =$ $(-a + a) + (-b + b)$	3. ___?___
4. $(-a + a) + (-b + b) =$ $0 + 0$	4. ___?___
5. $0 + 0 = 0$	5. ___?___
6. $[-a + (-b)]$ and $(a + b)$ are additive inverses.	6. ___?___
7. $-a + (-b) = -(a + b)$	7. ___?___

55. Prove: **If** $a = b$, **then** $a + c = b + c$ and $c + a = c + b$.

Statements	Reasons
1. $a + c = a + c$	1. ___?___
2. $a = b$	2. Given
3. $a + c = b + c$	3. ___?___
4. $a + c = c + a;$ $b + c = c + b$	4. ___?___
5. $c + a = c + b$	5. ___?___

CALCULATOR APPLICATIONS

Checking Equations

A calculator does not automatically follow the rules for the order of operations. Therefore, to check the answer to an equation, it may be necessary to rewrite the equation.

EXAMPLE Equation: $30 - 6t = 4$ **Answer:** $t = \frac{13}{3}$

SOLUTION Because multiplication is performed before addition or subtraction, rewrite the left side of the equation.

$$30 - 6t = -6t + 30$$
$$= -6\left(\tfrac{13}{3}\right) + 30$$

To enter -6, press the sign change key, $\boxed{+/-}$ (sometimes indicated as $\boxed{sc}$), *after* you enter the 6.

6 $\boxed{+/-}$ $\boxed{\times}$ 1 3 $\boxed{\div}$ 3 $\boxed{+}$ 3 0 $\boxed{=}$ $\boxed{4.}$

Since the two sides of the equation have the same value, $\frac{13}{3}$ is the correct answer.

EXERCISES

Check the given "answer" to each equation. Correct any incorrect answers.

1. $16 + 4n = -4$; -5 **2.** $3p - 5 = -7$; 4 **3.** $8 - \frac{7}{8}y = 6$; -16 **4.** $-16 = 1.2c - 2.2$; 11.5

Consumer Applications

Saving Energy: Heating Costs

For many people, heating costs make up the largest part of their total energy costs. To save money, it is recommended that thermostats are set no higher than **65°F**. For each degree Fahrenheit that a thermostat is lowered, heating costs are lowered by **3%**.

EXAMPLE 1   Last year the Jenkins family spent $1500 to heat their home with the thermostat set at 69°F. How much could they save by setting the thermostat at 65°F?

Solution: $69° - 65° = 4°$ lower

$4 \times 3\% = 12\%$

$\$1500 \times 12\% = \$1500 \times 0.12 = \$180$

They would save **$180**.

To help explain why the above savings occur, energy conservationists use the following formula that relates to the concept of **heat transfer**: a hotter object will give up its heat to a cooler one.

A = area of surface in ft²
U = heat transfer factor
i = inside temperature in °F
o = outside temperature in °F

$$\text{Heat Transfer} = A \cdot U(o - i) \longleftarrow$$

The thermogram below records the heat transfer of the house shown above. The brighter portions of the thermogram (for example, around windows and the chimney) indicate the location of the greatest amount of heat loss.

The variable U represents a number that depends on the surface through which the heat must pass. Heat transfer is measured in **British thermal units (Btu's) per hour**.

The table below gives the value of U for several different surfaces.

Surface	Value of *U*
Brick, 8 inches thick	0.41
Wood, 2 inches thick	0.43
Glass, double paned	0.50
Concrete, 6 inches thick	0.58
Glass, single paned	1.13

EXAMPLE 2 The side wall of the Carlton home is 6-inch concrete and is 20 feet long and 10 feet high. The outside temperature is 20°F. Estimate the rate of heat transfer when **a.** $i = 65°F$ **b.** $i = 69°F$

Solution: Calculate A: $A = 20 \times 10 = 200$ square feet

a. $HT = 200 \cdot 0.58(20 - 65)$
$= 200 \cdot 0.58(-45)$
$= -5220$ **Btu's per hour**

b. $HT = 200 \cdot 0.58(20 - 69)$
$= 200 \cdot 0.58(-49)$
$= -5684$ **Btu's per hour**

The negative signs in the answers indicate that heat is being lost from the inside. Notice that at the lower temperature, less heat is lost. This is one reason why savings occur.

EXERCISES

In Exercises 1–8, find how much each family could save on last year's heating costs.

Yearly Heating Costs	Last Year's Thermostat Setting	This Year's Thermostat Setting		Yearly Heating Costs	Last Year's Thermostat Setting	This Year's Thermostat Setting
1. $900	68°	65°	**5.**	$750	67°	65°
2. $1200	72°	67°	**6.**	$940	69°	66°
3. $800	69°	64°	**7.**	$1260	70°	64°
4. $1100	68°	66°	**8.**	$1150	71°	68°

In Exercises 9–12, use the table on page 92 to estimate the amount of heat transfer with the given conditions.

9. 2–inch solid wood wall
$l = 12$ feet
$h = 10$ feet
$i = 65°F; o = 30°F$

10. 8–inch brick wall
$l = 15$ feet
$h = 9$ feet
$i = 65°F; o = 24°F$

11. Double–paned glass window
$l = 10$ feet
$h = 7$ feet
$i = 66°F; o = 10°F$

12. 6–inch concrete wall
$l = 20$ feet
$h = 10$ feet
$i = 68°F; o = 36°F$

Insulation is installed in houses to reduce heat transfer. Proper insulation can help keep heat inside in winter and outside in summer.

3-4 Using Formulas to Solve Word Problems

In Chapter 1, you substituted for a variable in formulas. In this section, you will use formulas to solve word problems.

EXAMPLE 1 The Chic Tailoring Company uses this formula to find the width, M, of material needed to make n pleats where each pleat is p inches wide.

$$M = 3np$$

A worker is making $\frac{3}{4}$-inch pleats from material that is one yard wide. How many pleats can be made?

Solution:
$$M = 3np \quad \longleftarrow \quad \textbf{Replace } \textit{M} \textbf{ with 36 (36 inches = 1 yard) and } \textit{p} \textbf{ with } \frac{3}{4}.$$

$$36 = 3n\left(\frac{3}{4}\right) \quad \longleftarrow \quad \textbf{Solve for } \textit{n}.$$

$$36 = \frac{9}{4}n$$

$$\frac{4}{9} \cdot 36 = \frac{4}{9} \cdot \frac{9}{4}n \quad \longleftarrow \quad \textbf{By the Multiplication Property for equations}$$

$$16 = n$$

Check: $M = 3np \qquad 36 \overset{?}{=} 3 \cdot 16 \cdot \frac{3}{4}$

$$36 \overset{?}{=} 36 \quad \text{Yes } \vee \qquad \text{Thus, } \textbf{16} \text{ pleats can be made.}$$

The formula in Example 2 involves more than one operation.

EXAMPLE 2 The Trylon Theater uses this formula to calculate the total ticket receipts, R, each day. In the formula, A represents the number of adult tickets sold and C represents the number of children's tickets sold.

$$R = 3.50A + 1.50C$$

On Monday, 230 adult tickets were sold and the total receipts were \$962.50. How many children's tickets were sold?

Solution:
$$R = 3.50A + 1.50C \quad \longleftarrow \quad \textbf{Replace } \textit{R} \textbf{ with \$962.50 and } \textit{A} \textbf{ with 230.}$$

$$962.50 = 3.50(230) + 1.50C \quad \longleftarrow \quad \textbf{Solve for } \textit{C}.$$

$$962.50 = 805 + 1.50C$$

$$-805 + 962.50 = -805 + 805 + 1.50C \quad \longleftarrow \quad \textbf{By the Addition Property for equations}$$

$$157.50 = 1.50C$$

$$\frac{1}{1.50}(157.50) = \frac{1}{1.50}(1.50C) \quad \longleftarrow \quad \textbf{By the Multiplication Property for equations}$$

$$105 = C$$

Check:
$$R = 3.50A + 1.50C$$
$$962.50 \stackrel{?}{=} 3.50(230) + 1.50(105)$$
$$962.50 \stackrel{?}{=} 962.50 \quad \text{Yes} \; \text{✔}$$

Thus, **105** children's tickets were sold.

CLASSROOM EXERCISES

The yearly interest, i, in dollars on an investment, p, earning $14\frac{1}{2}\%$ interest is given by the formula $i = 0.145p$. Use this formula in Exercises 1–3.

1. What investment will earn \$181.25 in interest in 1 year?
2. What investment will earn \$391.50 in interest in 1 year?
3. What investment will earn \$812.00 in interest in 1 year?

The cost, C, in dollars of making n copies on a certain copying machine is given by the formula $C = 0.90 + 0.30n$. Use this formula in Exercises 4–6.

4. What is the cost of making 150 copies?
5. What is the cost of making 300 copies?
6. How many copies can be made for \$16.00?

WORD PROBLEMS

A   Use the formula from Example 1 in Exercises 1–4.

1. A worker is making $1\frac{1}{3}$-inch pleats from material that is one yard wide. How many pleats can be made?

2. A worker is making $\frac{5}{8}$-inch pleats from material that is 30 inches wide. How many pleats can be made?

3. A skirt having 24 pleats is to be made from material that is 24 inches wide. Find the width of each pleat.

4. A skirt having 8 pleats is to be made from material that is one yard wide. Find the width of each pleat.

Use the formula from Example 2 in Exercises 5–8.

5. On Wednesday, total receipts at the Trylon Theater amounted to \$623 and 151 adult tickets were sold. How many children's tickets were sold?

6. For the Saturday matinee, the Trylon Theater sold 472 children's tickets. Total receipts were \$1646. How many adult tickets were sold?

7. On Saturday evening, 452 adults tickets and 178 children's tickets were sold at the Trylon Theater. What were the total receipts that evening?

8. Total receipts at the Trylon Theater for one week in April were \$8089.50. During that week, 976 children's tickets were sold. How many adult tickets were sold?

A salesperson earns a base salary of $265 per week plus a 3% commission on sales. The formula

$$W = \$265 + 0.03A,$$

where W represents total weekly wages, A represents the amount of weekly sales, and $0.03A$ represents the amount of commission, can be used to find the salesperson's weekly wages. Use this formula in Exercises 9–12.

9. Last week, the salesperson's wages were $505. Find the total sales.

10. This week, the salesperson's wages were $460. Find the total sales.

11. What were the salesperson's total sales for a week in which the total weekly wages were $430?

12. What were the salesperson's total sales for a week in which the total weekly wages were $403.30?

B   A bank uses the formula

$$M = (1 - P)C$$

to calculate the amount of mortgage on a house. In the formula, M represents the amount of the mortgage, C represents the cost of the house, and P represents the per cent (expressed as a decimal) of the down payment (the initial amount paid toward the cost of the house). Use this formula in Exercises 13–16.

13. The mortgage on a house is $60,000 and the per cent of down payment is 25%. Find the cost of the house.

14. The mortgage on a house is $45,000 and the per cent of down payment is 20%. Find the cost of the house.

15. The mortgage on a house is $140,000 and the per cent of down payment is 30%. Find the cost of the house.

16. The mortgage on a house is $85,000 and the per cent of down payment is 50%. Find the cost of the house.

——— **Review** ———

Solve and check each equation. *(Section 3–1)*

1. $x + 9 = 7$

2. $-12 + n = 7$

3. $0.4 + v = 1.3$

4. $\frac{1}{2} + a = 6\frac{1}{2}$

(Section 3–2)

5. $5x = 10$

6. $-6b = 24$

7. $-3.1n = 12.4$

8. $\frac{y}{5} = -\frac{5}{2}$

(Section 3–3)

9. $3a + 4 = 13$

10. $5n + 20 = 10$

11. $9 = 6x - 3$

12. $-2 = 4 - 3m$

13. $8.0 = 1.4 - 3.3x$

14. $0 = 0.4a - 2.4$

15. $23 + \frac{5}{6}y = 3$

16. $10 + 2r = 6$

In Exercises 17–18, use the formula $d = rt$ where d represents the distance, d, in kilometers, r represents the rate in kilometers per hour and t represents the time in hours. *(Section 3–4)*

17. A car is traveling at 80 kilometers per hour. How far will it travel in 3 hours?

18. Find the time required for a jet to travel 45 kilometers at a speed of 900 kilometers per hour.

Combine like terms. *(Pages 60–63)*

1. $7x + 9x + 2$ **2.** $8y + y - 9$ **3.** $4a + 2a - a$ **4.** $8a + (-3a) - 9$

5. $6t - 5t + 1$ **6.** $-6y - y + 9y$ **7.** $-32 + 4r - 9r$ **8.** $-7 - 10b + 15b$

3-5 Solving Equations: Like Terms

In solving equations, you sometimes have to combine like terms. Usually it is better to do this first. Then you apply the addition and multiplication properties for equations.

EXAMPLE 1   Solve and check: $9m - 2m + 6 = 27$

Solution: $9m - 2m + 6 = 27$ ⟵   **Combine 9m and 2m.**

$7m + 6 = 27$ ⟵   **9m − 2m = (9 − 2)m = 7m**

$7m = 21$

$m = 3$

Check: $9m - 2m + 6 = 27$ ⟵   **Replace m with 3.**

$9(3) - 2(3) + 6 \overset{?}{=} 27$

$27 - 6 + 6 \overset{?}{=} 27$

$27 \overset{?}{=} 27$ Yes ✔   **Solution set: {3}**

Sometimes it is helpful to use parentheses to group the like terms.

EXAMPLE 2   Solve and check: $t + (3t - 9) + t + (3t - 9) = 62$

Solution: $t + (3t - 9) + t + (3t - 9) = 62$ ⟵   **Group the like terms.**

$(t + 3t + t + 3t) + [(-9) + (-9)] = 62$ ⟵   **Combine like terms.**

$8t + (-18) = 62$ ⟵   **t + 3t + t + 3t = 8t**

$8t = 80$

$t = 10$

Check: $t + (3t - 9) + t + (3t - 9) = 62$ ⟵   **Replace t with 10.**

$10 + (3 \cdot 10 - 9) + 10 + (3 \cdot 10 - 9) \overset{?}{=} 62$

$10 + 21 + 10 + 21 \overset{?}{=} 62$

$62 \overset{?}{=} 62$ Yes ✔   **Solution set: {10}**

When parentheses within an equation indicate multiplication, use the distributive postulate to multiply. For example,

$$-2(x - 5) = -2(x) + (-2)(-5)$$
$$= -2x + 10$$

Then you combine like terms and solve for the variable.

EXAMPLE 3 Solve and check: $4x - 3(x - 2) = 41$

Solution:
$$4x - 3(x - 2) = 41 \longleftarrow \text{ Write } -3(x - 2) \text{ as } + (-3)(x - 2).$$
$$4x + (-3)(x - 2) = 41$$
$$4x + (-3)(x) + (-3)(-2) = 41 \longleftarrow \text{ By the distributive postulate}$$
$$4x - 3x + 6 = 41$$
$$x + 6 = 41 \longleftarrow \text{ Solve for } x.$$
$$x + 6 + (-6) = 41 + (-6)$$
$$x = 35$$

Check:
$$4x - 3(x - 2) = 41 \longleftarrow \text{ Replace } x \text{ with 35.}$$
$$4(35) - 3(35 - 2) \overset{?}{=} 41$$
$$140 - 3(33) \overset{?}{=} 41$$
$$140 - 99 \overset{?}{=} 41$$
$$41 \overset{?}{=} 41 \quad \text{Yes} \ \checkmark \qquad \text{Solution set: } \{35\}$$

The following procedure summarizes the steps for solving equations.

Procedure

> **Steps for Solving Equations**
> 1 Remove parentheses by using the distributive postulate.
> 2 Combine like terms.
> 3 Use the addition property for equations.
> 4 Use the multiplication property for equations.
> 5 Check the equation.

CLASSROOM EXERCISES

Use the distributive property to find each product.

1. $9(x - 1)$ 2. $2(5x + 3)$ 3. $7(-2x - 1)$ 4. $8(3x - 10)$
5. $-2(x + 1)$ 6. $-3(x - 7)$ 7. $-5(x - 1)$ 8. $-2(x - 5)$

Solve and check.

9. $3a + a = 8$ 10. $6a - a + 3 = 15$ 11. $7b + 3b - b = 16$
12. $2(x + 3) = 9$ 13. $3(x - 5) = 21$ 14. $-2(-3 - 4x) = -10$

WRITTEN EXERCISES

A Use the distributive postulate to find each product.

1. $2(x - 3)$ 2. $4(x - 4)$ 3. $3(2x + 1)$ 4. $3(2x - 1)$
5. $4(5x - 7)$ 6. $4(2b - 3)$ 7. $4(b - 6)$ 8. $2(9 - b)$

Use the distributive postulate to find each product.

9. $-4(x - 9)$ **10.** $-2(y - 3)$ **11.** $-4(5 - n)$ **12.** $-5(y - 6)$

13. $-4(3 - x)$ **14.** $-1(5 - m)$ **15.** $-1(9 - 4m)$ **16.** $-2(m - 4)$

Solve and check each equation.

17. $7x - 3x = 8$ **18.** $5n - 2n = 12$ **19.** $3y + 2y - 4y = 6$

20. $8m - 2m + 7 = 19$ **21.** $15 = 7x - 2x$ **22.** $16 = 8a + 7a + a$

23. $2n - 5n = 12$ **24.** $-3n - 4n = -21$ **25.** $-5x - 4x + 3 = 12$

26. $7 - x + 2x = 7$ **27.** $2(x - 3) = -10$ **28.** $2(x - 5) = -8$

29. $2(x - 5) = 4$ **30.** $3(2x + 1) = -15$ **31.** $3(2x - 1) = 9$

32. $4(5x - 7) = 12$ **33.** $2(5 - 3n) = -14$ **34.** $4(7 - 2x) = 4$

35. $-7b + 4(2b - 3) = 16$ **36.** $2x + 3(x + 5) = 0$ **37.** $-3x + 6(x - 4) = 9$

38. $2y + 4(y - 5) = 4$ **39.** $2a - 5(a - 6) = 3$ **40.** $2b + 4(b - 6) = 12$

41. $-4(x - 9) + 5 = 1$ **42.** $2(9 - b) - 8 = 0$ **43.** $6m - 15m = 3$

44. $2b + 6b = 12$ **45.** $2(x - 6) = 3$ **46.** $-3(y + 5) = 10$

47. $b - 2(4 - b) = -5$ **48.** $x - 4(3 - x) = 0$ **49.** $5 - 2(m + 2) = 9$

B

50. $6 - (m - 4) = 18$ **51.** $-2 - (5 + 3m) = 20$ **52.** $-8 - (9 - 4m) = 15$

53. $\frac{1}{2}x + \frac{3}{4}x = 2\frac{1}{2}$ **54.** $0.04x + 0.96x = 4.80$ **55.** $1.6a + 2.4 - 7 = 3$

C   In Exercises 56–57, give the reason for each step of each proof. In these proofs, all variables represent real numbers.

56. If $ac = bc$ and $c \neq 0$, then $a = b$.

Statements	Reasons
1. $ac = bc$	1. Given
2. $(ac)\left(\frac{1}{c}\right) = bc\left(\frac{1}{c}\right)$	2. ___?___
3. $a\left[c\left(\frac{1}{c}\right)\right] = b\left[c\left(\frac{1}{c}\right)\right]$	3. ___?___
4. $a(1) = b(1)$	4. ___?___
5. $a = b$	5. ___?___

57. If $a + c = b + c$, then $a = b$.

Statements	Reasons
1. $a + b = b + c$	1. Given
2. $(a + c) + (-c) = b + c + (-c)$	2. ___?___
3. $a + [c + (-c)] = b + [c + (-c)]$	3. ___?___
4. $a + 0 = b + 0$	4. ___?___
5. $a = b$	5. ___?___

A set, S, of numbers is **closed under division** if the quotient of any two numbers in set S is also in set S. (Remember that division by zero is excluded.)

Which of the following sets are closed under division?

58. $\{1\}$ **59.** $\{-1, 0, 1\}$ **60.** $\{-1\}$ **61.** I   **62.** Q

63. Is the set $\{-1, 1\}$ closed under division?

Problem Solving and Applications

3–6 Formulas to Equations

Many problems that relate to geometry can be solved by writing an equation for a formula. For example,

the sum of the measures of the angles of a triangle is 180°.

That is,

$$A + B + C = 180°$$

where A, B, and C, represent the measures of the angles of a triangle.

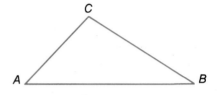

EXAMPLE Find the measure of each angle of this triangle.

Solution: Use the formula. Replace A with $2x$, B with x, and C with $2x + 5$.

$$A + B + C = 180°$$
$$2x + x + 2x + 5 = 180 \longleftarrow \text{ Combine like terms.}$$
$$5x + 5 = 180$$
$$5x = 175$$
$$x = 35 \longleftarrow \text{ Find 2x and 2x + 5.}$$
$$2x = 2(35) = 70$$
$$2x + 5 = 2(35) + 5 = 75$$

Check: Does the sum of the measures of the angles equal 180?

$35 + 70 + 75 = 180$? Yes ✔

Thus, the angle measures are **35°, 70°, and 75°**.

CLASSROOM EXERCISES

In Exercises 1–3, find the measure of each angle of the triangle.

1.

2.

3.

4. The measures of the angles of a triangle can be represented by a, $2a + 30$, and $a + 10$. Find the measure of each angle of the triangle.

5. The measures of the angles of a triangle can be represented by d, $d - 15$, and $d - 30$. Find the measure of each angle of the triangle.

WRITTEN EXERCISES

A   In Exercises 1–6, find the measure of each angle of the triangle.

1. Acute Triangle

2. Obtuse Triangle

3. Right Triangle

4. Isosceles Triangle

5. Equilateral Triangle

6. Isosceles Right Triangle

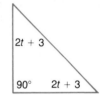

The sum of the measures of the angles of a quadrilateral (closed *polygon having four sides*) *is 360°. That is,*

$$A + B + C + D = 360°,$$

where A, B, C, and D represent the measures of the angles of the quadrilateral. In Exercises 7–12, refer to this formula to find the measure of each angle of the given quadrilateral.

7. Rectangle

$2y + 1$	$2y + 1$
$2y + 1$	$2y + 1$

8. Square

$\frac{3}{4}z$	$\frac{3}{4}z$
$\frac{3}{4}z$	$\frac{3}{4}z$

9. Parallelogram

$3x + 15$ $2x$

$2x$ $3x + 15$

10. Rhombus

$7x$ $3x - 10$

$3x - 10$ $7x$

11. Trapezoid

$7x - 25$ $6x$

$4x - 15$ $3x$

12. Quadrilateral

$3x$
$2x - 9$

$2x + 1$ $x - 24$

WORD PROBLEMS

13. The measures of the angles of a triangle can be represented by $s, \frac{1}{2}s$, and $3s$. Find the measure of each angle of the triangle.

14. The measure of one angle of a triangle is 70°. The measure of each of the other angles can be represented by $5x$. Find the measures of the two angles.

15. The measure of one angle of a triangle can be represented by $10p$. The measure of each of the other two angles is 15 more than the first angle. Find the measure of each angle of the triangle.

16. The sum of the measures of two angles is 90°. The measure of one of these angles is $2r$; the measure of the other angle is $2r - 18$. Find the measure of each of these angles.

17. The sum of two angles is 90°. The measures of the angles can be represented by x and $(x + 28)$. Find the measure of each angle.

18. The sum of two angles is 90°. The measures of the angles can be represented by t and $(t - 12)$. Find the measure of each angle.

19. The sum of two angles is 180°. Their measures can be represented by y and $(y + 36)$. Find the measure of each angle.

20. The sum of two angles is 180°. Their measures can be represented by w and $(3w + 18)$. Find the measure of each angle.

21. The measures of the angles of a parallelogram can be represented by $x, x, 3x$, and $3x$. Find the measure of each angle of the parallelogram.

22. The sum of the measures of two angles is 180°. The measure of one angle is $5x$. The measure of the other angle is twice the first. Find the measure of each angle.

23. The sum of the measures of two angles is 90°. The measure of one angle is $4q$. The measure of the second angle is three times the first. Find the measure of each angle.

24. The sum of the measures of two angles is 180°. The measure of one angle is $7t$. The measure of the second angle is 2 more than the first. Find the measure of each angle.

Puzzle

Solve each equation. Match each solution with a letter or "!" mark below. Then unscramble the letters in each word to find the secret message.

A: $x + \frac{3}{4} = 1$ **E:** $-x = -4$ **O:** $4x = -16$ **U:** $x - 5 = -10$ **L:** $x - 3x = \frac{1}{2}$

P: $12x + 7 = 16$ **R:** $2(x - 3) = 4$ **!:** $\frac{4}{5}x + 1 = \frac{2}{5}$ **S:** $4 = 2(5x + 1)$ **Y:** $10x = -2$

$$\overline{-4} \ \ \overline{-\frac{1}{5}} \ \ \overline{-5} \qquad \overline{4} \ \ \overline{\frac{1}{4}} \ \ \overline{5} \qquad \overline{-\frac{1}{4}} \ \ \overline{4} \ \ \overline{-\frac{1}{5}} \ \ \overline{\frac{1}{4}} \ \ \overline{5} \ \ \overline{-\frac{1}{4}}$$

$$\overline{4} \ \ \overline{\frac{3}{4}} \ \ \overline{\frac{1}{5}} \ \ \overline{5} \ \ \overline{-5} \qquad \overline{-\frac{3}{4}}$$

Write a two-place decimal for each fraction or mixed number.

Example: $\dfrac{9}{10} \longrightarrow 10\overline{)9.00}^{\,\mathbf{0.90}} \longleftarrow$ **Answer**

1. $\dfrac{7}{10}$ 　　　 2. $\dfrac{3}{5}$ 　　　 3. $\dfrac{3}{4}$ 　　　 4. $5\dfrac{1}{2}$ 　　　 5. $7\dfrac{1}{4}$ 　　　 6. $8\dfrac{3}{10}$

Write a fraction in lowest terms for each decimal.

Example: $0.32 = \dfrac{32}{100} = \dfrac{8}{25}$

7. 0.45 　　 8. 0.64 　　 9. 0.25 　　 10. 0.50 　　 11. 0.70 　　 12. 0.125

3-7　Equations and Per Cent

Per cent means **per hundred** or **hundredths**.

$$13\% = \frac{13}{100} = \mathbf{0.13} \qquad\qquad 6\% = \frac{6}{100} = \mathbf{0.06}$$

$$0.5\% = \frac{0.5}{100} = \frac{5}{1000} = \mathbf{0.005} \qquad 215\% = \frac{215}{100} = \mathbf{2.15}$$

There are three types of per cent problems. Each type involves three numbers. When you know two of the numbers, you can write an equation and solve it to find the third number.

Finding a Per Cent of a Number	**Finding What Per Cent a Number is of Another**	**Finding a Number Given its Per Cent**
What number is 75% of 900?	What per cent of 5 is 2?	72 is 9% of what number?
$n = 0.75 \cdot 900$	$n \cdot 5 = 2$	$72 = 0.09 \cdot n$

EXAMPLE 1　**a.** What number is 75% of 900?　　**b.** What per cent of 5 is 2?

c. 72 is 9% of what number?

Solutions:　**a.** Let $y =$ the number.　　　　**b.** Let $a =$ the per cent.

What number is 75% of 900?　　　　What per cent of 5 is 2?

$$y = 0.75 \cdot 900$$
$$y = 675$$

Thus, **675** is 75% of 900.

$$a \cdot 5 = 2$$
$$5a = 2$$
$$a = \frac{2}{5} = 0.40$$
$$a = 40\%$$

Thus, 2 is **40%** of 5.

c. Let $s =$ the number.

72 is 90% of <u>what number?</u>

$$72 = 0.90 \qquad s$$

$$\frac{72}{0.90} = \frac{0.90s}{0.90}$$

$$\textbf{80} = s$$

Thus, 72 is 90% of **80**.

NOTE: When finding what per cent one number is of another as in Example 1b and in Example 2, you can express the unknown as a decimal or as a fraction. Then you write a per cent for the decimal or fraction.

To find the per cent of increase or decrease, first find the *amount* of increase or decrease. Then compare this with the *original amount* and write a per cent.

EXAMPLE 2 In 1978, the cost for the first 3 ounces of first-class mail was 15¢. In 1981, the cost rose to 20¢. Find the per cent of increase.

Solution: $\boxed{1}$ Let $y =$ the per cent of increase.

$\boxed{2}$ Amount of increase: $20¢ - 15¢ = 5¢$

$\boxed{3}$ 5 is <u>what per cent</u> of 15? ◄────── **15 is the original amount.**

$$5 = \qquad y \qquad \cdot \ 15, \quad \text{or}$$

$$15y = 5$$

$$y = \frac{5}{15} = \frac{1}{3} \ \blacktriangleleft \text{─────── Write a per cent for } \tfrac{1}{3}.$$

Check: The per cent of increase is $33\frac{1}{3}\%$. Does $33\frac{1}{3}\%$ of $15 = 5$? Yes ✓

CLASSROOM EXERCISES

Complete.

1. $18 = 20\%$ of __?__

2. $6 = 15\%$ of __?__

3. __?__% of $20 = 15$

4. __?__% of $96 = 72$

5. 35% of $246 = $ __?__

6. 1% of $81 = $ __?__

7. __?__% of $20 = 12$

8. 45% of $120 = $ __?__

9. 18% of $150 = $ __?__

10. $72 = 9\%$ of __?__

11. $28 = $ __?__% of 70

12. $48.6 = 90\%$ of __?__

13. By raising the thermostat setting, the Arico family reduced their monthly costs for air conditioning from $170 to $100. Find the amount of decrease.

14. Last month, Carol earned $1250 selling vacuum cleaners for ABC Vac Corporation. This month she earned $1500. Find the amount of increase.

15. By lowering the thermostat setting, the Gould family reduced their monthly heating costs from $90 to $85. Find the per cent of decrease.

16. One-way train fare from Chicago to New Orleans cost $45 in 1970. By 1980, the fare was $75. Find the per cent of increase.

WRITTEN EXERCISES

A

$\cancel{\%} = \chi$

1. 35% of 28 is what number?
2. 40% of 25 is what number?
3. What per cent of 92 is 69?
4. What per cent of 65 is 39?
5. 15 is 20% of what number?
6. 21 is 30% of what number?
7. 125% of what number is 45?
8. 3 is what per cent of 3000?
9. $37\frac{1}{2}$% of 2400 is what number?
10. 3% of what number is 1.86?
11. What per cent of 35 is 28?
12. 2.5% of 400 is what number?

APPLICATIONS: Using Per Cent

13. The price of a new car is $6500. Mrs. Gomez made a down payment of 15% of the price of the car when she bought it. How much was the down payment?

14. In a factory, 54,600 parts were made in one week. When they were tested, 3% were found to be defective. How many were defective?

15. Mr. Garvey bought a suit for $180 and paid $10.80 as a sales tax. What per cent of the cost was the sales tax?

16. A baseball team won 8 games. This was 40% of the games played. How many games did the team play?

17. An advertisement claims that each serving of a brand of oatmeal contains 4 grams of protein. This is 6% of a person's daily recommended need. How many grams of protein make up a person's daily recommended need?

18. Jeff earns $1050 a month as a key punch operator for a bank. He spends $84 per month on his automobile insurance. What per cent of his monthly income is spent on automobile insurance?

19. Jennifer bought a coat at a "20% off" sale and saved $35. What was the original price of the coat?

20. How much silver is in 12.5 kilograms of an alloy (mixture) which is 8% silver?

21. A worker who earns $6.50 per hour receives a raise of $0.52 per hour. What is the per cent of increase in the worker's wages?

22. The list price (regular price) of a typewriter is $355. A discount (reduction in price) of $106.50 is given. What per cent of the list price is the discount?

23. The discount on a set of golf clubs is $69 and the rate of discount is 15%. What is the list price?

24. The list price on a camera is $60 but it is on sale for $44.40. What is the rate (per cent) of discount?

25. A sports car that originally cost $6000 is now valued at $8000. What is the per cent increase in value?

26. The monthly rent for an apartment rose from $425 to $476. What is the per cent of increase?

27. The price of pocket-size calculators decreased from $40 to $12 over a 9-year period. Find the per cent of decrease.

B

29. An art dealer bought an oil painting for $1200 and then sold it at an auction for a 40% profit. What was the selling price of the painting?

31. A business executive received a salary increase of 15%. This brought his salary to $27,600. What was the executive's salary before the raise?

33. After Kenneth Sims lost 20% of his real estate investment, he had $12,500 left. How much did he invest originally?

C

35. A store owner is trying to sell a $450 stereo. First the owner raises the price by 20%. Then the owner advertises a "20% off" sale on the new price. What is the final price of the stereo?

28. The value of a certain four-door car decreased from $7000 to $4550 in two years. Find the per cent of decrease.

30. The population of a village decreased from 21,000 to 16,000. Find the per cent of decrease. Round your answer to the nearest whole per cent.

32. After the price of a pound of meat was increased 12%, the new price was $1.68. What was the price per pound before the increase?

34. Shirley bought some stock valued at $62.50 per share and sold it for $67.50 per share. Find the per cent of profit.

36. On January 1, Tim's credit-card balance was $350. The interest rate is 1.5% per month and Tim pays $75 at the end of each month. How much will he owe on April 1?

CALCULATOR APPLICATIONS

Per Cent of Increase and Decrease

A calculator with a per cent key, $\boxed{\%}$, allows you to find the per cent of increase and decrease.

EXAMPLE A coat with a regular price of $75 is selling for $63.75. Find the per cent of decrease.

SOLUTION $\boxed{1}$ Find the amount of decrease.

$$7\ 5\ \boxed{-}\ 6\ 3\ .\ 7\ 5\ \boxed{=}$$

$$\boxed{11.25}$$

$\boxed{2}$ Find the per cent of decrease.

$$1\ 1\ .\ 2\ 5\ \boxed{\div}\ 7\ 5\ \boxed{\%}$$

$$\boxed{15.}$$

EXERCISES

1. A sedan that originally cost $10,500 is now valued at $8925. What is the per cent decrease in value?

2. A painting worth $750 ten years ago was auctioned for $4200. Find the per cent increase in value.

3–8 Integer Problems

To solve integer problems, you have to represent consecutive integers, consecutive even integers, and consecutive odd integers.

Word Expression	Algebraic Expression	Example
Three **consecutive** integers	Let x = the first integer Then $x + 1$ = the second integer, and $x + 2$ = the third integer.	$\begin{array}{ccc} -5 & -4 & -3 \\ \downarrow & \downarrow & \downarrow \\ x & x+1 & x+2 \end{array}$
Three **consecutive** even integers	Let t = the first even integer. Then $t + 2$ = the second even integer, and $t + 4$ = the third even integer.	$\begin{array}{ccc} 22 & 24 & 26 \\ \downarrow & \downarrow & \downarrow \\ t & t+2 & t+4 \end{array}$
Three **consecutive** odd integers	Let h = the first odd integer. Then $h + 2$ = the second odd integer, and $h + 4$ = the third odd integer	$\begin{array}{ccc} 3 & 5 & 7 \\ \downarrow & \downarrow & \downarrow \\ h & h+2 & h+4 \end{array}$

To solve word problems involving integers, follow these steps.

Procedure

> To solve word problems involving integers:
> 1. Choose a variable. Use the variable to represent the integers.
> 2. Write an equation for the word sentence.
> 3. Solve the equation and find the integers.
> 4. Check in the statement of the problem.

EXAMPLE 1 Find two consecutive integers whose sum is 147.

Solution:
1. Let t = the first integer. —— **Represent the integers.**
   Then $t + 1$ = the second integer.

2. $t + (t + 1) = 147$ —— **Their sum is 147.**

3. $2t + 1 = 147$

   $2t = 146$

   $t = 73$ —— **Find $t + 1$.**

   $t + 1 = 73 + 1 = 74$

Check:
4. Are the integers consecutive? Yes ✔

   Does $73 + 74 = 147$? Yes ✔ The integers are **73** and **74**.

Always check your solution with the original statement of the problem.

NOTE: The steps in Example 2 correspond to the steps in the procedure.

EXAMPLE 2 Find three consecutive odd integers whose sum is -15.

Solution: ☐1 Let $r =$ the first odd integer.
Then $r + 2 =$ the second odd integer,
and $r + 4 =$ the third odd integer.

☐2 $r + (r + 2) + (r + 4) = -15$ ⟵——— **Their sum is −15.**

☐3 $\qquad\qquad 3r + 6 = -15$

$\qquad\qquad\qquad 3r = -21$

$\qquad\qquad\qquad\quad r = -7$ ⟵——— **Don't forget to find**
$\qquad\qquad\qquad\qquad\qquad\qquad\qquad$ **$r + 2$ and $r + 4$.**

$\qquad\quad r + 2 = -7 + 2 = -5$

$\qquad\quad r + 4 = -7 + 4 = -3$

Check: ☐4 Are the integers consecutive odd integers? Yes ✔

Does $(-7) + (-5) + (-3) = -15$? Yes ✔

The integers are $-7, -5,$ and -3.

CLASSROOM EXERCISES

Beginning with the given integer, write the next four larger consecutive integers.

1. 18   **2.** 97   **3.** 0   **4.** -8 **5.** -1 **6.** r

Beginning with the given even integer, write the next four larger consecutive even integers.

7. 12   **8.** 100   **9.** -12 **10.** -66 **11.** q **12.** $b + 4$

Beginning with the given odd integer, write the next four larger consecutive odd integers.

13. 9   **14.** 1   **15.** -21 **16.** -101 **17.** k **18.** $k + 10$

In each of Exercises 19–22, write an algebraic expression to represent each integer. Then write the equation you would use to solve the problem.

19. The sum of two consecutive integers is 43.

20. The sum of two consecutive even integers is 86.

21. The sum of two consecutive odd integers is 0.

22. The sum of two consecutive integers is -29.

WORD PROBLEMS

A   Solve each problem.

1. The sum of two consecutive integers is −17. Find the integers.

2. The sum of three consecutive integers is 279. Find the integers.

3. Find four consecutive integers whose sum is −130.

4. Find two consecutive integers whose sum is −25.

5. Find three consecutive integers whose sum is 48.

6. The sum of two consecutive odd integers is 112. Find the integers.

7. The sum of three consecutive odd integers is −105. Find the integers.

8. The sum of four consecutive even integers is −420. Find the integers.

9. Find four consecutive odd integers whose sum is 0.

10. Find three consecutive even integers whose sum is 0.

11. Are there three consecutive integers whose sum is 40?

12. Are there three consecutive odd integers whose sum is 59?

B

13. Find two consecutive integers such that four times the smaller minus three times the larger equals 0.

14. Find three consecutive integers such that the sum of the first and third is 40.

15. Find four consecutive integers such that the sum of the second and fourth is 132.

16. Find three consecutive integers such that the sum of the first two decreased by the third equals 68.

17. Find two consecutive odd integers such that twice the smaller decreased by the larger equals 53.

18. Find three consecutive odd integers such that their sum decreased by the second equals 50.

19. If n is an integer, is $2n + 2$ even or odd?

20. If n is an integer, is $2n + 1$ even or odd?

21. If $2h + 1$ is an odd integer, what is the preceding even integer?

22. If $2h + 1$ is an odd integer, what is the preceding integer?

C   The French mathematician, Pierre de Fermat (1601–1665), proved this theorem about prime numbers.

> **If n is a natural number, prime numbers of the form $4n + 1$ can be expressed as the sum of the squares of two integers.**

Example: Prime number: **5**

Expressed as $4n + 1$: **4(1) + 1**

Expressed as the square of two integers: $2^2 + 1^2$

23. Express the numbers 13, 17, and 29 in the form $4n + 1$.

24. Express the numbers 13, 17, and 29 as the sum of the squares of two integers.

25. What other prime numbers less than 50 can be expressed as $4n + 1$?

26. Express the primes you found in Exercise 25 as the sum of the squares of two integers.

COMPUTER APPLICATIONS

BASIC: SOLVING AX + B = C

Problem: *Given a, b, and c, write a program which solves the equation ax + b = c. Include the possibilities that the solution set contains all real numbers or is the empty set.*

```
100 PRINT "FOR THE EQUATION AX + B = C, WHAT ARE"
110 PRINT "A, B, AND C";
120 INPUT A, B, C
130 IF A = 0 THEN 170
140 LET X = (C - B)/A
150 PRINT "X = ";X
160 GOTO 210
170 IF B = C THEN 200
180 PRINT "NO SOLUTION"
190 GOTO 210
200 PRINT "ALL REAL NUMBERS ARE SOLUTIONS."
210 PRINT
220 PRINT "ANY MORE EQUATIONS TO SOLVE (1=YES, 0=NO)";
230 INPUT Z
240 IF Z = 1 THEN 120
250 END
```

The following is the output from a sample run of the program above.

Output:
```
RUN
FOR THE EQUATION AX + B = C, WHAT ARE
A, B, AND C? 1,3,5
X =  2

ANY MORE EQUATIONS TO SOLVE (1=YES, 0=NO)? 1
? 4,8,6
X = -.5

ANY MORE EQUATIONS TO SOLVE (1=YES, 0=NO)? 1
? 0,5,-3
NO SOLUTION

ANY MORE EQUATIONS TO SOLVE (1=YES, 0=NO)? 1
? 0,6,6
ALL REAL NUMBERS ARE SOLUTIONS.

ANY MORE EQUATIONS TO SOLVE (1=YES, 0=NO)? 0
READY
```

Analysis: Before the program could be written, some preliminary algebra had to be done.

$$ax + b = c$$

$$ax = c - b \longleftarrow \text{Subtract } b \text{ from both sides.}$$

$$x = \frac{c - b}{a} \longleftarrow \text{Divide both sides by } a.$$

Statements 130, 170–200: The last step of the work above assumes that A ≠ 0. If A = 0, then the formula (C − B)/A cannot be used. Instead the solution set will either be empty (if B ≠ C) or all real numbers (if B = C). These two special cases are handled by statements 170–200.

Statements 140–160: If A ≠ 0, the computer ignores the "THEN 170" in statement 130 and instead moves in order to statement 140. Here the formula developed above is used to compute X. Then statement 150 prints the answer. Statement 160 sends the computer to the statements (210–240) that determine whether the user has any more equations to solve.

EXERCISES

A Write each equation in the form $ax + b = c$. Then use the program on page 110 to solve the equation.

1. $71 = 5x - 3$
2. $89 + 10x = 284$
3. $104 - 15x = 73$
4. $234 = 45 + 21x$
5. $804 = 66 - 34x$
6. $1245 - 125x = 1542$
7. $54 + 0x = 120$
8. $81 = 81 - 0x$
9. $99 = 12 + 0x$
10. $4x + 83 + 7x = 135$
11. $25x - 75 - 12x = 90$
12. $342 = 17x - 135 + 14x$

B Write a BASIC program for each problem.

13. Given the measures of two angles of a triangle, compute and print the measure of the third angle. Use the following formula. (See page 100.)
$$A + B + C = 180$$

14. Given the perimeter of a square, compute and print the length of the side. Use the following formula. (See page 10.)
$$P = 4s$$

15. Given the average of three numbers and two of the numbers, compute and print the third number. Use the following formula.
$$A = \frac{x + y + z}{3}$$

16. Given the winning percentage of a sports team, p, and the number of games played, g, compute and print the number of games won, w. Use the following formula.
$$P = \frac{w}{g} \cdot 100$$

Solve and check each equation. *(Section 3-5)*

1. $8x - 5x = 9$

2. $4y + 5y - 2y = 14$

3. $18 = 3(4a - 2)$

4. $0.02m + 0.83m = 1.70$

5. $\frac{1}{4}x + \frac{3}{8}x = 3\frac{1}{5}$

6. $-3 - 4(a - 3) = 17$

In Exercises 7–8 use the formula $A + B + C = 180°$ where A, B, and C represent the measures of the angles of a triangle. *(Section 3-6)*

7. The measure of one angle of a triangle is 30°. The measure of a second angle is 55°. Find the measure of the remaining angle.

8. The measure of one angle of a triangle is 120°. The measure of each of the other angles can be represented by $6x$. Find the measures of these angles.

Solve. *(Section 3-7)*

9. 30% of 40 is what number?

10. What per cent of 16 is 9?

11. Jaime bought a suit at a "15% off" sale and saved $30. What was the original price of the suit?

12. A living room set that originally cost $800 is on sale for $720. What is the rate of discount?

(Section 3-8)

13. Find three consecutive integers whose sum is 30.

14. The sum of two consecutive even integers is 46. Find the integers.

15. Find four consecutive integers such that the sum of the first and third is 84.

16. Find two consecutive odd integers whose sum is -28.

_____ **Chapter Summary** _____

IMPORTANT TERMS Equivalent equations (p. 84)   Solution set (p. 87)
Per cent (p. 103)

IMPORTANT IDEAS

1. **Addition Property for Equations:** Adding the same number to each side of an equation results in an equivalent equation.

2. The replacement set for the variables in equations is the set of real numbers, unless it is otherwise stated.

3. **Multiplication Property for Equations:** Multiplying each side of an equation by the same nonzero number results in an equivalent equation.

4. You solve a formula for one of the variables in the same way as you solve an equation.

5. When parentheses within an equation indicate multiplication, use the distributive postulate to multiply.

6. **Steps for Solving Equations**
   1. Use the distributive postulate.
   2. Combine like terms.
   3. Use the addition property for equations.
   4. Use the multiplication property for equations.
   5. Check the equation.
7. To find the per cent of increase or decrease, first find the amount of increase or decrease. Then compare with the original amount and write a per cent.
8. **Steps for Solving Word Problems Involving Integers**
   1. Choose a variable. Use the variable to represent the integers.
   2. Write an equation for the word sentence.
   3. Solve the equation and find the integers.
   4. Check in the statement of the problem.

——— Chapter Objectives and Review ———

Objective: *To use the addition property for equations to solve equations (Section 3–1)*

Solve and check each equation.

1. $x + 9 = 15$
2. $-8 + n = 0$
3. $-14 + t = 7$
4. $k - (-10) = 5\frac{1}{2}$
5. $r - \frac{1}{5} = 4\frac{4}{5}$
6. $-2.9 + z = 11.3$

Objective: *To use the multiplication property for equations to solve equations (Section 3–2)*

Solve and check each equation.

7. $4x = 12$
8. $-3c = 18$
9. $7.5x = 1.5$
10. $\frac{3}{5}t = 21$
11. $-m = \frac{4}{9}$
12. $-\frac{y}{8} = 1\frac{1}{16}$

Objective: *To use the addition and multiplication properties for equations to solve equations (Section 3–3)*

Solve and check each equation.

13. $3x + 7 = 19$
14. $11 - \frac{4}{5}m = 3$
15. $0.4t - 1.3 = 0.3$

Objective: *To use formulas to solve word problems (Section 3–4)*

16. The formula for the width of material, M, needed to make n pleats where each pleat is p inches wide is $M = 3np$. Find the number of $\frac{5}{8}$-inch pleats that can be made from material that is 45 inches wide.

17. The formula for a salesperson's weekly wages, W, is $W = \$315 + 0.05A$, where A represents the amount of total weekly sales. Find his total weekly sales if his wages for this week were $352.74.

Objective: *To solve equations involving like terms (Section 3–5)*

Use the distributive postulate to find each product.

18. $3(x - 7)$ **19.** $-1(m + 6)$ **20.** $11(3y - 2)$ **21.** $-5(5 - a)$

Solve and check each equation.

22. $14n - 3n = -44$ **23.** $3b + 11 - 8b = -24$ **24.** $8(4 + y) = 16$

25. $-9(7 - k) - 27 = -90$ **26.** $-4 - (6 - 2t) = -12$ **27.** $1.2r + 4 + 3.2 = 10.8$

Objective: *To use equations to solve word problems involving geometric formulas (Section 3–6)*

In Exercises 28–30, find the measure of each angle of the triangles. Use the formula $A + B + C = 180°$.

28. Right Triangle   **29.** Acute Triangle   **30.** Obtuse Triangle

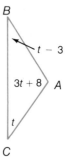

Objective: *To solve percent problems (Section 3–7)*

31. 25% of 68 is what number?

32. 3.5% of what number is 7?

33. What per cent of 38 is 57?

34. 2% of 75 is what number?

35. The price of a home computer is $1800. Ronald made a down payment of 20% when he bought it. How much was the down payment?

36. A basketball team won 15 games. That was $62\frac{1}{2}\%$ of the games played. How many games did the team play?

37. A dealer bought an antique clock for $375 and sold it for $450. What was the per cent of profit?

38. The enrollment at a college increased from 1850 to 2175. Find the per cent of increase, to the nearest whole per cent.

Objective: *To solve integer problems (Section 3–8)*

Solve each problem.

39. Find three consecutive even integers whose sum is 126.

40. Find two consecutive integers such that three times the smaller increased by twice the larger equals -43.

Solve and check each equation.

1. $5 + z = 23$

2. $9k = -72$

3. $t - (-4.3) = 0$

4. $\frac{r}{7} = 6$

5. $x - 3\frac{1}{4} = 11$

6. $-\frac{1}{9}y = 1\frac{2}{3}$

7. $\frac{1}{3}p - 4 = -2$

8. $14w + 6 = 13$

9. $\frac{v}{15} - 9 = -16$

10. $7a + 11a = 9$

11. $6b - 4b + 3 = 11$

12. $5(-3c - 8) = 35$

13. $12d - 3(d - 1) = 15$

14. $6 = 3 - (f + 7)$

15. $\frac{3}{4}g + 7 + \frac{1}{4}g = 7$

16. A broker's weekly wage, W, amounted to \$390.52. Use the formula $W = \$370 + 0.02A$ to find A, the broker's total amount of weekly sales.

17. The angles of a triangle measure b, $2b + 20$, and $b + 20$. Find the measure of each angle. Use the formula $A + B + C = 180°$, where A, B, and C represent the measures of the angles of the triangle.

18. Paul bought boots at a "30% off" sale. The original price was \$42. How much did he save?

19. Find two consecutive even integers whose sum is 70.

20. Find three consecutive odd integers whose sum is 171.

Additional Practice

Skills

Solve and check each equation. *(Sections 3–1, 3–2, 3–3)*

1. $x + 9 = 17$

2. $16 = r - 7$

3. $s + 3.1 = 0$

4. $t - (-7) = 21$

5. $y + \frac{1}{2} = 3\frac{1}{4}$

6. $\frac{2}{5} = b - 4\frac{1}{5}$

7. $8n = 32$

8. $2.2m = -8.8$

9. $-v = \frac{7}{8}$

10. $\frac{c}{10} = 15$

11. $\frac{d}{3} = -4.3$

12. $-\frac{5}{9} = \frac{f}{6}$

13. $4g + 7 = 27$

14. $3h - 3 = -15$

15. $\frac{2}{3}j + 6 = 16$

16. $3 = -\frac{2}{11}u + 9$

17. $1.7w - 0.44 = 5$

18. $-0.9k + 8 = 3.5$

19. If $z + 7 = 13$, find the value of $4z$.

20. If $6p - 9 = -39$, find the value of $2p$.

Use the distributive postulate to find each product. *(Section 3–5)*

21. $6(x - 9)$

22. $-4(n + 7)$

23. $(12 - y)6$

24. $-1(7x - 8)$

25. $-4(-3 + 4y)$

26. $8(2a - 6)$

27. $-3(4 - 5a)$

28. $-2(-8 - 5b)$

Solve and check each equation. *(Section 3–5)*

29. $3y + 5y = -40$ **30.** $-19 = 4a - 3$ **31.** $-36 = 7b - b$

32. $4(3x - 7) = 32$ **33.** $2c - 1(c + 6) = 11$ **34.** $-1.6r + 7(r - 1) = 3.8$

Solve. *(Section 3–7)*

35. 8% of 175 is what number?   **36.** What per cent of 120 is 45?

37. 27% of 200 is what number?   **38.** 32% of what number is 32?

Applications

In Exercises 39 and 40, use the formula $M = 3np$, where M is the width of material needed to make n pleats that are p inches wide. *(Section 3–4)*

39. A skirt having 25 pleats is to be made from material that is 50 inches wide. Find the width of each pleat.

40. How many $\frac{1}{2}$-inch pleats can be made from material that is 45 inches wide?

In Exercises 41 and 42, use the formula $R = 3.50A + 1.50C$, where R represents the total ticket receipts collected at the Trylon Theater when A adult tickets and C children's tickets are sold. *(Section 3–4)*

41. On Friday, total receipts at the Trylon Theater were $920 and 100 children's tickets were sold. How many adult tickets were sold?

42. For the Sunday matinee, 58 adult tickets were sold and total receipts were $542. How many children's tickets were sold?

In Exercises 43–45, find the measure of each angle. Use the formula $A + B + C = 180°$. *(Section 3–6)*

43. Acute Triangle   **44.** Isosceles Triangle   **45.** Isosceles Right Triangle

          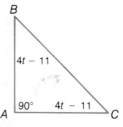

Solve each problem. *(Sections 3–7, 3–8)*

46. The value of an antique pewter pitcher increased 350% in the last ten years. If it was valued at $92 ten years ago, what is its value now?

47. Jill received a 6% increase in wages, bringing her earnings to $4.77 per hour. What did she earn per hour before she got the raise?

48. The sum of two consecutive integers is 49. Find the integers.

49. The sum of two consecutive odd integers is -32. Find the integers.

CHAPTER 4 Equations and Inequalities

Problem Solving and Applications

4-1 From Words to Symbols

Translating word expressions to algebraic expressions is an essential skill in solving word problems. This table shows that the *same* algebraic symbol of operation can be used to translate *more than one* word expression.

	Word Expression	Algebraic Expression
Addition Expressions	The **sum** of a number, t, and -3	$t + (-3)$
	$z°$ **plus** $1.9°$	$z + 1.9$
	Add $7\frac{1}{2}$ to k.	$k + 7\frac{1}{2}$
	$\$50$ **more than** d dollars	$d + 50$
	$-\frac{7}{8}$ **increased by** n	$-\frac{7}{8} + n$
	Increase t by 3.9.	$t + 3.9$
	The **total** of 16 and $-r$	$16 + (-r)$
Subtraction Expressions	x **minus** $2\frac{3}{8}$	$x - 2\frac{3}{8}$
	The **difference** of $\$60$ and $\$b$	$60 - b$
	The **difference between** $\$60$ and $\$b$	$60 - b$
	Subtract 7.8 from n.	$n - 7.8$
	t **decreased by** -8	$t - (-8)$
	a **diminished by** -1	$a - (-1)$
	$y°$ **less** $5°$	$y - 5$
	$y°$ **less than** $5°$	$5 - y$
Multiplication Expressions	1.7 **times** z	$1.7z$
	b **multiplied by** $\frac{2}{3}$	$\frac{2}{3}b$, or $\frac{2b}{3}$
	The **product** of 5 and g	$5g$
	Twice m centimeters	$2m$
	Triple the width, w	$3w$
Division Expressions	The **cost**, c, **divided by** 12	$c \div 12$, or $\frac{c}{12}$
	The **quotient** of y and 15	$y \div 15$, or $\frac{y}{15}$
	The **quotient** of 15 and y	$15 \div y$, or $\frac{15}{y}$

Note carefully how these two subtraction expressions differ.

$y°$ less $5°$ **is not the same as** $y°$ less than $5°$.

$y - 5$ **is not the same as** $5 - y$.

To translate a word expression to an algebraic expression, follow this procedure.

Procedure

> **To represent a word expression by algebraic symbols:**
> 1 Choose a variable. Tell what it represents.
> 2 Identify the key word or words that indicate which operation to use.
> 3 Represent the word expression by symbols.

EXAMPLE   Use algebraic symbols to represent each word expression.

a. 1.5 seconds more than Amy's record time.

b. The amount of the car loan divided by 36, the number of monthly payments.

Solutions: a. 1 Let $t =$ Amy's record time.

     2 1.5 seconds more than t 3 $t + 1.5$

b. 1 Let $a =$ the amount of the car loan.

     2 a divided by 36   3 $a \div 36$, or $\dfrac{a}{36}$

CLASSROOM EXERCISES

In Exercises 1–18, choose from the box at the right the algebraic expression that represents each word expression. More than one answer may be possible in some cases.

1. The product of y and (-6)
2. y minus 6
3. 6 plus y
4. y increased by 6
5. Subtract 6 from y.
6. The quotient of y and (-6)
7. Six times y
8. y more than 6
9. Subtract y from 6.
10. 6 less y
11. 6 less than y
12. The product of (-6) and y
13. The quotient of (-6) and y
14. -6 multiplied by y
15. y divided by (-6)
16. The sum of 6 and y
17. 6 divided by twice y
18. 6 diminished by y

$y + 6$	$6 + y$
$y - 6$	$6 - y$
$-6y$	$6y$
$\dfrac{y}{-6}$	$\dfrac{-6}{y}$
$y \div 6$	$6 \div y$
$\dfrac{2y}{6}$	$\dfrac{6}{2y}$

WORD PROBLEMS

A Represent each word expression by an algebraic expression.

1. The difference of 25 and n
2. 16 more than $(-r)$
3. The total of x and $(-6\frac{1}{4})$
4. y decreased by 19.3
5. Subtract b from (-9).
6. 19.1 increased by x
7. $\frac{1}{2}$ plus $(-a)$
8. $-18\frac{2}{3}$ minus $(-r)$
9. t less (-100)
10. t less than (-100)
11. n increased by $\frac{4}{5}$
12. The sum of x and $(-x)$
13. 4 less than r
14. a increased by $\frac{5}{8}$
15. 5 less s
16. -2 subtracted from m
17. Subtract (-30) from m.
18. Subtract m from (-30).
19. 12 decreased by $|y|$
20. $|y|$ decreased by 12
21. $9\frac{1}{2}$ more than q
22. q more than $9\frac{1}{2}$
23. -0.5 less than r
24. -0.5 less r
25. r less than (-0.5)
26. r less (-0.5)
27. The quotient of 9 and x
28. The quotient of x and 9
29. q multiplied by 7
30. The product of (-2) and q
31. Twice p
32. Three times r
33. 212 divided by $(-t)$
34. $(-t)$ divided by 212
35. z multiplied by $\frac{1}{5}$
36. $\frac{1}{5}$ multiplied by z
37. z divided by 5
38. The quotient of z and 5
39. -1 times p
40. p times (-1)
41. The product of r and $\frac{1}{12}$
42. The quotient of t and (-3)

In Exercises 43–58, first choose a variable and tell what it represents. Then write an algebraic expression for each word expression.

43. Five centimeters more than the width of a rectangle
44. The number of hours worked less $\frac{1}{2}$ hour
45. One-third the perimeter of the base of the Great Pyramid in Egypt
46. The quotient of the distance traveled and the rate, 50 miles per hour
47. The cost of the dinner plus a tip of $5.45
48. Four centimeters less than Bob's height
49. The cost of a new car less the depreciation, $1200
50. The distance traveled divided by the time, 3 hours
51. Twice the air distance from San Francisco to Chicago
52. Fifteen pounds more than the average weight
53. The cost of a tennis racquet minus the discount, $6.90
54. Nine degrees less than the average temperature

55. The number of quarts of oil multiplied by $1.10

56. The quotient of the number of dimes Sally has and 10

57. $20 more than the amount of Jeff's checking account

58. The quotient of $969.50 and the number of tickets sold

B

59. A car travels 6 hours at an average rate of k kilometers per hour. Represent the distance traveled.

60. A plane travels t hours at an average rate of 320 miles per hour. Represent the distance traveled.

61. The Nolan family repays a debt of $1200 in equal monthly payments over m months. Represent the amount of each monthly payment.

62. The Martinez family spent a total of $1500 for a vacation that lasted d days. Represent the average cost per day.

63. Last year, Glenda paid $3500 in gasoline and maintenance costs for her car. She used the car to travel m miles. Represent the average cost per mile.

64. Richard had a total of 23 hits in k times at bat. Represent his batting average. (HINT: Batting average = Number of hits ÷ Times at bat)

CALCULATOR APPLICATIONS

A Paper Caper

You can use a calculator to find the thickness of a folded piece of paper. You may be surprised at how quickly the thickness can build up!

EXAMPLE A sheet of paper 0.0015 inch thick is folded in half 15 times. Find the thickness.

SOLUTION Each fold doubles the thickness of the paper. For example,

$$1 \text{ fold} = 2 \times 0.0015 \text{ inch.}$$
$$2 \text{ folds} = 2 \times 2 \times 0.0015 \text{ inch (or } 2^2 \times 0.0015)$$

$$\vdots \qquad \vdots$$

$$15 \text{ folds} = 2^{15} \times 0.0015 \text{ inch}$$

Press $\boxed{=}$ 14 times.

$\boxed{49.152}$

The folded sheet will be **about 49 inches thick.**

EXERCISES

In Exercises 1–4, find the thickness of the sheet of paper. Round your answers to the nearest inch.

1. Folded 12 times   2. Folded 16 times   3. Folded 20 times   4. Folded 25 times

4-2 One Unknown

Sometimes a word expression involves more than one arithmetic operation.

Word Expression	Algebraic Expression
Five **more** than 3 **times** a number, n	$3n + 5$
Twice the distance, d, **subtracted from** 1800	$1800 - 2d$
Four times the number of students, s, **divided by** 15	$\dfrac{4s}{15}$, or $\dfrac{4}{15}s$
Three more than **twice** the number of girls, g, on the tennis team	$2g + 3$
Twice the amount, a, Earl budgeted for a vacation **less** \$125	$2a - 125$
The **quotient** of \$3500 and n, the number of monthly payments	$\dfrac{3500}{n}$

You can use equations to solve word problems. The table below shows word sentences with their corresponding equations. Note that the word "is" is replaced by the "=" symbol.

Word Sentence	Equation
Eighteen more than some number x is 54.	$x + 18 = 54$
16 is 10 less than twice some number, n.	$2n - 10 = 16$
The product of some number q and 0.3 is 78.	$0.3q = 78$
The quotient of three times an unknown number, p, and 5 is 21.	$\dfrac{3p}{5} = 21$
When the sum of 12 and an unknown number, t, is divided by 3, the result is 8.	$\dfrac{12 + t}{3} = 8$

This procedure will help you to solve word problems having one unknown.

Procedure

> **To solve word problems having one unknown:**
> 1. Choose a variable to represent the unknown.
> 2. Write an equation for the problem.
> 3. Solve the equation.
> 4. Check your answer with the statements in the problem. Answer the question.

NOTE: The steps in the Example correspond to the steps in the procedure.

EXAMPLE When $78 is subtracted from the amount in Fred's checking account, the balance (amount remaining) is $31. How much is in the account?

Solution: ① Let $a =$ the amount in the account.

② $a - 78 = 31$ ⟵——— **78 subtracted from a is 31.**

③ $a - 78 + 78 = 31 + 78$

$a = 109$

Check: ④ Does $109 - 78 = 31$? Yes ✓ There is **$109** in the account.

CLASSROOM EXERCISES

Use algebraic symbols to represent each word expression.

1. The quotient of twice an unknown number, p, and 7

2. Three times some number, g, less 48.1

3. The sum of 150 and three times the number of pages, p

4. Ten less than three times John's score, s

5. Twenty-five kilometers more than twice the distance, d, traveled by the Stealle family

6. The difference between the number of coins in the piggy bank, c, and 412

Write an equation to represent each word sentence.

7. An unknown number, z, increased by $1\frac{3}{4}$ equals 20.

8. The quotient of an unknown number, n, and 7 equals 6.9.

9. Two hundred decreased by an unknown number, t, is $71\frac{3}{4}$.

10. Two-thirds of a certain number, r, is 40.

11. The total of 9 and one-half of a certain number, n, is 29.

12. The product of a number, q, and 15 is 255.

WORD PROBLEMS

🅰 Use algebraic symbols to represent each word expression.

1. Three times Beth's age, a, minus 2 years

2. Three dollars more than four times the amount, t, that Phil has

3. Twenty less than twice the number of marathon runners, r

4. Five degrees more than twice the present temperature, t

5. The quotient of four times the amount of the loan, l, and 5

6. The product of the rate, r, and 3.5 divided by 4

7. The product of 25 and the number of quarters, n, divided by 100

8. Three times the amount budgeted for food, f, decreased by $25

9. The amount of the bill, b, increased by the product of 0.15 and b

10. The quotient of $1200 and five times a round-trip fare, r

Write an equation to represent each word sentence.

11. Nineteen more than an unknown number, t, is 42.6.

12. Ninety-seven is 17 less than a certain number, r.

13. The quotient of a number, n, and 14 is 9.

14. The product of some number, q, and 24 equals 356.

15. The difference between 4 times a number, z, and 3 is 35.

16. Two-thirds of a number, z, equals 40.

17. One-third of a number, t, increased by 7 equals 23.

18. The sum of 38 and $\frac{5}{9}$ of a certain number, p, is 128.

19. The quotient of 5 times a certain number, b, and 3 is 100.

20. Eight less than 6 times some number, p, is 10.

21. Twelve times a number, c, minus 6 equals 60.

22. The total of 9 and one-half of a certain number, c, is 29.

23. When the quotient of a certain number, q, and 6 is decreased by 14, the result is 4.

24. When the quotient of 3 times a certain number, t, and 2 is increased by 12, the result is 39.

25. When the product of 4 and a certain number, s, is diminished by 8, the result is −4.

26. When the sum of an unknown number, c, and 9 is multiplied by 5, the result is 35.

Solve each problem. Follow the steps of the procedure on page 122.

27. When $102 is added to the amount in Jill's checking account, the total is $461.70. How much is in Jill's account?

28. Thirty-nine kilometers more than the distance traveled by the Blair family is 721 kilometers. How far did they travel?

29. Last year's interest increased by $41.50 equals $72.80. Find the amount of last year's interest.

30. Seven and one-half times the number of voters in the election is 90,000. How many persons voted?

31. Twice the cost of a pair of skis decreased by $60 equals $225. Find the cost of the skis.

32. Four times the perimeter of the parking lot less 16 is 2000 yards. What is the perimeter of the lot?

33. The amount of the Ohira family's electric bill divided by 375 kilowatt-hours equals $0.22. Find the amount of the bill.

34. The amount of last month's telephone bill, decreased by the product of 3 and 0.30, equals $131.95. Find the amount of the bill.

35. Sixteen less than seven times the number of sandwiches is 264. How many sandwiches are there?

36. The quotient of four times the number of cars and 15 decreased by 7 is 105. Find the number of cars.

37. Three times the number of words Dot types per minute increased by 14 is 194. How many words does Dot type per minute?

38. The quotient of the number of pages in a telephone directory and 9 is increased by 500. The result is 2128. How many pages are in the directory?

39. The sum of three times a number and 33 is 51. Find the number.

40. One hundred less than 6 times a number is 26. Find the number.

Combine like terms. *(Pages 60-63)*

1. $7(5y + 4) + 8(1 + 3y)$ **2.** $5p - 2(4 + 3p) + 6p$ **3.** $-3(8 - 3z) + 9(4 - 3z)$

Solve and check each equation. *(Pages 97-99)*

4. $15 + 9 = 8d - 3d + 1$ **5.** $7x - 8x + 2 = -9$ **6.** $6 - 3x - x = 30$

7. $9t + 7 - t = 35$ **8.** $29 = 3t - 1 - t$ **9.** $4 - x - 3x = 0$

Problem Solving and Applications

4-3 Identifying Conditions

In some word problems, one condition tells how the unknown quantities are related. Call this Condition 1 and use this condition to represent the unknowns.

A second condition tells what quantities are equal. Call this Condition 2 and use this condition to write an equation. Then solve the equation.

EXAMPLE 1 Felipe is thinking of two numbers. The larger is 5 more than twice the smaller (Condition 1). Their sum is 47 (Condition 2). Find the numbers.

Solution: 1 Use Condition 1 to represent the unknowns.

Let x = the smaller number.
Then $2x + 5$ = the larger number.

2 Use Condition 2 to write an equation.

$x + (2x + 5) = 47$ ◄——— **The sum of the numbers is 47.**

3 Solve the equation.

$x + 2x + 5 = 47$ ◄——— **Combine like terms.**

$3x + 5 = 47$ ◄——— **Add (−5) to each side.**

$3x = 42$ ◄——— **Multiply each side by $\frac{1}{3}$.**

$x = 14$ ◄——— **Don't forget to find 2x + 5.**

$2x + 5 = 2(14) + 5 = 33$

Check: 4 **Condition 1** Does $33 = 2(14) + 5$? Yes ✔

Condition 2 $14 + 33 = 47$? Yes ✔

The numbers are **14** and **33**.

The procedure on page 126 summarizes the steps shown in Example 1.

Procedure	**Steps for Solving Word Problems**
	1. Identify Condition 1. Use this condition to represent the unknowns.
	2. Identify Condition 2. Use this condition to write an equation for the problem.
	3. Solve the equation.
	4. Check the results with the two conditions. Answer the question(s).

NOTE: The steps in the Examples correspond to the steps in the procedure.

EXAMPLE 2 The total number of apartments in two buildings is 348 (Condition 2). The Fair View apartment building has 12 less than three times the number of apartments in the Tulip Vista apartment complex (Condition 1). Find the number of apartments in Fair View.

Solution: 1. Let a = the number of apartments in Tulip Vista.
Then $3a - 12$ = the number in Fair View.

2. $a + (3a - 12) = 348$

3. $\quad\quad 4a - 12 = 348$

$\quad\quad\quad\quad 4a = 360$

$\quad\quad\quad\quad\quad a = 90$ ←——— **Don't forget to find $3a - 12$.**

$\quad\quad 3a - 12 = 258$

Check: 4. **Condition 1** Does $258 = 3(90) - 12$? Yes ✓

Condition 2 $90 + 258 = 348$? Yes ✓

Fair View has **258** apartments.

CLASSROOM EXERCISES

With each sentence in Exercises 1–8, match the corresponding item in **a–h**.

1. The larger number is 1 more than twice the smaller.

2. The smaller of two numbers is 1 less than the larger.

3. The larger of two numbers is 8 times the smaller.

4. The smaller of two numbers is 8 less than twice the larger.

5. One number is twice another.

a. Let h = first number.
Then $2h$ = second number.

b. Let q = larger number.
Then $q - 1$ = smaller number.

c. Let x = larger number.
Then $x - 2$ = smaller number.

d. Let p = smaller number.
Then $3p + 9$ = larger number.

e. Let t = smaller number.
Then $2t + 1$ = larger number.

6. One number is two less than another.

7. One number is 9 more than 3 times a second number.

8. One number is 3 less than 9 times another.

f. Let a = larger number.
   Then $2a - 8$ = smaller number.

g. Let w = first number.
   Then $9w - 3$ = second number.

h. Let r = smaller number.
   Then $8r$ = larger number.

WORD PROBLEMS

A   Solve each problem.

In some problems, one condition is <u>underscored once</u>. Use this condition to represent the unknowns. A second condition is <u>underscored twice</u>. Use this condition to write an equation for the problem.

1. <u>One number is 5 times another.</u> <u>The sum of the numbers is 72.</u> Find the numbers.

2. <u>One number is 5 more than a second number.</u> <u>The sum of the numbers is 115.</u> Find the numbers.

3. <u>One number is 4 less than another.</u> <u>The sum of the numbers is 20.</u> Find the numbers.

4. <u>The sum of two numbers is 21.</u> <u>One number is 3 less than the other.</u> Find the numbers.

5. <u>One number minus a smaller number is 18.</u> <u>The larger number is 3 times the smaller.</u> Find the numbers.

6. <u>The sum of two numbers is 110.</u> <u>One of the numbers is 7 less than twice the second.</u> Find the numbers.

7. <u>One number is $\frac{2}{3}$ of another.</u> <u>The sum of the numbers is 50.</u> What are the numbers?

8. <u>The larger of two numbers is 12 more than the smaller.</u> <u>The sum of the numbers is 36.</u> What are the numbers?

9. <u>The smaller of two numbers is 10 less than the larger.</u> <u>The sum of the numbers is 76.</u> What are the numbers?

10. <u>A number is 7 more than five times another number.</u> <u>The sum of the numbers is 55.</u> Find the numbers.

11. <u>The sum of three numbers is 72.</u> <u>The first is three times the second and the third is twice the result of subtracting 6 from the second.</u> Find the numbers.

12. The sum of three numbers is 64. The second number is 3 more than the first. The third number is 11 less than twice the first. Find the numbers.

13. <u>The second of three numbers is 4 times the first.</u> <u>The third number is 1 more than the second.</u> <u>Their sum is 73.</u> Find the numbers.

14. The second of two numbers is 16 less than 3 times the first. The sum of the two numbers is 64. What are the numbers?

15. Together, Bob and Dan earned $52. Bob earned 3 times as much as Dan. How much did each boy earn?

16. Louisa is $\frac{3}{4}$ as tall as Carla. The difference between their heights is 0.4 meters. How tall is each girl?

17. A coat costs $35.50 more than a dress. The total cost of both items is $161.30. How much does each cost?

18. A house and a lot are sold for $140,000. The house costs 1.5 times as much as the lot. How much does each cost?

19. The number of persons entering the A–Z Department Store at 10 A.M. one day was 235 more than at 10 A.M. the next day. The total for both days was 885. How many persons entered the store at 10 A.M. on each day?

20. Together, Carol and Dick own 152 shares of stock in Sierra Engineering Corporation. Carol owns 4 less than twice the number of shares that Dick owns. How many shares of stock does each person own?

21. The amount of the Yang family's electric bill for June was $14.81 less than the gas bill. The total bill for gas and electricity was $97.63. Find the amount of each bill.

22. The Harris family's telephone bill for October was $63.80. The cost of long distance calls was $41.96 more than the cost for local calls. Find the cost for long-distance calls.

B The following terms are used in Exercises 23–28. Be sure that you know the meaning of each term.

> The price of merchandise before it is offered to consumers at a reduced price is called the **list price** or **regular price**.
>
> The amount that an item is reduced is called the **discount**.
>
> The reduced price is called the **sale price**.

23. The rate of discount at a sale is 20%. Jim bought a lamp on sale for $40. Find the list price and the discount. (HINT: Let p = the list price. Then $0.20p$ = the amount of discount and $p - 0.20p = \underline{\ ?\ }$.)

24. At a kitchen appliance sale, the Gomez family bought a refrigerator that was on sale at a 10% discount. The sale price was $594. Find the list price and the amount of discount on the refrigerator.

25. A camera is on sale for $90.40. The rate of discount is 20%. Find the list price and the amount of discount.

26. An 8–track tape is on sale for $5.10. The rate of discount is 25%. Find the list price and the amount of discount.

27. A clock radio is on sale at a discount rate of 35%. The sale price is $45.50. Find the list price and the amount of discount.

28. The sale price of a television set is $360. The discount rate is 40%. Find the list price and the amount of discount.

C

29. Dick's bank contains an equal number of nickels, dimes and quarters. The total value is $10.00. How many of each kind of coin is there?

30. Elaine has only dimes and quarters in her purse. The total value is $2.50. There are 3 more quarters than dimes. How many quarters are there?

31. A piece of string, 60 centimeters long, is cut into 3 pieces. One piece is 2 centimeters longer than the shortest piece and 2 centimeters shorter than the longest piece. How long is each piece?

32. Gina has $2 more than three times the amount that Fred has. When Gina gave Fred $5, Fred than had one–half as much as Gina. How much did Gina have at first?

Problem Solving and Applications

4–4 Measurement Problems

The **perimeter**, P, of a geometric figure such as a triangle is the distance around it. To find this distance, add the lengths of the sides.

Triangle

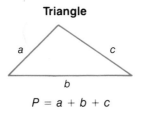

$P = a + b + c$

Rectangle

$P = l + w + l + w$
$P = 2l + 2w$

Square

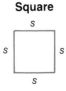

$P = s + s + s + s$
$P = 4s$

To solve problems that involve a geometric figure, follow the steps of this procedure.

Procedure

> **To solve problems involving a geometric figure:**
>
> 1 Draw and label the figure.
> 2–5 Follow Steps 1–4 of the Procedure in Section 4–3 on page 126.

The steps in the Example correspond to the steps in the procedure.

EXAMPLE The length of a tennis court for singles is 0.9 meter shorter than three times the width (Condition 1). The perimeter is 63.8 meters (Condition 2). Find the dimensions (length and width) of the court.

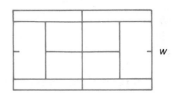

Solution:

1 Draw and label a figure.

2 Let w = the width. ← **Represent the unknowns.**
Then $3w - 0.9$ = the length.

3 $w + (3w - 0.9) + w + (3w - 0.9) = 63.8$ ← **The perimeter is 63.8 meters.**

4 $8w - 1.8 = 63.8$

$8w = 65.6$

$w = 8.2$ ← **Don't forget to find the length.**

$3w - 0.9 = 3(8.2) - 0.9 = 23.7$

Check:

5 **Condition 1** Does $23.7 = 3(8.2) - 0.9$? Yes ✓

Condition 2 $8.2 + 23.7 + 8.2 + 23.7 = 63.8$? Yes ✓

The width is **8.2 meters** and the length is **23.7 meters.**

Since the figure in the Example is a rectangle, you could also use the formula $P = 2l + 2w$ to find the perimeter. That is,

$$63.8 = 2(3w - 0.9) + 2w \quad \longleftarrow \quad \textbf{Solve for } \textit{w.}$$

CLASSROOM EXERCISES

Find the length of each side of each figure.

1.

$r - 25$ $r - 25$

$r - 25$ $r - 25$

Perimeter: 36 meters

2.

$3w + 1$

w w

$3w + 1$

Perimeter: 374 feet

3.

a

$a + 147$

$2a$

Perimeter: 623 meters

4.

x $3x$

$3x + 2$

Perimeter: 51 meters

5.

$2t$ $2t$

$t - 1$

Perimeter: 14 yards

6.

$2h + 1$ $2h + 1$

$2h + 1$

Perimeter: 27 inches

7.

l

$l - 1.4$ $l - 1.4$

l

Perimeter: 9.2 centimeters

8.

$\frac{3}{4}s$

$\frac{3}{4}s$ $\frac{3}{4}s$

$\frac{3}{4}s$

Perimeter: 144 feet

9.

b

$b - 5$ $b - 7.5$

$b + 12.5$

Perimeter: 56 meters

WORD PROBLEMS

A   Solve each problem.

In some problems, one condition is <u>underscored once</u>. Use this condition to represent the unknowns. A second condition is <u>underscored twice</u>. Use this condition to write the equation.

1. The length of a rectangle is 7 times its width. The perimeter of the rectangle is 64 centimeters. Find the dimensions of the rectangle.

2. The length of a rectangle is $2\frac{1}{2}$ times its width. The perimeter of the rectangle is 84 feet. Find the dimensions of the rectangle.

3. The perimeter of a triangle is 52 inches. The second side is three times the first side and the third side is $2\frac{1}{2}$ times the first side. Find the length of each side of the triangle.

4. The lengths of the sides of a triangle can be represented by three consecutive even integers. The perimeter of the triangle is 96 meters. Find the lengths of the sides of the triangle.

5. The length of a rectangle is 8 inches more than twice its width. The perimeter is 112 inches. Find the length and width of the rectangle.

6. The width of a badminton court is 8 yards less than its length. The perimeter is $42\frac{2}{3}$ yards. Find the length and width of the court.

7. An isosceles triangle has two equal sides. The third side of an isosceles triangle is 3 centimeters longer than each of the equal sides. The perimeter is 27 centimeters. Find the length of each side.

8. Each of the equal sides of an isosceles triangle is 2 feet more than three times the third side. The perimeter is 32 feet. Find the length of each side of the triangle.

9. A plane flies 1971 kilometers along a triangular route formed by three cities, Malone, Stockton, and Cooper. The distance from Malone to Stockton is 299 kilometers more than the distance from Stockton to Cooper and the distance from Malone to Cooper is 674 kilometers. Find the distance from Malone to Stockton.

10. A triangular, 764-kilometer course for a boat race is marked out by three buoys. The distance between the first and second buoys is 3 kilometers more than the distance between the second and third buoys. The distance between the first and third buoys is 281 kilometers. How far is it from the first to the second buoy?

11. The perimeter of a squash court (rectangular in shape) is 31.2 meters. The length of the court is 1.2 meters more than the width. Find the length and width of the court.

12. An artist is making a rectangular wooden frame for a painting. The perimeter is 250 centimeters and the length is 1.5 times the width. Find the width and length of the frame.

13. Surveyors working on a freeway placed stakes at points A, B, and C such that the distance from A to C equals the distance from B to C. The distance from A to B is 1.6 times the distance from A to C. The perimeter of the triangle is 1929.6 meters. Find all three distances.

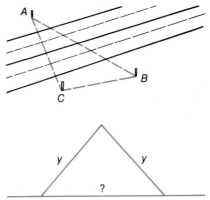

14. The frame of a garage roof forms a triangle having two sloping sides of equal length. The third side of the triangle is 4 feet longer than either of the equal sides and the perimeter of the triangle is 37 feet. Find the length of a sloping side.

B In Exercises 15–18, recall the following.

The sum of the measures of the angles of a triangle is 180°.

15. In triangle ABC, the measure of angle B is twice the measure of angle A and the measure of angle C is three times the measure of angle A. Find the measure of each angle.

16. An isosceles triangle has two angles of equal measure. In isosceles triangle ABC, angles A and B are equal in measure and each of these angles is 20° more than three times the measure of angle C. Find the measure of each angle.

17. In triangle ABC, angle B is 8° more than twice the measure of angle A and angle C is 12° less than the measure of angle A. Find the measure of each angle.

18. In triangle ABC, the measure of angle A is twice the measure of angle B and the measure of angle B is 20° more than the measure of angle C. How many degrees are there in each angle?

19. In triangle DEF, the measure of angle F is three times the measure of angle D and the measure of angle D is 80° less than the measure of angle E. Find the measure of each angle.

C

20. The length of a rectangle is twice its width. When the length is increased by 4 inches and the width is decreased by 1 inch, a new rectangle is formed. The perimeter of the new rectangle is 198 inches. Find the length and width of the original rectangle.

21. A square has four equal sides. When one side of the square is increased by 4 meters and the adjacent side is multiplied by 4, a rectangle is formed. The perimeter of the rectangle is 3 times the perimeter of the original square. Find the length of one side of the square.

22. The length of a rectangle is 4 feet more than the width. When the width is doubled and the length is decreased by 2 feet, the new rectangle that is formed has a perimeter that is 48 feet more than the perimeter of the original rectangle. Find the width of the original rectangle.

23. A hexagon has six sides. Each side of a certain hexagon is 4 centimeters less than the length of a side of a square. The perimeter of the hexagon equals the perimeter of the square. Find the length of a side of the hexagon.

── Puzzle ──

Maria invested some money and doubled the amount. After spending $4000, she reinvested the remaining money and tripled the amount. She then spent $5000, and had $10,000 left. How much money did she originally invest?

─── REVIEW CAPSULE FOR SECTION 4–5 ───

Multiply. *(Pages 30–33)*

1. $-4(2t + 5)$ **2.** $-3(4y - 5)$ **3.** $-3(2 - 6r)$ **4.** $-1(4 - 6n)$

5. $-1(6 - m)$ **6.** $-1(x + 9)$ **7.** $-1(-1 + b)$ **8.** $-1(-2x - 3)$

4-5 Solving Equations: Variable on Both Sides

In the following equation, terms with the variable, x, appear on both sides of the equation.

$$4x - 6 = x + 9$$

Use the addition property for equations to get these terms on the same side of the equation. Then solve for the variable.

EXAMPLE 1 Solve and check: $4x - 6 = x + 9$

Solution:

$$4x - 6 = x + 9 \qquad \longleftarrow \text{ Add } (-x) \text{ to each side.}$$
$$4x - 6 + (-x) = x + 9 + (-x) \longleftarrow \begin{array}{l}\textbf{Group and combine}\\\textbf{like terms.}\end{array}$$
$$[4x + (-x)] - 6 = [x + (-x)] + 9$$
$$3x - 6 = 9$$
$$3x - 6 + 6 = 9 + 6 \qquad \longleftarrow \begin{array}{l}\textbf{By the addition property}\\\textbf{for equations}\end{array}$$
$$3x = 15$$
$$\tfrac{1}{3}(3x) = \tfrac{1}{3}(15) \qquad \longleftarrow \begin{array}{l}\textbf{By the multiplication property}\\\textbf{for equations}\end{array}$$
$$x = 5$$

Check:

$$4x - 6 = x + 9$$
$$4(5) - 6 \overset{?}{=} 5 + 9$$
$$14 \overset{?}{=} 14 \quad \text{Yes } \checkmark \qquad \text{Solution set: } \{5\}$$

When an equation has no solution for the given replacement set, the solution is the **empty set**, or ϕ.

EXAMPLE 2 Solve and check: $-4(3x - 20) = -1 - 12x$

Solution:

$$-4(3x - 20) = -1 - 12x$$
$$-4(3x) + (-4)(-20) = -1 - 12x \longleftarrow \textbf{By the distributive postulate}$$
$$-12x + 80 \quad = -1 - 12x \longleftarrow \textbf{Add 12x to each side.}$$
$$-12x + 80 + 12x = -1 - 12x + 12x$$
$$80 \neq -1 \qquad \text{The solution is the \textbf{empty set}, or } \phi.$$

CLASSROOM EXERCISES

What would you add to each side of the equation in order to get the variable terms on the left side of the equation?

1. $2x + 8 = x + 9$

2. $4z + 7 = z - 2$

3. $-4y - 7 = -9y + 8$

4. $2x + 5 = -3x + 25$

5. $7a - 9 = 3a - 1$

6. $-3t + 5 = -4t - 7$

What would you add to each side of the equation in order to get the variable terms on the right side of the equation?

7. $5 - 2t = 3t$

8. $-r + 6 = 2r$

9. $100 - 9d = 41d$

10. $1 - 9m = 6m - 14$

11. $-5m + 6 = 7m - 6$

12. $2y + 1 = 3y - 2$

Solve each equation.

13. $3x + 5 = 2x - 6$

14. $m = 2m - 9$

15. $4 - 7n = 1 - 6n$

WRITTEN EXERCISES

A   Solve and check.

1. $5x = 2x + 12$

2. $7x = 3x + 24$

3. $4y + 12 = 7y$

4. $7y + 8 = 11y$

5. $5a - 9 = 2a$

6. $9y - 42 = 3y$

7. $12x + 15 = 7x$

8. $6y + 32 = 2y$

9. $7x + 4 = 9x + 24 - 2x$

10. $3y + 9 = 3y + 15$

11. $4a + 1 = 7a - 17$

12. $2b - 5 = 8b + 1$

13. $-7m = 9m - 12$

14. $-4p = 9p - 26$

15. $5x - 9 = 6x + 17$

16. $8y - 15 = 7y + 2$

17. $4a - 5 = 7a - 7$

18. $-6b + 9 = -4b - 3$

19. $-3r - 8 = -5r + 12$

20. $-6x - 7 = -5x + 3$

21. $4 - 3r = -16 + 2r$

22. $t - 7 = 3\frac{1}{2} + 2t$

23. $\frac{1}{2}y + 6 = y - 4$

24. $\frac{1}{4}b + \frac{3}{4}b = 0 - b$

25. $0.7a + 0.3a = 2a - 4$

26. $q + 7q = -12q + 10$

27. $6k - k = 9k - 42$

B

28. $4(x + 2) = 3x$

29. $7y = -2(y + 9)$

30. $-3(y - 8) = 2y - 1$

31. $-4(x + 2) = -6x + 2$

32. $5(m - 5) = 3(m + 1)$

33. $5(p - 6) = 3(p - 6)$

34. $2x + 3(x - 9) = 2(x + 3)$

35. $3y + 5(y + 3) = 5y$

36. $-4(a - 5) = -7(a - 2) + 6$

37. $3x - 5 = 2(x - 1) + 6$

38. $-5(y - 9) = -(3 + 5y)$

39. $6 - (8 - 4n) = 2(2n - 1)$

40. $3(1 - 2c) - 4 = -2(3c - 1)$

41. $7x - (x - 4) = 25$

42. $36 - 2(c - 28) = -4(2c + 52)$

43. $2(x - 3) + 3(x - 2) = 8$

44. $2(2n + 1) - 3(n - 5) = 0$

45. $1.3 + 9.4n - 9.03n = 3.52$

C   List the members in these sets. Note that **set-builder notation** is used. That is, $\{x: x + 2 = 7\}$ means the set of all real numbers x such that $x + 2 = 7$. This set has one member, 5. Thus, $\{x: x + 2 = 7\} = \{5\}$.

46. $\{x:\ 8x - 13x = 2x + 56\}$

47. $\{n:\ -6n + 13 = -5n + 12\}$

48. $\{n:\ 5n - 20 = -32 - 7n\}$

49. $\{n:\ -16 - 3n = 5n + 16\}$

50. $\{t:\ 11 - 2t - 16 = 8t\}$

51. $\{n:\ 14n = 14n - 5n + 6\}$

52. $\{n:\ 26n - 9n = 46 + 26n\}$

53. $\{c:\ 5c - 13 = 6c - 18\}$

54. $\{c:\ 4c + 12 = 7c + 3\}$

55. $\{x:\ 5 - 3x = 5x + 21\}$

56. $\{r:\ -5r + 2 = -9r - 16\}$

57. $\{s:\ -6s = -7 + 2s - 13\}$

Problem Solving and Applications

4-6 Age Problems

To solve age problems, you often have to represent a person's present age, the person's age a number of years ago, and the person's age a number of years from now.

	Age Now	Age 4 Years Ago	Age 7 Years From Now
Kiyo	15	15 − 4, or 11	15 + 7, or 22
Gordon	a	$a - 4$	$a + 7$
Rosa	$3t$	$3t - 4$	$3t + 7$

Thus, to represent a past age, *subtract* from the present age. To represent a future age, *add* to the present age.

To solve age problems, follow the steps of the procedure in Section 4-3 on page 126. The steps in the following Example correspond to the steps of this procedure. In the Example, Condition 1 is <u>underscored once</u>. Condition 2 is <u>underscored twice</u>.

EXAMPLE   Mrs. Garcia is now three times as old as her son, Tony. In 14 years, Mrs. Garcia's age will be twice Tony's age then. How old is each now?

Solution: Make a table. Use Condition 1.

1	Age Now	Age 14 Years From Now
Tony	y	$y + 14$
Mrs. Garcia	$3y$	$3y + 14$

2   Use the table and Condition 2 to write an equation.

Mrs. Garcia's age in 14 years	will be	twice Tony's age in 14 years.
↓	↓	↓
$3y + 14$	$=$	$2(y + 14)$

3
$$3y + 14 = 2(y + 14) \quad \longleftarrow \text{ Solve for y.}$$
$$3y + 14 = 2y + 28 \quad \longleftarrow \text{ By the distributive property}$$
$$(-2y) + 3y + 14 = (-2y) + 2y + 28$$
$$y + 14 + (-14) = 28 + (-14)$$
$$y = 14 \quad \longleftarrow \begin{array}{l}\text{Don't forget to find}\\ \text{Mrs. Garcia's age.}\end{array}$$
$$3y = 42$$

Check: 4   **Condition 1**   Does $42 = 3(14)$?   Yes ✔

   Condition 2 $42 + 14 = 2(14 + 14)$?   Yes ✔

Tony is now **14 years old** and Mrs. Garcia is **42.**

CLASSROOM EXERCISES

1. Charles is x years old now. Represent his age 12 years from now.

2. Jill is y years old now. Represent her age 8 years ago.

3. Peter is $2z$ years old now. Represent his age 2 years from now.

4. Eduardo is $5t$ years old now. Represent his age 4 years ago.

5. Miyako is $(2r - 3)$ years old now. Represent her age 9 years from now.

6. Gina is $(30 - q)$ years old now. Represent her age 7 years ago.

Meg is t years old. Ted is three times as old as Meg.

7. Represent Meg's age 6 years from now.

8. Represent Ted's age 6 years from now.

9. Represent Meg's age 5 years ago.

10. Represent Ted's age 5 years ago.

WORD PROBLEMS

A Solve each problem.

In some Exercises, Condition 1 is underscored once. Condition 2 is underscored twice.

1. Anna is now four times as old as her brother Ramon. In 4 years, Anna's age will be twice Ramon's age then. How old is each now?

2. Tom's present age is twice Sue's present age. Two years ago, Tom was three times as old as Sue was then. Find their present ages.

3. Skip is now three times as old as Paul. In 5 years, Skip will be twice as old as Paul will be then. What will their ages be in five years?

4. Carla is now twice as old as Jennifer. Seven years ago, the sum of their ages was 16. How old is each girl now?

5. Andy Anderson is now 25 years older than his brother, Bob. In 15 years, Andy's age will be twice Bob's age then. How old are Andy and Bob Anderson now?

6. Mrs. Montez is 20 years older than Mrs. Cooke. Sixteen years ago, Mrs. Montez was 3 times as old as Mrs. Cooke was then. How old are Mrs. Montez and Mrs. Cooke now?

7. The ages of two cousins can be represented as consecutive integers. Fifteen years from now, the sum of their ages will be 57. How old is each now?

8. The ages of two sisters can be represented as consecutive odd integers. Twelve years ago, the sum of their ages was 8. How old is each now?

9. An electrician has 5 times as many years experience as her apprentice. Four years from now, the electrician will have 3 times as many years experience as the apprentice. How many years experience does each have now?

10. One teacher has 4 times as many years experience as a second. Six years from now, the first teacher will have twice as many years experience as the second. How many years experience does each teacher have now?

11. Mr. Connors is 15 years younger than Mr. Saito. Five years from now, Mr. Saito will be $1\frac{1}{2}$ times as old as Mr. Connors will be then. Find their present ages.

12. Linda is 10 years younger than Harold. In 6 years, Harold's age will be $1\frac{1}{2}$ times Linda's age then. Find their present ages.

B

13. Sandra Klee was 25 years old when her son was born. Her present age is 7 years less than three times her son's present age. How old is Sandra now?

14. A man is 40 years old and his son is 8. In how many years will the father's age be exactly three times the son's age? (HINT: Let n = the number of years.)

15. A woman is now 40 years old and her daughter is 14 years old. In how many years will the mother be exactly twice as old as her daughter?

16. Mae Ying Chung is now 17 years old and her aunt is 50. In how many years will Mae be one half as old as her aunt?

17. A woman's age is 32 and her son's age is 2. In how many years will the mother be four times as old as her son?

18. The sum of Louellen's age and Fred's age is 20. Louellen's age one year from now will be nine times Fred's age one year ago. How old is each now?

_____ **Review** _____

Represent each word expression by an algebraic expression. *(Section 4–1)*

1. The product of -6 and m

2. The quotient of x and 12

3. The total of $2\frac{1}{4}$ and k

4. n less than 4.6

5. Fifteen dollars plus four times the daily rental charge for a boat is $79. What is the daily rental charge? *(Section 4–2)*

6. One number is $\frac{2}{3}$ of another number. The difference between the two numbers is 12. Find the numbers. *(Section 4–3)*

7. Together, Bob and Jane own 128 shares of Intek stock. Bob owns 4 more than three times the number of shares Jane owns. How many shares does each own? *(Section 4–3)*

8. The length of a rectangular park is three times the width. The perimeter of the park is 160 meters. Find the dimensions of the park. *(Section 4–4)*

Solve and check. *(Section 4–5)*

9. $9g + 7 = 2g$

10. $18 - n = 5n + 6$

11. $6 - \frac{1}{2}b = 1\frac{1}{2}b + 18$

12. $4(2n + 1) = 2(3n - 1)$

13. $4(0.5x - 3) = 9 + 2x$

14. $3(4 - c) - 6(2c + 1) = -9$

15. Maria is now 3 years younger than her sister, Ann. Four years ago Maria's age was one-half Ann's age. How old is each girl now? *(Section 4–6)*

Career Applications: Statistics

Statisticians are concerned with gathering data and analyzing the results. They sometimes research consumer topics on behalf of federal agencies and private companies.

For example, statisticians may study the effects a vehicle's speed, brakes, and the road conditions have on the ability of motorists to stop quickly in an emergency.

The **stopping distance**, s, of a vehicle is the sum of the reaction distance, D, and the braking distance, b.

$$s = D + b$$

Reaction distance is the distance a car travels during the time it takes a driver to begin braking. **Braking distance** is the distance a car travels when the brakes are applied and until the car stops completely.

A calculator is an important tool for a statistician.

Based on statistical research, it has been found that the formula

$$D = 1.1r$$

estimates the reaction distance in feet of a car traveling at r miles per hour.

EXAMPLE 1 Mary Sandoval was driving at 45 miles per hour when she saw a branch lying on the road. Estimate the reaction distance.

Solution: $D = 1.1r$ ←——— $r = 45$

$D = 1.1(45)$

$D = 49.5$

The reaction distance is about $49\frac{1}{2}$ **feet.**

Statisticians have also found that such factors as road surface and condition, as well as the brakes of the car, will affect braking distance. A formula that has been developed to estimate braking distance is

$$b = \frac{r^2}{30F},$$

where F is the **coefficient of friction**, a number based on the condition and surface of the road. The table at the right gives several values for F.

Type of Surface	Coefficient of Friction	
	Dry Road	Wet Road
Asphalt	0.85	0.65
Concrete	0.90	0.60
Gravel	0.65	0.65
Packed Snow	0.45	0.45

EXAMPLE 2 a. Mary was driving on a dry concrete road. Estimate the braking distance.

b. Estimate the total stopping distance of Mary's car.

Solutions: a. $b = \dfrac{r^2}{30F}$ ⟵ $r = 45;$
$F = 0.9$ from the table

$b = \dfrac{(45)^2}{30(0.9)}$

4 5 $\boxed{\times}$ $\boxed{=}$ $\boxed{\div}$ 3 0 $\boxed{\div}$. 9 $\boxed{=}$ $\boxed{75.}$

The braking distance is about **75 feet.**

b. $s = D + b$
$s = 49\frac{1}{2} + 75$
$s = 124\frac{1}{2}$

The stopping distance is about **$124\frac{1}{2}$ feet.**

NOTE: You can also express the formula for stopping distance as the sum of two formulas.

$$s = 1.1r + \frac{r^2}{30F}$$

EXERCISES

Estimate the reaction distance a car will travel at the following rates of speed.

1. 55 miles per hour
2. 30 miles per hour
3. 45 miles per hour
4. 42 miles per hour
5. 54 miles per hour
6. 28 miles per hour

Estimate the braking distance of a car traveling under the given conditions.

7. 54 mi/hr on wet concrete
8. 30 mi/hr on dry concrete
9. 42 mi/hr on wet concrete
10. 52 mi/hr on gravel

Complete the table below.

	Rate	Road Conditions	Reaction Distance	Braking Distance	Stopping Distance
11.	39 mi/hr	wet asphalt	?	?	?
12.	54 mi/hr	dry concrete	?	?	?
13.	45 mi/hr	wet concrete	?	?	?
14.	27 mi/hr	packed snow	?	?	?

Solve each inequality. The replacement set is $\{-4, -3, -2, -1, 0, 1, 2, 3, 4\}$. *(Pages 18–19)*

1. $3z < 9$
2. $2z > 4$
3. $z + 1 > 2$
4. $\frac{1}{2}z < 6$
5. $z - 1 < 0$
6. $1 - z > 0$
7. $|z| > 1$
8. $|z| \leq 3$

4-7 Solving Inequalities: Addition Property

Compare the solution sets and graphs for each pair of inequalities in the table below. The replacement set is $\{-1, 0, 1, 2, 3, 4, 5, 6, 7, 8\}$.

Inequalities	Solution Set	Graph
$x < 4$ $x + 7 < 4 + 7$ or $x + 7 < 11$	$\{-1, 0, 1, 2, 3\}$	
$x > 4$ $x + 7 > 4 + 7$ or $x + 7 > 11$	$\{5, 6, 7, 8\}$	

In the table, $x < 4$ is *equivalent* to $x + 7 < 11$, and
$x > 4$ is *equivalent* to $x + 7 > 11$,

because each pair has the *same solution set*. This suggests an addition property for inequalities similar to the addition property for equations.

Property

> **Addition Property for Inequalities**
>
> Adding the same number to each side of an inequality results in an **equivalent inequality.**

In solving inequalities, assume that the replacement set is the set of real numbers unless you are told otherwise.

EXAMPLE 1 Solve and graph: $x + 3 > 6$

Solution: $x + 3 > 6$ ⟵——— **Add −3 to each side.**
$x + 3 + (-3) > 6 + (-3)$
$x > 3$

Solution set: $\{$**all real numbers greater than 3**$\}$

Note that the open circle around the point 3 on the number line indicates that 3 is *not* a solution.

The symbol $\leq$ used in Example 2 is read: "is less than or equal to."

EXAMPLE 2   Solve and graph: $3x - 1 \le 2x + 3$

Solution: $3x - 1 \le 2x + 3$ ◄——— **Add (−2x) to each side.**

$-2x + 3x - 1 \le -2x + 2x + 3$

$x - 1 \le 3$ ◄——— **Add 1 to each side.**

$x - 1 + 1 \le 3 + 1$

$x \le 4$

Solution set: {**all real numbers less than or equal to 4**}

You can check an inequality by substituting two or more of its solutions in the original inequality. Here is a check for Example 2, using the solutions $x = 0$ and $x = -5$.

Check: $3x - 1 \le 2x + 3$ ◄——— **Replace x with 0.**
         $\overset{?}{ }$
$3(0) - 1 \le 2(0) + 3$
$\overset{?}{ }$
$-1 \le 3$ Yes ✔

$3x - 1 \le 2x + 3$ ◄——— **Replace x with (−5).**
$\overset{?}{ }$
$3(-5) - 1 \le 2(-5) + 3$
$\overset{?}{ }$
$-16 \le -7$ Yes ✔

CLASSROOM EXERCISES

Complete each statement. Use $>$ or $<$.

1. Since $18 > 12$, $18 + (-5) \underline{\quad?\quad} 12 + (-5)$.

2. Since $21 < 30$, $21 + 15 \underline{\quad?\quad} 30 + 15$.

3. Since $-8 > -10$, $-8 + 2 \underline{\quad?\quad} -10 + 2$.

4. Since $-21 < -18$, $-21 + (-5) \underline{\quad?\quad} -18 + (-5)$.

5. If $z + 3 > 5$, then $z + 3 + (-3) \underline{\quad?\quad} 5 + (-3)$, or $z \underline{\quad?\quad} 2$.

6. If $t - 8 < 2$, then $t - 8 + 8 \underline{\quad?\quad} 2 + 8$, or $t \underline{\quad?\quad} 10$.

7. If $q - 21 > -106$, then $q - 21 + 21 \underline{\quad?\quad} -106 + 21$, or $q \underline{\quad?\quad} -85$.

8. If $r + 9 < 0$, then $r + 9 + (-9) \underline{\quad?\quad} 0 + (-9)$, or $r \underline{\quad?\quad} -9$.

9. If $w + 5 < -7$, then $w + 5 + (-5) \underline{\quad?\quad} -7 + (-5)$, or $w \underline{\quad?\quad} -12$.

10. If $s + 2 < 2$, then $s + 2 + (-2) \underline{\quad?\quad} 2 + (-2)$, or $s \underline{\quad?\quad} 0$.

WRITTEN EXERCISES

A   Solve and graph each inequality.

1. $t + 4 > 1$

2. $n + 3 < 4$

3. $y - 5 > 7$

4. $x + 7 > 16$

5. $r + 9 < 16$

6. $x - 15 > -22$

7. $r - 1.5 < 3.5$

8. $m + 0.1 < 2.1$

9. $-5\frac{1}{2} > c + 1\frac{1}{2}$

Solve and graph each inequality.

10. $q + \frac{1}{4} > 3$ **11.** $z - 8 > 8$ **12.** $19 < y + 14$

13. $x + 2 < 8$ **14.** $6d + 1 \leq 5d - 3$ **15.** $x - 3 \geq 5$

16. $6x + 2 \geq 14 + 5x$ **17.** $3.5r - 10 \geq 2.5r + 9$ **18.** $\frac{1}{3}t - 1 < 1\frac{1}{3}t - 1$

B

19. $3n - 2(n - 1) \geq 0$ **20.** $4t - 3(t + 6) > -5$

21. $3(2z - 1) + 8 < 5z$ **22.** $7 + 4(2y) \leq 7y - 5$

23. $1 + 2(y - 1) \geq 3y$ **24.** $6(r - \frac{1}{2}) \geq 5(r + \frac{3}{5})$

25. $5q + 2(9 - 2q) \leq 0$ **26.** $0 \leq 4(1 - 7n) + 29n$

27. $-2(4x - 8) > -3(3x + 5)$ **28.** $-5(1 - 5x) > -12(1 - 2x)$

29. $9x + 1 \leq 4(2x + \frac{1}{4})$ **30.** $3(7y - \frac{1}{3}) \geq 20y - 1$

Complete each statement. In each statement, the variables represent real numbers.

31. If $x > y$, then $x + z$ __?__ $y + z$. (Addition Property for Inequalities)

32. If $x < y$, then $x + z$ __?__ $y + z$. (Addition Property for Inequalities)

C

33. If $x < y$ and $y < z$, then $x <$ __?__. (Transitive Property for Inequalities)

34. If $z > y$ and $y > x$, then $z >$ __?__. (Transitive Property for Inequalities)

35. If $a > 2$, then $a - 2 >$ __?__.

36. If $a - 3 < 0$, then $a <$ __?__.

37. If $a + 5 > 0$, then $a >$ __?__.

38. If $a - 3 < 0$, which is greater, a or 3?

39. If $a + 5 > 0$, which is greater, a or -5?

40. If $b < 0$, which is greater, $b + 3$ or b?

41. If $b < 0$, which is greater, $b + 3$ or 3?

42. The reflexive property of equality states that $a = a$. Is there a similar reflexive property for $>$ and $<$?

43. Show by using examples that if $a > b$ and $c > d$, then it is not always true that $a - c > b - d$.

<hr/>

REVIEW CAPSULE FOR SECTION 4–8

In Exercises 1–6, solve each inequality. Use the given replacement set. *(Pages 18–19)*

1. $2x > -1$; $\{-2, 0, 2\}$ **2.** $2x + 3 > 9$; $\{-4, -3, -2, -1, 0\}$

3. $6 - 3x < 0$; $\{-2, -1, 0, 1, 2\}$ **4.** $7 - 4x \geq 0$; $\{-2, -1, 0, 1, 2\}$

5. $3(x + 1) \leq 3x + 3$; $\{-3, -1, 1, 3\}$ **6.** $-2(p + 1) > 2p - 2$; $\{-6, -3, 0, 3, 6\}$

4-8 Solving Inequalities: Multiplication Property

The table below shows that *multiplying each* side of an inequality by the *same positive number* does not change the order of the inequality.

**Multiplying each side by a negative number,
however, reverses the order of the inequality.**

Inequality	Multiply by 1.	Multiply by 3.	Multiply by -1.	Multiply by -3.
$3 < 7$	$3 < 7$	$9 < 21$	$-3 > -7$	$-9 > -21$
$-3 < 2$	$-3 < 2$	$-9 < 6$	$3 > -2$	$9 > -6$
$4 > -6$	$4 > -6$	$12 > -18$	$-4 < 6$	$-12 < 18$

The table suggests the following.

Properties

> **Multiplication Properties for Inequalities**
>
> 1. For all real numbers a, b, and c, if $a > b$ and $c > 0$, then $ac > bc$.
>
> 2. For all real numbers a, b, and c, if $a > b$ and $c < 0$, then $ac < bc$.

EXAMPLE 1 Solve and graph: $-\dfrac{1}{2}x > 1$

Solution:

$$-\frac{1}{2}x > 1 \longleftarrow \text{Multiply each side by } (-2).$$
Change > to <.

$$(-2)\left(-\frac{1}{2}x\right) < (-2)(1)$$

$$x < -2$$

Solution set: {all real numbers less than -2}

In Example 2, both the addition and multiplication properties of inequalities are used. As when solving equations, it is usually easier to apply the addition property first.

EXAMPLE 2 Solve: $5 - 4x \leq 17$

Solution:

$$5 - 4x \leq 17 \longleftarrow \text{Add } (-5) \text{ to each side.}$$

$$-4x \leq 12 \longleftarrow \text{Multiply each side by } \left(-\frac{1}{4}\right).$$
Change $\leq$ to $\geq$.

$$-\frac{1}{4}(-4x) \geq -\frac{1}{4}(12)$$

$$x \geq -3$$

Solution set: {all real numbers greater than or equal to -3}

In Examples 1 and 2, the check is left for you.

CLASSROOM EXERCISES

Complete each statement.

1. Since $12 > 3$, $\frac{1}{3}(12)$ __?__ $\frac{1}{3}(3)$.
2. Since $16 > 12$, $(-\frac{1}{4})(16)$ __?__ $(-\frac{1}{4})(12)$.
3. Since $-1 < 5$, $10(-1)$ __?__ $10(5)$.
4. Since $-8 < -4$, $(-\frac{1}{8})(-8)$ __?__ $(-\frac{1}{8})(-4)$.
5. Since $\frac{1}{5} < 10$, $(-5)(\frac{1}{5})$ __?__ $(-5)(10)$.
6. Since $-\frac{1}{4} > -\frac{3}{4}$, $(-4)(-\frac{1}{4})$ __?__ $(-4)(-\frac{3}{4})$.
7. If $2x > 9$, then $\frac{1}{2}(2x)$ __?__ $\frac{1}{2}(9)$, or x __?__ $\frac{9}{2}$.
8. If $-\frac{1}{3}t < 27$, then $(-3)(-\frac{1}{3}t)$ __?__ $(-3)(27)$, or t __?__ -81.
9. If $-6p < 1.5$, then $(-\frac{1}{6})(-6p)$ __?__ $(-\frac{1}{6})(1.5)$, or p __?__ -0.25.

WRITTEN EXERCISES

A   Solve and graph each inequality.

1. $2x < 8$
2. $5z > 45$
3. $7q > 14$
4. $-4z > 8$
5. $-4d < 8$
6. $-4n > 12$
7. $-6x \le 0$
8. $-9y \ge 0$
9. $-9t \le -36$
10. $-10w \ge -20$
11. $\frac{1}{3}z > 2$
12. $-\frac{2}{3}r > 6$
13. $2a + 2\frac{1}{2} > 10\frac{1}{2}$
14. $2c - 5 \ge 10$
15. $3h + 7 \le 16$
16. $16 < 3x + 4$
17. $7y < 20 - 3y$
18. $5 + 2p < 17$

Solve each inequality.

19. $2t + 3 > 4t - 7$
20. $3y + 9 > -2$
21. $-2x + 5 > 10$
22. $-3a - 4a > -21$
23. $8r - 3r + 1 \le 29$
24. $5 - 6x \le 17$
25. $4(5a + 7) \le 13$
26. $8t \le 5(2t + 4)$
27. $-3m + 6(m - 4) > 9$

B

28. $8z - 2(2z + 3) > 0$
29. $-2y - 5 \ge 10$
30. $4 - 3p \ge 16 + p$
31. $-2x - 5 < -x + 10$
32. $12x + 3 < 3x - 9$
33. $-4x + 2 < x + 9$
34. $3(x + 2) < -x + 4$
35. $-7(-3x + 4) < 0$
36. $3(x + 2) \ge -2(x + 1)$
37. $3(y + 2) + 8 < 10 - (2 - y)$
38. $-3(2m - 8) < 2(m + 14)$
39. $15x - 2(x - 4) > 3$
40. $-2(n - 3) < 6n - 7(n - 4)$
41. $3(k - 4) - 3 \ge 2k + 1$
42. $5s \le 10 + 2(3s - 4)$
43. $4 - 5(r - 2) \le -2(-9 + 2r)$
44. $-3(t + 1) - 5(t + 2) \ge 0$
45. $3z + 7 \ge 8z - 2(5z - 2)$
46. $2(2r + 5) + 1 \le 5 - 2(3 - r)$
47. $1 - (4d - 1) > 2(d - 3)$
48. $k - 3(2k + 1) < 5(1 + k) + 2$

Complete each statement. In each statement, x, y, and z represent real numbers. (Exercises 49–52 express the Multiplication Property for Inequalities in generalized form.)

49. If $x > y$ and z is positive $(z > 0)$, then $xz \underline{\quad?\quad} yz$.

50. If $x < y$ and z is positive $(z > 0)$, then $xz \underline{\quad?\quad} yz$.

51. If $x > y$ and z is negative $(z < 0)$, then $xz \underline{\quad?\quad} yz$.

52. If $x < y$ and z is negative $(z < 0)$, then $xz \underline{\quad?\quad} yz$.

In Exercises 53–62, classify each statement as true, T, or false, F. When a statement is false, give an example that shows why it is false. In these Exercises, x and y represent real numbers where $x > y$.

53. $y < x$ **54.** $x > 0$ **55.** $y^2 > 0$ **56.** $y^2 > y$ **57.** $xy > 0$

58. $x + y > y$ **59.** $y^2 > x$ **60.** $y^2 < xy$ **61.** $xy < x^2$ **62.** $x^3 < x^2$

CALCULATOR APPLICATIONS

Checking Inequalities

You can use a calculator to check whether a given number is in the solution set of an inequality.

EXAMPLE Is -9.5 a solution of $4p - 6 > -20$?

SOLUTION Substitute -9.5 in the left side of the inequality.

$$4 \;[\times]\; 9.5 \;[\underline{+}/\underline{-}]\; [-]\; 6 \;[=]$$

$$\boxed{-44.}$$

Since $-44 > -20$ is *false*, -9.5 **is not** a solution.

EXERCISES

Check the given "answer" to each inequality.

1. $2b + 4 \geq -9$; -6.5 **2.** $-8 + 4d < 5$; 1 **3.** $5q + 7 > -5$; -2

4. $5(2 - 3n) \leq -8$; -4 **5.** $10 - 4k \geq 16$; 5.2 **6.** $6 - 3(4 + z) < -9$; 1

REVIEW CAPSULE FOR SECTION 4–9

Choose a variable to represent one unknown and tell what it represents. Represent the second unknown in terms of the variable. *(Pages 118–121)*

1. The sum of two consecutive integers.

2. Nadia bought 7 more pencils than pens.

3. One number is 36 more than three times a second number.

4. Room 203 has 5 more than twice the number of students that Room 201 has.

5. The entertainment part of a TV program lasted 10 minutes less than four times the length of the advertising part.

6. Each side of a triangle is 4 meters shorter than twice the length of each side of a square.

Problem Solving and Applications

4-9   Using Inequalities

Many word problems can be solved by using inequalities.

EXAMPLE 1 Ellen plans to spend less than $120 for a dress and a pair of shoes (Condition 2). The cost of the dress Ellen would like to buy is $30 more than twice the cost of a pair of shoes (Condition 1). What is the greatest amount she can spend for the shoes?

Solution: Let p = the cost of the shoes.
Then $2p + 30$ = the cost of the dress. ⟵ **Condition 1**

$$p + 2p + 30 < 120 \qquad \longleftarrow \textbf{Condition 2}$$
$$3p + 30 < 120 \qquad \longleftarrow \textbf{Add (−30) to each side.}$$
$$3p < 90 \qquad \longleftarrow \textbf{Multiply each side by } \tfrac{1}{3}.$$
$$p < 30$$

Since $p < 30$, the greatest amount Ellen can spend for shoes is **$29.99**.

Check: Amount for shoes: $29.99   Amount for dress: $2(\$29.99) + \$30 = \$89.98$
Is $\$29.99 + \$89.98 < \$120$?   Yes ✔

Recall that the *average* of two or more scores is the sum of the scores divided by the number of scores.

EXAMPLE 2 Tom's scores on four tests were 87, 92, 88, and 86. What is the lowest score Tom needs to achieve on the next test in order to have an average score greater than 90?

Solution: Let x = Tom's score on the next test.
$$\frac{87 + 92 + 88 + 86 + x}{5} > 90 \quad \longleftarrow \textbf{Multiply each side by 5.}$$
$$5\left(\frac{87 + 92 + 88 + 86 + x}{5}\right) > 5(90)$$
$$87 + 92 + 88 + 86 + x > 450$$
$$353 + x > 450$$
$$x > 97 \qquad \text{Tom's next score must be } \textbf{greater than 97.}$$

Check: Will a score of 98 give Tom an average greater than 90?
Is $\dfrac{87 + 92 + 88 + 86 + 98}{5} > 90$? $\dfrac{451}{5} > 90$?   Yes ✔

Will a score of 97 give Tom an average greater than 90?
Is $\dfrac{87 + 92 + 88 + 86 + 97}{5} > 90$? $\dfrac{450}{5} > 90$?   No

The check for Example 2 shows another way to check the solution set of an inequality. First replace the variable with a number in the solution set. This number *should satisfy* the inequality. Then replace the variable with a number *not* in the solution set. This number *should not satisfy* the inequality.

CLASSROOM EXERCISES

In Exercises 1–5, choose a variable to represent the unknown(s). Then write the inequality you would use to represent the given situation.

1. Several pipe sections, each 8 meters long, are to be joined to form a pipe greater than 110 meters long.

2. Claude is 5 years older than Tom. The sum of their ages is less than 53, Tom's mother's age.

3. George has two test scores of 82 and 91. What must be his score on the next test in order to have an average of 90 or greater?

4. A trailer can safely carry 1000 kilograms. A number of 40-kilogram bags are being loaded onto the trailer. How many bags can be loaded?

WORD PROBLEMS

A Solve each problem. For some problems, Condition 1 is underscored once. Condition 2 is underscored twice.

1. Larry plans to spend no more than $140 for a jacket and a sweater. Suppose that the cost of a jacket is $10 less than twice the cost of a sweater. What is the greatest amount that Larry can spend for the sweater?

2. Beth and Sara estimate that they should spend less than $600 each month for rent and food and that the amount budgeted for rent should be $30 more than twice the amount budgeted for food. What is the greatest amount budgeted for food?

3. Rosa's scores on three quizzes were 78, 81 and 93. What must be her lowest score on the next quiz in order to have an average greater than 85?

4. Peter's grades on four tests were 68, 82, 78 and 80. What must be his lowest grade on the next test in order to have an average greater than 80?

5. Bob's scores for three games in bowling were 76, 103, and 121. What must be his lowest score in the next game in order to have an average greater than 100 for the four games?

6. Roseanne's scores for three games she bowled were 147, 137, and 130. What must be her lowest score in the next game in order to have an average greater than 140 for the four games?

7. Ada had a sum of money in a savings account. After she deposited an additional $130, there was more than $750 in the account. What is the smallest amount that could have been in the account originally?

8. A drama club agreed to buy more than 250 tickets for a theater party. The number of orchestra seats they bought was 80 fewer than the number of balcony tickets. What was the least number of balcony tickets bought?

9. The sum of two consecutive positive integers is less than or equal to 10. Find the integers.

10. The sum of two consecutive positive integers is less than 50. Find the pair with the greatest sum.

11. The sum of two consecutive odd integers is greater than 55. Find the pair with the smallest sum.

12. The sum of two consecutive even integers is less than 100. Find the pair with the greatest sum.

13. Philip is paid $225 a week plus a $15 commission on each piece of photographic equipment that he sells. How many pieces of equipment must he sell in order to make at least $400 per week?

14. A gain of 2 pounds would put a certain amateur boxer in the welterweight class. What is the least amount the boxer must weigh now if the minimum welterweight class weight is 140 pounds?

B

15. The product of 3 and any number from a set of numbers is greater than 12. Find the set of numbers.

16. The product of 4 and any number from a set of numbers is increased by 7. The result is less than 19. Find the set of numbers.

C

17. The sum of two consecutive even integers is greater than 98 decreased by twice the larger integer. Find the smallest possible values for the integers.

18. Find the largest possible values for three consecutive integers if the sum of the two smaller integers is less than 32 decreased by half the largest integer.

───── **Review** ─────────────────

Solve and graph each inequality. *(Section 4–7)*

1. $n + 8 < 11$

2. $-4.8 > x - 2.3$

3. $3g + 4 \le 2g - 1$

Solve each inequality. *(Section 4–7)*

4. $6(a - 1) > 5a - 9$

5. $2(2 - a) + 3a \ge 0$

6. $2(1\frac{1}{2} - 4p) < 3(1 - 3p)$

Solve and graph each inequality. *(Section 4–8)*

7. $4h > 12$

8. $6y - 4 \ge -10$

9. $3 + 7s < 2(4s + 1)$

Solve each inequality. *(Section 4–8)*

10. $2(b + 3) + 8 > 7 - (b - 4)$

11. $t - 2(3t + 1) \le 5(4 + t) + 8$

12. Paula's grades on three tests were 85, 92, and 75. What is the lowest grade she can get on the next test in order to have an average greater than 85? *(Section 4–9)*

13. One integer is five times as great as a second integer. Their sum is less than 78. What are the greatest possible values of the two integers? *(Section 4–9)*

BASIC: SOLVING INEQUALITIES

One use of the computer is the solution of inequalities.

Problem: *Write a program to solve any inequality of the following form.*

$$ax + b < c$$

Include the possibilities that the solution set may be all real numbers or the empty set.

```
100 PRINT "ENTER VALUES FOR A, B, C"
110 PRINT "(IN THAT ORDER, SEPARATED BY COMMAS)";
120 INPUT A, B, C
130 IF A = 0 THEN 200
140 LET X = (C - B)/A
150 IF A < 0 THEN 180
160 PRINT "X < ";X
170 GOTO 240
180 PRINT "X > ";X
190 GOTO 240
200 IF B < C THEN 230
210 PRINT "NO SOLUTION"
220 GOTO 240
230 PRINT "ALL REAL NUMBERS ARE SOLUTIONS."
240 PRINT "ANY MORE INEQUALITIES TO SOLVE (1=YES, 0=NO)";
250 INPUT Z
260 IF Z = 1 THEN 120
270 END
```

Analysis

Statement 130: If A = 0, the solution set will be either the null set or all real numbers. So when A = 0, the computer is told to jump to statement 200, where it will compare B and C to decide between these two possibilities.

Statement 140: The computer reaches this statement when A ≠ 0. The programmer must solve the inequality for the computer and give it the correct formula. The following steps justify the formula in statement 140.

$$ax + b < c \quad \longleftarrow \text{Subtract } b \text{ from both sides.}$$
$$ax < c - b \quad \longleftarrow \text{Divide both sides by } a.$$
$$x < \frac{c - b}{a} \quad \text{if } a > 0,$$
or
$$x > \frac{c - b}{a} \quad \text{if } a < 0$$

Statements 150–190:	In the work just shown, the inequality sign must be reversed if A < 0. In this case, statement 150 sends the computer to statement 180, which prints the answer with a ">" sign. If A > 0, the computer moves to statement 160, which prints the answer with a "<" sign. In either case, the computer is told (statements 170 and 190) to jump to statement 240, which asks the user if there are more inequalities to be solved.
Statements 200–230:	The computer can get to statement 200 only from statement 130, when A = 0. In this case, the inequality becomes B < C, which will be true either all the time or never. So, in statement 200, if B < C, the computer goes to statement 230 and prints ALL REAL NUMBERS ARE SOLUTIONS. But if B is not less than C, statement 210 is executed, printing NO SOLUTION. In either event the computer moves to statement 240 to see if the user has any more data to enter.

In IF...THEN statements in BASIC, the IF part contains an equation or inequality in which the following symbols are used.

Algebraic symbol	=	<	>	≤	≥	≠
BASIC Symbol	=	<	>	<=	>=	<>

Either or both sides of the equation or inequality in the IF part may include operation symbols. For example, 130 IF C/D <= 2*(A + B) THEN 20 is a valid statement.

EXERCISES

A   Run the program on page 149 for the following values of a, b, and c.

1. $a = 2; b = 5; c = 9$ **2.** $a = 3; b = 4; c = 10$ **3.** $a = 2; b = -6; c = 0$

4. $a = -2; b = 5; c = 9$ **5.** $a = 0; b = 7; c = 8$ **6.** $a = 0; b = 8; c = 7$

Write each of the following inequalities in the form $ax + b < c$.
Then use the program on page 149 to solve the inequality.

7. $6 + 4x < 12$ **8.** $18 > 3x - 2$ **9.** $25 > 7 + 11x$

10. $112 < 16x - 123$ **11.** $254 < 24x + 123$ **12.** $82 - 9x < 233$

13. Write REM statements that can be added to the sample program on page 149 to explain what the program is doing. For example,

145 REM LINES 150-190 DECIDE WHETHER TO REVERSE THE < SIGN.

14. Change the problem in the example on page 149 to solve $ax + b \leq c$. What statements in the program must be changed and how?

B   Write a BASIC program for each problem.

15. Solve equations of the form $ax + b = cx + d$. Include the possibilities that the solution set may be all real numbers or the null set.

16. Given a real number, print its absolute value. Do not use any "built-in" absolute value function that your computer may have.

Chapter Summary

IMPORTANT IDEAS

1. **Steps in Representing a Word Expression by Algebraic Symbols**
   - 1 Choose a variable. Tell what it represents.
   - 2 Identify the key word or words that indicate which operation to use.
   - 3 Represent the word expressions by symbols.

2. **Steps in Solving a Word Problem with One Unknown**
   - 1 Choose a variable to represent the unknown.
   - 2 Write an equation for the problem.
   - 3 Solve the equation.
   - 4 Check your answer with the statements in the problem. Answer the question.

3. **Steps in Solving a Word Problem with Two Conditions**
   - 1 Identify Condition 1. Use this condition to represent the unknowns.
   - 2 Identify Condition 2. Use this condition to write an equation for the problem.
   - 3 Solve the equation.
   - 4 Check the results with the two conditions. Answer the question(s).

4. When terms with the variable occur on both sides of an equation, use the addition property for equations to get the terms on the same side. Then combine like terms.

5. **Addition Property for Inequalities:** Adding the same number to each side of an inequality results in an equivalent inequality.

6. **Multiplication Property for Inequalities:** Multiplying each side of an inequality by the same positive number gives an equivalent inequality. Multiplying each side of an inequality by the same negative number gives an equivalent inequality *when the inequality sign is reversed.*

Chapter Objectives and Review

Objective: *To represent word expressions by algebraic symbols (Section 4–1)*

Represent each word expression by an algebraic expression.

1. 4.5 less w

2. p divided by -7

3. 5 increased by x

4. c multiplied by $\frac{1}{4}$

Objective: *To use equations to solve word problems with one unknown*
(Section 4–2)

5. The cost of a battery, plus $2.49 sales tax, is $43.99. What is the price of the battery?

6. The quotient of a certain number and 9, decreased by 4, is 6. Find the number.

7. Twenty-four more than twice the number of people at a movie is 850. How many people were at the movie?

8. Three times the perimeter of the garden plus 12 yards is 57 yards. What is the perimeter of the garden?

Objective: *To solve word problems by first identifying two conditions*
(Section 4–3)

9. One number plus another number is 75. The smaller number is 13 less than the larger number. Find the numbers.

10. Together, Bill and Jim earned $95. Jim earned $4 less than twice what Bill did. How much did each earn?

11. Profits for the Solatech Company this month were $500 less than twice the profits last month. The total profits for the two months were $4300. What were the profits for each of the two months?

12. The larger of two hospitals has 1.8 times as many beds as the smaller hospital. The larger hospital has 116 more beds than the smaller one. Find the number of beds in each hospital.

Objective: *To solve measurement problems (Section 4–4)*

13. The width of a swimming pool is 20 meters less than its length. The perimeter is 160 meters. Find the length and width of the pool.

14. In triangle XYZ, angles X and Y have the same measure. The sum of the measures of angles Y and Z is 100°. How many degrees are there in each of the three angles?

15. The lengths of the sides of a triangle can be represented by three consecutive odd integers. The perimeter of the triangle is 87 feet. Find the lengths of the sides of the triangle.

16. A mason is building a wall around a rectangular patio. The perimeter of the patio is 70 feet and the length is 2.5 times the width. Find the length and width of the patio.

Objective: *To solve equations in which the variable occurs on both sides*
(Section 4–5)

Solve and check.

17. $8x = 3x + 15$

18. $2y + 5 = 2(y - 1)$

19. $3(n + 2) - 16 = 8n$

20. $4 - (6 - 5n) = 2(n + 5)$

Objective: *To solve age problems (Section 4–6)*

21. Jim's present age is three times Tony's present age. Five years ago, the sum of their ages was 14. What is each boy's present age?

22. John Lukas was 50 years old when his granddaughter was born. Now he is 2 years more than four times his granddaughter's age. How old is his granddaughter now?

23. The ages of two friends can be represented as consecutive even integers. Twelve years from now, the sum of their ages will be 46. How old is each now?

24. A man is now 38 years old and his son is 14 years old. In how many years will the father be exactly twice as old as his son?

Objective: *To solve inequalities using the addition property of inequality (Section 4–7)*

Solve and graph each inequality.

25. $y - 4 > 2$ **26.** $6 \leq 9 + t$ **27.** $-2 + 3b < 2b + 3$

Solve each inequality.

28. $3(2 - n) < 9$ **29.** $6(f + \frac{1}{2}) - 5(1 + f) \geq 0$

30. $-3(4 - p) \leq 2(p + 1)$ **31.** $3(2n + 4) - 12 < 5n$

Objective: *To solve inequalities using the multiplication property of inequality (Section 4–8)*

Solve and graph each inequality.

32. $8d < -16$ **33.** $3 - 2r > 7$ **34.** $-\frac{3}{4}x \leq -3$

Solve each inequality.

35. $2(y - 4) \geq 7 - y$ **36.** $3m - 4 < 2(5m + 6) - 3m$

Objective: *To solve word problems using inequalities (Section 4–9)*

37. The charge to rent a car for a day is $25. There is an additional charge of $0.06 per mile. What is the greatest number of miles that a rented car can be driven in a day if the total bill is to be less than $40?

38. Andrea scored 18 points in one basketball game and 13 points in another. What is the least number of points she must score in the next game if her average for the 3 games is to be more than 14 points?

—— Chapter Test ——

Represent each word expression by an algebraic expression.

1. 9 more than t **2.** y decreased by 1.5

3. The quotient of -6 and w **4.** Twice n, less 58

Solve and check.

5. $6d = 20 - 4d$ **6.** $8 - x = 3x + 12$

7. $2(3y + 1) = -2(y - 5)$ **8.** $3(3 - a) - 1 = a + 8$

Solve and graph each inequality.

9. $x + 9 < 8$ **10.** $-5c > 10$ **11.** $4r - 7 \leq -3$ **12.** $3t + 2 \geq 11$

Solve each inequality.

13. $3(x + 4) - 4 > 2$

14. $5(n - 1) < 2(2n + 1)$

15. $6 + 2y - (5y - 3) < 0$

16. $2(2z + 6) \geq 3(4 - z)$

17. The number of tickets printed, less 76, is 424. Find the number of tickets printed.

18. Last week Jean earned $24 more than Laura. Together, they earned $96. How much did each girl earn?

19. The length of a table top is 26 centimeters longer than its width. Its perimeter is 612 centimeters. Find the length and width.

20. Keith is 10 years older than Mark. Five years ago, Keith was twice as old as Mark was then. How old are Keith and Mark now?

———— More Challenging Problems ————

1. Simplify: $\dfrac{(-12)\left(\frac{1}{4}\right)}{(-18)\left(-\frac{1}{3}\right)} \div \dfrac{(16)\left(-\frac{1}{2}\right)}{\left(-\frac{1}{5}\right)(-25)}$

2. Solve for x and graph the solution set: $7 - [4 - (3 + x)] > 3 - (9 + x)$. The replacement set is the set of real numbers.

3. Solve for x: $7(b + 5d) = 5(x - 3b)$

4. Simplify: $6 + 7[4(3a + 2b - 6) - 3(-4b + 6a - 7) + 2]$

5. How many feet are there in y yards, f feet, and i inches?

6. Show that these are equivalent formulas.
$$\tfrac{9}{5}C + 32 = F \text{ and } C = \tfrac{5}{9}(F - 32)$$

7. Simplify: $5x - y + 3 \cdot 5z - 1\tfrac{1}{6}z + 2\tfrac{1}{2}x + 3\tfrac{1}{2}y$

8. After selling $\frac{1}{4}$ of his crop, a farmer sold the remainder for $900 at the same price per bushel. What was the value of the crop?

9. The three digit number $2a3$ is added to the number 326 to give the three digit number $5b9$. If $5b9$ is divisible by 9, find $a + b$.

10. A positive number is mistakenly divided by 6 instead of being multiplied by 6. Based on the correct answer, what is the per cent of error?

11. Find the sum of the solutions of $|x + 2| = 2|x - 2|$.

12. A rectangular field is half as wide as it is long. Its perimeter is x yards. Find its area in terms of x.

13. A house and store were sold for $12,000 each. The house was sold at a loss of 20% of the cost, and the store was sold at a gain of 20% of the cost. Find the result of the entire transaction and state whether it was a loss or a gain.

14. In a group of cows and chickens, the number of legs was 14 more than twice the number of heads. Find the number of cows.

Additional Practice

Skills

Represent each word expression by an algebraic expression. *(Section 4-1)*

1. 6.5 less x

2. The product of -5 and n

3. 28 divided by c

4. p increased by $3\frac{1}{2}$

Solve and check. *(Section 4-5)*

5. $9a - 4 = 5a$

6. $5 - 3n = 2n + 15$

7. $2x - 3 = 3(x - 2)$

8. $4(a + 2) = 6(a - 3)$

9. $2(\frac{1}{2}y + 7) = 8y$

10. $2(x + 1) - 3(2x - 2) = 4$

Solve each inequality. *(Section 4-7)*

11. $2(x - 3) > 4 + x$

12. $-2(4 - n) < 3n$

13. $5(a + 1) - 2(2a - 1) \le 0$

14. $3(2n + 1) - 5n \ge 2n - 1$

Solve each inequality. *(Section 4-8)*

15. $3x \le 5x - 8$

16. $6(2 - n) < 12 + 5n$

17. $1 + n > 3(1 - n)$

18. $5(3 - n) \ge 2(n + \frac{1}{2})$

Applications

19. Five dollars, plus three times the daily rental charge for a rug cleaning machine, is $47. What is the daily rental charge? *(Section 4-2)*

20. The sale price of a book is $9.72. The rate of discount is 25%. Find the list price and the amount of discount. *(Section 4-3)*

21. Jean and Emily have 110 old coins in their combined collections. Jean has 25 less than twice the number of coins that Emily has. How many coins does each girl have? *(Section 4-3)*

22. The width of a rug is 2 meters less than the length. The perimeter of the rug is 28 meters. Find the length and width of the rug. *(Section 4-4)*

23. In triangle ABC, the measure of angle B is three times the measure of angle A, and the measure of angle C is five times the measure of angle A. Find the measure of each angle. *(Section 4-4)*

24. Mr. Sanchez is 25 years older than his son. In 15 years he will be twice as old as his son. Find their present ages. *(Section 4-6)*

25. Jim threw the javelin four times for distances of 165, 170, 158, and 178 feet. What is the least distance he must get on his fifth throw in order to average at least 170 feet for the five throws? *(Section 4-9)*

26. Sally is paid $245 per week plus an $8 commission on each major appliance she sells. How many major appliances must she sell in order to make at least $325 per week? *(Section 4-9)*

Review of Word Problems: Chapters 1–4

1. A 946–milliliter bottle of lemon juice costs $1.29. A 315–milliliter bottle of the same brand of lemon juice costs $0.49. Which size is the better buy? *(Section 1–4)*

2. At sunrise, the temperature was −5°C. At noon, the temperature had risen 8 degrees, and by sunset it had fallen 6 degrees. What was the temperature at sunset? *(Section 2–3)*

3. The average temperature on Monday was 4°C. The average temperature on Tuesday was −3°C. Find the difference between the two temperatures. *(Section 2–4)*

4. In five consecutive days, the following gains and losses in the price of a stock were reported: $+1\frac{1}{2}, -\frac{3}{4}, -\frac{1}{4}, +\frac{1}{2}, -\frac{3}{8}$. Find the average change over the five days. *(Section 2–7)*

5. John Hammond earns $1450 per month plus a 5% commission on the sales he makes. Last month he earned a total of $1720. What were his sales that month? *(Section 3–4)*

6. The sum of the measures of two angles is 180°. Their measures can be represented by x and $(2x + 15)$. Find the measure of each angle. *(Section 3–6)*

7. Maria earns $1120 a month as a computer programmer. She spends $56 per month on entertainment. What per cent of her monthly income is spent on entertainment? *(Section 3–7)*

8. A basketball team won 24 games. This was 60% of all the games they played. How many games did the team play? *(Section 3–7)*

9. The sum of three consecutive odd integers is 93. Find the integers. *(Section 3–8)*

10. Five times the cost of a ticket, decreased by $2, equals $16.75. Find the cost of a ticket. *(Section 4–2)*

11. Janet bought skis and ski boots for $175. The boots cost $23 more than the skis. What was the price of the skis? *(Section 4–3)*

12. The sale price of a typewriter is $230. The discount rate is 20%. Find the list price and the amount of discount. *(Section 4–3)*

13. The length of a rectangular court is 10 meters less than twice its width. The perimeter of the court is 106 meters. Find the length and width of the court. *(Section 4–4)*

14. Keith is 8 years younger than Sean. In 4 years, Keith will be $\frac{2}{3}$ as old as Sean is then. Find their present ages. *(Section 4–6)*

15. In the last three weeks, Carla earned $38, $45, and $52. How much must she earn this week in order to have average earnings of at least $48 per week for the four weeks? *(Section 4–9)*

Cumulative Review: Chapters 1–4

Choose the best answer. Choose *a, b, c,* or *d.*

1. What is the cost in dollars of *r* stamps at 30¢ each?

   a. $30r$ b. $0.30r$ c. $\dfrac{r}{30}$ d. $\dfrac{r}{0.30}$

2. Find the value of $m - 3n$ when $m = 18$ and $n = 5$.

   a. 75   b. -3 c. 3   d. -49

3. What is the value of A in the formula $A = P(1 + 0.06t)$ when $P = \$700$ and $t = 2.5$ years?

   a. $805   b. $8050   c. $1750   d. $743.75

4. What is the solution set of $3(4 + x) = 12 + 3x$, where the replacement set is $\{0, -4, 8, -12\}$?

   a. $\{0\}$ b. $\{-4\}$ c. ϕ d. $\{0, -4, 8, -12\}$

5. Which statement is false?

   a. $N \subset Q$ b. $Ir \subset R$ c. $I \subset N$ d. $N \subset W$

6. Which number is a rational number?

   a. π b. $\sqrt{49}$ c. $\sqrt{7}$ d. $\sqrt{9 \cdot 2}$

7. What is the name of the postulate illustrated by $-2(x + 3) = -2x + (-2 \cdot 3)$?

   a. Commutative for Multiplication   b. Multiplicative Inverse

   c. Additive Inverse   d. Distributive

8. What is the solution set of $-y = 13$?

   a. $\{13\}$ b. $\{-13\}$ c. $\{12\}$ d. $\{14\}$

9. Which can replace __?__ in $|-7\frac{1}{2}|$ __?__ -8 and make a true sentence?

   a. $>$ b. $<$ c. $=$ d. $\leq$

10. Which expression does not equal -8?

    a. $2 \cdot -4$ b. $-16 - (-8)$ c. $0 - (-8)$ d. $0 - 8$

11. Simplify: $7 - [4 + (2 \cdot -6)]$

    a. -9 b. -15 c. -1 d. 15

12. Evaluate $2r - 7s - 9$ when $r = -1.5$ and $s = -3$.

    a. 9   b. -9 c. -19 d. 9.5

13. For which of the numbers -5, 0, and 5 is $|x|$ positive?

    a. -5, 0, and 5   b. 5   c. -5 and 5   d. 0

14. Solve $8 + 7a - 5a = 2a + 8$, where the replacement set is $\{-10, 0, 10\}$.

    a. All three   b. Only 0   c. Only -10 and 10   d. Only 10

15. Simplify: $1.8m - 6n + 3m + 2.4n$

    a. $4.8m^2 - 3.6n^2$ **b.** $1.2mn$ **c.** $4.8m - 3.6n$ **d.** $4.8m - 4.6n$

16. Which expression is equal to y?

    a. $\frac{4}{3}(-\frac{3}{4}y)$ **b.** $-\frac{3}{4}y + \frac{3}{4}$ **c.** $-\frac{3}{4}y - \frac{3}{4}$ **d.** $-\frac{4}{3}(-\frac{3}{4}y)$

17. If t is an integer, which of the following represents three consecutive integers?

    a. $t, 2t, 3t$ **b.** $t, t+2, t+4$ **c.** $t, t+1, t+2$ **d.** $t, t+1, t+4$

18. Which equation does not have $\{-7\}$ as its solution set?

    a. $\frac{1}{2}x = -14$ **b.** $x + (-7) = -14$ **c.** $2x = -14$ **d.** $-x + 7 = 14$

19. What is the solution set of $5a - 2 = 17$?

    a. $\{3\}$ **b.** $\{3\frac{4}{5}\}$ **c.** $\{-3\}$ **d.** $\{-3\frac{4}{5}\}$

20. Which of the following has the same solution set as $8 - 3(2x - 5) = 6$?

    a. $8 - 6x - 15 = 6$ **b.** $8 - 6x + 5 = 6$ **c.** $8 - 6x + 15 = 6$ **d.** $10x - 25 = 6$

21. The equation $5m + 7m - 8 = 4.7$ is equivalent to which of the following equations?

    a. $12m^2 - 8 = 4.7$ **b.** $12m = 12.7$ **c.** $12m = -3.3$ **d.** $4m = 4.7$

22. The measures of the angles of a triangle are represented by x, $2x$, and $3x - 60$. Find the measure of the smallest angle.

    a. $20°$ **b.** $40°$ **c.** $60°$ **d.** $80°$

23. At an average speed of 70 kilometers per hour, how many hours will it take to travel 455 kilometers?

    a. 6   **b.** 7   **c.** 6.5   **d.** $\frac{455}{140}$

24. A number is 0.86 less than r. Represent the number by an algebraic expression.

    a. $0.86 - r$ **b.** $r + 0.86$ **c.** $n - r - 0.86$ **d.** $r - 0.86$

25. Twice Mary's allowance decreased by $6.82 is $3.18. How much is Mary's allowance?

    a. $5.00   **b.** $10.00   **c.** $3.64   **d.** $1.82

26. The length of a rectangle is three times its width. If the perimeter is 240 centimeters, what is the length of the rectangle?

    a. 30 cm   **b.** 60 cm   **c.** 90 cm   **d.** 180 cm

27. What is the solution set of $-3(2x - 8) = -5x + 2$?

    a. $\{-10\}$ **b.** $\{-22\}$ **c.** $\{22\}$ **d.** $\{-26\}$

28. Solve: $n + 7 < -15$

    a. $n < -22$ **b.** $n < -8$ **c.** $n < 8$ **d.** $n > -22$

29. Solve: $-4n + 6 > -n - 30$

    a. $n < -12$ **b.** $n > 12$ **c.** $n < 12$ **d.** $n > -12$

Preparing for College Entrance Tests

Accuracy and **speed** are important in College Entrance tests. If you can recognize situations in which the basic postulates for the real numbers can be applied, it is often possible to reduce the amount of time needed to determine a correct answer.

REMEMBER: The fewer the computations, the less possibility there is for error!

EXAMPLE: $\dfrac{12(16-8)-8(16-8)}{4} = \underline{\ ?\ }$ (a) 2 (b) 4 (c) 8 (d) 16

Solution: By the distributive postulate, $12x - 8x = (12-8)x = 4x$.

$$\text{Thus, } \frac{12(16-8)-8(16-8)}{4} = \frac{\overset{1}{\cancel{4}}(16-8)}{\underset{1}{\cancel{4}}}$$

$$= 16 - 8, \text{ or } \mathbf{8} \qquad \textbf{Answer: c}$$

Choose the best answer. Choose *a, b, c,* or *d.*

1. $\dfrac{6(15-3)-3(15-3)}{3} = \underline{\ ?\ }$

(a) 12   (b) 24   (c) 45   (d) 72

2. $\dfrac{2(21+3)-4(21+3)}{2} = \underline{\ ?\ }$

(a) −72   (b) −48   (c) −24   (d) 24

3. $\dfrac{3(38-14)+5(38-14)}{24} = \underline{\ ?\ }$

(a) 8   (b) 15   (c) 18   (d) 24

4. $\dfrac{6(31-29)-2(31-29)}{2} = \underline{\ ?\ }$

(a) 2   (b) 4   (c) 6   (d) 8

5. $3(20-5)-4(20-5)+(20-5) = \underline{\ ?\ }$

(a) −30   (b) −15   (c) 0   (d) 15

6. $\dfrac{42+42+42+42}{4} = \underline{\ ?\ }$ (Think: $\dfrac{4(42)}{4} = \underline{\ ?\ }$)

(a) 4   (b) $40\frac{1}{2}$ (c) 42   (d) 84

7. $\dfrac{36+36+36+36+36}{36} = \underline{\ ?\ }$

(a) 5   (b) 18   (c) 36   (d) 72

8. $(25-38)-(20-38) = \underline{\ ?\ }$

(a) −91   (b) −71   (c) 0   (d) 5

Preparing for College Entrance Tests

It is not always necessary to solve an equation for the variable in order to answer a question about the variable.

REMEMBER: It is important to watch for ways to save yourself time and work on College Entrance tests!

EXAMPLE: If $2n - 6 = 1$, what is the value of $n - 3$?

(a) $3\frac{1}{2}$ (b) 2   (c) $\frac{1}{2}$ (d) -1

Think: By the distributive postulate, $2(n - 3) = 2n - 6$.
Thus, $2n - 6 = 2(n - 3)$. Solve for $n - 3$.

Solution: $2(n - 3) = 1$
$n - 3 = \frac{1}{2}$ **Answer: c**

Choose the best answer. Choose *a*, *b*, *c*, or *d*.

1. If $2x + 4 = 6$, what is the value of $x + 2$?

 (a) 1   (b) 3   (c) 6   (d) 12

2. If $3y - 3 = 2$, what is the value of $y - 1$?

 (a) -1 (b) $\frac{2}{3}$ (c) $1\frac{2}{3}$ (d) 2

3. If $4n - 12 = -8$, what is the value of $n - 3$?

 (a) 2   (b) 1   (c) -2 (d) -8

4. If $4 - 8a = 5$, what is the value of $1 - 2a$?

 (a) $-\frac{1}{8}$ (b) $\frac{1}{8}$ (c) $\frac{3}{4}$ (d) $1\frac{1}{4}$

5. If $6c + 8 = 3$, what is the value of $3c + 4$?

 (a) -1 (b) $-\frac{5}{6}$ (c) $1\frac{1}{2}$ (d) 3

6. If $9p - 6 = -1$, what is the value of $3p - 2$?

 (a) 1   (b) $\frac{1}{3}$ (c) $-\frac{1}{3}$ (d) -4

7. If $4p - 4 = \frac{1}{2}$, what is the value of $p - 1$?

 (a) $\frac{1}{8}$ (b) $\frac{1}{4}$ (c) $1\frac{1}{8}$ (d) 2

8. If $\frac{1}{3}x + \frac{1}{3} = 1$, what is the value of $x + 1$?

 (a) $\frac{1}{3}$ (b) $\frac{2}{3}$ (c) 2   (d) 3

9. If $\frac{n}{4} = 3$, what is the value of $\frac{n}{3}$?

 (a) $\frac{1}{4}$ (b) $\frac{3}{4}$ (c) 4   (d) 12

10. If $\frac{y}{6} = 4$, what is the value of $\frac{y}{4}$?

 (a) $\frac{1}{6}$ (b) $\frac{2}{3}$ (c) $\frac{3}{2}$ (d) 6

CHAPTER 5 Graphing Relations and Functions

5–1 Solving Equations for a Variable

Problems in science and business often involve solving an equation for one variable in terms of the others. The procedures for solving are illustrated in the table below. To solve for x in the equation

$$x + a = b,$$

you find x in terms of a and b. Compare the solutions of the given equations in the table with those of the general equations.

Given Equation	**General Equation**
Solve for x.	Solve for x.
$x + 7 = 12$	$x + a = b$
$x + 7 + (-7) = 12 + (-7)$	$x + a + (-a) = b + (-a)$
$x = 5$	$x = b + (-a)$
Check: $x + 7 = 12$	**Check:** $x + a = b$
$5 + 7 \overset{?}{=} 12$	$b + (-a) + a \overset{?}{=} b$
$12 \overset{?}{=} 12$ Yes ✔	$b \overset{?}{=} b$ Yes ✔
The solution is **5**.	The solution is $b + (-a)$, or $\boldsymbol{b - a}$.
Solve for w.	Solve for w.
$38 = 16 + 2w$	$p = 2 + 2w$
$-16 + 38 = -16 + 16 + 2w$	$p - 2 = 2w$
$22 = 2w$	$\frac{1}{2}(p - 2) = \frac{1}{2}(2w)$
$\frac{1}{2}(22) = \frac{1}{2}(2w)$	$\frac{p - 2}{2} = w$
$w = 11$	
Check: $38 = 16 + 2w$	**Check:** $p = 2 + 2w$
$38 \overset{?}{=} 16 + 2(11)$	$p \overset{?}{=} 2 + 2\left(\frac{p - 2}{2}\right)$
$38 \overset{?}{=} 38$ Yes ✔	$p \overset{?}{=} 2 + p - 2$
The solution is **11**.	$p \overset{?}{=} p$ Yes ✔
	The solution is $\dfrac{p - 2}{2}$.
Solve for t.	Solve for t.
$-12 = -3t$	$d = rt$
$4 = t$ The solution is **4**.	$\dfrac{d}{r} = t$ The solution is $\dfrac{d}{r}$.
The check is left for you.	The check is left for you.

CLASSROOM EXERCISES

Solve each equation for x. Check.

1. $x + b = 7$

2. $x + a = c$

3. $x - t = 2$

4. $x - a = b$

5. $3x = a$

6. $ax = b$

WRITTEN EXERCISES

A Solve the first equation in each pair. Then use the same procedure to solve the second equation for x. Check each solution.

1. $\dfrac{x}{6} = 24; \dfrac{x}{a} = b$

2. $5x + 4 = 10; ax + b = c$

3. $\dfrac{3x}{5} = 2; \dfrac{ax}{b} = c$

4. $x + 6 = 8 + \dfrac{1}{4}; x + a = b + c$

5. $5x + 4 = 10; 5x + a = b$

6. $-2x = 16; -ax = b$

7. $3(x + 4) = 8; 3(x + a) = b$

8. $-x + 4 = -5; -x + a = b$

9. $-2x + 6 = 0; -2x + a = b$

10. $3x + 5 = -7; 3x + a = -b$

Solve each formula for the variable indicated.

11. Formula for the circumference of a circle: $C = \pi d$ Solve for d.

12. Formula for the area of a parallelogram: $A = bh$ Solve for b.

13. Formula for the area of a triangle: $A = \frac{1}{2}bh$ Solve for h.

14. Formula for the perimeter of a rectangle: $P = 2l + 2w$ Solve for w.

15. Distance/rate/time formula: $d = rt$ Solve for r.

16. Simple interest formula: $i = prt$ Solve for t.

17. Simple interest formula: $i = prt$ Solve for r.

18. Formula for the volume of a rectangular box: $V = lwh$ Solve for h.

19. Formula for calculating a Celsius temperature from a Fahrenheit temperature: $C = \frac{5}{9}(F - 32)$ Solve for F.

20. Formula for the sum of the measures of the angles of a triangle: $a + b + c = 180°$ Solve for b.

Solve each formula for the unknown variable. Then substitute the given values to find the required length.

21. $C = \pi d$

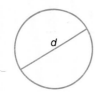

$C = 22.6\pi ; d = \underline{\quad ? \quad}$

22. $P = a + b + c$

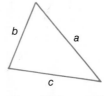

$P = 29.9; a = 11.4;$
$b = 7.9: c = \underline{\quad ? \quad}$

23. $P = 2l + 2w$

$P = 84; w = 20;$
$l = \underline{\quad ? \quad}$

Solve each formula for the unknown variable. Then find the required length.

24. $A = bh$

$A = 36.34$ square units;
$h = 4.6; b = \underline{\quad ? \quad}$

25. $A = lw$

$A = 36.4$ square units;
$l = 13; w = \underline{\quad ? \quad}$

26. $A = \frac{1}{2}bh$

$A = 72$ square units;
$b = 9; h = \underline{\quad ? \quad}$

B Solve each equation for *n*. Check each solution.

27. $2n + a = b$

28. $2n + 5a = 8a$

29. $6a + 2b = 2n$

30. $2n - a = b$

31. $3a + n = 5b$

32. $2n - b = 5a$

33. $n + a = b + c$

34. $2a + 2n = b + c$

35. $-n = -4b$

36. $-n + a = b$

37. $an = b + c$

38. $an + ac = b$

C Solve each equation for the variable indicated. Check each solution.

39. $a(b + n) = c$ for b

40. $\frac{n}{a} = b + n$ for a

41. $(a + b)n = c$ for a

42. $b(n - a) = c$ for n

43. $A = \frac{1}{2}h(b + b')$ for b

44. $A = p(1 + rt)$ for r

Puzzle

Unscramble the letters below to form 10 words introduced in Chapters 1–4. Then use the circled letters to find someone whose name lives on after 2400 years.

1. ☐ ☐ ☐ ☐ ⊙ ☐ ☐
   T E N G I R E

2. ☐ ☐ ☐ ☐ ⊙
   M Y P T E

3. ☐ ⊙ ☐ ☐ ☐ ☐ ☐ ☐
   B A R A L I V E

4. ☐ ☐ ☐ ☐ ⊙ ☐ ☐ ☐
   T A R A L I O N

5. ☐ ☐ ☐ ☐ ☐ ☐ ☐ ⊙
   P E N T E X O N

6. ⊙ ☐ ☐ ☐ ☐ ☐ ☐ ☐ ☐
   M E R E T R I P E

7. ☐ ⊙ ☐ ☐ ☐
   H E L O W

8. ⊙ ☐ ☐ ☐ ☐ ☐ ☐ ☐
   L I O N O U S T

9. ☐ ☐ ☐ ☐ ⊙ ☐ ☐
   H O M E T E R

10. ☐ ☐ ☐ ☐ ☐ ☐ ⊙
    R O A M F U L

Answer: ☐ ☐ ☐ ☐ ☐ ☐ ☐ ☐ ☐ ☐

Problem Solving and Applications

5–2 Distance/Rate/Time

To solve distance/rate/time problems, you use the following formula.

Distance = Rate · Time   or $d = rt$

In solving distance/rate/time problems, it is helpful to organize the given information in a table. This will help you to represent the unknowns (Condition 1). Drawing a figure will help you to write the equation (Condition 2).

EXAMPLE 1 Two cars 635 kilometers apart start at the same time and travel toward each other (Condition 2). One car travels at a rate of 75 kilometers per hour (abbreviated: 75 km/h); the other travels at a rate of 52 kilometers per hour. In how many hours will the cars meet (Condition 1)?

Solution: $\boxed{1}$ Organize the information in a table. Represent the unknowns.

Let t = the number of hours each car travels.

	Rate r	Time t	Distance $d = rt$
Car A	75	t	$75t$
Car B	52	t	$52t$

$\boxed{2}$ Draw a figure. Use the figure and the table to write an equation.

Car A ⟶   ⟵ Car B
|⟵ 635 km ⟶|

$$\underset{\text{Car A}}{\text{Distance for}} + \underset{\text{Car B}}{\text{Distance for}} = \underset{\text{Distance}}{\text{Total}}$$

$$75t + 52t = 635$$

$\boxed{3}$ Solve the equation.

$$127t = 635$$
$$t = 5$$

Check: $\boxed{4}$ Does the total distance covered equal 635 kilometers?

$75(5) + 52(5) = 635$?   Yes ✓   The cars will meet in **5 hours.**

The following procedure summarizes the steps shown in Example 1.

Procedure

To solve distance/rate/time problems:

$\boxed{1}$ Organize the given information in a table. Use this information to represent the unknowns (Condition 1).

$\boxed{2}$ Draw a figure to represent the information. Use this figure and the table to write an equation for the problem (Condition 2).

$\boxed{3}$ Solve the equation.

$\boxed{4}$ Check your answer with the conditions of the problem. Answer the question.

EXAMPLE 2   Marsha and her brother Don left home by car at the same time, traveling in opposite directions. Don's rate was 6 miles per hour (abbreviated mph) less than Marsha's rate. After 10 hours, they were 940 miles apart. Find the rate of travel for each person.

Solution: $\boxed{1}$ Let r = Marsha's rate.
          Then $r - 6$ = Don's rate.

	Rate r	Time t	Distance $d = rt$
Marsha	r	10	$10r$
Don	$r - 6$	10	$10(r - 6)$

$\boxed{2}$ Draw a figure.

$\boxed{3}$ $10r + 10(r - 6) = 940$ ◄——— $\underset{\textbf{Distance}}{\textbf{Marsha's}} + \underset{\textbf{Distance}}{\textbf{Don's}} = \underset{\textbf{Distance}}{\textbf{Total}}$

$10r + 10r - 60 = 940$

$20r - 60 = 940$

$20r = 1000$

$r = 50$ ◄——— **Don't forget to find Don's rate.**

$r - 6 = 44$

Check: $\boxed{4}$ Is Don's rate 6 mph less than Marsha's?
          $44 = 50 - 6$?   Yes ✔

          After 10 hours, were they 940 miles apart?
          $50(10) + 44(10) = 940$?   Yes ✔

          Marsha's rate is **50 mph** and Don's rate is **44 mph**.

CLASSROOM EXERCISES

In Exercises 1–4, use the given information to complete the table.

1. Two hikers start toward each other at the same time from different towns. They meet in 6 hours. The rate of one hiker is twice the rate of the other.

	r	t	$d = rt$
Hiker A	?	?	?
Hiker B	?	?	?

2. Susan and Joann leave from the same place driving in opposite directions, but Joann leaves 3 hours later than Susan. Susan's average rate of speed is 45 kilometers per hour and Joann's average rate is 50 kilometers per hour.

	r	t	$d = rt$
Susan	?	?	?
Joann	?	?	?

3. A passenger train and a freight train start at the same time from stations which are 648 kilometers apart. The rate of the passenger train is twice the rate of the freight train. They pass each other in 3 hours.

	r	t	$d = rt$
Passenger	?	?	?
Freight	?	?	?

166   *Chapter 5*

4. Jack and Harry started on bicycles at the same time from two different places and rode toward each other. Jack traveled at 12 kilometers per hour and Harry traveled at 16 kilometers per hour. They met in 5 hours.

	r	t	d = rt
Jack	?	?	?
Harry	?	?	?

WORD PROBLEMS

A Solve each problem.

1. Two automobiles start at the same time at the same place and travel in opposite directions. One travels at the rate of 45 kilometers per hour and the other at the rate of 40 kilometers per hour. In how many hours will they be 255 kilometers apart?

2. Two boys on bicycles start from the same place at the same time. One rides at the rate of 12 kilometers per hour and the other at 8 kilometers per hour. They travel in opposite directions. In how many hours will they be 24 kilometers apart?

3. One car traveling 40 kilometers an hour left a certain place 4 hours later than another car traveling in the same direction at the rate of 30 kilometers an hour. In how many hours will the faster car overtake the other?

4. Frank and Bob start from home in their cars and travel in opposite directions. Frank's rate of speed is twice Bob's. In 4 hours they are 480 kilometers apart. Find the rate at which each travels.

5. A freight train traveling at an average rate of 30 kilometers per hour is followed two hours later from the same station by a passenger train traveling at an average rate of 50 kilometers per hour. How many hours after the passenger train leaves will it pass the freight train?

6. Two jets leave Chicago at the same time, one flying east and one flying west. The rate of the second jet is 100 kilometers per hour faster than the first. In 3 hours, they are 4800 kilometers apart. Find the rate at which each is traveling.

7. A plane leaves an airport at ten o'clock, flying due north. Another plane starts from the same airport at twelve o'clock, flying due south at twice the speed of the other plane. At two o'clock they are 1920 kilometers apart. Find the rate of speed of each.

8. Mildred left camp 4 hours after Margaret did. They traveled in opposite directions. Mildred drove at 48 kilometers per hour and Margaret at 72 kilometers per hour. How many hours after Mildred left were the two girls 1008 kilometers apart?

9. Ann starts from a certain place, traveling at 4 kilometers per hour. Five hours later, Fred starts from the same place and travels in the same direction at 6 kilometers per hour. In how many hours will Fred overtake Ann?

10. A freight train leaves a station and travels at a rate of 30 miles per hour. Two hours later, an express train leaves the same station traveling in the same direction at a rate of 50 miles per hour. In how many hours will the express train overtake the freight train?

11. Meg left home on her bicycle traveling at the rate of 6 miles per hour. One hour later, her twin sister, Mary, set out on the same route traveling at the rate of 8 miles per hour. In how many hours will Mary overtake Meg?

B

12. How far can a person drive out into the country at an average rate of 64 kilometers per hour and return over the same road at an average rate of 48 kilometers per hour if the total trip takes 7 hours? (HINT: Use the table at the right. Remember that the distance going is the same as the distance returning.)

	r	t	d = rt
Going	64	t	64t
Returning	48	7 − t	48(7 − t)

13. A round trip in a helicopter lasted $4\frac{1}{2}$ hours. The average rate going was 160 km/h; the average rate returning was 80 km/h. What was the helicopter's greatest distance from the heliport?

14. A pilot plans to make a round-trip flight lasting 2.5 hours. How far can the pilot plan to go if the rate going is 480 kilometers per hour and the rate returning is 320 kilometers per hour?

15. Lisa left home in a car that was traveling at the rate of 48 kilometers per hour. She walked home at the rate of 6 kilometers per hour. The round trip took 1.5 hours. How far did Lisa ride?

16. A cyclist had been traveling 24 km/h for 8 hours when he was overtaken by a motorist who left the same starting point 5 hours after the cyclist. Find the motorist's speed.

17. Dick jogs from his house to school at a rate of 9 kilometers per hour. On the return trip from school, he jogs at a rate of 6 kilometers per hour. The round trip takes 1 hour 15 minutes. How far is the school from Dick's house?

18. A train traveling at 80 kilometers per hour started from Westville toward Easton. An hour later, a train traveling at 64 kilometers per hour started from Easton toward Westville. Westville and Easton are 656 kilometers apart. How long will it take the engines of the two trains to pass each other? (The trains are on parallel tracks.)

5-3 Graphing Ordered Pairs

A flat surface, such as a chalkboard, can be thought of as representing a **plane.** A plane extends on and on in all directions. To locate, or **graph,** points on a plane, you use two number lines that are **perpendicular** to each other. (That is, they meet at a 90° angle.) The horizontal number line is called the **x axis;** the vertical number line is called the **y axis.**

To graph a point P in a plane, you use an **ordered pair** of numbers

$$(x, y).$$

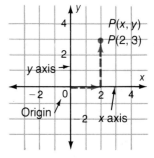

The first number, x, shows distance to the right or left of the vertical axis. The second number, y, shows distance above or below the horizontal axis. Thus, in the figure at the right, $P(2, 3)$ is 2 units to the right of the y axis and 3 units above the x axis.

The axes cross at the **origin.** The origin is represented by the ordered pair $(0, 0)$.

EXAMPLE 1 Graph each point on the same set of axes.

    a. $Q(3, 4)$ **b.** $R(-6, -2)$ **c.** $S(6, -1)$ **d.** $T(-5, 5)$

Solutions: **a.** For $Q(3, 4)$: Start at the origin. Move 3 units to the right, then 4 units up.

    b. For $R(-6, -2)$: Start at the origin. Move 6 units to the left, then 2 units down.

    c. For $S(6, -1)$: Start at the origin. Move 6 units to the right, then 1 unit down.

    d. For $T(-5, 5)$: Start at the origin. Move 5 units to the left, then 5 units up.

The numbers of an ordered pair are the **coordinates** of a point. The first number, or **x coordinate,** is the **abscissa;** the second number, or **y coordinate,** is the **ordinate.** Because the plane associates number pairs or coordinates with points, it is called the **coordinate plane.** The axes separate the coordinate plane into four regions or **quadrants.** *The axes are not in any quadrant.*

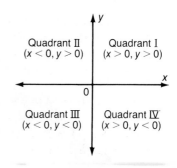

EXAMPLE 2 Name the quadrant or axis on which each point lies.

      a. $S(-1, -2)$ **b.** $P(6, -5)$ **c.** $V(0, -4)$ **d.** $T(5, 0)$

Solutions: Graph the points.

    a. S is in **Quadrant III.**

    b. P is in **Quadrant IV.**

    c. V is on the **y axis.**

    d. T is on the **x axis.**

CLASSROOM EXERCISES

One coordinate of each point shown on the diagram is given. What is the other coordinate?

1. $A(4, ?)$ 2. $B(?, 6)$ 3. $C(-3.5, ?)$

4. $D(?, 6)$ 5. $E(-6, ?)$ 6. $F(?, -5)$

7. $G(?, -5.5)$ 8. $H(4, ?)$ 9. $I(?, -4.5)$

10. $J(?, 0)$ 11. $K(?, 4)$ 12. $L(?, -6)$

Name the quadrant or axis on which each point lies.

13. $R(0, 4)$ 14. $S(-8, -1)$ 15. $T(3, 3)$ 16. $U(-2, 0)$ 17. $V(-4, 5)$

18. $W(5, -6)$ 19. $A(0, -2)$ 20. $B(-3, 7)$ 21. $D(-6, 5)$ 22. $E(5, -4)$

WRITTEN EXERCISES

1. Graph these points on the same pair of coordinate axes.

    a. $A(-3, 4)$ **b.** $B(5, 2)$ **c.** $C(4, -3)$ **d.** $D(+5, -4)$ **e.** $E(6, 0)$

    f. $F(-4, 0)$ **g.** $G(0, 5)$ **h.** $H(0, -3)$ **i.** $I(-4, -4)$ **j.** $J(0, 0)$

2. Name the quadrant or axis on which each point in Exercise 1 lies.

Give the abscissa and the ordinate for these points in Exercise 1.

3. A 4. D 5. G 6. I 7. J

8. Name the coordinates for each point graphed at the right.

9. Name the ordinate of every point on the x axis.

10. Name the abscissa of every point on the y axis.

Name the quadrant or axis on which each point lies.

11. $(-3, -2)$ **12.** $(4, -1)$ **13.** $(-5, 6)$ **14.** $(2, 5)$ **15.** $(5, -4)$

16. $(3, 0)$ **17.** $(0, -\pi)$ **18.** $(0, 0)$ **19.** $(-1, 4)$ **20.** $(\pi, -\pi)$

21. $P(x, y)$ when $x > 0$ and $y > 0$ **22.** $Q(x, y)$ when $x < 0$ and $y < 0$

23. $R(x, y)$ when $x > 9$ and $y < 0$ **24.** $T(x, y)$ when $x < 0$ and $y > 0$

25. Plot each set of points A–E. Connect the points of each set in order. The result should be a familiar picture.

A: $\{(-2, 6), (1, 6), (4, 5), (6, 4), (7, 2), (7, 0), (6, -2\frac{1}{4}), (5, -4), (5, -9),$
$(2, -9), (3, -4), (3, -3), (1, -3), (-2, -2\frac{1}{4}), (-3, -2), (-4, -4),$
$(-5, -9), (-8, -9), (-6, -3), (-6, 1), (-9, 1), (-8\frac{1}{2}, 2\frac{1}{4}), (-11, 3),$
$(-12, 4), (-13, 6), (-12, 8), (-10, 10), (-9, 9), (-11, 7), (-11, 5),$
$(-10, 5), (-8, 7), (-5, 7), (-4, 8), (-3, 8), (-2, 7), (-2, 6), (-2, 5),$
$(-3, 3), (-4, 1), (-5, 0), (-6, 2), (-6, 3\frac{1}{2})\}$

B: $\{(7, 2), (8, 0), (9, -2), (10, -3), (11, -3)\}$

C: $\{(6, -2\frac{1}{4}), (6, -9), (5, -9)\}$

D: $\{(-2, -2\frac{1}{4}), (-3, -4), (-4, -9), (-5, -9)\}$ **E:** $\{(-7, 5)\}$

B

A fly walks along a certain path in the coordinate plane. List the coordinates, $P(x, y)$, of three points in its path. Draw a graph of the path and describe the graph.

Example: The fly walks along points with an ordinate of 2.

Solution: $(5, 2)$; $(0, 2)$; $(-7\frac{1}{2}, 2)$ ⟵ **Choose some points on the path.**

⟵ **Graph the points. Connect them with a line.**

A horizontal line 2 units above the x axis.

26. The fly walks along points with an abscissa of 3.

27. The fly walks along points with an ordinate of -4.

28. The fly walks along points with an ordinate of 0.

29. The fly walks along points with an abscissa of 0.

30. The fly walks along points whose x coordinates are positive and whose y coordinates are 5.

31. The fly walks along points whose x and y coordinates are opposites. (HINT: See the figure at the right.)

32. The fly walks along points whose distance from the origin is 6.

33. Describe the graph of the set of all points that have the same ordinate.

34. Describe the graph of the set of all points that have the same abscissa.

35. What is the graph of the set of all points that have negative abscissas?

Each of Exercises 36–41 lists three vertices of a rectangle. Graph the vertices. Then sketch the rectangle and give the coordinate of the fourth vertex.

36. $(-3, -3)$, $(-7, -5)$, $(-7, -3)$
37. $(-7, 3)$, $(-4, 3)$, $(-7, 5)$
38. $(6, 8)$, $(7, 2)$, $(7, 8)$
39. $(0, 3\frac{1}{2})$, $(6, -4)$, $(6, 3\frac{1}{2})$
40. $(-6, 1)$, $(-1, 5)$, $(-6, 5)$
41. $(-5, -1)$, $(-8, -4)$, $(-6, -6)$

Ⓒ Each of Exercises 42–47 lists three vertices of a parallelogram. Graph the vertices. Then locate three points, each of which could be the fourth vertex. Give the coordinates of all three points.

42. $(-3, -3)$, $(-7, -5)$, $(-7, -3)$
43. $(-7, 3)$, $(-4, 3)$, $(-7, 5)$
44. $(6, 8)$, $(7, 2)$, $(7, 8)$
45. $(3, 4)$, $(2, 7)$, $(3, 7)$
46. $(-6, 1)$, $(-1, 5)$, $(-6, 5)$
47. $(-6, 8)$, $(-8, 5)$, $(-1, 6)$

Points in a plane can also be located by using an ordered pair of numbers to show distance along a ray and to show angle measure.

Example: Begin with a horizontal ray to represent 0°. Choose a unit of length and mark off distances along the way.

To locate $A(3, 30°)$ draw a second ray that makes an angle of 30° with the first. Mark the second ray, 30°. Mark off three units on the 30° ray.

Coordinates such as (3, 30°) are called **polar coordinates.** Note that distance is given first in the ordered pair, and the angle measure is second.

48. Use polar coordinates to locate each point in the figure at the right.

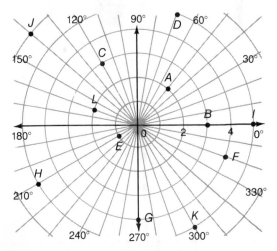

Review

Solve each equation for x. Check each solution. *(Section 5-1)*

1. $\frac{x}{4} = 9$ **2.** $x + 7 = 24$ **3.** $-3x + 1 = 10$ **4.** $4x - 6 = 16$

Solve each problem. *(Section 5-2)*

5. Jackie and Joel started out from the same place at the same time. Jackie jogged at 6 miles per hour, and Joel bicycled at 20 miles per hour in the opposite direction. In how many hours will they be 65 miles apart?

6. A local bus traveling at a rate of 50 kilometers per hour was passed by an express bus traveling at a rate of 75 kilometers per hour. The express bus left the terminal one hour later than the local bus. How far had the buses traveled?

7. Graph these points on the same coordinate axes. *(Section 5-3)*

  a. $A(10, 0)$ **b.** $B(12, -5)$ **c.** $C(4, -9)$ **d.** $D(-4, -9)$ **e.** $E(-9, 0)$
  f. $F(-9, 4)$ **g.** $G(4, 9)$ **h.** $H(0, 9)$ **i.** $I(0, 10)$ **j.** $J(12, 5)$

8. Name the quadrant or axis on which each point in Exercise 1 lies. *(Section 5-3)*

9. Name the abscissa and the ordinate for each point in Exercise 1. *(Section 5-3)*

Puzzle

Copy the coordinate axes shown at the right. Graph the ordered pairs in set **A** in the order listed and join each point to the next.

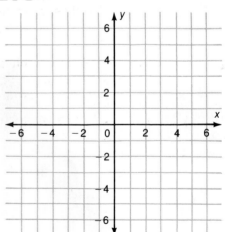

A: $\{(0, 6), (\frac{1}{2}, 5\frac{1}{2}), (\frac{1}{2}, 4), (1\frac{1}{2}, 4\frac{1}{2}), (2, 4),$
$(\frac{1}{2}, 3), (\frac{1}{2}, 2), (1\frac{1}{2}, 1\frac{1}{2}), (2\frac{1}{2}, 2), (2\frac{1}{2}, 3\frac{1}{2}),$
$(3\frac{1}{4}, 4), (3\frac{1}{4}, 2\frac{1}{2}), (4\frac{1}{4}, 3\frac{1}{4}), (5, 3), (5, 2\frac{1}{4}),$
$(4, 1\frac{1}{2}), (5, 1), (4, \frac{1}{2}), (3, 1), (2, \frac{1}{2}), (2, 0)\}$

Now graph the points in sets **B, C,** and **D** to obtain a reflection of the first graph. Use the same axes.

  B: $\{(0, 6), (-\frac{1}{2}, 5\frac{1}{2}), (-\frac{1}{2}, 4), \cdots, (-2, 0)\}$

  C: $\{(0, -6), (\frac{1}{2}, -5\frac{1}{2}), (\frac{1}{2}, -4), \cdots, (2, 0)\}$

  D: $\{(0, -6), (-\frac{1}{2}, -5\frac{1}{2}), (-\frac{1}{2}, -4), \cdots, (-2, 0)\}$

Career Applications: Navigation

Airplane pilots, ship captains, and others use a special coordinate system to describe the location of points on the surface of the earth. The system uses degrees of <u>latitude</u> and <u>longitude</u> to locate points.

Latitudes measure distance in degrees north (°N) or south (°S) of the **equator** (Latitude 0°). **Longitudes** measure distance in degrees east (°E) or west (°W) of the **prime meridian** (Longitude 0°). Points on the globe are described by the ordered pair (latitude, longitude). You can see from the globe at the right that the origin (Lat. 0°, Long. 0°) is the point where the equator and the prime meridian meet.

The table below gives the ordered pairs for several cities.

City	Location (Latitude, Longitude)	City	Location (Latitude, Longitude)
Cairo	(30°N, 31°E)	Paris	(49°N, 2°E)
Calcutta	(23°N, 88°E)	Rio de Janeiro	(23°S, 43°W)
Chicago	(42°N, 88°W)	Rome	(42°N, 13°E)
London	(52°N, 0°)	Sydney	(34°S, 151°E)
Los Angeles	(34°N, 118°W)	Tokyo	(36°N, 140°E)
New York	(41°N, 74°W)	Vancouver	(49°N, 123°W)

You can use the ordered pairs to compare the location of the cities in the table.

EXAMPLE 1 Use the table to find each of the following.

  a. The city directly east of Chicago

  b. The two cities that are the same distance from the equator

Solutions: **a. Rome** (same latitude as Chicago, 42°N)

  b. Los Angeles (34°N) and **Sydney** (34°S)

You can also use the measure of longitude of the cities to compare the time in each place. The diagram at the right shows how the longitude of a place affects its time zone. Note that each zone spans 15° of longitude.

The **zone description (ZD)** of a point is an integer between 12 and −12. The ZD is positive for points west of the prime meridian, and negative for points east. Comparing the ZD of two points allows you to find the difference in local times. (A point in Zone +1 is one hour earlier than a point in Zone 0.)

EXAMPLE 2 Use the table on page 174 to find the ZD of Chicago and Rome. Then find the difference in local times.

Solution: 1 Chicago's longitude is 88°W, and Rome's longitude is 13°E.

2 Divide the longitude of each city by 15. Find the quotient to the nearest whole number.

Chicago: $\frac{88}{15} \approx 5.87 \approx 6$ Rome: $\frac{13}{15} \approx 0.87 \approx 1$

3 Assign a positive or negative number to each ZD.

ZD for Chicago: +6 ZD for Rome: −1

4 Find the difference between the zone factors.

$6 - (-1) = 7$

Chicago and Rome are **7 hours** apart.

EXERCISES

In Exercises 1–22, use the table on page 174.

1. Find the city that is farthest from the equator.

2. Find the city that is farthest from the prime meridian.

3. Find the city that is located on the prime meridian

4. Find the city that is farthest from London.

5. Find the two cities that are the same distance from the prime meridian.

6. Find the city that is the same distance from the equator as Calcutta.

7. Find the city that is directly east of Vancouver.

8. Find the city that is directly north of Bogotá (5°N, 74°W).

Find the ZD of each of the following cities.

9. London   10. Chicago   11. Calcutta   12. Tokyo

13. Sydney   14. Los Angeles   15. Rio de Janeiro   16. Rome

Find the difference in local times between each pair of cities.

17. Chicago and London

18. Sydney and Tokyo

19. Los Angeles and Calcutta

20. Rio de Janeiro and London

21. Find the local time in New York when it is 10:30 A.M. in Vancouver.

22. Find the local time in Cairo when it is 7:15 P.M. in Tokyo.

5-4 Relations and Functions

At his part time job, Jim Noble is paid at the rate of $6.00 per hour. The equation

$$e = 6h$$

shows the relation between Jim's earnings, e, and the number of hours worked, h.

TIME CARD	*Jim Noble*
Monday	3 hours
Tuesday	
Wednesday	2 hours
Thursday	
Friday	
Saturday	4 hours
TOTAL	9 hours

This relation can be shown in several ways.

Kind of Description	Description
1. Words	1. Multiply 6 and the number of hours worked.
2. Equation	2. $e = 6h$
3. Table of ordered pairs	3. <table><tr><td>h</td><td>0</td><td>1</td><td>2</td><td>3</td><td>4</td><td>5</td><td>6</td><td>7</td><td>8</td><td>9</td></tr><tr><td>e</td><td>0</td><td>6</td><td>12</td><td>18</td><td>24</td><td>30</td><td>36</td><td>42</td><td>48</td><td>54</td></tr></table>
4. Graph	4.

Some relations cannot be described by an equation. For this reason, we use ordered pairs to define a *relation*.

Definition

> A **relation** is a set of ordered pairs.

EXAMPLE 1 A railroad divided its line into zones and charged one fare to any station in the zone.

Station	1, 2, or 3	4 or 5	6, 7, or 8
Fare	$3.50	$5.00	$7.10

List the ordered pairs of the relation and graph the relation.

Solution: $\{(1, 3.50), (2, 3.50), (3, 3.50), (4, 5.00),$ ← **Associate each station with a fare.**
$(5, 5.00), (6, 7.10), (7, 7.10), (8, 7.10)\}$

← **Graph the relation.**

For the ordered pairs of a relation, the set of all first coordinates is the **domain** of the relation. The set of all second coordinates of the ordered pairs is the **range** of the relation. The letter, D, is often used to represent the domain of a relation; the letter, R, is used to represent the range.

EXAMPLE 2 Give the domain and range of the relation described in Example 1.

Solution: {(1, 3.50), (2, 3.50), (3, 3.50), (4, 5.00) ←————— **Relation**
(5, 5.00), (6, 7.10), (7, 7.10), (8, 7.10)}

D = {1, 2, 3, 4, 5, 6, 7, 8} ←————— **Domain: Set of all first coordinates of each ordered pair**

R = {3.50, 5.00, 7.10} ←————— **Range: Set of all second coordinates of each ordered pair**

You can find the domain and range of a relation from its graph.

EXAMPLE 3 The graph at the right defines a relation.

Express the relation as a set of ordered pairs. Then give the domain and range of the relation.

Solution: Read the set of ordered pairs from the graph.

{(−3, 3), (−2, 2), (−1, 1), (0, 0),
(1, −1), (2, −2), (3, −3)}

D = {−3, −2, −1, 0, 1, 2, 3} ←————— **Domain: Set of all first coordinates of each ordered pair**

R = {3, 2, 1, 0, −1, −2, −3} ←————— **Range: Set of all second coordinates of each ordered pair**

A *function* is a special kind of relation.

Definition | A **function** is a relation for which no two ordered pairs have the same first element.

Relation	Ordered Pairs with the Same First Elements	Is the Relation a Function?
{(0, 0, (1, 11), (2, 22), (3, 33), (4, 44)}	None	**Yes**
{(1, 7), (1, 14), (1, 21)}	(1, 7), (1, 14), (1, 21)	**No**
{(0, 0), (1, 1), (2, 4), (3, 9), (4, 16)}	None	**Yes**
{(1, 1.50), (2, 1.50), (3, 1.50), (4, 1.75)}	None	**Yes**
{(10, 20), (11, 30), (12, 40), (10, 50)}	(10, 20), (10, 50)	**No**
{(−2, −2), (−1, −2), (0, −2), (3, −2)}	None	**Yes**

The graph of a relation shows whether it is a function. If a vertical line can be drawn through two or more points of the graph, the points have the same *x* coordinate, so the relation is *not* a function. This is called the **Vertical Line Test.**

EXAMPLE 4   Use the graphs to tell whether each relation is a function.

  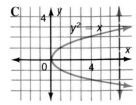

Solutions: **A** and **B** are functions.
C is not a function because a vertical line will intersect its graph in more than one point.

CLASSROOM EXERCISES

Give the domain and range for each relation.

1. $\{(0, 1), (2, 3), (4, 5), (6, 7)\}$
2. $\{(-1, 1), (-2, 2), (-3, 3), (-4, 4)\}$
3. $\{(0, -2), (1, -2), (2, -2), (3, -2)\}$
4. $\{(\frac{1}{2}, \frac{1}{4}), (\frac{3}{2}, \frac{1}{8}), (2, \frac{7}{2})\}$

State whether the given set of ordered pairs is a function. When a relation is not a function, tell why it is not.

5. $\{(1, 2), (0, 1), (1, 3), (2, 1)\}$
6. $\{(0, 0), (-1, -1), (2, 2), (3, 3)\}$
7. $\{(-3, 5), (-1, 5), (3, 5), (7, 5)\}$
8. $\{(-6, -5), (-6, -2), (-6, 0), (-6, 3)\}$

WRITTEN EXERCISES

A   Give the domain and range for each relation.

1. $\{(1, 50), (2, 100), (3, 150), (4, 200), (5, 250)\}$
2. $\{(-1, 1), (-2, 4), (-3, 9), (-4, 16), (-5, 25)\}$
3. $\{(1, \pi), (2, 4\pi), (3, 9\pi), (4, 16\pi), (5, 25\pi)\}$
4. $\{(1, \pi), (2, 2\pi), (3, 3\pi), (4, 4\pi), (5, 5\pi)\}$
5. The graph at the right defines a relation. Define this relation by listing the ordered pairs that are the coordinates of the points.
6. The relation in Exercise 5 cannot be defined easily by a simple sentence, but it can be defined easily by a table. Construct such a table for this relation.
7. Give the domain and range of the relation in Exercise 5.

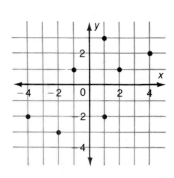

In Exercises 8–10, write the set of ordered pairs for each relation. Then give the domain and range for each relation.

 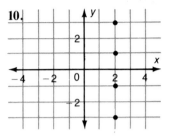

8. **9.** **10.**

Write a relation for the given domain and range. Write all the possible ordered pairs for the relation.

11. Domain: $\{1, 2, 3\}$; range: $\{4\}$

12. Domain: $\{-6\}$; range: $\{-2, 0, 5\}$

13. Domain: $\{-5, 0\}$; range: $\{0, 5\}$

14. Domain: $\{-2, -1, 0\}$; range: $\{3, 5\}$

Write *Yes* or *No* to tell whether the relation is also a function.

15. **16.** **17.** **18.** **19.**

Determine whether each relation in Exercises 20–27 is also a function. When a relation is not a function, state why it is not.

20. $\{(-1, 1), (-2, 4), (-3, 9), (-4, 16), (-5, 25)\}$

21. $\{(-3, -3), (0, 0), (3, 3), (5, 5)\}$

22. $\{(1, 5¢), (2, 10¢), (3, 10¢), (4, 15¢), (5, 20¢), (6, 20¢)\}$

23. $\{(-5, 5), (-1, 1), (2, -2), (4, -4)\}$

24. $\{(5, 8), (5, 9), (6, 10), (6, 11), (7, 12), (7, 13)\}$

25. $\{(3, -2), (3, -1), (3, 0), (3, 1), (3, 2)\}$

26. $\{(-2, 4), (-1, 4), (0, 4), (1, 4), (2, 4)\}$

27. $\{(-7, 7), (-5, 5), (0, 0), (5, 5), (7, 7)\}$

APPLICATIONS: Using Functions and Relations

In Exercises 28–33, write the ordered pairs for each relation. Then give the domain and range of the relation.

28. **Time (t)**	8 A.M.	9 A.M.	10 A.M.	11 A.M.	12 noon
Temperature (T)	4°	8°	8°	10°	11°

29.

Year (y)	1976	1978	1980	1982	1984 (est.)
Population (P)	11,000	12,000	13,000	15,000	16,000

B

30. $N = \dfrac{A}{30}$, a formula for finding the number of rolls of wallpaper needed to cover a rectangular wall, where A is the area of the wall and $A \in \{150, 180, 210\}$

31. $s = 16t^2$, the formula for the distance, s, a freely falling object falls in t seconds, where $t \in \{4, 6, 8, 10\}$

32. $A = 6s^2$, the formula for the surface area, A, of a cube, where $s \in \{5, 10, 15, 20\}$

33. $V = \dfrac{4}{3}\pi r^3$, the formula for the volume, V, of a sphere, where r is the length of the radius and $r \in \{1, 2, 3, 5\}$. Use 3.14 for π and round each value for V to the nearest whole number.

34. Pencils are selling at 3 for 25¢ or at 10¢ each.

a. Complete the table below showing the cost in cents of x pencils if x is 10 or less.

When x is	0	1	2	3	4	5	6	7	8	9	10
Cost is	0	10	20	25	?	?	?	?	?	?	?

b. Give the domain and range of this relation.

35. Which of the relations in Exercises 28–34 are also functions?

36. A brand of soup sells at 3 cans for 89¢ or at 30¢ per can.

a. Make a table that shows the cost of n cans if n is 10 or less.

b. Give the domain and range of this relation.

37. Suppose that the cost of mailing a package is 20¢ per ounce or fraction of an ounce. Thus, the cost for $2\frac{1}{4}$ ounces is $3 \times 20¢$, or 60¢.

a. Complete this table that shows the cost, C, in cents for a package weighing w ounces.

W	0	$\frac{1}{2}$	$\frac{3}{4}$	1	$1\frac{1}{2}$	$1\frac{7}{8}$	2	$2\frac{1}{8}$	3	$3\frac{1}{2}$	4	5
C	0	20	20	20	?	?	?	?	?	?	?	?

b. Complete this sentence: If the amount is 5 ounces or less, then the cost of mail will be any one of the numbers __?__.

c. Part of the graph is shown at the right. Complete the graph for values of w from $w = 0$ through $w = 4$.

5-5 Graphing Linear Equations

An equation such as

$$5x - 9 = 11$$

is an equation in one variable, x. It has *one solution*, 4, because $5 \cdot 4 - 9 = 11$ and this is the only value of x for which $5x - 9 = 11$. An equation such as

$$y - 2x = 3$$

has two variables, x and y. The solution of this equation is the *set of ordered pairs* (x, y) for which $y - 2x = 3$. For example, the ordered pairs $(0, 3)$, $\left(-\frac{3}{2}, 0\right)$, and $(2, 7)$ are some of the solutions of $y - 2x = 3$.

Check: $y - 2x = 3$ $\qquad$ $y - 2x = 3$ $\qquad$ $y - 2x = 3$

$3 - 2(0) \overset{?}{=} 3$ $\qquad$ $0 - 2(-\frac{3}{2}) \overset{?}{=} 3$ $\qquad$ $7 - 2(2) \overset{?}{=} 3$

$3 \overset{?}{=} 3$ Yes ✔ $\qquad$ $3 \overset{?}{=} 3$ Yes ✔ $\qquad$ $3 \overset{?}{=} 3$ Yes ✔

To solve an equation such as $y - 2x = 3$, you find *all* its solutions for the given replacement set. When the replacement set for x is {real numbers}, there is an infinite number of ordered pairs that are solutions. In such cases, you usually show the solution set as a graph.

EXAMPLE 1 Graph the equation $y - 2x = 3$.

Solution: ① Solve the equation for y. ⟶ $y - 2x = 3$

$$y = 2x + 3$$

② Make a table. First, choose values for x. To find y, substitute these values in $y = 2x + 3$.

Replace x with -3. $\qquad$ Replace x with 0. $\qquad$ Replace x with 1.

$y = 2x + 3$ $\qquad\qquad$ $y = 2x + 3$ $\qquad\qquad$ $y = 2x + 3$

$y = 2(-3) + 3$ $\qquad$ $y = 2(0) + 3$ $\qquad$ $y = 2(1) + 3$

$y = -6 + 3$ $\qquad\quad$ $y = 0 + 3$ $\qquad\quad$ $y = 2 + 3$

$y = -3$ $\qquad\qquad\;$ $y = 3$ $\qquad\qquad\;$ $y = 5$

x	-3	0	1
y	-3	3	5

③ Graph the points.

Since x can be any real number, draw a line containing the points.

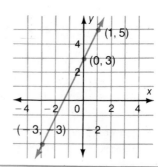

An equation whose graph is a straight line is a **linear equation.** Since two points determine a straight line, you need to plot only two points to graph a linear equation. However, it is useful to plot a third point as a check.

EXAMPLE 2 Graph each of the following in the coordinate plane.

a. $x = 2$

b. $y = -3$

Solutions:

a. All ordered pairs with an x coordinate of 2 are solutions of the equation. Thus, the graph is a vertical line.

b. All ordered pairs with a y coordinate of -3 are solutions of the equation. Thus, the graph is a horizontal line.

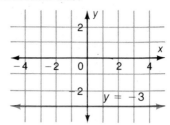

Unless stated otherwise, assume that the replacement set for each variable in a linear equation is {real numbers}.

Here is another way to describe a linear equation.

Definition

> An equation that can be written in the form
> $$Ax + By = C$$
> where A, B, and C are real numbers and A and B are not both zero, is a **linear equation in two variables.**

Thus, by definition, equations such as $3x - 2y = -6$ and $y - 5 = 0$ are linear equations; equations such as $x^2 + y = 9$ and $xy = 4$ are not.

A function whose ordered pairs satisfy a linear equation is a **linear function.** Thus, the equation $y - 2x = 3$ defines a linear function.

CLASSROOM EXERCISES

Complete the tables.

1. $y = 2x$

x	0	2	4	6
y	0	4	?	?

2. $y = 4x$

x	0	1	2	3	4
y	?	?	?	?	?

3. $y = 3x$

x	0	-1	-2	-3
y	0	-3	?	?

4. $y = -2x + 3$

x	-3	-1	0	1	3
y	9	?	?	?	?

Complete the tables.

5. $y = 2x + 4$

x	-3	-1	0	1	3
y	-2	2	?	?	?

6. $y = -2x + 4$

x	-3	-1	0	1	3
y	10	?	?	?	?

7. $y = -3x + 5$

x	-3	-2	-1	0	1
y	?	?	?	?	?

8. $y = 3x + 5$

x	-3	-2	-1	0	1
y	?	?	?	?	?

Determine whether the given ordered pair of numbers is a solution of the given sentence. Answer *Yes* or *No*.

9. $x + y = 5$; $(0, 3)$

10. $x - 3y = 16$; $(16, 0)$

11. $y - x = 10$; $(-\frac{1}{2}, 9\frac{1}{2})$

12. $y - x = 0$; $(2.6, 2.6)$

13. $4x + 3y = -12$; $(3, 0)$

14. $2x + y = 10$; $(-5, 0)$

15. $y = 7x$; $(0, 0)$

16. $y - 7x = 0$; $(\frac{1}{7}, -1)$

17. $y - 8 = 0$; $(3, 8)$

State whether each equation is linear. Answer *Yes* or *No*.

18. $3x + 7y = 19$

19. $y = 4x^2 - 7$

20. $7x^2 - 5xy + 9y^2 = 15$

21. $y = 3x$

22. $y - 8x = 0$

23. $\frac{y}{3} = 2x + 1$

State whether the graph of each equation is a straight line. Answer *Yes* or *No*.

24. $y + 1 = 5$

25. $2x - y = 8$

26. $y = \frac{4}{3}x - 1$

27. $y = 2x^2 - 1$

28. $xy = 1$

29. $x - y = 0$

WRITTEN EXERCISES

A   Graph each linear equation in the coordinate plane.

1. $y = 4x - 3$

2. $y = -3x$

3. $y = -2x - 4$

4. $y = -2x + 3$

5. $y = x - 5$

6. $y = 5 - x$

7. $x + y = 10$

8. $x + y = 4$

9. $y = \frac{1}{2}x$

10. $y = \frac{1}{3}x$

11. $y = -\frac{1}{4}x$

12. $y = -\frac{1}{2}x$

13. $2x + y = 4$

14. $3x + y = 6$

15. $2x + 3y = 6$

16. $3x + 4y = 12$

17. $2x - y = 4$

18. $3x - 2y = 0$

19. $y = -4$

20. $y = 7$

21. $y = -9$

22. $x = 3$

23. $x = 6\frac{1}{2}$

24. $x = -8$

B   Equations of the form **By = C** where $B \neq 0$ define **constant functions.**

In Exercises 25-28, complete the table of values for each constant function. Then graph each function.

25. $y = 3$

x	-2	0	2
y	?	?	?

26. $y + 5 = 0$

x	-1	0	3
y	?	?	?

27. $y = 0$

x	−4	0	4
y	?	?	?

28. $2y - 3 = 0$

x	−3	0	6
y	?	?	?

Refer to the graphs in Exercises 25–28 to complete the statements in Exercises 29–31.

29. The graph of a constant function is the __?__ axis or a line parallel to the __?__ axis.

30. The domain of a constant function is __?__ .

31. The range of a constant function is __?__ .

Complete the table for each relation in Exercises 32–35. Then graph the relation.

32. $x = 3$

x	?	?	?
y	−3	0	4

33. $x - 8 = 0$

x	?	?	?
y	−3	0	4

34. $x = 0$

x	?	?	?
y	−5	0	5

35. $\frac{2}{3}x = -6$

x	?	?	?
y	−2	0	2

Refer to the tables and graphs in Exercises 32–35 to complete the statements in Exercises 36–39.

36. The graph of each relation in Exercises 32–35 is the __?__ axis, or a line parallel to the __?__ axis.

37. The range of each relation in Exercises 32–35 is __?__ .

38. An equation of the form $Ax = C$, $A \neq 0$ defines a __?__ (relation or function).

39. A relation of the form $Ax = C$, $A \neq 0$ does *not* define a function because __?__ .

C For each equation, write the coordinates of the points (0, y) and (x, 0).

40. $y = 2x - 6$

41. $9y - 26 = 2x$

42. $2x + 3y = 6$

43. $3x + y = 4$

44. $y = -2x$

45. $3(2x - 4) = 2(y - 5)$

In Exercises 46–50, graph each function. Tell whether each function is a linear function. Give the domain and range of each function.

46. The function pairs each positive real number with the number 1, the number 0 with 0, and each negative real number with the number −1.

47. The function pairs each positive real number with the number 0, and each negative real number x with itself.

48. The function pairs each nonnegative real number x, with itself, and each negative real number x with the opposite of x.

49. The function pairs each real number x with its absolute value, $|x|$.

50. The function pairs each real number with $-|x|$.

5-6 Graphs and Estimation

Graphs of functions can be useful in estimating answers. For example, to determine the distance to an approaching thunderstorm.

1. Count the number of seconds between a flash of lightning and the resulting sound of thunder.

2. Use this number to read the distance from a graph that shows the distance sound travels in air as a function of time.

EXAMPLE For every 3 seconds, sound travels about 1 kilometer. That is, $s = \frac{1}{3}t$ where s is the distance in kilometers and t is the time in seconds.

Questions	Solutions

a. Write three ordered pairs for this function. Note that t cannot be negative.

a.

t	0	2	4
s	0	$\frac{2}{3}$	$1\frac{1}{3}$

b. Use the ordered pairs to graph the function. (Note the scale on each axis.)

b.

c. Use the graph to estimate the distance to an approaching thunderstorm when a person counts 6 seconds between the lightning and the thunder.

c. Read from the graph. For $t = 6$, s is about **2 kilometers**.

d. Use the graph to estimate the distance when $t = 7.5$ seconds.

d. For $t = 7.5$, s is about **2.5 kilometers**.

CLASSROOM EXERCISES

Suppose that a new oil filter for a car costs $6.00 and that oil costs $1.00 per quart. That is, $C = 6 + q$, where C is the total cost of a new filter and an oil change, and q is the number of quarts of oil used.

1. Write three ordered pairs for the function. Let $q = 0$, 2, and 3.

2. Use the ordered pairs in Exercise 1 to graph the function.

3. Use the graph to estimate C when $q = 2\frac{1}{2}$.

4. Use the graph to estimate C when $q = 3\frac{3}{4}$.

WORD PROBLEMS

A   Sound travels in water at a rate of about
1.5 kilometers per second. That is,
$s = 1.5t$, where t is the time in seconds
and s is the distance in kilometers. Use
this function in Exercises 1–5.

Distance (kilometers) vs **Time (seconds)**

1. Write three ordered pairs for this function.
   Let $t = 0$, 4, and 6.

2. Use the ordered pairs in Exercise 1 to graph
   the function.

3. A ship using sonar finds that it takes sound waves
   0.5 second to reach the bottom of a lake. Use the graph in Exercise 2 to estimate the depth of the lake at this point.

4. A ship using sonar finds that it takes sound waves 7 seconds to reach a point
   at the bottom of a body of water. Use the graph in Exercise 2 to estimate
   the depth at this point.

5. Use the graph in Exercise 2 to estimate how long it would take sound waves
   to reach a point 4 kilometers below the surface of the ocean.

The function $d = 0.2r$ represents the distance, d, in meters covered by a car traveling at a rate of r kilometers per hour
during the average driver's reaction time
of $\frac{3}{4}$ second. **Reaction time** is the length
of time between the moment a driver de-
cides to stop the car and the moment the
brakes are applied.

Distance (meters) vs **Speed (kilometers per hour)**

6. Write three ordered pairs for this function.
   Let $r = 16$, 48, and 80.

7. Use the ordered pairs in Exercise 6 to graph the function.

Use the graph in Exercise 7 to estimate how many meters a car traveling
at each rate will cover during a reaction time of $\frac{3}{4}$ second.

8. 32 kilometers per hour   9. 64 kilometers per hour   10. 88 kilometers per hour

The rate of sales tax for a certain state is
5%. Use this information in Exercises
11–19.

Amount of Tax (dollars) vs **Amount of Sales (dollars)**

11. Complete the table.

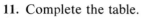

Amount of Sales, S	$100	$200	$300
Amount of Tax, t	?	?	?

12. Use the ordered pairs in Exercise 11 to graph the function. Assume that the graph is linear.

Use the graph in Exercise 12 to estimate the tax on each amount.

13. $50   14. $150   15. $400   16. $375   17. $225   18. $75

19. Write an equation that describes the amount of sales, S, as a function of the amount of tax, t.

The basic fee for renting a floor polisher is $5 plus an additional $2.50 for each hour of rental. Use this information for Exercises 20–25.

20. Complete the table.

Number of Hours (h)	2	4	6
Cost (C)	?	?	?

21. Use the ordered pairs in Exercise 20 to graph the function. Assume that the graph is linear.

Use the graph in Exercise 21 to estimate the rental cost for each number of hours.

22. 3 hours   23. 5 hours   24. $4\frac{1}{2}$ hours   25. $5\frac{1}{4}$ hours

26. Write an equation that describes the cost of rental, C, as a function of the number of hours, h.

B   A plane at an altitude of 22,000 feet begins to climb at the rate of 50 feet per second. Use this information for Exercises 27–32.

27. Complete the table.

Time, t, in seconds	2	4	6
Altitude, A, in feet	?	?	?

28. Use the ordered pairs in the table for Exercise 27 to graph the function. Assume that the graph is linear.

Use the graph in Exercise 28 to estimate the altitude of the plane for each time, t.

29. $t = 3$ seconds   30. $t = 5$ seconds   31. $t = 2.5$ seconds   32. $t = 8$ seconds

33. Write an equation that describes the altitude, A, of the plane as a function of the time, t, in seconds.

C   The cost of first class mail is a function of weight. In 1981, the cost for any weight up to, and including, 1 ounce rose to 20¢. Each additional ounce or fraction thereof cost 17¢. For example, 1.6 ounces cost 37¢ and 3.2 ounces cost 71¢.

Use this information and the graph at the right for Exercises 34–36.

34. Complete the table.

Weight	1.4 oz	2.7 oz	5.8 oz
Costs	?	?	?

35. This rate holds for 12 ounces and less. Thus, the domain of this function is all possible weights of mail less than or equal to 12 ounces. List the 12 numbers in the range of this function.

36. Graph this function for weights up to, and including, 5 ounces.

Review

Give the domain and range for each relation. *(Section 5-4)*

1. $\{(1, 12°), (2, 14°), (3, 8°), (4, 4°), (5, 6°), (6, -2°)\}$

2. $\{(1, \$10), (2, \$15), (3, \$25), (4, \$40), (5, \$60), (6, \$85)\}$

3. $\{(1, \pi), (2, \frac{3\pi}{2}), (2, 2\pi), (3, \frac{5\pi}{2}), (4, 3\pi)\}$

4. Write *Yes* or *No* to indicate whether each relation in Exercises 1–3 is also a function. *(Section 5-4)*

Graph each linear equation in the coordinate plane. *(Section 5-5)*

5. $y = 2x$ **6.** $y = -3x - 7$ **7.** $y = -3$ **8.** $x = 2$

In a movie theater, the projector is placed so that the picture is the same size as the screen. In a certain theater, the function $w = \frac{4}{9}d$ represents the relationship between the distance, d, from the projector to the screen and the width, w, of the picture.

Use this information for Exercises 9–11. *(Section 5-6)*

9. Write three ordered pairs for this function. Let $d = 9$, 18, and 36.

10. Use the ordered pairs to graph the function.

11. Estimate the width of the picture when the distance from the projector is 15 units.

REVIEW CAPSULE FOR SECTION 5-7

Simplify. *(Pages 56–58, 68–71)*

1. $-9 - (-4)$ **2.** $2 - 5$ **3.** $3 - (-2)$ **4.** $-6 - 3$

5. $0 - 10$ **6.** $0 - (-2)$ **7.** $9 - (-1)$ **8.** $-8 - (-11)$

9. $\frac{2-4}{4+2}$ **10.** $\frac{-6-2}{3-2}$ **11.** $\frac{-8-(-2)}{7-5}$ **12.** $\frac{2-2}{8-4}$

13. $\frac{-1-(-1)}{-2-6}$ **14.** $\frac{3-3}{2-(-1)}$ **15.** $\frac{3-(-1)}{2-3}$ **16.** $\frac{3-(-2)}{0-(-4)}$

5-7 Slope of a Line

When you talk about the grade, or steepness, of a certain road you can say that it rises a vertical distance of 100 feet over a horizontal distance of 400 feet. That is,

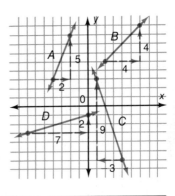

rise: 100
run: 400

$$\text{steepness} = \frac{\text{rise}}{\text{run}} = \frac{\text{vertical change}}{\text{horizontal change}} = \frac{100}{400} = \frac{1}{4}.$$

The measure of steepness is a ratio called *slope*. **A ratio** is the quotient of two numbers, such as $\frac{2}{5}$.

Definition

> The **slope** of a line is the ratio of the vertical change to the horizontal change between any two points on the line. That is,
>
> $$\text{slope} = \frac{\text{vertical change}}{\text{horizontal change}}, \ \textbf{(horizontal change} \neq \textbf{0).}$$

EXAMPLE 1 Find the slope of each line graphed at the right below.

Solutions:

Line	Vertical Change	Horizontal Change	Slope = $\dfrac{\text{Vertical Change}}{\text{Horizontal Change}}$
A	5	2	$\dfrac{5}{2}$
B	4	4	$\dfrac{4}{4}$, or 1
C	9	-3	$\dfrac{9}{-3}$, or -3
D	2	7	$\dfrac{2}{7}$

When you know the coordinates of any two points on a line, you can determine the slope of a line. First, you find the difference between the y coordinates, or the vertical change, and the difference between the x coordinates, or the horizontal change. Then you write the ratio of these differences.

EXAMPLE 2 Find the slope of the line containing the points $(1, 3)$ and $(6, 7)$.

Solution: Subtract the y coordinates first. Then subtract the x coordinates.

Graphing Relations and Functions **189**

$$7 - 3 = 4 \longleftarrow \text{Vertical change: difference of } y \text{ coordinates}$$
$$6 - 1 = 5 \longleftarrow \text{Horizontal change: difference of } x \text{ coordinates}$$
$$\text{slope} = \frac{4}{5} \longleftarrow \textbf{Slope} = \frac{\text{vertical change}}{\text{horizontal change}}$$

The ratio of the vertical change to the horizontal change is the same everywhere, no matter which two points are chosen. Thus, the slope of a given line is a constant.

Let $P_1(x_1, \ y_1)$ and $P_2(x_2, \ y_2)$ be any two points on the line graphed at the right. Determine the slope of the line.

$$y_2 - y_1 \longleftarrow \textbf{Vertical change}$$
$$x_2 - x_1 \longleftarrow \textbf{Horizontal change}$$
$$\text{slope} = \frac{y_2 - y_1}{x_2 - x_1} \longleftarrow \textbf{Slope} = \frac{\text{vertical change}}{\text{horizontal change}}$$

The letter m is customarily used to denote slope.

Definition

For any two points in a line, $P_1(x_1, \ y_1)$ and $P_2(x_2, \ y_2)$,

$$\text{slope} = m = \frac{\text{vertical change}}{\text{horizontal change}} = \frac{y_2 - y_1}{x_2 - x_1}, \ (x_2 - x_1 \ne 0).$$

EXAMPLE 3 Find the slope of the line containing the points $P_1(-4, 3)$ and $P_2(6, -9)$.

Solution: $m = \dfrac{y_2 - y_1}{x_2 - x_1}$

$$m = \frac{\overset{y_2 \quad y_1}{\overbrace{\downarrow \quad \downarrow}}}{\underset{x_2 \quad x_1}{\underbrace{6 - (-4)}}}$$

$$= \frac{-9 + (-3)}{6 + 4}$$

$$= \frac{-12}{10}, \text{ or } -\frac{6}{5}$$

Lines with positive slope rise from left to right.
Lines with negative slope fall from left to right.

Thus, the line in Example 3 falls from left to right.

EXAMPLE 4   Find the slope of the lines containing each pair of points.

a. $S(-1, -3)$ and $T(2, -3)$ **b.** $P(4, 5)$ and $N(4, 9)$

Solutions: **a.** $m = \dfrac{y_2 - y_1}{x_2 - x_1}$ **b.** $m = \dfrac{y_2 - y_1}{x_2 - x_1}$

$m = \dfrac{-3 - (-3)}{2 - (-1)}$ $m = \dfrac{9 - 5}{4 - 4}$ ⟵ **Cannot divide by 0**

$m = \dfrac{0}{2 + 1} = 0$ The slope of the line is **undefined.**

Example 4 suggests the following.

> The slope of any horizontal line is **0.**
>
> The slope of a vertical line is **undefined.**

CLASSROOM EXERCISES

Classify the slope of each line as *positive, negative,* or *equal to zero.* If the slope of a line is undefined, write *ND.*

1.   **2.**   **3.**   **4.**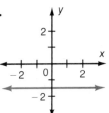

Find the slope of the line containing the given points.

5. $P(1, 2)$; $Q(-3, 5)$ **6.** $R(-5, -1)$; $S(-2, -4)$ **7.** $T(-3, -11)$; $V(2, -7)$

8. $M(4, -2)$; $R(3, 2)$ **9.** $W(6, -9)$; $N(-1, -1)$ **10.** $A(8, -2)$; $P(12, 1)$

11. $C(0, 0)$; $D(-4, 2)$ **12.** $F(3, -2)$; $H(0, 0)$ **13.** $E(7, 3)$; $G(9, 1)$

WRITTEN EXERCISES

A   Find the slope of each line from its graph.

1.   **2.**   **3.**   **4.**

5.   **6.**   **7.**   **8.**

Find the slope of the line containing the given points.

9. $R(3, 2)$; $N(6, 8)$ **10.** $S(7, 1)$; $T(5, 9)$ **11.** $A(-4, 3)$; $B(-8, 6)$

12. $Q(5, -2)$; $S(-7, 4)$ **13.** $G(-5, -1)$; $W(-11, -4)$ **14.** $T(-6, 3)$; $Q(-2, -9)$

15. $H(2, 6)$; $T(-2, -3)$ **16.** $J(3, -5)$; $K(-4, 9)$ **17.** $B(-8, 2)$; $C(10, -4)$

18. $P(0, 4)$; $S(-6, 4)$ **19.** $D(2, -8)$; $G(-1, -8)$ **20.** $E(-6, -2)$; $F(-6, 9)$

Find the slope, if it exists, of each side of the given figure.

21.   Triangle

22.   Rectangle

23.   Parallelogram

24.   Square

25.   Rhombus

26.   Trapezoid

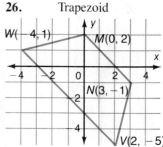

B   Determine whether the given points lie on the same line. (HINT: The slope is the same for all pairs of points on a line.)

27. $(-5, 11)$, $(0, 8)$, $(5, 5)$ **28.** $(0, 1)$, $(4, -2)$, $(6, -4)$

29. $(6, 3)$, $(3, 2)$, $(0, 0)$ **30.** $(4, 1)$, $(-1, 7)$, $(3, 3)$

31. Find y so that the line containing $(2, y)$ and $(-3, 4)$ has a slope of 2.

32. Find y so that the line containing $(5, 1)$ and $(6, y)$ has a slope of -3.

33. Find the slope of a line passing through $(a, 0)$ and $(0, a)$.

34. Find the slope of a line containing the origin and the point $P(40{,}000, -20{,}000)$.

35. Let $P_1(x_1, y_1)$ and $P_2(x_2, y_2)$ be any two points on the line graphed at the right. Write a formula for m, the slope of the line.

36. Suppose that the line in Exercise 35 is horizontal. How will y_1 and y_2 be related?

37. Suppose that the line in Exercise 35 is vertical. How will x_1 and x_2 be related?

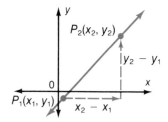

38. What is the slope of all lines defined by equations of the form $By = C$, $B \neq 0$?

39. What is the slope of all lines defined by equations of the form $Ax = C$, $A \neq 0$?

CALCULATOR APPLICATIONS

Computing y Values for Functions

You can use a calculator to compute y values for a function, given the function's formula and domain.

EXAMPLE Complete the table of values. $\qquad y = -5x - 15$

x	−6	−4	0	3
y	?	?	?	?

SOLUTION Substitute x values from the table in the formula.

$$y = -5x - 15 \longrightarrow y = -5(-6) - 15$$

5 [+⁄−] [×] 6 [+⁄−] [−] 1 5 [=] | 15. |

Repeat the procedure above for $x = -4$, $x = 0$, and $x = 3$.
The range is $\{15, 5, -15, -30\}$.

EXERCISES

Complete the tables.

1. $y = \frac{1}{2}x - 17$

x	−3	0	1	4
y	?	?	?	?

2. $y = -6x - 11$

x	−2	−1	2	5
y	?	?	?	?

3. $y = 2\frac{1}{4}x - 6$

x	−6	−4	5	8
y	?	?	?	?

4. $y = 9x + 21$

x	−4	−1	0	3
y	?	?	?	?

_____ **REVIEW CAPSULE FOR SECTION 5-8** _____

Solve each equation for y. *(Pages 162–164)*

1. $3x - y = 4$ 2. $2y = 5(x + 1)$ 3. $4x - 3y = 0$ 4. $2x + 3y = 7$

For each equation, find y when $x = 0$. *(Pages 9–11)*

5. $2y - 4x = 9$ 6. $y - 4x = 3$ 7. $y - 3x = 2$ 8. $2x - 3y - 6 = 0$

5-8 Slope-Intercept Form of a Line

The graphs of each of these linear functions show that when the x coordinates differ by 1, the y coordinates differ by 3.

$y = 3x$

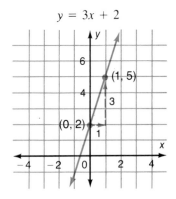

$y = 3x + 2$

Since, for each linear function,

$$\text{slope} = \frac{\text{vertical change}}{\text{horizontal change}} = \frac{3}{1} = 3,$$

it appears that in the equations

$$y = 3x \quad \text{and} \quad y = 3x + 2$$

the "3" represents the slope of the line.

More generally, if a line l is the graph of an equation of the form

$$y = mx + b,$$

m represents the slope of the line. In the equation $y = mx + b$, note that the coefficient of y is 1.

EXAMPLE 1 Find the slope of the line defined by the equation $2x + y = 18$.

Solution: Solve for y in order to write the equation in the form $y = mx + b$.

$$2x + y = 18$$
$$y = -2x + 18 \quad \longleftarrow \quad \textbf{Compare with } y = mx + b.$$
$$y = mx + b$$
$$m = -2$$

The y coordinate at which a line crosses the y axis is called the **y intercept.** Since $x = 0$ for any point on the y axis, you can find the y intercept of a linear function by replacing x with 0 in its equation.

$$y = mx + b \quad \longleftarrow \quad \textbf{Replace x with 0.}$$
$$y = m(0) + b$$
$$y = b \quad \longleftarrow \quad \textbf{y intercept}$$

<table>
<tr><td>Slope-
Intercept
Form</td><td>The equation $y = mx + b$ is called the **slope-intercept form** of the linear equation.
Its graph is a straight line with **slope m** and **y intercept b**.</td></tr>
</table>

EXAMPLE 2 Find the slope and y intercept of the graph of $5x + y = 6$.

Solution: Rewrite the equation in the form $y = mx + b$.

$y = -5x + 6$ ◄——— $m = -5; b = 6$ Slope: **−5** y intercept: **6**

You can use the slope and y intercept of a line to draw its graph.

EXAMPLE 3 Graph the line with slope -2 and y intercept 3.

Solution: $\boxed{1}$ The y intercept is 3. Therefore, graph the point $P(0, 3)$.

$\boxed{2}$ Since the slope is -2,

$$\frac{\text{vertical change}}{\text{horizontal change}} = -2 = \frac{-2}{1}.$$

Start at P. Move 1 unit to the right and 2 units down. Label the point Q.

$\boxed{3}$ Connect points P and Q with a straight line.

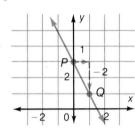

NOTE: In Example 3, you could also start at point P, move 2 units down and then 1 unit to the right. You would arrive at the same point, Q.

You can also write the slope as $-2 = \frac{2}{-1}$. The graph would be the same.

EXAMPLE 4 Use the slope and y intercept of $2x - 3y = 9$ to draw its graph.

Solution: $\boxed{1}$ $2x - 3y = 9$ ◄——— **Solve for y.**

$-3y = -2x + 9$

$y = \frac{2}{3}x - 3$ ◄——— **Compare with $y = mx + b$.**

Slope: $\frac{2}{3}$ y intercept: -3

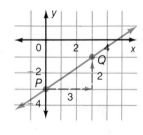

$\boxed{2}$ The y intercept is -3. Therefore, graph the point $P(0, -3)$.

Since $m = \frac{2}{3}$, start at P. Move 3 units to the right and 2 units up. Label point Q.

$\boxed{3}$ Connect points P and Q with a straight line.

CLASSROOM EXERCISES

Give the slope and y intercept of the graph of each equation.

1. $y = 2x + 5$ **2.** $y = 6x - 7$ **3.** $y = 3x + 2$ **4.** $y = 4x$

5. $y = \frac{2}{3}x + \frac{1}{2}$ **6.** $y = -\frac{1}{2}x - 5$ **7.** $y = 3$ **8.** $y + 8 = 0$

WRITTEN EXERCISES

A First write each equation in the form $y = mx + b$. Then give the slope and y intercept of its graph.

1. $2x + y = 4$ **2.** $3x + y = 8$ **3.** $5x + y = -3$

4. $y - 4x = 1$ **5.** $y - 2x = -4$ **6.** $2y = 6x - 2$

7. $-2y = 4x + 5$ **8.** $6 + 2y = 8x$ **9.** $9 - 3y = 3x$

10. $4x - 2y = 12$ **11.** $2y + 8 = 0$ **12.** $2y - 4x + 6 = 0$

Graph the line whose slope and y intercept are given.

13. $m = 9,\ b = 6$ **14.** $m = -8,\ b = -2$ **15.** $m = 3,\ b = 1$

16. $m = \frac{1}{2},\ b = 1$ **17.** $m = -\frac{2}{3}\ b = 0$ **18.** $m = \frac{1}{4},\ b = -2$

19. $m = 0,\ b = -2$ **20.** $m = 0,\ b = 5$ **21.** $m = -\frac{2}{5},\ b = -1$

Use the slope and y intercept to graph each line.

22. $y = 3x - 2$ **23.** $y = -6x$ **24.** $y = 5x - 6$

25. $-2x + y = 4$ **26.** $y = -\frac{2}{3}x - 6$ **27.** $3x = y + 6$

28. $y - 3x = 1$ **29.** $4y = 5x + 12$ **30.** $2x - y = 3$

B Use this theorem from geometry to tell whether each pair of lines in Exercises 31–36 is parallel.

Theorem	**Parallel lines have the same slope.**

31. $2x + y = 1$ **32.** $x - 3y = 4$ **33.** $3x - 2y = 2$
$\ 6x + 3y = 4$ $\ 6y + 2x = 8$ $\ 6x = 4y - 9$

34. $2y = 4x - 5$ **35.** $3y + 10 = 2x$ **36.** $y + 6 = 0$
$\ 3y - 6x = 7$ $\ 2y - 3x = 0$ $\ y - 2 = 0$

37. What is the slope of all lines parallel to $y = -\frac{3}{4}x$?

38. What is the equation of a line whose slope is -2 and whose y intercept is 0?

39. What is the equation of a line whose slope is $-\frac{1}{3}$ and whose y intercept is 5?

40. What is the equation of a line whose slope is $-\frac{5}{6}$ and whose y intercept is -3?

C

41. Write the general form of the linear equation $Ax + By = C$ in the form $y = mx + b$.

42. Use your answer to Exercise 41 to represent the slope m of the line $Ax + By = C$ in terms of A and B.

5-9 Direct Variation

$$T = 5h$$

$$T = 10h + 12$$

For one of the examples above, doubling the number of hours, h, doubles the total cost, T. Do you recognize $T = 5h$ as the equation that defines this relationship?

The equation $T = 5h$ expresses *direct variation*. It is called **direct variation** because only multiplication by a constant is involved.

	Direct Variation $T = 5h$	Not Direct Variation $T = 10h + 12$
Let $h = 3$.	$T = 15$	$T = 42$
Let $h = 6$.	$T = 30$	$T = 72$
Let $h = 12$.	$T = 60$	$T = 132$
Let $h = 24$.	$T = 120$	$T = 252$
	T is doubled when h is doubled.	T is not doubled when h is doubled.

Direct variation is a special case of the linear function $y = mx + b$, with $b = 0$. Thus, the graph of a linear function expressing direct variation will always pass through the origin.

The equation $y = kx$ expresses **direct variation between x and y.** That is, y is said to vary directly as x, and k is called the **constant of variation.** Note that k is the slope of the graph of $y = kx$.

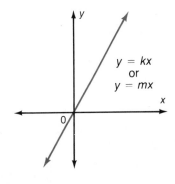

EXAMPLE 1   **a.** If y varies directly as x, and $y = 8$ when $x = 3$, find k.

b. Write the equation that expresses the variation.

Solution: **a.** $y = kx$ ◄——— **y varies directly as x.**

            $8 = k(3)$ ◄——— **When y = 8, x = 3.**

            $\dfrac{8}{3} = k$ ◄——— **Constant of variation**

       b. $y = \dfrac{8}{3}x$ ◄——— **Write the equation with $k = \dfrac{8}{3}$.**

After you have found the equation that expresses the direct variation, you can find ordered pairs (x, y) that satisfy the equation.

EXAMPLE 2   If y varies directly as x, and $y = 21$ when $x = 1\frac{1}{2}$, find y when $x = 9$.

Solution:

$$y = kx \quad \longleftarrow \quad \textbf{Linear direct variation}$$

$$21 = k\left(\frac{3}{2}\right) \quad \longleftarrow \quad \textbf{Multiply each side by } \frac{2}{3}.$$

$$21\left(\frac{2}{3}\right) = k\left(\frac{3}{2}\right)\left(\frac{2}{3}\right)$$

$$14 = k \quad \longleftarrow \quad \textbf{Constant of variation}$$

Thus, $y = 14x.$ $\quad \longleftarrow \quad$ **Find y when x = 9.**

$$y = 14(9)$$

$$y = \textbf{126}$$

CLASSROOM EXERCISES

Determine whether each set of ordered pairs (x, y) is an example of direct variation. Answer *Yes* or *No*.

1.

x	1	2	3	4
y	3	6	9	12

2.

x	0	1	2	3
y	5	6	7	8

3.

x	−1	−2	−3	−4
y	−7	−14	−21	−28

Determine whether each equation is an example of direct variation. Answer *Yes* or *No*.

4. $x = 4y$ **5.** $x + y = 6$ **6.** $y = 6x$ **7.** $x - y = 4$

8. $\dfrac{x}{4} = y$ **9.** $x + 5y = 10$ **10.** $x - 8y = 0$ **11.** $xy = 10$

If y varies directly as x, find the constant of variation, k, for the given values of x and y.

12. $x = 3, y = 2$ **13.** $x = -1, y = 4$ **14.** $x = 5, y = -2$ **15.** $x = -\frac{1}{2}, y = -1$

WRITTEN EXERCISES

A   In Exercises 1–2, determine whether the relation between the variables is that of direct variation. Explain your answer.

1. P is the perimeter of a square and s is the length of one side.

2. John earns \$3.25 an hour mowing lawns. The amount that he earns in cents is A. The number of hours that he works is n.

In Exercises 3–6, refer to the table at the right.

x	0	1	2	3	4	5	6
y	0	$2\frac{1}{2}$	5	$7\frac{1}{2}$	10	$12\frac{1}{2}$	15

3. Does each number for y equal a constant times the corresponding number for x? Does y vary directly as x? Explain.

4. Write an equation that shows the relation between x and y. ($y = $ _?_)

5. When x is 4, y is 10. When x is 8, y is _?_ . If you double the value of x, is the corresponding value of y doubled? If you choose any value of x and double it, the corresponding value of y is _?_ .

6. When x is 2, y is _?_ . When x is 6, y is _?_ . If you triple any value of x, the corresponding value of y is _?_ .

Determine whether each equation is an example of direct variation. Answer Yes or No.

7. $x = 12y$

8. $5x = y$

9. $y = \frac{1}{8}x$

10. $y + 3x = 0$

11. $xy + 4 = y$

12. $y = \frac{x}{4}$

13. $\frac{x}{y} = 7$

14. $y = \frac{18}{x}$

Express each relationship as an equation. Use k as the constant of variation.

15. y varies directly as x.

16. p varies directly as q.

17. r varies directly as s.

18. s varies directly as t.

In Exercises 19–30, assume that y varies directly as x.

19. If $x = 2$ when $y = 3$, find k.

20. If $x = 5$ when $y = 2$, find k.

21. If $x = -3$ when $y = 6$, find k.

22. If $x = 1$ when $y = -4$, find k.

23. If $x = \frac{1}{2}$ when $y = \frac{2}{3}$, find k.

24. If $x = -2$ when $y = -8$, find k.

25. If $y = 9$ when $x = 3$, find k. Then find y when x is 1.

26. If $y = 10$ when $x = 2$, find k. Then find y when x is -2.

27. If $y = 6$ when $x = 4$, find y when x is 10.

28. If $y = -2$ when $x = -1$, find y when x is 5.

29. If $x = -3$ when $y = -2$, find x when y is -4.

30. If $x = 4$ when $y = -3$, find x when y is 0.

B In Exercises 31–33, refer to the figure at the right. The figure shows the graph of $y = kx$ for various values of k.

31. As k increases from $\frac{1}{5}$ to 9, what happens to the graph of $y = kx$?

32. As k increases from $-2\frac{1}{2}$ to $-\frac{1}{3}$, what happens to the graph of $y = kx$?

33. Why does the graph of an equation expressing direct variation always pass through the origin?

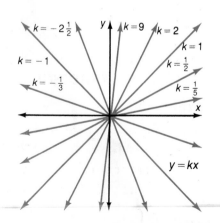

In Exercises 34–35, use the fact that $C = \pi d$ expresses the relation between the circumference of a circle and the length of a diameter.

34. Does C vary directly as d? Explain.

35. When d is 10, C is 10π. When d is 20, C is __?__. If you take one circle and draw another circle that has a diameter twice that of the first, its circumference is __?__ the circumference of the first circle.

C　　In Exercises 36–39, assume that y equals a negative number times x.

36. As x increases, does y increase or decrease?

37. As x decreases, does y increase or decrease?

38. Complete: When any number for x is doubled, the corresponding number for y is __?__.

39. Complete: When any number for x is multiplied by n, the corresponding number for y is __?__.

CALCULATOR APPLICATIONS

Direct Variation

You can use the memory keys on a calculator, [M+] and [MR], to check whether a relation is an example of direct variation.

EXAMPLE Determine whether each set of ordered pairs at the right is an example of direct variation. If so, write an equation that expresses the variation.

x	−3	0	2.5	7.5
y	−16.5	0	13.75	41.25

SOLUTION First find the quotient, $\frac{y}{x}$, in the first ordered pair, and store in memory. Then test the value of k for each ordered pair in the relation.

1 6 . 5 [+/-] [÷] 3 [+/-] [=] [M+]　　　5.5　　◄——— Value of $\frac{y}{x}$.

0 [×] [MR] [=] 2 . 5 [×] [MR] [=] 7 . 5 [×] [MR] [=]　　　41.25

Since each ordered pair checks, the relation is an example of direct variation. The equation is **y = 5.5x.**

EXERCISES

Determine whether each relation is an example of direct variation. If so, write an equation that expresses the variation.

1.

x	−5	−1	4	9
y	$-2\frac{1}{2}$	$-\frac{1}{2}$	2	$4\frac{1}{2}$

2.

x	−2	−1	0	1
y	12	6	0	6

3.

x	−2	0	1	8
y	−13.5	0	6.75	54

5-10 Using Direct Variation

You can use direct variation to solve word problems.

EXAMPLE The length of an official flag of the United States varies directly with its width, and the constant of variation is fixed by Federal law. If an official flag is 3 meters wide and 5.7 meters long, what should be the length of an official flag that is 1.5 meters wide?

Solution: Let l = the length of the flag and let w = the width.

Then $l = kw$. ⟵——— **Replace l with 5.7 and w with 3.**

$\quad\quad 5.7 = k(3)$

$\quad\quad 1.9 = k$ ⟵———— **Use k to write the direct linear variation.**

Thus, $l = 1.9w$.

$\quad\quad l = 1.9(1.5)$

$\quad\quad l = 2.85$ The length should be **2.85 meters.**

In the Exercises that follow, assume that all variations are linear.

CLASSROOM EXERCISES

1. David paid an import tax of $160 on a $25,000 car. The tax varies directly as the cost of the car. At that rate, how much import tax would be owed on a car that cost $17,000?

2. The labor costs for an automobile repair job vary directly as the number of hours a mechanic works on the car. If labor costs for 3 hours amount to $87, what will be the labor costs for 7 hours?

3. The estimated cost of building a house varies directly as the number of square feet of floor space. If 1200 square feet cost $60,000, how many square feet could you expect to get for $100,000?

4. A real estate dealer makes a commission of $6720 on a sale of $112,000. At the same rate, how much could the dealer expect to make on a sale of $85,000?

5. Operating costs for driving a car 20,000 kilometers per year total $4800. At the same rate, how much will it cost to drive the car 36,804 kilometers?

WORD PROBLEMS

A   Solve each problem.

1. The amount of pay, A, that Sue earns varies directly with the number of hours, h, that she works. Last week, she earned $108.75 for 25 hours of work. How much pay will she earn for 120 hours of work? Assume that the pay rate remains the same.

2. The weight of an object on the moon varies directly as its weight on earth. Thus, an object with a weight of 14.4 kilograms on the moon will have a weight of 90 kilograms on earth. If an object has a weight of 120 kilograms on earth, find its weight on the moon.

3. On a scale drawing, 2 centimeters represent 50 meters. How many meters will 5 centimeters represent?

4. The cost of gold varies directly as its mass. If 3 grams of gold cost $235, how much will 5 grams cost?

5. The gas consumption of a car varies directly as the distance traveled. If a certain car uses 20 liters of gas to travel 200 kilometers, how many liters of gasoline will be used on a trip of 700 kilometers?

6. The amount of stretch, S, in a spring varies directly as the weight attached, w. A certain spring stretches 5 inches when a weight of 15 pounds is attached. Find the weight needed for a stretch of $7\frac{1}{2}$ inches.

7. The distance between two towns on a map varies directly with the actual distance between the towns. If $2\frac{1}{2}$ inches on the map represent 150 miles, what is the actual distance represented by 7 inches on the map?

8. The number of calories in a container of milk varies directly with the amount of milk in the container. If a 10-ounce glass of milk contains 180 calories, how many calories are there in a 14-ounce glass?

9. The toll, T, on a bridge varies directly with the number of axles on a vehicle. On a certain bridge, the toll for a 4-axle truck is $3.00. What will be the toll for a 6-axle truck?

10. The speed of the blade tips of a windmill varies directly with the speed of the wind. In a 20 mile-per-hour wind, the speed of the blade tips of a windmill near Sandusky, Ohio is 180 miles per hour. Find the speed of the blade tips in a 5 mile-per-hour wind.

11. The amount of time, T, that it takes to read an article varies directly with the length of the article. Ted takes 3 minutes to read an article of 315 words. How many minutes will it take him to read an article of 945 words if he reads at the same rate?

12. The cost, c, of cleaning a carpet varies directly with the area, A, of the carpet. The cost of cleaning a 9-foot by 12-foot carpet is $21.60. At the same rate per square foot, how much will it cost to clean a carpet 18 feet long by 10 feet wide?

13. The weight, w, of a steer being raised for food varies directly with the number of pounds of feed, f, consumed. It takes 96 pounds of fodder to produce a 6-pound roast of beef. How many pounds of fodder does it take to produce 15 pounds of beef?

14. The amount of antifreeze required to prevent freezing at $-25°C$ varies directly with the capacity of the cooling system. A 20-liter cooling system requires 6.2 liters of antifreeze. How much antifreeze is needed in a 25-liter system?

_____ Review _____

Find the slope of the line containing the given points. *(Section 5–7)*

1. $(5, -1)$; $(8, 2)$ 2. $(0, 0)$; $(-1, 1)$ 3. $(-8, 6)$; $(3, -9)$ 4. $(-5, 9)$; $(3, 9)$

Write each equation in the form $y = mx + b$. Then give the slope and y intercept of its graph. *(Section 5–8)*

5. $3x + y = 5$ 6. $3x - 2y = 8$ 7. $y + 8 = 0$ 8. $-5y = 3x$

9. Use the slope and y intercept of $2x + y = 8$ to draw its graph. *(Section 5–8)*

Determine whether each equation is an example of direct variation. Answer *Yes* or *No*. *(Section 5–9)*

10. $y = 4x$ 11. $2y = x$ 12. $y = -\dfrac{x}{5}$ 13. $y = 3x - 1$

14. If y varies directly as x, and $y = 40$ when $x = 5$, find y when $x = 20$. *(Section 5–9)*

Solve. *(Section 5–10)*

15. The cost, C, of keeping a lamp lit for 24 hours varies directly with the number of watts, w, of the lamp bulb. It costs 10 cents a day to keep a 100-watt bulb burning for 24 hours. How much would you save each day if the bulb were changed to 60 watts?

Puzzle

Without actually graphing, tell whether each line would intersect the graph of the house shown in 1 point, 0 points, or infinitely many points.

1. $y = 1$ 2. $y = 2$ 3. $y = 3$

4. $x = 1$ 5. $x = 2$ 6. $y = x + 3$

7. $y = x + 2$ 8. $y = x - 2$ 9. $y = x + 8$

10. $y + x = 8$ 11. $y + x = 3$ 12. $y = 4x$

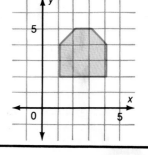

BASIC: DIRECT VARIATION

Problem: *y varies directly as x. Given the constant of variation and the smallest and largest x values, write a program which prints a table of ordered pairs.*

Program:
```
100 PRINT "Y VARIES DIRECTLY AS X. WHAT ARE"
110 PRINT "THE CONSTANT OF VARIATION AND THE"
120 PRINT "SMALLEST AND LARGEST X VALUES";
130 INPUT K, X1, X2
140 PRINT
150 PRINT " X", " Y"
160 PRINT
170 FOR X = X1 TO X2
180 LET Y = K * X
190 PRINT X, Y
200 NEXT X
210 PRINT
220 END
```

The following is the output from a sample run of the program above.

Output:
```
RUN
Y VARIES DIRECTLY AS X.  WHAT ARE
THE CONSTANT OF VARIATION AND THE
SMALLEST AND LARGEST X VALUES? 5,0,10

   X              Y

   0              0
   1              5
   2              10
   3              15
   4              20
   5              25
   6              30
   7              35
   8              40
   9              45
   10             50

READY
```

Analysis

Statements 140–160: These print the heading for the table. Statement 140 skips a line. Then statement 150 puts the titles on the columns before statement 160 skips another line.

Statements 170–200: These form a FOR–NEXT loop. This section of the program is executed over and over, one time for each X value. The first time the computer reaches statement 170, X is set to its starting value (X1, which is 0 for the sample run on page 204). Statements 180 and 190 are done. Then statement 200 sends the computer back to statement 170, where X is increased by 1. Statements 180 and 190 are executed again. The loop continues like this until X reaches X2, its final value. Statements 180–190 are done one last time before the computer moves to statement 210, which skips a line at the end of the printout.

If statement 170 were changed to 170 FOR X = X1 TO X2 STEP .5, the difference between successive X values would be 0.5 instead of 1. Thus, for the data in the sample run, X would take on the values 0, 0.5, 1, 1.5, $\cdots$, 9.5, 10.

Examples of valid FOR statements are shown below.

```
110 FOR J = I+1 TO N          235 FOR K = A-B TO C*C STEP 2
340 FOR D = 100 TO 1 STEP -1  432 FOR R = 2*X TO X+10 STEP J/2
```

EXERCISES

A Run the program on page 204 for the following values of k, x_1, and x_2.

1. $k = 4$; $x_1 = 1$; $x_2 = 5$ 2. $k = 2.5$; $x_1 = 0$; $x_2 = 4$ 3. $k = 10$; $x_1 = -3$; $x_2 = 3$
4. $k = -4$; $x_1 = 10$; $x_2 = 15$ 5. $k = -1.5$; $x_1 = -5$; $x_2 = 0$ 6. $k = -6$; $x_1 = -2$; $x_2 = 2$

Write a BASIC program for each problem.

7. y varies directly as x. The input is an x value and its corresponding y value, along with another x value. Print the y value that corresponds to the second x value.

8. Given two ordered pairs, print whether the set of ordered pairs is an example of direct variation.

9. For the equation $y = mx + b$, print a table of values that can be used to draw the graph of the equation. Let the user specify the smallest and largest x values.

10. Given the x and y coordinates of a point, print the quadrant in which the point lies or the axis on which the point lies. (See page 170.)

B

11. For the equation $Ax + By = C$, input A, B, and C. Print the slope and the y intercept of the line with that equation. Include the possibility that the slope may be undefined.

12. Given the slope and y intercept of a line, print the equation of the line in the form $y = mx + b$. Print the equation as "neatly" as possible. For example, print Y = 3 X - 2 and not Y = 3 X + -2; print Y = -2 X and not Y = -2 X + 0; print Y = -4 and not Y = 0 X - 4.

Chapter Summary

IMPORTANT IDEAS

1. **Distance Formula:** distance = rate · time, or $d = rt$

2. **Steps in Solving Distance/Rate/Time Problems**

   $\boxed{1}$ Organize the given information in a table. Use this information to represent the unknowns (Condition 1).

   $\boxed{2}$ Draw a figure to represent the information. Use this figure and the table to write an equation for the problem (Condition 2).

   $\boxed{3}$ Solve the equation.

   $\boxed{4}$ Check your answer with the conditions of the problem. Answer the question.

3. In an ordered pair, the first number, x, shows distance to the right or left of the vertical axis. The second number, y, shows distance above or below the horizontal axis.

4. It is necessary to plot only two points to graph a linear equation. However, a third point should be plotted as a check.

5. For any two points on a line, $P_1(x_1, y_1)$ and $P_2(x_2, y_2)$,

$$\text{slope} = m = \frac{\text{vertical change}}{\text{horizontal change}} = \frac{y_2 - y_1}{x_2 - x_1}, \; (x_2 - x_1 \neq 0)$$

6. Lines with positive slope rise from left to right.

   Lines with negative slope fall from left to right.

   The slope of a horizontal line is 0.

   A vertical line has no slope.

7. The graph of an equation of the form $y = mx + b$ is a straight line with slope m and y intercept b.

8. Parallel lines have the same slope.

Chapter Objectives and Review

Objective: *To solve an equation for one variable in terms of the other variables (Section 5–1)*

Solve each equation for *n*. Check each solution.

1. $s = \dfrac{n}{t}$

2. $4n - c = d$

3. $a - n = 2b$

4. $-n = a - b$

5. $3h = 2n + g$

6. $cn - d = 1 - e$

Solve the formula for the variable indicated.

7. Formula for the area of a parallelogram: $A = bh$ Solve for *h*.

8. Formula for the perimeter of a rectangle: $P = 2l + 2w$ Solve for *l*.

Objective: *To solve distance/rate/time problems (Section 5–2)*

9. Two runners going in opposite directions pass each other along a straight trail. The speed of the faster runner is $1\frac{1}{4}$ times that of the slower runner. In one hour they are 18 kilometers apart. Find the rate of each runner.

10. Two buses leave Atlanta at the same time, headed in the same direction. One bus averages 80 kilometers per hour, and the other averages 85 kilometers per hour. In how many hours will the buses be 15 kilometers apart?

Objective: *To graph ordered pairs on the coordinate plane (Section 5–3)*

11. Graph these points on the same pair of coordinate axes.

   a. $Q(3, -7)$ **b.** $R(-3, 7)$ **c.** $S(0, -2)$ **d.** $T(6, -5)$ **e.** $U(-6, -6)$
   f. $V(7, 5)$ **g.** $W(6\frac{1}{2}, 0)$,   **h.** $X(-2, -5)$ **i.** $Y(-1, 4)$ **j.** $Z(3\frac{1}{2}, -5)$

12. Describe the graph of the set of all points with an abscissa of -2.

13. The coordinates of three vertices of a square are $(2, 3)$, $(-5, -4)$, and $(2, -4)$. Graph the vertices, sketch the square, and give the coordinates of the fourth vertex.

Objective: *To identify the domain and range of a relation and to identify functions (Section 5–4)*

Give the domain and range for each relation.

14. $\{(1, 2), (1, 4), (2, 6), (2, 8), (3, 10), (3, 12)\}$

15. $\{(-2, 1), (-1, \frac{1}{2}), (0, 0), (1, -\frac{1}{2}), (2, -1)\}$

16. $\{(-2, 4), (-1, 1), (0, 0), (1, 1), (2, 4)\}$

17. Write *Yes* or *No* to indicate whether each relation in Exercises 14–16 is also a function.

Objective: *To graph linear equations (Section 5–5)*

Graph each linear equation in the coordinate plane.

18. $y = 3x - 1$

19. $y = -4x$

20. $4x + 2y = -4$

21. $3x + 9 = 0$

Objective: *To estimate answers to problems using the graph of a linear equation (Section 5–6)*

The yearly property taxes on private homes in one city are set at 2% of the value of the property. The relationship between the amount of the tax, t, and the property value, p, is expressed by the function $t = 0.02p$. Use this information to complete the table in Exercise 22 and to complete Exercises 23–24.

22.

Property Value (p)	$40,000	$60,000	$80,000
Amount of Tax (t)	?	?	?

23. Use the ordered pairs in the table in Exercise 22 to graph the function.

24. Use the graph from Exercise 23 to estimate the amount of tax when the property value is $50,000.

Objective: *To find the slope of a line (Section 5–7)*

Find the slope of the line containing the given points.

25. $(-7, 16)$; $(1, 0)$ 26. $(8, 2)$; $(4, -1)$ 27. $(-3, 2)$; $(0, 2)$

Objective: *To graph a line using the slope–intercept form of its equation (Section 5–8)*

Write each equation in the form $y = mx + b$. Then give the slope and y intercept of its graph.

28. $3y = 2x - 9$ 29. $x + y = 0$ 30. $4x - 2y = 8$

Use the slope and y intercept to graph each line.

31. $y = x + 2$ 32. $y = 2x + 1$ 33. $x + 2y = -4$

34. $3y - 9 = x$ 35. $4x + 6 = y$ 36. $x - 2y = 11$

Objective: *To write an equation expressing direct variation and find ordered pairs that satisfy the equation. (Section 5–9)*

Determine whether each equation is an example of direct variation. Answer *Yes* or *No*.

37. $x = 4y$ 38. $x = 2y + 7$ 39. $y = x$ 40. $xy = -8$

41. If y varies directly as x, and $y = 4\frac{1}{2}$ when $x = -2$, find y when $x = 8$.

Objective: *To solve problems involving direct variation (Section 5–10)*

42. On a scale drawing, 3 centimeters represent 90 meters. How many meters will 5 centimeters represent?

43. The cost of silver varies directly as its weight. If 4 ounces of silver cost $56, how much will 7 ounces cost?

44. The distance traveled in a given time varies directly as the rate of travel, r. Mr. Anders drove 260 miles at an average rate of 50 miles per hour. How far could he drive in the same amount of time at an average rate of 55 miles per hour?

45. The length of a steel beam shown on a blueprint varies directly with its actual length. On the blueprint, 5 centimeters represent 1 meter. If the length of the beam on the blueprint is 21.5 centimeters, what is the actual length of the steel beam?

_____ Chapter Test _____

Solve each equation for x. Check each solution.

1. $\dfrac{x}{p} = k$ **2.** $2x - a = b$ **3.** $y - x = z$

4. Graph these points on the same coordinate axes.

  a. $A(4, -3)$ **b.** $B(-3, 4)$ **c.** $C(0, -2)$ **d.** $D(-5, -5)$

Give the domain and range of each relation. Then state whether each relation is a function.

5. $\{(0, 0), (1, 1), (2, 2), (3, 2), (4, 3), (5, 3)\}$
6. $\{(5, 0), (0, -5), (-3, 4), (-3, -4), (-5, 0), (0, 5)\}$

Find the slope of the line containing the given points.

7. $(7, -4); (-5, -4)$ **8.** $(0, -4); (-2, -5)$ **9.** $(3, -2); (-4, 7)$

Write each equation in the form $y = mx + b$. Then give the slope and y intercept of its graph.

10. $x - y = 2$ **11.** $3x + 4y = 4$ **12.** $2y = 4x - 6$

Graph each linear equation in the coordinate plane.

13. $y = x + 4$ **14.** $y = -2x - 1$

Determine whether each equation is an example of direct variation. Answer *Yes* or *No*.

15. $3y = x$ **16.** $x - y = 8$ **17.** $xy = 7$
18. If y varies directly as x, and $y = 12$ when $x = 3$, find y when $x = 5$.

19. Two automobiles leave the same place at the same time, one headed north and one south. One travels at an average rate of 60 kilometers per hour and the other at an average rate of 70 kilometers per hour. In how many hours will they be 325 kilometers apart?

20. The weight of a steel cable varies directly with its length. How heavy is a 150–meter roll of cable, if the weight of a 2–meter section is 0.8 kilogram?

Additional Practice

Skills

Solve each equation for n. *(Section 5–1)*

1. $a = nb$ **2.** $y - n = 4h$ **3.** $3n + c = d$

Graph these points on the same pair of coordinate axes. *(Section 5–3)*

4. $A(3, -5)$ **5.** $B(0, 6)$ **6.** $C(-1, -1)$ **7.** $D(6, 7)$ **8.** $E(-2, 2)$

Give the domain and range for each relation. Then tell if each relation is a function. *(Section 5–4)*

9. $\{(-13, 0), (-12, 5), (0, 13), (0, -13), (5, 12), (12, 5)\}$

10. $\{(-2, 2), (-1, 3), (0, 0), (1, -3), (2, -2)\}$

Graph each linear equation in the coordinate plane. *(Section 5–5)*

11. $y = -3x$ **12.** $y + 3x = -6$ **13.** $x = 6$ **14.** $y - 2x = 4$

Find the slope of the line containing the given points. *(Section 5–7)*

15. $(2, 6); (-4, -6)$ **16.** $(3, -4); (5, -4)$ **17.** $(0, -4); (4, -6)$

Write each equation in the form $y = mx + b$. Then give the slope and y intercept of its graph. *(Section 5–8)*

18. $4x + y + 3 = 0$ **19.** $5 - y = 2x$ **20.** $3y - 6 = 2x$

21. If y varies directly as x and $y = -3$ when $x = 1$, find y when $x = 4$. *(Section 5–9)*

Applications

The cost, c, of running a classified ad in a newspaper is $3 plus 50 cents for each line of print, l, required.

Use this information for Exercises 22–23. *(Section 5–6)*

22. Write three ordered pairs for this function. Let l equal 4, 8, and 12. Graph the function.

23. Use the graph in Exercise 22 to estimate the cost for a fourteen-line ad.

24. Frank leaves home at 8 A.M. and drives at a speed of 40 miles per hour. His sister leaves home at 9:30 A.M. driving in the same direction at a speed of 46 miles per hour. At what time will Frank's sister overtake him? *(Section 5–2)*

25. The actual distance between cities varies directly with the distance shown on a map. On the map, 2 centimeters represent 5 kilometers. If the distance between two cities on the map is 14 centimeters, what is the actual distance between the cities? *(Section 5–10)*

Intersecting lines have *different slopes* and the *same, or different, y inter-cepts*. (See Figure 1.) Parallel lines have the *same slope* and *different y intercepts*. (See Figure 2.) Coincident lines have the *same slope* and the *same y intercept*. (See Figure 3.) Thus, to determine whether a system of linear equations has one, none, or an infinite number of solutions, examine the slope and y intercept of each line.

EXAMPLE 2   Determine the number of solutions for each system.

a. $\begin{cases} y = \frac{1}{3}x + 7 \\ y = 2x - 5 \end{cases}$ b. $\begin{cases} y + x = 5 \\ 3x = 15 - 3y \end{cases}$ c. $\begin{cases} y = 2x - 5 \\ y = 2x + 10 \end{cases}$

Solutions: a. The slopes, $\frac{1}{3}$ and 2, are different. The y intercepts, 7 and -5, are dif-ferent. Thus, the graphs are intersecting lines and there is **one solution**.

b. Write each equation in the form $y = mx + b$.

$\begin{cases} y = -x + 5 \\ y = -x + 5 \end{cases}$ ◄———— **Same equation**

Since the slopes are the same and the y intercepts are the same, the graphs coincide. Every point on the graph is a solution and there are an **infinite number of solutions**.

c. The slopes, 2 and 2, are the same. The y intercepts, -5 and 10, are different. Thus, the graphs are parallel lines, and there are **no solutions**.

This table summarizes how to determine the number of solutions for a system of two linear equations.

Graphs of the Equations		Number of Solutions	Graph of the System
Slopes	y intercepts		
Different	Same or different	One	Two intersecting lines
Same	Different	None	Two parallel lines
Same	Same	Infinitely many	Same line

A system of equations having no solutions is called an **inconsistent system**. Systems that have solutions are called **consistent systems**.

CLASSROOM EXERCISES

Complete the tables for each exercise. Give the point of intersection of each pair of equations.

1. $x + y = 5$

x	0	1	2	3	4
y	?	?	?	?	?

$x - y = 3$

x	0	1	2	3	4
y	?	?	?	?	?

2. $2x - y = 7$

x	−1	0	1	2	3	4
y	?	?	?	?	?	?

$x + 2y = 6$

x	−1	0	1	2	3	4
y	?	?	?	?	?	?

Determine whether the ordered pair (3, 7) is a solution of each system.

3. $\begin{cases} x + y = 4 \\ x - y = 10 \end{cases}$ **4.** $\begin{cases} y - x = 4 \\ y + x = 10 \end{cases}$ **5.** $\begin{cases} x + y = -4 \\ x - y = -10 \end{cases}$

Determine whether each system graphed below has one solution, an infinite number of solutions, or no solution.

6.   **7.**   **8.**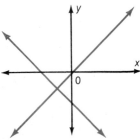

Determine the number of solutions for each system.

9. $\begin{cases} y = 3x + 7 \\ y = 2x - 5 \end{cases}$ **10.** $\begin{cases} y = 2x - 5 \\ y = 2x + 10 \end{cases}$ **11.** $\begin{cases} 2y = 8 - 7x \\ 4y = 16 - 14x \end{cases}$

WRITTEN EXERCISES

A   Read the solution set of each system of equations from its graph. Check by substituting in both equations.

1. $\begin{cases} x + y = 10 \\ x - y = 4 \end{cases}$ **2.** $\begin{cases} 2x - y = 3 \\ 3x + y = 7 \end{cases}$ **3.** $\begin{cases} x + 2y = 4 \\ 2x - y = 8 \end{cases}$

4. $\begin{cases} 2x + y = 3 \\ x - 3y = 5 \end{cases}$ **5.** $\begin{cases} x + y = 6 \\ x = 5 \end{cases}$ **6.** $\begin{cases} x = -3 \\ y = 2 \end{cases}$

Solve each system by graphing. Check your solutions.

7. $\begin{cases} x+y=6 \\ x-y=4 \end{cases}$ **8.** $\begin{cases} x-y=5 \\ x+y=7 \end{cases}$ **9.** $\begin{cases} x+y=4 \\ y-x=2 \end{cases}$

10. $\begin{cases} x-y=9 \\ 2x+y=6 \end{cases}$ **11.** $\begin{cases} x+y=2 \\ 2y-x=10 \end{cases}$ **12.** $\begin{cases} 3x+y=6 \\ x-2y=2 \end{cases}$

13. $\begin{cases} 2x-y=10 \\ x+2y=-5 \end{cases}$ **14.** $\begin{cases} 3x+y=3 \\ x-4y=1 \end{cases}$ **15.** $\begin{cases} x-5y=-14 \\ 3x+y=6 \end{cases}$

16. $\begin{cases} 3x+2y=4 \\ 2x-3y=7 \end{cases}$ **17.** $\begin{cases} y=-x+5 \\ y=\frac{1}{3}x+1 \end{cases}$ **18.** $\begin{cases} x+4y=-5 \\ 3x+y=-4 \end{cases}$

19. $\begin{cases} x+y=1 \\ y=x+1 \end{cases}$ **20.** $\begin{cases} y=2x-3 \\ x-y=-6 \end{cases}$ **21.** $\begin{cases} y=x-6 \\ y=-2 \end{cases}$

Write *one, none,* or *infinitely many* to describe the number of solutions for each system.

22. $\begin{cases} y=-3x+7 \\ y=-3x+5 \end{cases}$ **23.** $\begin{cases} y=3x+7 \\ y=-3x+5 \end{cases}$ **24.** $\begin{cases} y=7-3x \\ 2y+6x=14 \end{cases}$

25. $\begin{cases} y=-x+10 \\ y=-x+4 \end{cases}$ **26.** $\begin{cases} y=x+10 \\ y=x-1 \end{cases}$ **27.** $\begin{cases} y=-x \\ y=-x+1 \end{cases}$

28. $\begin{cases} 4x+4y=7 \\ x+y=\frac{7}{4} \end{cases}$ **29.** $\begin{cases} y=-2x+2 \\ y=-2x \end{cases}$ **30.** $\begin{cases} y=2x-8 \\ y=2x+10 \end{cases}$

31. $\begin{cases} y=5 \\ y=-1 \end{cases}$ **32.** $\begin{cases} y-9=0 \\ y+1=0 \end{cases}$ **33.** $\begin{cases} y-3x=0 \\ 5y-15x=0 \end{cases}$

B

34. $\begin{cases} x+y=9 \\ x-y=9 \end{cases}$ **35.** $\begin{cases} y=2x-8 \\ 2x-y=10 \end{cases}$ **36.** $\begin{cases} y=-4x+5 \\ 8x+2y=10 \end{cases}$

37. $\begin{cases} x=y+5 \\ 2x-2y=7 \end{cases}$ **38.** $\begin{cases} y=4x-2 \\ x-4y=2 \end{cases}$ **39.** $\begin{cases} 2\frac{1}{2}x-4=3y \\ 6y+8=5x \end{cases}$

APPLICATIONS: Using Systems of Equations

The Q Street Flea Market charges $1 per hour to rent a display area. Residents of Q Street pay no base fee. Town residents, not from Q Street, pay a base fee of $2.00. Out-of-town residents pay a base fee of $5.00.

Use this information and the figure at the right in Exercises 40–42.

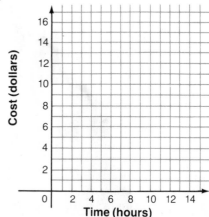

40. On the same set of coordinate axes, draw graphs showing the rental fees for residents of Q Street, town residents, and out-of-town residents for 1 to 12 hours.

41. How are the slopes of the graphs related?

42. Use the graphs to determine how much more it costs an out-of-town person than a Q Street resident to rent a display area for 8 hours.

Suppose that the cost of using solar energy to heat a home involves an initial cost of $10,000 with an average yearly cost of $200 for every year after the first. Suppose also that heating with oil involves an initial cost of $4000 with an average yearly cost of $800 for every year after the first.

Use this information and the figure at the right in Exercises 43–47.

43. On the same coordinate axes, draw graphs showing yearly costs for heating with solar energy and with oil for 12 years.

44. Which graph has the greater slope?

45. For how many years does it cost less to heat with oil than with solar energy? (Include the initial costs.)

46. How many years does it take for the costs to be equal? (Include the initial costs.)

Ⓒ

47. About how much more does it cost to heat with oil than with solar energy during the twelfth year?

A supermarket offers two plans for renting a floor polisher. Under Plan A, the charge is $5 per hour. Under Plan B, there is a basic fee of $6 and an additional charge of $2 per hour.

Use this information in Exercises 48–52.

48. On the same set of coordinate axes, draw a graph showing rental costs under each plan for 0 to 6 hours.

49. When will the costs for both plans be the same?

50. When will it cost less to use Plan A?   **51.** When will it cost less to use Plan B?

52. For which plan do costs increase the fastest for $t > 2$?

Write *one, none,* or *infinitely many* to describe the number of solutions for each system.

53. $\begin{cases} Ax + By = C \\ Ax + By = D, \ C \neq D \end{cases}$ **54.** $\begin{cases} Ax + By = C \\ NAx + NBy = NC, \ N \neq 0 \end{cases}$ **55.** $\begin{cases} Ax + By = C \\ Ax - By = C, \ B \neq 0 \end{cases}$

―――――― **REVIEW CAPSULE FOR SECTION 6-2** ――――――

Combine like terms. *(Pages 60–63)*

1. $3x + y - (2x - y)$ **2.** $4x + y + (-4x + 3y)$ **3.** $2x + y - (x - y)$

4. $-4a + 2b + (a - 2b)$ **5.** $9r - 3t - (-9r + 8t)$ **6.** $-3.5v + s - (-v - 1.2s)$

6-2 Addition Method

When you add the left sides of the two equations of a system and then add the right sides, the resulting **sum equation** will have the same solution set as the original system. For example, for

$$\begin{cases} x = 5 \\ y = 2 \end{cases}$$

the sum equation is $x + y = 7$.

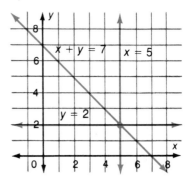

The graph shows that the ordered pair $(5, 2)$ is a solution of each equation. Thus, a system consisting of any two of the equations is *equivalent* to the original system. **Equivalent systems have the same solution set.**

$$\begin{cases} x = 5 \\ y = 2 \end{cases} \qquad \begin{cases} x = 5 \\ x + y = 7 \end{cases} \qquad \begin{cases} y = 2 \\ x + y = 7 \end{cases} \longleftarrow \quad \textbf{Equivalent systems}$$

To solve a system of equations algebraically, you find an equivalent system from which you can read the solution directly.

Example 1 shows how to use the **addition method** to do this. The addition method is useful when the coefficients of either the x terms or of the y terms are additive inverses of each other.

EXAMPLE 1 Solve by the addition method: $\begin{cases} 3x + y = 10 & \quad 1 \\ 2x - y = 5 & \quad 2 \end{cases}$

Solution: Since the coefficients of the y terms are additive inverses, adding the corresponding sides of the equations will **eliminate** the y terms.

$$\begin{array}{ll} 3x + y = 10 & \quad 1 \\ \underline{2x - y = 5} & \quad 2 \\ 5x = 15 \end{array}$$

$$x = 3 \qquad 3 \longleftarrow \quad \textbf{Substitute } x = 3 \textbf{ in Equation } 1 \text{ or in Equation } 2.$$

$$3x + y = 10 \qquad 1$$
$$3(3) + y = 10$$
$$y = 1 \qquad 4$$

Thus, $\begin{cases} x = 3 \\ y = 1 \end{cases}$ is an equivalent system. Check in the original equations.

Check:

$$\begin{array}{ll} 3x + y = 10 & \qquad 2x - y = 5 \\ 3(3) + 1 \overset{?}{=} 10 & \qquad 2(3) - 1 \overset{?}{=} 5 \\ 9 + 1 \overset{?}{=} 10 & \qquad 6 - 1 \overset{?}{=} 5 \\ 10 \overset{?}{=} 10 \quad \text{Yes } \checkmark & \qquad 5 \overset{?}{=} 5 \quad \text{Yes } \checkmark \qquad \textbf{Solution set: } \{(3, 1)\} \end{array}$$

When a and b in the solution (a, b) of a system of linear equations are not integers, it is sometimes difficult to read the solutions accurately from a graph. In such cases, the addition method gives more accurate results.

EXAMPLE 2 Solve by the addition method: $\begin{cases} p + q = 4 & 1 \\ -p + q = 7 & 2 \end{cases}$

Solution:

$\begin{array}{ll} p + q = 4 & 1 \\ \underline{-p + q = 7} & 2 \\ \quad 2q = 11 \end{array}$ ⟵ **Add to eliminate p.**

$\begin{array}{ll} q = 5\frac{1}{2} & 3 \\ p + q = 4 & 1 \\ p + 5\frac{1}{2} = 4 \\ \qquad p = -1\frac{1}{2} & 4 \end{array}$

⟵ **Substitute in Equation 1 or Equation 2.**

⟵ **Check the values for p and q in the original system.**

Check:

$\begin{array}{l} p + q \quad = 4 \\ -1\frac{1}{2} + 5\frac{1}{2} \overset{?}{=} 4 \\ \qquad 4 \overset{?}{=} 4 \quad \text{Yes} \checkmark \end{array}$
$\begin{array}{l} -p + q = 7 \\ -(-1\frac{1}{2}) + 5\frac{1}{2} \overset{?}{=} 7 \\ \qquad 7 \overset{?}{=} 7 \quad \text{Yes} \checkmark \end{array}$

Solution set: $\{(-1\frac{1}{2}, 5\frac{1}{2})\}$

NOTE: It is customary to give the solution(s) of the system in the alphabetical order of the variables involved. In Example 2, the variables used were p and q. Thus, the solution is given as $(-1\frac{1}{2}, 5\frac{1}{2})$.

Procedure

To solve a system of two linear equations by the addition method:

1 Add to eliminate one of the variables. Solve the resulting equation.

2 Substitute the known value of one variable in one of the original equations of the system. Solve for the other variable.

3 Check the solution in both equations of the system.

CLASSROOM EXERCISES

Write the sum equation for each system.

1. $\begin{cases} x = -2 \\ y = 3 \end{cases}$
2. $\begin{cases} x + y = 7 \\ x - y = 2 \end{cases}$
3. $\begin{cases} p + q = \frac{1}{2} \\ -p + q = -\frac{3}{2} \end{cases}$
4. $\begin{cases} -r + s = 6 \\ r + s = 2 \end{cases}$

WRITTEN EXERCISES

Use the addition method to solve each system.

1. $\begin{cases} x - y = 4 \\ x \cdots \end{cases}$
2. $\begin{cases} 2x + y = 7 \\ 3x - y = 3 \end{cases}$
3. $\begin{cases} y - 4x = 8 \\ y + 4x = 0 \end{cases}$

4. $\begin{cases} a + 5b = 10 \\ -a + 4b = 8 \end{cases}$

5. $\begin{cases} y = 3x + 6 \\ 2y = -3x + 3 \end{cases}$

6. $\begin{cases} 3y = -7x + 7 \\ 2y = 7x - 7 \end{cases}$

7. $\begin{cases} 2t + 3n = 9 \\ 5t - 3n = 5 \end{cases}$

8. $\begin{cases} -7c - 8d = 8 \\ 7c - 8d = 8 \end{cases}$

9. $\begin{cases} y = 2x - 4 \\ y = -2x + 3 \end{cases}$

10. $\begin{cases} c + d = 12 \\ -d = 8 \end{cases}$

11. $\begin{cases} x - y = 8 \\ y = 7 \end{cases}$

12. $\begin{cases} x - y = 2\frac{1}{2} \\ y = 4 \end{cases}$

13. $\begin{cases} x - 2y = 2\frac{1}{2} \\ x + 2y = 3 \end{cases}$

14. $\begin{cases} x + 3y = 9 \\ -x + 2y = 6 \end{cases}$

15. $\begin{cases} 2x - 3y = 8 \\ 2x + 3y = 4 \end{cases}$

16. $\begin{cases} 7x + 3y = 19 \\ 4x - 3y = 3 \end{cases}$

17. $\begin{cases} -6x + 3y = 5 \\ 6x - 5y = 7 \end{cases}$

18. $\begin{cases} 7a + 6b = 0 \\ 15a - 6b = 0 \end{cases}$

B

19. $\begin{cases} \frac{1}{2}x + y = 9 \\ \frac{3}{4}x - y = 0 \end{cases}$

20. $\begin{cases} 0.4x + y = 1.2 \\ 0.6x - y = 3.9 \end{cases}$

21. $\begin{cases} \frac{3}{4}x - \frac{1}{2}y = 4 \\ \frac{1}{4}x + \frac{1}{2}y = 2\frac{1}{2} \end{cases}$

22. $\begin{cases} 0.1x - 0.01y = 0.1 \\ 0.3x + 0.01y = 0.3 \end{cases}$

23. $\begin{cases} 5\frac{1}{2}x - y = 8 \\ 3\frac{1}{2}x + y = 1 \end{cases}$

24. $\begin{cases} a - b = -1 \\ -a - b = 1 \end{cases}$

Puzzle

Solve each system in 1–3 below by the addition method and graph its solution set. Connect the points associated with each solution set in order. The answers form a secret message.

1. $\begin{cases} x + y = -7 \\ x - y = -5 \end{cases}$
  $\begin{cases} -x + 2y = 10 \\ x - 3y = -13 \end{cases}$
  $\begin{cases} 6x = 4y - 8 \\ -x = -4y - 2 \end{cases}$

  $\begin{cases} x + 2y = -1 \\ -x + 3y = 6 \end{cases}$
  $\begin{cases} y = x + 6 \\ -y = x + 4 \end{cases}$

2. $\begin{cases} x = y - 2 \\ x = -y \end{cases}$
  $\begin{cases} 2y - x = 1 \\ -2y + 3x = 1 \end{cases}$

3. $\begin{cases} 2x - 3y = 0 \\ -2x + 2y = -2 \end{cases}$
  $\begin{cases} 9x + 15y = 81 \\ -9x - 2y = -42 \end{cases}$
  $\begin{cases} 8x - 10y = 42 \\ -8x - 3y = -29 \end{cases}$

  $\begin{cases} 3y = -4x + 5 \\ -2y = 4x - 6 \end{cases}$
  $\begin{cases} 6x + 21y = 15 \\ -6x + 10y = -46 \end{cases}$

REVIEW CAPSULE FOR SECTION 6

Write the additive inverse of each number. *(Pages 47–50)*

1. 21   **2.** -9 **3.** 0   **4.** -11 **5.** 18.3   **6.** $-\frac{1}{3}$

Multiply. *(Pages 97–99)*

7. $2(3x - 2y)$ **8.** $-3(6a + b)$ **9.** $-1(2w - 3s)$ **10.** $-1(r + 3t)$

11. $-1(-v + 7q)$ **12.** $-1(7q - 9)$ **13.** $-\frac{1}{2}(4r - 6p)$ **14.** $-\frac{1}{4}(s - t)$

6–3 Using Multiplication with the Addition Method

Adding the corresponding sides of the two equations in a linear system *does not always eliminate* one of the variables. To obtain a sum equation having a single variable in such cases, multiply each side of one or both equations of the system by a number or numbers, so that, after multiplying, the coefficients of one of the variables will be additive inverses.

EXAMPLE 1 Solve: $\begin{cases} 3x + y = 10 & \quad 1 \\ 2x + y = 15 & \quad 2 \end{cases}$

Solution: Multiply each side of Equation 1 by -1.

$$\begin{array}{rl} -3x - y = -10 & \quad 1 \\ \underline{2x + y = \quad 15} & \quad 2 \\ -x \quad = \quad 5 \end{array}$$ ← **Now the coefficients of the y terms are additive inverses.**

$x = -5$ 3 ← **Substitute $x = -5$ in Equation 1 or in Equation 2.**

$2x + y = 15$ 2

$2(-5) + y = 15$

$y = 25$ 4 ← **The check is left for you.**

Solution set: $\{(-5, 25)\}$

Sometimes it is necessary to multiply Equation 1 by one number and to multiply Equation 2 by another number.

EXAMPLE 2 Solve: $\begin{cases} 2x + 3y = -1 & \quad 1 \\ 5x - 2y = -12 & \quad 2 \end{cases}$

Solution: Multiply each side of Equation 1 by 2 and multiply each side of Equation 2 by 3. Then *the y terms will be additive inverses* of each other.

$$\begin{array}{rl} 4x + 6y = -2 & \\ \underline{15x - 6y = -36} & \\ 19x \end{array}$$ ← **$2(2x + 3y) = 2(-1)$**
← **$3(5x - 2y) = 3(-12)$**

3 ← **Substitute $x = -2$ in Equation 1.**
1

$2(-2) \qquad -1$

$3y = 3$

$y = 1$ 4 ← **The check is left for you.**

Solution set: $\{(-2, 1)\}$

The following procedure summarizes the steps for solving a system of two linear equations by this method.

Procedure

> To solve a system of two linear equations using multiplication with addition:
>
> 1 Multiply each side of one of the equations by a number, and, if necessary, multiply each side of the second equation by another number. Choose the two numbers so that, after multiplying, the coefficients of one of the variables will be additive inverses of each other.
>
> 2 Use the addition method to solve the new system.

CLASSROOM EXERCISES

Determine the number by which you could multiply *one* equation in each pair in order to eliminate one of the variables.

1. $\begin{cases} 5x + 2y = 14 & 1 \\ 4x - y = 6 & 2 \end{cases}$

2. $\begin{cases} 2p + 3q = 1 & 1 \\ 3p - q = 18 & 2 \end{cases}$

3. $\begin{cases} 9a - 3b = 3 & 1 \\ a + 5b = 11 & 2 \end{cases}$

Determine the number by which each of the equations in **a** has been multiplied in order to obtain the corresponding equation in **b**.

	a	**b**		**a**	**b**

4. $\begin{cases} 3x - 2y = -4 & 1 \\ -5x + 3y = -1 & 2 \end{cases}$ $\begin{cases} 15x - 10y = -20 & 1 \\ -15x + 9y = -3 & 2 \end{cases}$

5. $\begin{cases} 3x - 2y = -9 & 1 \\ 3x - 5y = -10 & 2 \end{cases}$ $\begin{cases} 15x - 10y = -45 & 1 \\ -6x + 10y = 20 & 2 \end{cases}$

6. $\begin{cases} 3r + 7t = 22 & 1 \\ 2r - 8t = 2 & 2 \end{cases}$ $\begin{cases} 6r + 14t = 44 & 1 \\ -6r + 24t = -6 & 2 \end{cases}$

7. $\begin{cases} 5p + 3q = 17 & 1 \\ 4p - 5q = 21 & 2 \end{cases}$ $\begin{cases} 25p + 15q = 85 & 1 \\ 12p - 15q = 63 & 2 \end{cases}$

WRITTEN EXERCISES

A　　　Solve each system.

1. $\begin{cases} 3x + y = 9 \\ 2x + y = 1 \end{cases}$

2. $\begin{cases} 3x + y = 10 \\ 2x + y = 7 \end{cases}$

3. $\begin{cases} 5r - s = -23 \\ 3r - s = -15 \end{cases}$

4. $\begin{cases} 2a + 3b = -5 \\ 5a + 3b = 1 \end{cases}$

5. $\begin{cases} 3x + 2y = -7 \\ 5x - 2y = -1 \end{cases}$

6. $\begin{cases} x + 3y = 14 \\ x - 2y = -1 \end{cases}$

7. $\begin{cases} 2t + 3v = 6 \\ 2t - 5v = 22 \end{cases}$

8. $\begin{cases} 2x + 3y = 8 \\ 3x + y = 5 \end{cases}$

9. $\begin{cases} 2x + y = 3 \\ 7x - 4y = 18 \end{cases}$

10. $\begin{cases} 5x + y = 15 \\ 3x + 2y = 9 \end{cases}$

11. $\begin{cases} 7r - 5t = -2 \\ -8r - t = 9 \end{cases}$

12. $\begin{cases} 4p - 2q = 20 \\ p + 5q = -17 \end{cases}$

13. $\begin{cases} 2a + 5b = 18 \\ -5a + b = -18 \end{cases}$

14. $\begin{cases} 2u + 2z = 8 \\ 5u - 3z = 4 \end{cases}$

15. $\begin{cases} 4a + 3b = -2 \\ 8a - 2b = 12 \end{cases}$

16. $\begin{cases} 2x - 5y = 7 \\ 3x - 2y = -17 \end{cases}$

17. $\begin{cases} 9c + 7d = 14 \\ -6c - d = -2 \end{cases}$

18. $\begin{cases} 4r + 3s = 7 \\ 4r + 4s = 12 \end{cases}$

19. $\begin{cases} 4x - 3y - 5 = 0 \\ -2x + 9y + 1 = 0 \end{cases}$

20. $\begin{cases} 5a - 2b - 11 = 0 \\ 3a + 5b - 19 = 0 \end{cases}$

21. $\begin{cases} 6n - 2k + 3 = 0 \\ 2n + 4k - 5 = 0 \end{cases}$

22. $\begin{cases} 9x - 2y = 2\frac{1}{2} \\ 5x - 6y = -3\frac{1}{2} \end{cases}$

23. $\begin{cases} 3x + 5y = 4\frac{1}{2} \\ -9x - 2y = -7 \end{cases}$

24. $\begin{cases} 8x + 6y = 10 \\ -4x + 3y = -1 \end{cases}$

25. $\begin{cases} 5x + 4y = -\frac{1}{3} \\ 7x + 2y = \frac{4}{3} \end{cases}$

26. $\begin{cases} 2x - 3y = 9.4 \\ -5x + 9y = -12.4 \end{cases}$

27. $\begin{cases} x + 3y = 17.3 \\ 2x - 7y = -36.9 \end{cases}$

28. $\begin{cases} 2r - 7t = 8 \\ 4r - 9t = 19 \end{cases}$

29. $\begin{cases} 4c - 6d = 8 \\ -9c - 6d = -96 \end{cases}$

30. $\begin{cases} 2w - 3q = 8 \\ 3w - 7q = 7 \end{cases}$

What values of *r* and *s* will eliminate the *y* term?

31. $r(-2x + y - 5) + s(x + 3y - 1) = 0$

32. $r(2x + 3y - 3) + s(3x - 5y + 2) = 0$

33. $r(3x + 4y - 10) + s(2x - y + 8) = 0$

34. $r(3x + 2y - 2) + s(2x + 3y + 2) = 0$

Solve each system.

35. $\begin{cases} 2x + 1.5y = -1 \\ 0.5x + 2y = 3 \end{cases}$

36. $\begin{cases} x - 2.3 = -5y \\ 2x - 2 = 3y \end{cases}$

37. $\begin{cases} 2a - 1.5b = 10 \\ 0.3a - 0.05b = 0.8 \end{cases}$

38. $\begin{cases} 2x - 3y = 0.1 \\ 3x - 3 = -5y \end{cases}$

39. $\begin{cases} 1.25s + 8.25t = 107.5 \\ 2.5s - t = 0.8 \end{cases}$

40. $\begin{cases} 10x + 5y = 3.5 \\ 3y - 0.6 = 3x \end{cases}$

41. Solve the system: $\begin{cases} -3x - y + 10\frac{1}{2} = 0 \\ 6x - 2y - 7 = 0 \end{cases}$

42. Show that for all real numbers *f* and *g*, the solution of the system in Exercise 41 is also a solution of

$$f(-3x - y + 10\tfrac{1}{2}) + g(6x - 2y - 7) = 0.$$

43. Prove this statement.

For all real numbers *A*, *B*, *C*, and *D* where $A \ne 0$, $B \ne 0$, and $C \ne D$, the following system has no solutions.

$$\begin{cases} Ax + By = C \\ Ax + By = D \end{cases}$$

―――― **REVIEW CAPSULE FOR SECTION 6-4** ――――

Choose a variable to represent one unknown and tell what it represents. Then represent the second unknown in terms of the variable. *(Pages 122–124)*

1. Nancy invested $2,100 more than Hal.

2. Emily is one-half as old as Roger.

3. Jim has three times as many shirts as he has pants.

4. Suzanne had four more dollars than Joe had.

5. The bookcase is twice as high as it is wide.

6. Cindy owns three fewer pairs of shoes than her mother does.

7. The Owens have one more than twice as many children as the Bakers.

8. The swimming pool is two-thirds as wide as it is long.

Problem Solving and Applications

6-4 Using Two Variables

You can use systems of equations to solve word problems. First, you use Condition 1 to represent the unknowns by two variables. You also use this condition to write one equation of the system.

Condition 1	Represent the unknowns	Equation for Condition 1
The sum of two numbers is 12.	Let x = the first number. Let y = the second number.	$x + y = 12$
The length of a rectangle is 3 meters less than twice its width.	Let l = the length. Let w = the width.	$l = 2w - 3$
Jaime's age exceeds his sister's age by 8 years.	Let a = Jaime's age. Let b = his sister's age.	$a = b + 8$, or $a - b = 8$
The total number of balcony and orchestra seats sold was 685.	Let a = the number of balcony seats. Let c = the number of orchestra seats.	$a + b = 685$
A trucker buys 200 fewer crates of apples than pears.	Let c = the number of crates of apples. Let p = the number of crates of pears.	$c = p - 200$

You use Condition 2 to write the second equation for the system. The Example shows you how to do this.

EXAMPLE Joe has 6 fewer EE bonds than Art (Condition 1). Twice the number Art has is 5 more than three times the number Joe has (Condition 2). How many EE bonds does each have?

Solution: Let x = the number Art has. ⟵ **Represent the unknowns.**
Let y = the number Joe has.

$$\begin{cases} x - y = 6 & \quad 1 \\ 2x = 3y + 5 & \quad 2 \end{cases}$$

⟵ **Equation for Condition 1**
⟵ **Equation for Condition 2**

To solve the system, multiply Equation 1 by -3.

$$\begin{array}{ll} -3x + 3y = -18 & 1 \\ \underline{2x - 3y = 5} & 2 \\ -x = -13 & \end{array}$$

$x = 13$ ⟵ **Don't forget to find y.**

$x - y = 6$ ⟵ **Replace x with 13.**

$13 - y = 6$

$-y = -7$

$y = 7$

The procedure that follows summarizes the steps for using a system of equations in two variables to solve word problems.

Procedure

To solve word problems using a system of equations in two variables:

1. Use Condition 1 and two variables to represent the unknowns. Write an equation in two variables that expresses Condition 1.

2. Write a second equation in two variables that expresses Condition 2.

3. Solve the system of equations.

4. Check your solution in the original conditions of the problem. Answer the question.

CLASSROOM EXERCISES

Choose two variables to represent the unknowns. Then write an equation to express Condition 1.

1. The sum of two numbers is 16.

2. Two angles have a sum of 90°.

3. The difference between the heights of two boys is 4 centimeters.

4. A service station operator sells twice as much regular as premium gas.

5. A cup of cooked macaroni contains 105 calories more than an ounce of cheese.

6. Amy sold a total of 870 adult and student tickets for the senior class play.

7. The length of a rectangle is twice the width.

8. The perimeter of a rectangular picture frame is 246 centimeters.

9. A truck is loaded to capacity with apples and peaches. The capacity of the truck is 5000 pounds.

10. A health store has a mixture of 40 kilograms of walnuts and pecans on hand.

WORD PROBLEMS

A   Solve each problem. In some problems, Condition 1 is <u>underscored once</u>. Condition 2 is <u>underscored twice</u>.

1. <u>The sum of two numbers is 52.</u> <u><u>The difference of the same two numbers is 20.</u></u> Find the numbers.

2. <u>One number is 5 more than a second number.</u> <u><u>The sum of the numbers is 115.</u></u> What are the numbers?

3. One number is 3 times a second number. The larger number decreased by the smaller is 18. Find the numbers.

4. The sum of two numbers is 21. One number is 3 less than the other. Find the numbers.

5. The difference between two numbers is 4. Three times the larger is 2 more than five times the smaller. Find the numbers.

6. The sum of two unknown numbers is 20. Twice the larger number is three times the smaller number. Find each of the numbers.

7. The width of a rectangle is 6 inches less than the length. The perimeter is 72 inches. Find the length and the width.

8. The length of a rectangle is 4 feet more than the width. The perimeter is 40 feet. Find the length and width.

9. The distance from St. Louis to Chicago is 111 miles more than the distance from Chicago to Minneapolis. The sum of the two distances is 697 miles. Find the distance from St. Louis to Chicago.

10. The distance by air from New York to London is 545 kilometers more than twice the distance from London to Moscow. The sum of the two distances is 8105 kilometers. Find the distance from New York to London.

11. Two sides of a triangle are equal. Each of the two equal sides is 5 inches more than the third side. The perimeter is 35 inches. Find the length of each side.

12. Each of the two equal sides of a triangle is 1.2 centimeters longer than the third side. The perimeter is 17.4 centimeters. Find the length of each side.

B

13. Two angles are **supplementary; that is,** the sum of their measures is 180°. The measure of one angle is 30° more than twice the other. What is the measure of each angle?

14. Two angles are **complementary; that is,** the sum of their measures is 90°. The measure of one angle is twice the measure of the other. What is the measure of each angle?

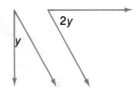

15. Seven times the sum of two numbers is 28. When the second number is multiplied by 3 and added to the first number, the sum equals the second number. Find each number.

16. An oak tree is 20 years older than a pine tree. In eight years, the oak tree will be 3 times as old as the pine tree will be then. Find the present age of each tree.

17. Enrico's father is now twice his age. In 20 years, Enrico will be two-thirds his father's age then. How old is each now?

18. Find two numbers such that one is as much more than 30 as the other is less than 30, and 8 times their difference is equal to the larger.

Problem Solving and Applications

6-5 Digit Problems

Systems of equations in two variables are particularly useful in solving problems related to numbers and their digits. Suppose that you are asked to represent a two-digit number.

Two–Digit Number

Example: 85	**In General:** $10t + u$
Tens digit: 8	Tens digit: t
Units digit: 5	Units digit: u
Number: $10 \cdot 8 + 5$, or 85	Number: $10t + u$
Sum of digits: $8 + 5$	Sum of digits: $t + u$

When solving digit problems, be careful to distinguish between representing the *sum of the digits* and representing *the number*.

EXAMPLE   The sum of the digits of a two-digit number is 6 (Condition 1). The number is six times the units digit (Condition 2). Find the number.

Solution: Follow the steps of the procedure in Section 6–4 on page 224.

$\boxed{1}$ Let t = the tens digit.
Let u = the units digit.   ⟵—————— **Represent the unknowns.**
Then $10t + u$ = the number.

$\boxed{2}$ $\begin{cases} t + u = 6 & 1 \leftarrow\!\!\!-\!\!\!- \textbf{The sum of the digits is 6.} \\ 10t + u = 6u & 2 \leftarrow\!\!\!-\!\!\!- \textbf{The number is 6 times the units digit.} \end{cases}$

$\boxed{3}$ Combine like terms in Equation 2.

$10t - 5u = 0 \qquad 2$

To eliminate the variable u, multiply Equation 1 by 5.

$$\begin{array}{ll} 5t + 5u = 30 & 1 \\ \underline{10t - 5u = 0} & 2 \\ 15t = 30 \end{array}$$

$t = 2$ ⟵————— **Don't forget to find u.**

$t + u = 6$ 1 ⟵————— **Replace t with 2 in Equation 1.**

$2 + u = 6$

$u = 4$ ⟵————— **Don't forget to find the number.**

Number: $10t + u = 10 \cdot 2 + 4 = 24$

Check: $\boxed{4}$ **Condition 1**   Is the sum of the digits equal to 6? $2 + 4 = 6$?   Yes ✔

Condition 2   Is the number six times the units digit?

$24 = 6 \cdot 4$?   Yes ✔   The number is **24**.

To represent a three-digit number, let h represent the hundreds digit, t represent the tens digit and u represent the units digit. Then the number is

$$100h + 10t + u. \longleftarrow \textbf{Three-digit number}$$

CLASSROOM EXERCISES

For each problem in Exercises 1–6, let t represent the tens digit and let u represent the units digit. Write the system of equations you would use to solve the problem.

1. The sum of the digits of a two-digit number is 12. The number is 12 times the tens digit.

2. The sum of the digits of a two-digit number is 9. The number is 6 times the units digit.

3. The sum of the digits of a two-digit number is 10. The tens digit is 4 more than the units digit.

4. The sum of the digits of a two-digit number is 9. The units digit is 7 more than the tens digit.

5. The units digit of a two-digit number is twice the tens digit. The number is 6 more than 5 times the units digit.

6. The tens digit of a two-digit number is 2 more than the units digit. The number is 5 more than 7 times the tens digit.

WORD PROBLEMS

A   Write a system of equations in two variables for each problem. Then solve the problem. For some problems, Condition 1 is <u>underscored once</u>, Condition 2 is <u>underscored twice</u>.

1. The sum of the digits of a two-digit number is 12. The number is 12 times the tens digit. Find the number.

2. The sum of the digits of a two-digit number is 10. The tens digit is 4 more than the units digit. Find the number.

3. The units digit of a two-digit number is twice the tens digit. The difference between the digits is 4. Find the number.

4. The units digit of a two-digit number is 2 less than the tens digit. The number is 2 more than 6 times the sum of the digits. Find the number.

5. The units digit of a two-digit number is 11 less than twice the tens digit. The number is 6 less than 7 times the sum of the digits of the number. Find the number.

6. The tens digit of a two-digit number is 14 less than twice the units digit. The number is 3 less than 4 times the sum of the digits of the number. Find the number.

7. The sum of the digits of a two-digit number is 9. The number is 27 more than the original number with its digits reversed. Find the number. (HINT: The number with its digits reversed is $10u + t$.)

8. A two-digit number is 5 times the sum of its digits. When 9 is added to the number, the result is the original number with its digits reversed. Find the number.

9. The sum of the digits of a two-digit number is 11. When 45 is added to the number, the result is the original number with its digits reversed. Find the number.

10. When 63 is subtracted from a two-digit number, the result is the original number with its digits reversed. The tens digit of the original number exceeds 4 times the units digit by 1. Find the number.

B

11. A two-digit number is 5 times the sum of its digits. The digits from left to right name consecutive integers. Find the number.

12. A two-digit number is 6 more than 4 times the sum of its digits. The digits from left to right are consecutive even integers. Find the number.

C

13. The sum of the digits of a certain three-digit number is 8. The tens digit is two less than the hundreds digit, and the units digit is three times the hundreds digit. Find the number.

14. The sum of the digits of a three-digit number is 14. The tens digit is one more than twice the hundreds digit and the units digit is one less than 4 times the hundreds digit. Find the number.

15. Represent the difference between any two-digit number and the number with its digits reversed.

16. Represent the sum of any two-digit number and the number with its digits reversed.

17. Use your answer to Exercise 15 to show that the difference between any two-digit number and the number with the digits reversed is divisible by 9.

18. Use your answer to Exercise 16 to show that the sum of a two-digit number and the number with its digits reversed is divisible by 11.

19. Show that the difference between a three-digit number and the number with its digits reversed is divisible by 99.

20. Show that the difference between a four-digit number and the number with its digits reversed is divisible by 9.

───── **Review** ─────────────────

Solve each system by graphing. *(Section 6–1)*

1. $\begin{cases} 2x - y = 8 \\ x + y = 4 \end{cases}$

2. $\begin{cases} x + y = 9 \\ x - y = 5 \end{cases}$

3. $\begin{cases} 3x = 9 \\ x + y = -1 \end{cases}$

Write *one, none,* or *infinitely many* to describe the number of solutions for each system. *(Section 6–1)*

4. $\begin{cases} y = 3x - 1 \\ y = 5x \end{cases}$

5. $\begin{cases} y = 4x - 1 \\ 8x = 2y + 2 \end{cases}$

6. $\begin{cases} x = 2y - 4 \\ y = x + 7 \end{cases}$

Use the addition method to solve each system. *(Section 6–2)*

7. $\begin{cases} x + 2y = -4 \\ -x + y = 1 \end{cases}$

8. $\begin{cases} 2a - 7b = 41 \\ a + 7b = -32 \end{cases}$

9. $\begin{cases} 0.6x + 0.5y = 0 \\ 0.2x - 0.5y = 0.4 \end{cases}$

In Exercises 10–12, use multiplication with the addition method to solve each system. *(Section 6–3)*

10. $\begin{cases} 2x + y = 7 \\ -x + y = 4 \end{cases}$

11. $\begin{cases} 4r - 7s = 18 \\ r + 3s = -5 \end{cases}$

12. $\begin{cases} 4x + 3y = -2 \\ 3x + 2y = 1 \end{cases}$

13. The length of a rectangular desk is 11 inches less than twice the width. The perimeter of the desk is 206 centimeters. Find the length and the width. *(Section 6–4)*

14. Karl's age is now 2 years more than twice his brother's. In 5 years, Karl's age will equal three times his brother's age now. How old is each now? *(Section 6–4)*

15. The sum of the digits of a two-digit number is 12. The ones digit is one-half as large as the tens digit. Find the number. *(Section 6–5)*

16. The sum of the digits of a two-digit number is 15. The number is 9 less than the number obtained by reversing the digits. Find the number. *(Section 6–5)*

CALCULATOR APPLICATIONS

Checking Systems of Equations

You can use a calculator to check whether a given ordered pair is a solution of a system of equations.

EXAMPLE Check the solution set, $\{(-2, 1)\}$, of Example 2 on page 220.

SOLUTION 1. $2x + 3y = -1$

$\boxed{-1.}$

2. $5x - 2y = -12$

$\boxed{-12.}$

EXERCISES

Check each given solution set. Correct any incorrect solutions.

1. $\begin{cases} x + y = 5 \\ 2x - y = -2 \end{cases}; \{(1, 4)\}$

2. $\begin{cases} 2x + y = 1 \\ 2x - y = 7 \end{cases}; \{(-2, 3)\}$

3. $\begin{cases} -2x + y = 1 \\ 4x + 3y = 23 \end{cases}; \{(2, -5)\}$

4. $\begin{cases} -x - 5y = -6 \\ 2y - 3x = 16 \end{cases}; \{(-4, 2)\}$

—————— **REVIEW CAPSULE FOR SECTION 6–6** ——————

Solve each equation for x in terms of y. *(Pages 162–164)*

1. $2x + 4y = 6$

2. $-x + 3y = 7$

3. $3x + 5y = 9$

4. $2y - x = 1$

5. $y = 3 - x$

6. $y = \frac{1}{3}x$

7. $y - x = -3$

8. $-12x = 7y$

Consumer Applications

Saving Energy: Cooling Costs

To save energy in warm weather, power companies recommend a setting of **78° Fahrenheit** on your air conditioner. The table at the right shows the per cent of savings and loss with respect to 78°F for settings from 72°F to 80°F. A loss is indicated by a negative per cent.

Setting	Savings Loss (−)
80°F	16%
79	8%
78	0
77	−8%
76	−18%
75	−28%
74	−39%
73	−50%
72	−63%

EXAMPLE 1 Last year the Carlton family spent $800 to operate their air conditioner with the thermostat set at 75°F. How much would they save by setting the thermostat at 79°F?

Solution: Subtract to find the per cent of change.

$8\% - (-28\%) = 36\%$ savings ◄——— **From the table**

$800 \times 36\% = 800 \times 0.36 = \$288$

They would save **$288**.

Example 1 assumes that the Carlton family has an air conditioner with the correct cooling capacity. The **cooling capacity** is the amount of heat (measured in Btu's) that an air conditioning unit can remove from the air in an hour. If the air conditioner is too small, it will run constantly and still not cool the room. If it is too large, the air conditioner will stop and start, lower the temperature quickly, but not remove the humidity from the room. So you will still be uncomfortable.

The graph at the right can be used to estimate the cooling capacity needed for a given room of a house or apartment. (The graph can be used for any room that is about 8 feet high, provided that it is not directly below an attic floor.) The exposure of the room's exterior wall determines which part of the shaded band you should use.

EXAMPLE 2 A room of a house has a northern exposure. Its floor area is 300 square feet. What must be the size (cooling capacity) of the air conditioner for this room?

Solution: $\boxed{1}$ On the vertical scale, find the room's floor area, 300 square feet.

$\boxed{2}$ Since the room has a northern exposure, find the point on the <u>left</u> portion of the band directly to the right of the 300 reading.

$\boxed{3}$ From this point on the band read directly <u>down</u> on the horizontal scale to find the correct cooling capacity, **5500 Btu's per hour.**

Cooling Capacity
(thousands of Btu's per hour)

EXERCISES

In Exercises 1–8, use the table on page 230 to find how much each family would save over last year's air conditioning costs.

	Yearly Cooling Costs	Last Year's Thermostat Setting	This Year's Thermostat Setting
1.	$700	74°F	79°F
2.	$480	77°F	80°F
3.	$850	72°F	77°F
4.	$640	76°F	79°F
5.	$900	73°F	78°F
6.	$570	75°F	76°F
7.	$540	74°F	77°F
8.	$620	73°F	79°F

Monitoring a Large Air Conditioning Unit

In Exercises 9–17, estimate the size of an air conditioner needed to cool each room described. Round each answer to the nearest 500 Btu's.

9. Western exposure
   300 square feet

10. Northern exposure
    100 square feet

11. Southern exposure
    200 square feet

12. Eastern exposure
    150 square feet

13. Western exposure
    250 square feet

14. Northern exposure
    350 square feet

15. Southern exposure
    300 square feet

16. Western exposure
    700 square feet

17. Eastern exposure
    400 square feet

6-6 Substitution Method

The **substitution method** is another way to solve a system of two linear equations. First you solve one of the equations for one of the variables. Then you substitute the value of this variable in the other equation.

EXAMPLE   Solve by the substitution method: $\begin{cases} -x + 2y = 4 & 1 \\ 5x - 3y = 1 & 2 \end{cases}$

Solution: Since the x term in Equation 1 has a coefficient of -1, it will probably be simpler to solve this equation for x.

$$-x + 2y = 4 \qquad 1$$
$$-x = 4 - 2y \qquad \longleftarrow \quad \textbf{Multiply each side by (−1).}$$
$$x = 2y - 4$$
$$5x - 3y = 1 \qquad 2 \longleftarrow \quad \textbf{Replace x with (2y − 4).}$$
$$5(2y - 4) - 3y = 1 \qquad \longleftarrow \quad \textbf{Solve for y.}$$
$$10y - 20 - 3y = 1$$
$$7y = 21$$
$$y = 3 \qquad 3 \longleftarrow \quad \textbf{Replace y with 3 in Equation 1.}$$
$$-x + 2y = 4 \qquad 1$$
$$-x + 2(3) = 4$$
$$x = 2 \qquad 4 \longleftarrow \quad \textbf{The check is left for you.}$$

Solution set: $\{(2, 3)\}$

The following procedure summarizes the steps for solving a system of two linear equations by the substitution method.

Procedure

> **To solve a system of two linear equations by the substitution method:**
> 1. Solve one equation for one of the variables.
> 2. Substitute the resulting expression in the other equation.
> 3. Solve the resulting equation.
> 4. Find the values of the variables.

CLASSROOM EXERCISES

Determine the solution set of each system.

1. $\begin{cases} 3x + y = 5 \\ x = 1 \end{cases}$

2. $\begin{cases} b = 4 \\ a - b = 7 \end{cases}$

3. $\begin{cases} 2p - q = 2 \\ p = -1 \end{cases}$

4. $\begin{cases} 3x - 2y = 7 \\ -y = 1 \end{cases}$

5. $\begin{cases} p + 2r = -1 \\ p = 5 \end{cases}$

6. $\begin{cases} s - t = -5 \\ -t = 3 \end{cases}$

WRITTEN EXERCISES

A Use the substitution method to solve each system.

1. $\begin{cases} x = y + 4 \\ 2x - 5y = 2 \end{cases}$

2. $\begin{cases} y = 3 - x \\ 5x + 3y = -1 \end{cases}$

3. $\begin{cases} x = 8y \\ x - 4y = 12 \end{cases}$

4. $\begin{cases} 5x - y = 1 \\ 3x + 2y = 13 \end{cases}$

5. $\begin{cases} 5a = b \\ a = 10b + 5 \end{cases}$

6. $\begin{cases} r = 5 - s \\ 2r + 7s = 0 \end{cases}$

7. $\begin{cases} c = d + 4 \\ 2c + 3d = -2 \end{cases}$

8. $\begin{cases} x + 3y = 5 \\ -3x + 2y = 18 \end{cases}$

9. $\begin{cases} c = d - 4 \\ 3c + d = 4 \end{cases}$

10. $\begin{cases} 3x + y = 7 \\ x - y = 1 \end{cases}$

11. $\begin{cases} 4x - y = 7 \\ 5x - 8y = 2 \end{cases}$

12. $\begin{cases} r + s = 3 \\ r - s = 1 \end{cases}$

13. $\begin{cases} 2a + b = 5 \\ 8a - b = 45 \end{cases}$

14. $\begin{cases} p - 3q = 0 \\ 2p - 5q = 4 \end{cases}$

15. $\begin{cases} 5c - 3d + 1 = 0 \\ -c + 3d + 7 = 0 \end{cases}$

B

16. $\begin{cases} y + 2x = 0 \\ x + 2y - 9 = 0 \end{cases}$

17. $\begin{cases} r + t = 0 \\ 3r + 2t - 5 = 0 \end{cases}$

18. $\begin{cases} 3t - u = 0 \\ t + u = 12 \end{cases}$

19. $\begin{cases} y = 8 - x \\ 4x - 3y = -3 \end{cases}$

20. $\begin{cases} 3x + 2y = 16 \\ 7x + y = 19 \end{cases}$

21. $\begin{cases} c + 2d = 4 \\ 3c - 4d = 7 \end{cases}$

22. $\begin{cases} 2r + s = 11 \\ r - s = 2 \end{cases}$

23. $\begin{cases} 4x - 2y = 3 \\ 3x - y = 4 \end{cases}$

24. $\begin{cases} 5a - b = -9 \\ 4a + 3b = -11 \end{cases}$

25. $\begin{cases} 4a + b - 8 = 0 \\ 5a + 3b - 3 = 0 \end{cases}$

26. $\begin{cases} 2u - r + 2 = 0 \\ 6u + 12r - 1 = 0 \end{cases}$

27. $\begin{cases} 4s + 3t - 1 = 0 \\ 8s + 6t - 2 = 0 \end{cases}$

C Use the substitution method to solve each system. Solve for x and y in terms of the other variables.

28. $\begin{cases} 6x - 4y = 2d \\ x - y + d = 0 \end{cases}$

29. $\begin{cases} 3x = y + h \\ 5x = 3y + 7h \end{cases}$

30. $\begin{cases} 5x - 3y = -2a \\ 2x + 5y = 24a \end{cases}$

REVIEW CAPSULE FOR SECTION 6–7

Write an algebraic expression to represent the value of each word expression. *(Pages 118–121)*

Example: The number of cents in n dimes   Solution: **10 · n**   or   **10n**

1. The number of cents in k nickels.

2. The number of cents in t quarters

3. The number of dollars in b half-dollars

4. The number of dollars in k \$5.00-raffle tickets

5. The number of cents in m 20¢ stamps

6. The number of dollars in p \$1000-bonds

7. The number of cents in q quarters and d dimes

8. The number of cents in d dimes and n nickels

9. The number of dollars in r raffle tickets at \$2.50 each and t tickets at \$5.00 each

10. The number of dollars in b \$100–bonds and q \$1000–bonds

6-7 Money Problems

Problems that involve the cost of two items can often be solved by using a system of equations in two variables. In solving such problems, it is helpful to make a table showing the number of items (Condition 1) and the value of the items (Condition 2).

EXAMPLE 1 An auditorium seats 2500 persons. How many balcony tickets must be sold for $4.50 each and how many orchestra tickets must be sold for $5.25 each in order to receive total receipts of $12,675 each time the auditorium is full?

Solution: $\boxed{1}$ Follow the steps of the procedure on page 224.

	Number (Condition 1)	Price per Ticket	Total Sales (Condition 2)
Balcony tickets	x	$4.50	$4.50x$
Orchestra tickets	y	$5.25	$5.25y$
TOTAL	2500		$12,675

Use Conditions 1 and 2 to write a system of equations.

$\boxed{2}$ $\begin{cases} x + y = 2500 & \text{1} \longleftarrow \textbf{Number of tickets sold} \\ 4.50x + 5.25y = 12{,}675 & \text{2} \longleftarrow \textbf{Total sales} \end{cases}$

$\boxed{3}$ Solve the system. The substitution method is used below.

$x + y = 2500$ 1 $\longleftarrow$ **Solve for x in terms of y.**

$\qquad x = 2500 - y$

$\qquad\qquad 4.50x + 5.25y = 12{,}675$ 2 $\longleftarrow$ **Replace x with (2500 − y).**

$\qquad 4.50(2500 - y) + 5.25y = 12{,}675$

$\qquad 11{,}250 - 4.50y + 5.25y = 12{,}675$

$\qquad\qquad 11{,}250 + 0.75y = 12{,}675$

$\qquad\qquad\qquad 0.75y = 1425$

$\qquad\qquad\qquad\qquad y = 1900$ $\longleftarrow$ **Don't forget to find x.**

$\qquad\qquad\qquad x + y = 2500$ $\longleftarrow$ **Replace y with 1900.**

$\qquad\qquad\quad x + 1900 = 2500$

$\qquad\qquad\qquad\qquad x = 600$

Check: $\boxed{4}$ **Condition 1** Were 2500 tickets sold? $600 + 1900 = 2500$? Yes ✔

$\qquad$ **Condition 2** Do total receipts equal $12,675?

$\qquad\qquad 600(\$4.50) + 1900(\$5.25) = \$12{,}675$? Yes ✔

Thus, **600 balcony seats** and **1900 orchestra seats** must be sold.

Investment problems are based on the simple interest formula,

$$i = prt.$$

Since the time, t, in these problems is usually one year, multiply the principal or amount invested, p, and the rate, r, (expressed as a decimal) to find the interest. That is,

$$i = pr.$$

As in Example 1, making a table will help you to organize the given information and to write the equations for the system. Use the method you prefer to solve the system.

EXAMPLE 2 Cora invested $5000, part at a yearly interest rate of 8.5% and part at a yearly interest rate of 9% (Condition 1). The total interest earned in one year was $442.50 (Condition 2). Find the amount invested at each rate.

Solution: **1**

	Amount Invested (Condition 1)	Interest Rate	Interest (Condition 2)
Lower rate	x	8.5% or 0.085	$0.085x$
Higher rate	y	9% or 0.09	$0.09y$
TOTAL	$5000		$442.50

2 $\begin{cases} x + y = 5000 \\ 0.085x + 0.09y = 442.50 \end{cases}$ 1 ⟵——— **Amount invested**
   2 ⟵——— **Total interest**

3 Solve the system. The substitution method is used below.

$x + y = 5000$ 1 ⟵—— **Solve for x in terms of y.**

$x = 5000 - y$

$0.085x + 0.09y = 442.50$ 2 ⟵—— **Replace x with (5000 − y).**

$0.085(5000 - y) + 0.09y = 442.50$

$425 - 0.085y + 0.09y = 442.50$

$425 + 0.005y = 442.50$

$0.005y = 17.50$

$y = 3500$ ⟵——— **Don't forget to find x.**

$x + y = 5000$

$x + 3500 = 5000$

$x = 1500$

Check: **4** **Condition 1** Does $1500 + $3500 = $5000?   Yes ✔

Condition 2 Does $0.085($1500) + 0.09($3500) = $442.50?

$127.50 + $315.00 = $442.50?   Yes ✔

Thus, **$1500** was invested at 8.5% and **$3500** was invested at 9%.

An equation such as

$$0.005y = 17.50$$

in Example 2 is sometimes easier to solve by multiplying each side by 10, by 100, by 1000, and so on, in order to eliminate the decimal coefficient of y. Thus,

$$0.005y = 17.50 \longleftarrow \textbf{Multiply each side by 1000.}$$
$$5y = 17{,}500$$
$$y = \textbf{3500}$$

CLASSROOM EXERCISES

In Exercises 1–4, first complete the table. Then write a system of equations that could be used to solve for x and y.

1. Eugene has 12 coins in dimes and quarters. The total value of the coins is $1.95.

	Number of Coins	Value of Each	Total Value
Dimes	x	$0.10	?
Quarters	y	?	?
TOTAL	?		?

2. Martha bought 13 stamps having a total value of $2.85. She bought 15¢ stamps and 25¢ stamps.

	Number of Stamps	Value of Each	Total Value
15¢ stamps	x	$0.15	?
25¢ stamps	y	?	?
TOTAL	?		?

3. Gina worked a total of 57 hours on two jobs. One job paid $4.50 an hour and the other paid $4.75 an hour. Her total pay for the 57 hours amounted to $260.75.

	Number of Hours	Wages per Hour	Total Wages
First job	x	$4.50	?
Second job	y	?	?
TOTAL	?		?

4. The Ciara family invested a sum of money, part at a yearly interest rate of 7.5% and part at a yearly interest rate of 9.6%. The total investment of $15,500 earned $1425 in one year.

	Amount Invested	Interest Rate	Interest
Lower rate	x	7.5%, or __?__	__?__
Higher rate	y	9.6%, or __?__	__?__
TOTAL	__?__		__?__

WORD PROBLEMS

A Solve each problem.

1. Melissa has 45 coins in dimes and quarters. The total value of the coins is $7.65. How many coins of each kind does she have?

2. José puts quarters and nickels aside for paying tolls. He has a total of 18 coins with a total value of $2.90. How many quarters does he have?

3. Dick Arico invested $5000, part at a yearly rate of 7% and part at a yearly rate of 9%. The total interest earned for one year was $368. How much did he invest at each rate?

4. Partners in a business agreed to take out two loans totaling $35,000. The yearly interest rates were 12% and 15% and the total yearly interest was $4650. Find the amount of each loan.

5. A total of 7500 tickets were sold for a concert. Total receipts amounted to $45,000. Tickets sold for $5.50 and $7.00. How many of each type of ticket were sold?

6. Five full-fare bus tickets and one half-fare ticket cost $90.75. Four full-fare tickets and two half-fare tickets cost $82.50. How much does a full-fare ticket cost?

7. Rachel makes a bank deposit of $595 with 96 five- and ten-dollar bills. How many of each kind of bill did she deposit?

8. Maria paid $6.60 for some 15¢ stamps and some 20¢ stamps. She bought 37 stamps in all. How many of each kind did she buy?

9. A store had a special sale on two models of calculators. One model sold for $22.75 and another model for $15.95. In all, thirty-one calculators were sold. The total amount of sales, not including tax, was $576.05. How many of each model were sold?

10. A door-to-door salesperson sells dictionaries at $15 each and almanacs at $6.50 each. Sales over three days amounted to 36 books sold with total sales amounting to $361.50. How many of each kind of book were sold?

B

11. A lending library charges a fixed amount for the first day that a book is overdue and an additional charge for each day thereafter. Raoul paid $0.75 for one book that was 7 days overdue and $1.95 for a book that was 19 days overdue. Find the fixed charge and the charge for each additional day.

12. Bob West loaned $7800 to a bank customer for one year, part at 10% and the rest at 12%. If the rates of interest were interchanged, the interest for one year would have been $24 more. Find the amount he loaned at each rate.

6-8 Mixture Problems

Mixture problems involve two or more ingredients that are combined to produce a given mixture with a given value. Making a table to show the *amount* of each ingredient (Condition 1) and the *total value* of each ingredient (Condition 2) will help you to organize the information and to write a system of equations for the problem.

EXAMPLE 1   The owner of Corner Health Foods wishes to mix raisins that sell at $5.75 per kilogram with nuts that sell at $4.00 per kilogram to make a 100-kilogram mixture that sells at $4.70 per kilogram. How many kilograms of raisins and how many kilograms of nuts must be used?

Solution: $\boxed{1}$ Follow the steps of the procedure given on page 224.

	Number of Kilograms (Condition 1)	Value per Kilogram	Total Value (Condition 2)
Raisins	x	$5.75	$5.75x$
Nuts	y	$4.00	$4.00y$
Mixture	100	$4.70	$4.70(100)$

$\boxed{2}$ $\begin{cases} x + y = 100 \\ 5.75x + 4.00y = 4.70(100) \end{cases}$ 1 ◄——— **Amount**
                                                                        2 ◄——— **Value**

$\boxed{3}$ Solve the system. The substitution method is used below.

$$x + y = 100 \qquad\qquad 1 \longleftarrow \textbf{Solve for x in terms of y.}$$
$$x = 100 - y$$
$$5.75x + 4.00y = 470 \qquad 2 \longleftarrow \textbf{Replace x with (100 - y).}$$
$$5.75(100 - y) + 4.00y = 470$$
$$575 - 5.75y + 4.00y = 470$$
$$575 - 1.75y = 470$$
$$-1.75y = -105$$
$$y = 60 \qquad \longleftarrow \textbf{Don't forget to find x.}$$
$$x + y = 100 \qquad 1$$
$$x + 60 = 100$$
$$x = 40$$

Check: $\boxed{4}$ **Condition 1**   Are there 100 kilograms in all? $40 + 60 = 100$?   Yes ✔

Condition 2   Does the total value equal $4.70(100)$ or 470?
$40($5.75) + 60($4.00) = 470?   Yes ✔

The owner should mix **40 kg** of raisins with **60 kg** of nuts.

Per cents are often used to express the strength of a solution or the amount of a specific ingredient in a solution or mixture. In such problems, one condition expresses the amounts of the two ingredients in the solution or mixture. The other condition expresses the strength of the solution or the per cent of a substance in the mixture.

EXAMPLE 2 A soil analysis of a lawn determines that 50 pounds of fertilizer containing 20% nitrogen is needed. How can this mixture be made from two different fertilizers, one containing 15% nitrogen and the other containing 24% nitrogen?

Solution: 1

	Number of Pounds (Condition 1)	Per Cent of Nitrogen	Amount of Nitrogen (Condition 2)
Fertilizer A	x	15%	$0.15x$
Fertilizer B	y	24%	$0.24y$
Mixture	50	20%	$0.20(50)$

2 $\begin{cases} x + y = 50 \\ 0.15x + 0.24y = 10 \end{cases}$ 1 ⟵——— **Condition 1**
2 ⟵——— **Condition 2**

3 The addition method is used below to solve the system. To eliminate the decimals, multiply each side of Equation **2** by 100.

$$15x + 24y = 1000 \qquad 2$$
$$\underline{-15x - 15y \quad -750} \qquad 1 \longleftarrow \text{—— } -15(x + y) = -15(50)$$
$$9y = \quad 250$$
$$y = 27.7 \text{ or } 28 \quad \longleftarrow \text{ Rounded to the nearest pound}$$
$$x + y = 50$$
$$x + 28 = 50$$
$$x = 22$$

4 The check is left for you.

About **22 pounds** of Fertilizer A and **28 pounds** of Fertilizer B are needed.

CLASSROOM EXERCISES

Read the problem and complete the table. Then write the system of equations you would use to solve each problem.

1. Cashews that sell for $6.50 per kilogram are mixed with almonds that sell for $8.00 per kilogram to make a 100-kilogram mixture. The mixture will sell for $7.40 per kilogram. How many kilograms of cashews and how many kilograms of almonds must be used? (See the table on page 240.)

	Number of Kilograms	Value per Kilogram	Total Value
Cashews	x	$6.50	?
Almonds	y	$8.00	?
Mixture	?	$7.40	?

2. A 20-kilogram mixture of coffee is made from two brands. Brand A sells at $5.50 per kilogram and Brand B at $6.50 per kilogram. The mixture will sell at $6.10 per kilogram. How many kilograms of Brand A and of Brand B must be used?

	Number of Kilograms	Value per Kilogram	Total Value
Brand A	x	?	?
Brand B	y	?	?
Mixture	?	?	?

WORD PROBLEMS

A Solve each problem.

1. A baker mixes cookies worth $0.95 per pound with cookies worth $1.70 per pound. How many of each kind must be used to produce a 45-pound mixture that sells for $1.25 per pound?

2. How many kilograms of cashews selling at $6.00 per kilogram must be mixed with 20 kilograms of peanuts selling at $3.25 per kilogram to produce a mixture worth $4.50 per kilogram?

3. A seed company sells one-ounce packets of a mixture of marigold seeds. Pretty Face marigolds sell at 50¢ per ounce and Golden Face marigolds sell at 40¢ per ounce. The mixture will sell at 45¢ per packet. How many ounces of each kind of seed must be used?

4. Solution A, which is 10% iodine, is mixed with Solution B, which is 18% iodine, to obtain 320 grams of a solution that is 15% iodine. How many grams of Solution A and how many grams of Solution B are needed for the 15%-solution?

5. A 4% salt solution is mixed with an 8% salt solution. How many grams of each solution are needed to obtain 400 grams of a 5% solution?

6. A 25% silver alloy is to be melted with a 55% silver alloy. How many grams of each must be used to obtain 30 grams of a 32% silver alloy?

7. An alloy that is 35% copper is melted with a second alloy that is 65% copper. How many kilograms of each alloy must be melted to obtain 20 kilograms of an alloy that is 41% copper?

8. A milk distributor has cream that is 24% butterfat and cream that is 18% butterfat. How many quarts of each must be used to obtain 90 quarts of cream that is 22% butterfat?

9. A chemist has one solution that is 40% acid and a second solution that is 15% acid. How many grams of each should be used to obtain 40 grams of a solution that is 25% acid?

10. Pecans priced at $5.85 per kilogram are mixed with almonds priced at $4.93 per kilogram to make a 40-kilogram mixture that is to sell at $5.62 per kilogram. How many kilograms of each kind of nut must be used?

B

11. A solution contains 8 grams of acid and 32 grams of water. How many grams of water must be evaporated to obtain a solution that is 40% acid?

12. A tank contains 100 liters of a solution of acid and water. The solution is 20% acid. How much water must be evaporated to obtain a solution that is 50% acid?

_____ Review _____

Use the substitution method to solve each system. *(Section 6–6)*

1. $\begin{cases} x + y = 10 \\ 3x - 2y = 5 \end{cases}$

2. $\begin{cases} 2r + t = 0 \\ 4r - 3t = -10 \end{cases}$

3. $\begin{cases} p - 2q = 1 \\ 2p + q = 12 \end{cases}$

4. $\begin{cases} p - 2n = 3 \\ 2p + n = 1 \end{cases}$

5. $\begin{cases} 3c + 2d = 0 \\ 2c - d = 7 \end{cases}$

6. $\begin{cases} 3a + b - 1 = 0 \\ 2a - 6b - 4 = 0 \end{cases}$

Solve.

7. Timothy has $5.00 in dimes and nickels. He has exactly 66 coins. How many coins of each kind does he have? *(Section 6–7)*

8. Rosita made a bank deposit of $250 with 17 ten– and twenty–dollar bills. How many bills of each type did she deposit? *(Section 6–7)*

9. Bob invested $1500, part at a yearly interest rate of 10% and the rest at a yearly interest rate of 9.5%. The total interest earned in one year was $145. How much did he invest at each rate? *(Section 6–7)*

10. Wild rice worth $9.50 per pound is mixed with brown rice worth $2.25 per pound. How many pounds of each kind of rice must be used to produce a 50-pound mixture selling for $3.70 per pound? *(Section 6–8)*

11. A 12% tin alloy is to be melted with an 18% tin alloy. How many kilograms of each alloy must be used to obtain 15 kilograms of an alloy that is 14% tin? *(Section 6–8)*

12. An 8% plant food solution is mixed with a 12% solution. How many liters of each solution are needed to obtain 10 liters of a 9% solution? *(Section 6–8)*

_____ Puzzle _____

Cristina can buy a bracelet and a watch band for $55, or the watch band and a locket for $46, or the locket and the bracelet for $37. What does the bracelet cost?

BASIC: SOLVING SYSTEMS OF EQUATIONS

One of the most common uses of computers is in solving systems of equations. For a system of the form

$$\begin{cases} A_1x + B_1y = C_1 \\ A_2x + B_2y = C_2 \end{cases}$$

the general solution is the following.

$$x = \frac{B_2C_1 - B_1C_2}{A_1B_2 - A_2B_1} \qquad y = \frac{A_1C_2 - A_2C_1}{A_1B_2 - A_2B_1}$$

Problem: *Write a program which solves systems of two linear equations in two variables.*

```
100 REM SOLVE A1*X + B1*Y = C1
110 REM          A2*X + B2*Y = C2
120 REM
130 PRINT "ENTER THE COEFFICIENTS OF THE FIRST EQUATION";
140 INPUT A1, B1, C1
150 PRINT "ENTER THE COEFFICIENTS OF THE SECOND EQUATION";
160 INPUT A2, B2, C2
170 LET D = A1*B2 - A2*B1
180 IF D = 0 THEN 230
190 LET X = (B2*C1 - B1*C2)/D
200 LET Y = (A1*C2 - A2*C1)/D
210 PRINT "SOLUTION IS (";X;",";Y;")"
220 GOTO 240
230 PRINT "NO UNIQUE SOLUTION"
240 PRINT "ANY MORE SYSTEMS TO SOLVE (1=YES, 0=NO)";
250 INPUT Z
260 IF Z = 1 THEN 130
270 END
```

The following is the output from a sample run of the program above.

```
RUN
ENTER THE COEFFICIENTS OF THE FIRST EQUATION? 1,1,1
ENTER THE COEFFICIENTS OF THE SECOND EQUATION? 2,2,2
NO UNIQUE SOLUTION

ANY MORE SYSTEMS TO SOLVE (1=YES, 0=NO)? 1
ENTER THE COEFFICIENTS OF THE FIRST EQUATION? 1,1,1
ENTER THE COEFFICIENTS OF THE SECOND EQUATION? 2,2,-7
NO UNIQUE SOLUTION
```

```
ANY MORE SYSTEMS TO SOLVE (1=YES, 0=NO)? 1
ENTER THE COEFFICIENTS OF THE FIRST EQUATION? 1,1,1
ENTER THE COEFFICIENTS OF THE SECOND EQUATION? 2,-1,2
SOLUTION IS ( 1 , 0 )

ANY MORE SYSTEMS TO SOLVE (1=YES, 0=NO)? 0
READY
```

Analysis

Statement 170: D is the denominator of the fraction used in statements 190 and 200.

Statements 180 and 230: If $D = 0$, the computer prints NO UNIQUE SOLUTION. The program does not decide whether the system has no solution or infinitely many solutions. (See Exercise 16 below.)

Statements 190–210: If $D \neq 0$, then X and Y are computed. In statement 210, because the parentheses and the comma are inside quotation marks, the solution is printed as an ordered pair. (Notice the output for the last set of data in the sample run.)

EXERCISES

A

In Exercises 1–15, write each system in the following form.

$$\begin{cases} A_1x + B_1y = C_1 \\ A_2x + B_2y = C_2 \end{cases}$$

Then use the program on page 242 to solve each system.

1. $\begin{cases} 3x = 2y + 8 \\ 5y = 4x - 6 \end{cases}$
2. $\begin{cases} y = 5x + 1 \\ x - 2y + 6 = 0 \end{cases}$
3. $\begin{cases} x = y + 6 \\ 4y + 4x = 15 \end{cases}$

4. $\begin{cases} y = 2x + 4 \\ 2x = 4 - y \end{cases}$
5. $\begin{cases} 2x + y = -2 \\ 2y = 4x - 1 \end{cases}$
6. $\begin{cases} 3y + 4x = 0 \\ 5 + 6y = 2x \end{cases}$

7. $\begin{cases} 4x - 17 = -3y \\ 3y + 2x - 13 = 0 \end{cases}$
8. $\begin{cases} y = 9 - x \\ y = 5x - 3 \end{cases}$
9. $\begin{cases} 8x + 13 = -5y \\ 3x = 2y - 1 \end{cases}$

10. $\begin{cases} 4x = 3y - 2 \\ 6 + 12x = 9y \end{cases}$
11. $\begin{cases} x = -2 \\ y = 2x + 4 \end{cases}$
12. $\begin{cases} x = 4y \\ \frac{1}{4}x = 20 - y \end{cases}$

13. $\begin{cases} x + y = 12 \\ -y = 8 \end{cases}$
14. $\begin{cases} 0.4x = 1.2 - y \\ 0.6x = y + 3.9 \end{cases}$
15. $\begin{cases} 0.5y = 0.75x - 4 \\ 0.25x + 0.5y = 2.5 \end{cases}$

B

16. Expand the program on page 242 so that, when $D = 0$, it prints whether the system has no solution or infinitely many solutions. For the first set of data in the sample run of the program on page 242, the revised program should print DEPENDENT SYSTEM--INFINITELY MANY SOLUTIONS. For the second set of data in the sample run, the revised program should print INCONSISTENT SYSTEM--NO SOLUTION.

Chapter Summary

IMPORTANT IDEAS

1. **In a system of two linear equations:**

   If the slopes of the lines for the two equations are different, the system has one solution.

   If the slopes are the same and the y intercepts are different, the system has no solutions.

   If the slopes are the same and the y intercepts are the same, the system has an infinite number of solutions.

2. **Steps in Solving a System of Two Linear Equations by the Addition Method**

   1. Add to eliminate one of the variables. Solve the resulting equation.
   2. Substitute the known value of one variable in one of the original equations of the system. Solve for the other variable.
   3. Check the solution in both equations of the system.

3. **Steps in Solving a System of Two Linear Equations Using Multiplication with the Addition Method**

   1. Multiply each side of one of the equations by a number, and, if necessary, multiply each side of the second equation by another number. Choose the two numbers so that, after multiplying, the coefficients of one of the variables will be additive inverses of each other.
   2. Use the addition method to solve the new system.

4. **Steps in Solving Word Problems Using Systems of Equations in Two Variables**

   1. Use Condition 1 and two variables to represent the unknowns.
   2. Write an equation in two variables that expresses Condition 1.
   3. Write a second equation in two variables that expresses Condition 2.
   4. Solve the system of equations.
   5. Check your solution in the original conditions of the problem.
   6. Answer the question.

5. A two-digit number may be expressed as $10t + u$, where t represents the tens digit and u the units digit.

   A three-digit number may be expressed as $100h + 10t + u$, where h represents the hundreds digit.

6. Steps in Solving a System of Two Linear Equations by the Substitution Method

$\boxed{1}$ Solve one equation for one of the variables.

$\boxed{2}$ Substitute the resulting expression in the other equation.

$\boxed{3}$ Solve the resulting equation.

$\boxed{4}$ Find the values of the variables.

7. Simple Interest Formula: interest = principal $\cdot$ rate $\cdot$ time, or $i = prt$.

Chapter Objectives and Review

Objective: *To solve systems of equations by graphing (Section 6–1)*

Solve each system by graphing.

1. $\begin{cases} x - y = 2 \\ 2x + y = 4 \end{cases}$
2. $\begin{cases} y = 3x - 4 \\ y = -2x + 1 \end{cases}$
3. $\begin{cases} 2x + y = -3 \\ 3x + 4y = 3 \end{cases}$

Write *one*, *none*, or *infinitely many* to describe the number of solutions for each system.

4. $\begin{cases} y = 2x - 5 \\ y = -x - 5 \end{cases}$
5. $\begin{cases} 2y - x = 6 \\ 2x + 6 = 4y \end{cases}$
6. $\begin{cases} 2x + y = 1 \\ 3y = 3 - 6x \end{cases}$

Objective: *To solve systems of equations by the addition method (Section 6–2)*

Use the addition method to solve each system.

7. $\begin{cases} x + y = 4 \\ 3x - y = -6 \end{cases}$
8. $\begin{cases} 2x - 3y = -2 \\ -2x + 5y = 2 \end{cases}$
9. $\begin{cases} \frac{2}{3}x - 2y = 5 \\ \frac{1}{3}x + 2y = 1 \end{cases}$

Objective: *To solve systems of equations using multiplication with the addition method (Section 6–3)*

Use multiplication with the addition method to solve each system.

10. $\begin{cases} 2x + 3y = 8 \\ 7x + 3y = -2 \end{cases}$
11. $\begin{cases} 2p - 3q = 2 \\ -6p + 4q = 9 \end{cases}$
12. $\begin{cases} 3a + 5b = -19 \\ 5a - 7b = 45 \end{cases}$

Objective: *To solve word problems using systems of equations (Section 6–4)*

13. The sum of two numbers is 22. Four times the greater number is equal to seven times the smaller number. Find the two numbers.

14. Eighty-five more student tickets than adult tickets were sold for a concert. The total number sold was 343. How many tickets of each type were sold?

Objective: *To solve digit problems using systems of equations (Section 6–5)*

15. The tens digit of a two-digit number is 3 less than the units digit. The sum of the digits is 13. Find the number.

16. A two-digit number is 4 times the sum of its digits. The number is 18 less than the number obtained when the digits are reversed. Find the number.

Objective: *To solve systems of equations using the substitution method (Section 6–6)*

Use the substitution method to solve each system.

17. $\begin{cases} y - 2x = 3 \\ y + 3x = 8 \end{cases}$

18. $\begin{cases} c + 2d = 0 \\ 4c - 7d = 15 \end{cases}$

19. $\begin{cases} 2r - 3s - 1 = 0 \\ r + 6s - 3 = 0 \end{cases}$

Objective: *To solve money problems using systems of equations (Section 6–7)*

20. The Lawn and Garden Shop sold 40 bags of lawn seed one week for a total of $263. Large bags of lawn seed sell for $8.50 each and smaller bags for $5.75 each. How many bags of each size were sold that week?

21. Ralph Minton borrowed $4000 for one year, part at 12% interest and the rest at 15% interest. If he had borrowed the entire amount at 12% interest, Ralph would owe $30 less interest for the year. Find the amount borrowed at each rate.

Objective: *To solve mixture problems using systems of equations (Section 6–8)*

22. A 25-kilogram mixture of tea is made from one brand that sells for $4.50 per kilogram and another brand that sells for $5.75 per kilogram. How many kilograms of each must be used to make a mixture that sells at $4.90 per kilogram?

23. Solution A, which is 5% sugar, is mixed with Solution B which is 10% sugar to obtain 10 liters of a solution that is 8% sugar. How many liters of Solution A and how many liters of Solution B are needed for the 8% solution?

Chapter Test

1. Solve this system by graphing: $\begin{cases} 2x - y = 8 \\ x + y = 1 \end{cases}$

Use the addition method to solve.

2. $\begin{cases} -2x + y = -4 \\ 5x - y = -1 \end{cases}$

3. $\begin{cases} -3x + 2y = -3 \\ 5x - 3y = 5 \end{cases}$

4. Use the substitution method to solve: $\begin{cases} 3a - b = -6 \\ 6a + 2b = 0 \end{cases}$

Use any method to solve each system.

5. $\begin{cases} 4x + y = 10 \\ y = -x + 1 \end{cases}$

6. $\begin{cases} 3m + 2n = -8 \\ 5m - 8 = 2n \end{cases}$

Solve each problem.

7. Tony worked 6 hours more than Carl last week. Together, the two boys worked a total of 58 hours. How many hours did each of them work?

8. The sum of the digits of a two-digit number is 9. The value of the number is 6 times the value of its units digit. Find the number.

9. A restaurant owner bought 24 new tables, some large and some smaller. The large tables cost $145 each, while the smaller ones cost $120 each. The total cost of the tables was $3080. How many tables of each size did he buy?

10. A mixture of birdseed contains sunflower seeds worth $1.30 per kilogram and other seeds worth $0.90 per kilogram. How many kilograms of each kind must be used to produce 100 kilograms of a mixture that sells for $1.00 per kilogram?

_____ More Challenging Problems _____

Solve each system.

1. $\begin{cases} x - 5y = 27 \\ 2x + 3y = 2 \\ 5x + 8y = 3 \end{cases}$

2. $\begin{cases} 9x + 4y = 0 \\ 5x - 2y = 19 \\ 3x + 4y = -12 \end{cases}$

3. $\begin{cases} 6x - 5y = 3 \\ 2y + 10 = 2x \\ 12 - 4y = 12x \end{cases}$

Solve each system for x and y in terms of a, b, and c.

4. $\begin{cases} ax + by = c \\ bx - ay = 7c \end{cases}$

5. $\begin{cases} ax + by + a^2 + b^2 = 0 \\ bx + ay + 2ab = 0 \end{cases}$

6. $\begin{cases} cy + (b + c)x = 2bc \\ by + (b - c)x = 2^2 - b^2 \end{cases}$

7. At what two times between 7:00 P.M. and 8:00 P.M. will the minute hand and the hour hand of a clock be exactly 15 minute spaces apart?

8. Mr. Teal has a 99-year lease on his farm. When asked how much of the lease had expired, he said: "Two thirds of the time past is equal to four fifths of the time to come." How much of the lease had expired?

Additional Practice

Skills

Solve each system by graphing. *(Section 6–1)*

1. $\begin{cases} x + y = 5 \\ 2x - y = 4 \end{cases}$

2. $\begin{cases} y = -2 \\ 4x - y = 6 \end{cases}$

3. $\begin{cases} x - 2y = 8 \\ 2x + y = 6 \end{cases}$

Write *one*, *none*, or *infinitely many* to describe the number of solutions for each system. *(Section 6–1)*

4. $\begin{cases} x + y = 5 \\ 2y = -2x + 10 \end{cases}$

5. $\begin{cases} 2y = x - 8 \\ y - 3 = \frac{1}{2}x \end{cases}$

6. $\begin{cases} y - 3x = 2 \\ y + \frac{1}{3}x + 1 = 0 \end{cases}$

Use the addition method to solve each system. *(Section 6–2)*

7. $\begin{cases} x - y = 14 \\ 3x + y = 6 \end{cases}$

8. $\begin{cases} 2x - y = -2 \\ -2x + 3y = 0 \end{cases}$

9. $\begin{cases} 5x - 4y = 0 \\ -x + 4y = 2 \end{cases}$

10. $\begin{cases} 3x - 2y = 12 \\ 4x + 2y = 2 \end{cases}$

11. $\begin{cases} -5x + 3y = 20 \\ 5x + 9y = 4 \end{cases}$

12. $\begin{cases} 4x - 2y = 25 \\ x + 2y = 10 \end{cases}$

Use multiplication with the addition method to solve each system.
(Section 6–3)

13. $\begin{cases} 4x - y = 3 \\ 3x + 2y = 5 \end{cases}$ 14. $\begin{cases} 3x + 5y = 7 \\ -x + 3y = 0 \end{cases}$ 15. $\begin{cases} 3x + 4y = 5 \\ 2x + 3y = 5 \end{cases}$

16. $\begin{cases} 2x + y = 6 \\ x + 3y = -2 \end{cases}$ 17. $\begin{cases} 4x - 5y = 2 \\ 7x - 11y = -1 \end{cases}$ 18. $\begin{cases} 3x - 2y = 22 \\ 2x - 5y = 0 \end{cases}$

Use the substitution method to solve each system. *(Section 6–6)*

19. $\begin{cases} 3x + 2y = 5 \\ 2x - y = 8 \end{cases}$ 20. $\begin{cases} x + 2y = 0 \\ 5x - 6y = -4 \end{cases}$ 21. $\begin{cases} 6x - y = 10 \\ -4x - 6y = -5 \end{cases}$

22. $\begin{cases} x - 5y = 20 \\ 3x + 7y = -6 \end{cases}$ 23. $\begin{cases} 7x - y = 14 \\ 2x + 5y = 41 \end{cases}$ 24. $\begin{cases} 3x - 4y = 43 \\ x + y = -9 \end{cases}$

Applications

A $550 refrigerator costs $85 per year to operate. A $650 refrigerator costs $60 per year to operate. Use this information for Exercises 25 and 26.

25. On the same set of coordinate axes, draw graphs showing the total cost after each of the first 10 years for each refrigerator. (Include the initial cost of each.) *(Section 6–1)*

26. Use the graph to determine after which year the total costs for each refrigerator are the same. *(Section 6–1)*

27. Voting District A has 146 more registered voters than District B. In all, the two districts have 6432 registered voters. How many are there in each district? *(Section 6–4)*

28. The length of a rectangle is 8 centimeters more than its width. The perimeter is 68 centimeters. Find the length and width of the rectangle. *(Section 6–4)*

29. The units digit of a two-digit number is 5 more than the tens digit. The sum of the two digits is 13. Find the number. *(Section 6–5)*

30. A two-digit number is 7 times the sum of its digits. The number is 36 more than the number obtained when its digits are reversed. Find the number. *(Section 6–5)*

31. Sandra borrowed $10,000, part at a 12% yearly interest rate and the rest at 14%. She paid $1270 in interest for a year. Find the amount of each loan. *(Section 6–7)*

32. Thomas has 56 coins in dimes and quarters. The total value of the coins is $8.00. How many coins of each kind does he have? *(Section 6–7)*

33. A 10% salt solution and a 5% salt solution are available. How many liters of each must be used in order to make 25 liters of an 8% salt solution? *(Section 6–8)*

34. A 7% iodine solution is to be mixed with a 12% iodine solution. How many liters of each must be used to obtain 5 liters of a 10% solution? *(Section 6–8)*

CHAPTER **7** **Inequalities**

7-1 Combined Inequalities

A sentence such as

$$x \geq 5 \longleftarrow \text{Read: "x is greater than or equal to 5."}$$

combines an inequality with an equation. Because $x \geq 5$ can be written as two simple sentences with the connective or, it is called a **compound sentence**. A compound sentence with or is a **disjunction**.

$$x \geq 5 \text{ means } x = 5 \quad \text{or} \quad x > 5.$$

The solution set of $x \geq 5$ is the set that makes $x = 5$ true or the set that makes $x > 5$ true. This means that the solution set of $x \geq 5$ is the *union* of the solution sets of $x = 5$ and $x > 5$.

In general, the **union of two sets A and B** (in symbols: $A \cup B$) is the set that contains all the elements in set A or in set B.

In the graph for $x \geq 5$, the solid dot indicates that the graph includes $x = 5$.

EXAMPLE 1 Solve and graph: $2x \geq -6$

Solution: Write the inequality with or. Then solve for x.

$$2x \geq -6 \quad \text{means} \quad 2x = -6 \quad \text{or} \quad 2x > -6$$
$$x = -3 \quad \text{or} \quad x > -3$$

Solution set: {all real numbers greater than or equal to -3}

A sentence such as

$$-6 < x < 2$$

combines two inequalities. Because the sentence can be written as two simple sentences with the connective and, it is also a compound sentence. A compound sentence with and is a **conjunction**.

$$-6 < x < 2 \quad \text{means} \quad -6 < x \quad \text{and} \quad x < 2.$$

The solution set of $-6 < x < 2$ is the set that makes both $-6 < x$ true and $x < 2$ true. Thus, the solution of a compound and sentence is the *intersection of two sets*.

In general, the **intersection of two sets A and B** (in symbols: $A \cap B$) is the set that contains the elements belonging to <u>both</u> set A <u>and</u> set B.

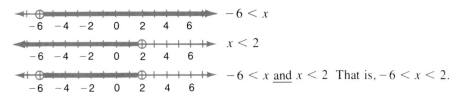

$-6 < x$

$x < 2$

$-6 < x$ and $x < 2$ That is, $-6 < x < 2$.

EXAMPLE 2 Solve and graph: $-9 < 2x - 1 < 5$

Solution: Write the inequality with and. Then solve for x.

$$-9 < 2x - 1 < 5 \quad \text{means} \quad -9 < 2x - 1 \quad \text{and} \quad 2x - 1 < 5$$

$$-8 < 2x \qquad\qquad 2x < 6$$

$$-4 < x \qquad\qquad \text{and} \qquad x < 3$$

Solution set: **{all real numbers greater than −4 and less than 3}**

CLASSROOM EXERCISES

Write each compound sentence as two simple sentences joined by <u>or</u> or <u>and</u>.

1. $x \leq 3$ **2.** $1 < x < 5$ **3.** $x \geq -1$ **4.** $-3 < x < 0$

5. $3y \leq 12$ **6.** $5 \geq p - 2$ **7.** $x + 2 \leq 8$ **8.** $-a \leq 5$

Write each compound sentence without <u>or</u>.

9. $x < 5$ <u>or</u> $x = 5$ **10.** $x < 0$ <u>or</u> $x = 0$

11. $x < -3$ <u>or</u> $x = -3$ **12.** $x < 2$ <u>or</u> $x = 2$

Write each compound sentence without <u>and</u>.

13. $x < 4$ <u>and</u> $x > 1$ **14.** $a > -1$ <u>and</u> $a < 0$

15. $t > -1$ <u>and</u> $t < 3$ **16.** $-3 < x$ <u>and</u> $x < 0$

Match each graph in Exercises 17–22 with one of the compound sentences given in a–f.

17.
a. $-2 \leq x$ <u>and</u> $x < 1$

18.
b. $x < -3$ <u>or</u> $x > 3$

19.
c. $x < -1$ <u>or</u> $x \geq 0$

20.
d. $0 \leq x$ <u>and</u> $x \leq 2$

21.
e. $0 \leq x$ <u>and</u> $x < 3$

22.
f. $x < -2$ <u>or</u> $x > 0$

WRITTEN EXERCISES

A Write each compound sentence as two simple sentences joined by <u>or</u> or <u>and</u>.

1. $3x - 1 \leq 11$

2. $\frac{1}{3}m \geq 4$

3. $3 < y < 8$

4. $-1 < a < 0$

5. $t - \frac{1}{2} \geq 3\frac{1}{2}$

6. $-5 < 2x < 10$

7. $-3 < x + 2 < 1$

8. $-2 < -\frac{1}{2}x < -1$

9. $-9 < 3k < 15$

Graph the solution set of each compound sentence.

10. $x > 2$ <u>or</u> $x < -2$

11. $-2 < x$ <u>and</u> $x < 2$

12. $w > -3$ <u>and</u> $w < 4$

13. $a > 3$ <u>and</u> $a < 5$

14. $y < 4$ <u>or</u> $-y < 4$

15. $y \geq 1$ <u>or</u> $y > 0$

16. $t < -1$ <u>or</u> $t < -3$

17. $t \leq -1$ <u>or</u> $t \leq -3$

18. $3a - 4 < 2$ <u>or</u> $5a + 1 < -4$

Solve and graph each inequality.

19. $3x \geq 21$

20. $-5x < 20$

21. $-5 < 2x < 10$

22. $-9 < -2x - 3 < -1$

23. $-2 < -\frac{1}{2}x \leq -1$

24. $\frac{1}{3}m \leq -4$

25. $-3 < t \leq 6$

26. $-2 \leq x \leq 8$

27. $2y + 1 \leq 7$

28. $-\frac{1}{2} \leq w < \frac{3}{2}$

29. $2c + 1 \geq 6$

30. $3(p + 2) \leq 6$

31. $-(x - 2) \geq 3$

32. $-14 \leq 4x - 2 \leq -6$

33. $-19 \leq 5m - 4 < -4$

34. $9 \leq 2a + 5 < 15$

35. $1 \leq 3m - 2 \leq 16$

36. $3 < 2x - 1 < 8$

APPLICATIONS: Using Combined Inequalities

37. The weight of each boy on a football team is more than 130 pounds and less than 205 pounds. If x represents the weight of any player, then __?__ $< x <$ __?__ is true.

38. In one high school wrestling weight class, wrestlers may weigh more than 167 pounds but no more than 185 pounds. Represent this weight class as an inequality, where w is the weight of any wrestler.

Olympic boxers compete in classes based on mass (weight) expressed in kilograms. In a particular class, a boxer's mass must be greater than the maximum of the next lighter class and no more than the maximum limit for the particular class.

Use this information in Exercises 39–42 to express each class as an inequality where y represents the mass of a boxer in kilograms.

39. Light heavyweight: 76–81

40. Welterweight: 64–67

41. Lightweight: 58–60

42. Bantamweight: 52–54

B

43. Stocks are sold only in integral numbers of dollars and eighths of a dollar. The inequality $51\frac{1}{8} < x < 52\frac{3}{4}$ indicates that a stock sold on a particular day above $51\frac{1}{8}$ and below $52\frac{3}{4}$. What is the solution set for the inequality?

Solve each inequality. Graph the solution set.

44. $3x - 7 < 28$ <u>and</u> $9x - 4 > x + 4$

45. $5 + 2y < -1$ <u>or</u> $-3 + 2y \geq 3$

46. $3 - 4a \leq 5$ <u>or</u> $2a - 3 \leq 7$

47. $3n - 9 > -3$ <u>and</u> $-9n > -27$

48. $-4 \geq 2y + 8$ <u>and</u> $3y + 10 \geq 7$

49. $3 + 4x < 3x - 2$ <u>and</u> $2 + x \geq -6$

50. $6y - 9 \leq 17y + 13$ <u>and</u> $3(y - 4) \leq 2(3y - 9)$

51. $3 - 2n > n$ <u>or</u> $2n < 6 + 8$

Puzzle

Some numbers have very interesting properties, as you can see in 1–3 below.

1. a. Think of a three-digit number. (For example, 293)

  b. Make a six-digit number by writing the number twice. (293293)

  c. Divide the new number by 7.

  d. Divide by 11.

  e. Divide by 13. What number do you get?

2. Look at the pattern below.

$$2^2 = 4 = 1^2 + 1 + 2 \qquad 4^2 = 16 = 3^2 + 3 + 4$$
$$3^2 = 9 = 2^2 + 2 + 3 \qquad 5^2 = 25 = 4^2 + 4 + 5$$

Use the pattern to find 25^2 without multiplying. (HINT: $24^2 = 576$)

3. Look at the pattern below.

$$999 \times 2 = 1998 \qquad 999 \times 4 = 3996$$
$$999 \times 3 = 2997 \qquad 999 \times 5 = 4995$$

Use the pattern to evaluate each expression below without using pencil and paper.

  a. 999×6 **b.** 999×8 **c.** $8991 \div 2997$ **d.** $3996 \div 7992$

REVIEW CAPSULE FOR SECTION 7–2

Tell whether the given ordered pair is a solution of the given equation. *(Pages 181–184)*

1. $y = x$; $(-4, 4)$

2. $y = -x$; $(-1, 1)$

3. $y - x = 5$; $(0, 5)$

4. $x = 5$; $(5, 0)$

5. $y = -2$; $(8, -2)$

6. $3y + 2x = 7$; $(\frac{1}{2}, 2)$

In Exercises 7–10, solve for y in terms of x. *(Pages 162–164)*

7. $y - 5x = 0$ **8.** $x + 2y = 6$ **9.** $-y + 2x - 1 = 0$ **10.** $5x - y + 3 = 0$

In Exercises 11–15, give the slope and y intercept of each line. *(Pages 194–196)*

11. $y - 5 = 0$ **12.** $3x - 4y = 12$ **13.** $2y + x - 1 = 0$ **14.** $2x - 3y + 6 = 0$

7-2   Graphing Linear Inequalities

The graph of a linear equation separates the coordinate plane into three sets of points: the points in the two **half-planes** and the points on the line. Thus, every point on the coordinate plane is either in one of the half-planes or on the line.

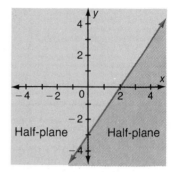

The equation of the line graphed at the right is $y = \frac{3}{2}x - 3$. Thus, the coordinates of every point in the plane make one of these sentences true.

$$y = \frac{3}{2}x - 3 \qquad y > \frac{3}{2}x - 3 \qquad y < \frac{3}{2}x - 3$$

The graph of an inequality that uses $>$ or $<$ *does not include* the graph of the related equation. To show this, the graph of the related equation is dashed.

EXAMPLE 1   Graph $y > 2x - 1$.

> **Solution:**
>
> 1. Draw the graph of $y = 2x - 1$ as a dashed line.
> 2. To identify the half-plane for which $y > 2x - 1$, test a point in each half-plane.
>
> | Try $(0, 1)$. | Try $(3, 0)$. |
> |---|---|
> | $1 > 2(0) - 1$? | $0 > 2(3) - 1$? |
> | $1 > -1$?   Yes ✔ | $0 > 5$?   No |
>
> 3. Shade the half-plane containing $(0, 1)$.

Since the graph of $y > 2x - 1$ *does not include* the graph of the related equation, the graph is an **open half-plane.**

The graph of an inequality that uses $\geq$ or $\leq$ *includes* the graph of the related equation. To show this, the graph of the related equation is a solid line. This line is the **edge** or **boundary** of the half-plane.

EXAMPLE 2   Graph $3x - 4y \leq 12$.

> **Solution:**
>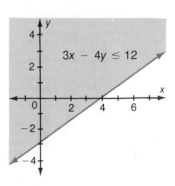
> 1. Draw the graph of $3x - 4y = 12$ as a **solid** line.
> 2. To identify the half-plane for which $3x - 4y < 12$, test a point in each half-plane.
>
> | Try $(0, 0)$. | Try $(3, -2)$. |
> |---|---|
> | $3(0) - 4(0) < 12$? | $3(3) - 4(-2) < 12$? |
> | $0 < 12$?   Yes ✔ | $9 + 8 < 12$?   No |
>
> 3. Shade the half-plane containing $(0, 0)$.

Since the graph of $3x - 4y \leq 12$ includes the edge or boundary of the half-plane, the graph is a **closed half-plane**.

CLASSROOM EXERCISES

Determine whether the given point belongs to the graph of the given inequality.

1. $y > x - 3;\ (0, 0)$ **2.** $y > 3x - 4;\ (2, 3)$ **3.** $x \geq 6;\ (-1, 5)$

4. $y \leq 5;\ (0, -7)$ **5.** $y \leq -\frac{1}{2}x + 1;\ (-4, 3)$ **6.** $3x - y \leq 5;\ (0, -5)$

WRITTEN EXERCISES

A   Determine which of the given points, if any, belong to the graph of the given inequality.

1. $y < 3x - 2;\ (0, 0);\ (-5, -7)$ **2.** $y \geq 3x - 2;\ (-1, -1);\ (9, 0)$

3. $y > -2x + 1;\ (1, -6);\ (-2, 1)$ **4.** $y \leq -2x + 1;\ (2, -2);\ (-2, 2)$

5. $x - y \leq 2;\ (1, 0);\ (0, 1)$ **6.** $x + y \geq 1;\ (1, 0);\ (0, -1)$

7. $y - x \leq 0;\ (1, -1);\ (0, 0)$ **8.** $y - x > 0;\ (0, 0);\ (-4, -3)$

9. $2x - 3y \geq 6;\ (9, 2);\ (-1, -7)$ **10.** $2x + y - 4 < 0;\ (-8, 1);\ (8, -1)$

Graph each inequality in the coordinate plane.

11. $y > x - 3$ **12.** $y < x + 3$ **13.** $y > 3x - 4$ **14.** $y < 2x + 4$

15. $y > -3x$ **16.** $y < -4x$ **17.** $y < -2x - 4$ **18.** $y > -4x + 5$

19. $x + y > 4$ **20.** $x - y > 2$ **21.** $2x + 3y > 6$ **22.** $4x - y < 5$

23. $y > 0 \cdot x + 4$ **24.** $y < 0 \cdot x - 5$ **25.** $y < -4$ **26.** $y > -5$

27. $x < 8$ **28.** $x > -6$ **29.** $x < -4$ **30.** $x > 6$

31. $y \geq -4$ **32.** $y \geq 2x - 5$ **33.** $y \leq 3x - 9$ **34.** $y \geq 2$

35. $y \leq -5$ **36.** $x + y \geq 4$ **37.** $2x - y \leq -6$ **38.** $3x + y < 5$

B   Write the inequality that defines the shaded portion of each plane.

39.

40.

41.

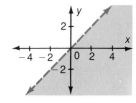

C   In Exercises 42–50, describe the graph of each inequality. Use one of the word descriptions below. In these exercises, $A \neq 0$, $B \neq 0$.

      A straight line   *An open half-plane*   *A closed half-plane*

42. $Ax + By = C$ **43.** $Ax + By \leq C$ **44.** $Ax + By < C$

45. $Ax + By \geq C$ **46.** $Ax + By > C$ **47.** $Ax = C$

48. $By = C$ **49.** $Ax \leq C$ **50.** $By > C$

Solve each system by graphing. Check your solutions. *(Pages 212–216)*

1. $\begin{cases} x = 4 \\ y = -1 \end{cases}$
2. $\begin{cases} y = 2x \\ y = 3x - 3 \end{cases}$
3. $\begin{cases} x + y = -4 \\ x - y = 6 \end{cases}$
4. $\begin{cases} y + 2x + 6 = 0 \\ y - 2x = 0 \end{cases}$

Determine whether the given point is a solution of the given system. Answer *Yes* or *No. (Pages 212–216)*

5. $\begin{cases} a + 2b = 1 \\ 3a + b = 8 \end{cases}; \ (3, -1)$
6. $\begin{cases} 3p + 5q = 9 \\ 9p + 2q = -12 \end{cases}; \ (-2, 3)$
7. $\begin{cases} -5s + 3v = 25 \\ 4s + 2v = 2 \end{cases}; \ (-2, -5)$

7-3 Systems of Inequalities

A system of linear inequalities in two variables is usually solved by graphing.

EXAMPLE 1 Solve by graphing: $\begin{cases} x + y > 10 \\ x - y > -4 \end{cases}$

Solution:
$\boxed{1}$ Graph $x + y > 10$. Any point in half-plane E is a solution of $x + y > 10$. Note that the graph of $x + y = 10$ is dashed to show that it is not included in the half-plane.

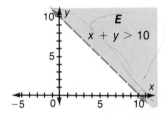

$\boxed{2}$ Graph $x - y > -4$. Any point in half-plane F is a solution of $x - y > -4$. Note that the points on the graph of $x - y = -4$ are not included in the half-plane.

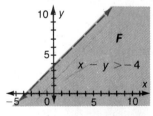

$\boxed{3}$ Any point in the intersection of the half-planes E and F (double shading) is a solution of $x + y > 10$ <u>and</u> $x - y > -4$.

Thus, **all points in the darkest region** (but no points on the lines) are solutions of the system.

Sometimes points on a line are included in the solutions of a system of linear inequalities. You indicate these points by showing all or part of the graph of the line as a solid line (see Example 2).

EXAMPLE 2 Solve by graphing: $\begin{cases} y \geq 2x - 4 \\ x + y \leq 5 \end{cases}$

Solution: **1** Graph $y \geq 2x - 4$.

Any point in half-plane E <u>or</u> on the line $y = 2x - 4$ (edge of half-plane E) is a solution of $y \geq 2x - 4$.

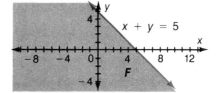

2 Graph $x + y \leq 5$.

Any point in half-plane F <u>or</u> on the line $x + y = 5$ (edge of half-plane F) is a solution of $x + y \leq 5$.

3 Any point **in the intersection of half-planes E and F** (double-shading) and **any point on the lines that border the intersection** is a solution of $y \geq 2x - 4$ <u>and</u> $x + y \leq 5$.

CLASSROOM EXERCISES

Match each graph in Exercises 1–4 with one of the systems given in a–d.

1.

2.

3.

4.

a. $\begin{cases} x \geq 0 \\ y \geq 0 \end{cases}$

b. $\begin{cases} x \geq 0 \\ y \leq 0 \end{cases}$

c. $\begin{cases} x > 2 \\ y > 2 \end{cases}$

d. $\begin{cases} x < -2 \\ y \geq -2 \end{cases}$

WRITTEN EXERCISES

A Solve each system by graphing.

1. $\begin{cases} x + y \leq 2 \\ x - y \leq 4 \end{cases}$

2. $\begin{cases} y > 3x \\ y \leq -3x \end{cases}$

3. $\begin{cases} x - y < 8 \\ x + y > 3 \end{cases}$

4. $\begin{cases} x + y > 10 \\ x + y < 4 \end{cases}$

Solve by graphing.

5. $\begin{cases} y > 3x \\ y > 3x + 2 \end{cases}$
6. $\begin{cases} 2x + 3y \geq 6 \\ y \leq 4 \end{cases}$
7. $\begin{cases} x + 2y \geq 4 \\ 2x - y \leq -2 \end{cases}$
8. $\begin{cases} x - 2y \leq 6 \\ 3x + y \geq 9 \end{cases}$

9. $\begin{cases} 2x + y > -8 \\ y < -2 \end{cases}$
10. $\begin{cases} y \leq 4x - 1 \\ y > 2x + 1 \end{cases}$
11. $\begin{cases} y < x \\ y \geq 3 - x \end{cases}$
12. $\begin{cases} 3x - y \leq 6 \\ x - 4y \geq 8 \end{cases}$

B

13. $y > -x$ <u>and</u> $y > \frac{1}{2}x - 4$

14. $\frac{1}{3}y - x \leq -9$ <u>and</u> $3x - 2y - 6 \geq 0$

15. $-2 < x < 2$ <u>and</u> $-2 < y < 2$

16. $0 \leq x \leq 6$ <u>and</u> $0 \leq y \leq 4$

17. $\begin{cases} y \geq x \\ y < 3 \\ x > 0 \end{cases}$
18. $\begin{cases} y < x + 1 \\ y - 2x > 1 \\ y \leq 1 \end{cases}$
19. $\begin{cases} x + y < 3 \\ x - y > 1 \\ 2x + y > -4 \end{cases}$
20. $\begin{cases} 2y > x + 2 \\ 2y + x < 6 \\ y > 0 \end{cases}$

C

21. $\begin{cases} x \geq 0 \\ x \leq 2 \\ y \geq 0 \\ y \leq 2 \end{cases}$
22. $\begin{cases} x \leq -2 \\ x \geq -5 \\ y \leq 6 \\ y \geq 4 \end{cases}$
23. $\begin{cases} y = x \\ x \leq 4 \\ y \geq 0 \end{cases}$
24. $\begin{cases} y - x > 0 \\ x > -1 \\ y < 5 \end{cases}$

CALCULATOR APPLICATIONS

Graphing Systems of Inequalities

A calculator can help you to find the region containing the points that are solutions of a system of inequalities.

EXAMPLE The graph at the right shows the linear equations $y = 4x + 2$ and $y = \frac{1}{3}x$. Find the region that contains the solution of the following system.

$$\begin{cases} y > 4x + 2 & \quad 1 \\ y < \frac{1}{3}x & \quad 2 \end{cases}$$

SOLUTION Choose a point in each region. Substitute in each inequality to test whether the point satisfies both inequalities.

Region **A**: $(-2, 2)$ 1 4 ⊗ 2 ⊞ ⊕ 2 ⊜ $-6.$

Test: Is $y > 4x + 2$? $2 > -6$?   Yes ✓

2 1 ⊘ 3 ⊗ 2 ⊞ ⊜ -0.6666666

Test: Is $y < \frac{1}{3}x$? $2 < -0.\overline{6}$?   No

Thus, the point in region **A** does not satisfy the system.

Repeat the procedure for points in regions **B, C,** and **D. Region C** contains the solution of the system.

EXERCISES

Use a calculator to check your answers to the Classroom Exercises on page 255.

Problem Solving and Applications

7-4 Linear Programming

Linear programming is a method of solving problems that contain restrictions, called **constraints**, which are often expressed as linear inequalities.

EXAMPLE A small company has five 3-ton trucks and four 5-ton trucks for hauling gravel. Only 7 crews are available at any one time to operate the trucks. How many of each kind of truck should be used to haul the maximum amount of gravel per trip?

Solution: ① Use two variables to represent the unknowns.

Let $x =$ the number of 3-ton trucks used.
Let $y =$ the number of 5-ton trucks used.
Then the number of tons of gravel hauled per trip is $3x + 5y$.

② Write a system of inequalities to represent the constraints.

$$\begin{cases} x \le 5 \\ y \le 4 \\ x + y \le 7 \\ x \ge 0 \\ y \ge 0 \end{cases}$$

⟵ **Only five 3-ton trucks are available.**
⟵ **Only four 5-ton trucks are available.**
⟵ **Only 7 crews are available.**
⟵ **A negative number of trucks is not possible.**

③ Graph these inequalities on the same coordinate axes. The intersection of the solution sets forms the shaded region (called a **polygonal region**) shown in the graph. *Any point in the region satisfies the system of inequalities.*

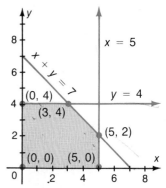

④ To find how many of each kind of truck are needed to haul the maximum amount of gravel per load means to find the ordered pair (x, y) for which $3x + 5y$ is a *maximum.*

It has been proved that a maximum or minimum always occurs at one of the vertices or corners of the polygon. In this case, there are 5 vertices.
Check the ordered pair for each vertex in $k = 3x + 5y$.

Vertex	$k = 3x + 5y$	Value of k
$(0, 0)$	$k = 3 \cdot 0 + 5 \cdot 0$	0
$(5, 0)$	$k = 3 \cdot 5 + 5 \cdot 0$	15
$(5, 2)$	$k = 3 \cdot 5 + 5 \cdot 2$	25
$(3, 4)$	$k = 3 \cdot 3 + 5 \cdot 4$	29 ⟵ **Maximum value**
$(0, 4)$	$k = 3 \cdot 0 + 5 \cdot 4$	20

Thus, **three 3-ton trucks** and **four 5-ton trucks** are needed.

Of course, common sense would give you the answer to the Example without the use of linear programming techniques. The techniques are shown when the answer is obvious to help you understand how to apply them when the answer is not so obvious.

CLASSROOM EXERCISES

In Exercises 1–4, the vertices of a polygonal region are given. For each exercise, find the maximum and minimum values of k over the given region.

1. $(0, 0)$; $(0, 5)$; $(6, 0)$; $k = 4x + y$
2. $(0, 0)$; $(0, 6)$; $(4, 8)$; $(2, 0)$; $k = 4x + y$
3. $(1, -1)$; $(0, 2)$; $(3, 0)$; $y = 2x + 3k$
4. $(1, 1)$; $(0, 4)$; $(4, 5)$; $(3, 0)$; $y = -x + k$

WRITTEN EXERCISES

A

In Exercises 1–4, find the maximum and minimum values for k, given the constraints shown in the graph.

1. $k = x + 2y$
2. $k = 3x + 5y$
3. $k = 2x + 3y$
4. $k = 50x + 10y$

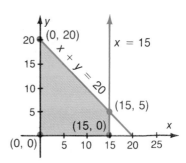

In Exercises 5–8:

a. Graph the solution set of each system of inequalities and determine the coordinates of the resulting polygonal region.

b. Find the minimum value of $k = 2x + y$ over the region graphed.

5. $\begin{cases} x \geq 0 \\ y \geq 0 \\ x + y \leq 4 \end{cases}$

6. $\begin{cases} y \leq 5 - \frac{1}{2}x \\ x \geq 0 \\ x \leq 7 \\ y \geq 0 \end{cases}$

7. $\begin{cases} y \leq 5 - x \\ x \leq 4 \\ x \geq 0 \\ y \geq 0 \end{cases}$

8. $\begin{cases} y \leq 2 - \frac{1}{2}x \\ y \geq 1 \\ x \leq 0 \end{cases}$

WORD PROBLEMS

A manufacturer makes two models of a bicycle. The profit on Model A is $15 per bicycle and the profit on Model B is $18 per bicycle. Because of a labor shortage, the manufacturer can produce no more than 200 bicycles per week. To meet the market demand, at least 50 Model A bicycles and 80 Model B bicycles must be available each week.

Use this information in Exercises 9–13.

9. Let x represent the number of Model A bicycles and let y represent the number of Model B bicycles produced per week. Write an expression to represent the total weekly profit.

10. Write a system of inequalities that shows the constraints on x and y.

11. Graph the system of inequalities you wrote in Exercise 10.

12. State the coordinates of the vertices of the polygonal region graphed in Exercise 11.

13. What is the maximum profit possible?

> The manager of a small toy shop decides to make up two types of variety packages in order to sell off 12 whistles and 32 small cars left in the shop. Each type A package contains 2 whistles and 8 small cars and sells for $6.50. Each type B package contains 3 whistles and 5 small cars and sells for $5.75.
>
> Use this information in Exercises 14–18.

14. Let x represent the number of type A packages and let y represent the number of type B packages. Write an expression to represent the store's income from the sale of these packages.

15. Write a system of linear equations to show the constraints on x and y.

16. Graph the system of inequalities from Exercise 15.

17. State the coordinates of the vertices (corners) of the region graphed in Exercise 16.

18. What is the store's maximum possible income from the sale of the packages?

_____ Review _____

Solve and graph each inequality on a number line. *(Section 7–1)*

1. $2n \geq 6$

2. $-9 < 3x < 6$

3. $2(y - 3) \geq -10$

Graph each inequality on the coordinate plane. *(Section 7–2)*

4. $3x \geq 6$

5. $x - y > 4$

6. $y > 2x + 5$

7. $4x - 2y < 6$

Solve each system by graphing. *(Section 7–3)*

8. $\begin{cases} x + y > 3 \\ x - y > -5 \end{cases}$

9. $\begin{cases} y \leq 2x \\ y \geq -x + 2 \end{cases}$

10. $\begin{cases} 2x - y < 1 \\ 3x + y > 4 \end{cases}$

11. $\begin{cases} y - 3x > 1 \\ y < -1 \\ x > -4 \end{cases}$

> Pamela makes and sells small woolen rugs. Plain rugs sell for $25 and take two hours to make. The fancier rugs take three hours to make and sell for $36 each. This week, Pamela plans to make a maximum of 10 rugs and to spend a maximum of 24 hours working on them. Use this information for Exercises 12–15. *(Section 7–4)*

12. Let x represent the number of plain rugs, and let y represent the number of fancier rugs. Write an expression to represent the total amount of money Pam will make on these rugs.

13. Write a system of inequalities that shows the constraints on x and y.

14. Graph the system of inequalities you wrote in Exercise 13.

15. How many of each type of rug should Pamela make in order to make the maximum amount of money?

Consumer Applications

Automobile Maintenance

The radiator of an automobile uses water, which has a **boiling point of 212°F**, or **100°C**, and a **freezing point of 32°F**, or **0°C**. Since this is not a wide enough temperature range, a solution is added to the water. This solution is referred to as **coolant** because it raises the boiling temperature of the water, or as **antifreeze** because it lowers the freezing temperature of the water.

The table below shows the changes in boiling point with different amounts of coolant.

Per Cent of Coolant	Boiling Point
50%	265°F
60%	270°F
70%	275°F

EXAMPLE 1 A car radiator holds 15 quarts. How many quarts of coolant must be mixed with the water to raise the boiling point to 270°F?

Solution: Find 270°F in the table. Read the entry at the left: 60%

Find 60% of 15.   60% of $15 = 0.60 \times 15 = $ **9**

Amount of coolant needed: **9 quarts with 6 quarts of water.**

The opposite effect happens to the freezing temperatures when antifreeze is mixed with water in the radiator.

EXAMPLE 2 A solution of water and antifreeze (Solution A) has a freezing point of 17°C higher than the freezing point of a stronger solution (Solution B). The freezing point of Solution B is 22°C lower than one half the freezing point of Solution A. Find the freezing point of both solutions.

Solution: Let f equal the freezing point of Solution A. Then $\frac{1}{2}f - 22$ equals the freezing point of Solution B.

$$f = (\tfrac{1}{2}f - 22) + 17 \quad \longleftarrow \quad \text{A's freezing point is}$$
$$\text{17°C higher than B's.}$$
$$f = \tfrac{1}{2}f - 5$$
$$\tfrac{1}{2}f = -5$$
$$f = -10 \qquad \tfrac{1}{2}f - 22 = -27$$

Freezing point of Solution A: $-10°C$ Freezing point of Solution B: $-27°C$

EXERCISES

In Exercises 1–4, find the number of quarts of coolant needed to raise the boiling point of the water in a car radiator with the given capacity to 265°F.

1. 10 quarts   **2.** 18 quarts   **3.** 20 quarts   **4.** 14 quarts

In Exercises 5–8, find the number of quarts of coolant needed to raise the boiling point of the water in a car radiator with the given capacity to 270°F.

5. 19 quarts   **6.** 12 quarts   **7.** 13 quarts   **8.** 16 quarts

In Exercises 9–12, find the number of quarts of coolant needed to raise the boiling point of the water in a car radiator with the given capacity to 275°F.

9. 15 quarts   **10.** 14 quarts   **11.** 18 quarts   **12.** 20 quarts

13. A 15-quart radiator contains 10.5 quarts of coolant and 4.5 quarts of water. What is the boiling point?

14. A 20-quart radiator contains 12 quarts of coolant and 8 quarts of water. What is the boiling point?

15. A solution of water and antifreeze (Solution C) freezes at a point 10°F lower than a weaker solution (Solution D). The freezing point of Solution C is 4°F lower than four times Solution D's freezing point. Find the freezing points of both solutions.

16. A solution of water and antifreeze (Solution Y) freezes at a point 8°C higher than a stronger solution (Solution Z). The freezing point of Solution Z is 5°C higher than three times one half of Solution Y's freezing point. Find the two freezing points.

17. A solution of water and antifreeze (Solution A) freezes at a point 12°C lower than a weaker solution (Solution B). The freezing point of Solution B is 2°C higher than one half the freezing point of Solution A. Find the two freezing points.

18. A solution of water and antifreeze (Solution W) freezes at a point 8°F higher than a stronger solution (Solution X). The freezing point of Solution X is 12°F lower than twice the freezing point of Solution W. Find the two freezing points.

Evaluate. *(Pages 47–50)*

1. $|6|$ 2. $|-3|$ 3. $|0|$ 4. $-|7|$ 5. $-|-10|$

6. $-|9-(-2)|$ 7. $|5-6|$ 8. $|5|-|7|$ 9. $|-6|+|3|$ 10. $-|\frac{1}{2}|-|-\frac{1}{2}|$

Solve and check. *(Pages 47–50)*

11. $|x|=5$ 12. $y=|-4|$ 13. $n=-|-5.7|$ 14. $|n|=|-2|$ 15. $r+|-5|=6$

7-5   Solving Absolute Value Equations

Sentences involving absolute value can also be written as compound sentences. Consider an equation such as $|x|=3$.

The distance from 0 is 3 units.

$|x|=3$ means $x=3$ <u>or</u> $x=-3$.

Thus, to solve an equation involving absolute value, write it as two simpler equations with the connective <u>or</u>. Then solve these equations.

EXAMPLE 1   Solve: $|2x+6|=14$

Solution: $|2x+6|=14$ means $2x+6=14$ <u>or</u> $2x+6=-14$

$\qquad\qquad\qquad\qquad\qquad\qquad\quad 2x=8 \qquad\qquad\qquad\quad 2x=-20$

$\qquad\qquad\qquad\qquad\qquad\qquad\quad\; x=4 \quad$ <u>or</u> $\qquad\quad x=-10$

Check: $|2x+6|=14$ ⟵ **Replace x with 4.** $|2x+6|=14$ ⟵ **Replace x with −10.**

$\qquad\qquad |2(4)+6| \overset{?}{=} 14 \qquad\qquad\qquad\qquad |2(-10)+6| \overset{?}{=} 14$

$\qquad\qquad\qquad\quad 14 \overset{?}{=} 14 \quad$ Yes ✔ $\qquad\qquad\qquad 14 \overset{?}{=} 14 \quad$ Yes ✔

Solution set: $\{-10, 4\}$

Combine like terms *within* the absolute value symbols as a first step in solving equations involving absolute value.

EXAMPLE 2   Solve: $|2k+k|-12=5$

Solution: $|2k+k|-12=5$ ⟵ **Combine like terms.**

$\qquad\qquad\quad |3k|-12=5$ ⟵ **Add 12 to each side.**

$\qquad\qquad\qquad\quad |3k|=17$ ⟵ **Write with "or."**

$\qquad\quad |3k|=17$ means $3k=17$ <u>or</u> $3k=-17$

$\qquad\qquad\qquad\qquad\qquad\quad k=\frac{17}{3}$ <u>or</u> $k=-\frac{17}{3}$ ⟵ **The check is left for you.**

Solution set: $\left\{-\frac{17}{3}, \frac{17}{3}\right\}$

CLASSROOM EXERCISES

Solve and check.

1. $|x + 5| = 10$ 2. $|x - 5| = 11$ 3. $|2t| = 4$ 4. $|6r| = 18$
5. $|5n - n| + 1 = 9$ 6. $|-3t + 7t| - 1 = 15$ 7. $|5y - 10| = 0$ 8. $|1 + h| = 0$
9. $|1 - 4q| = 12$ 10. $|7 - r| = 3$ 11. $|2k - 9| = 1$ 12. $|2p - 10| = 6$

WRITTEN EXERCISES

A   Solve and check each equation.

1. $|a + 3| = 2$ 2. $|\frac{1}{2}k| = 6$ 3. $|5y| = 10$ 4. $|-2v| = 2$
5. $|3k - 6| = 2$ 6. $|2y + 6| = 0$ 7. $12 = |3 - x|$ 8. $|\frac{5}{6} + y| = \frac{2}{3}$
9. $|\frac{1}{5}(2 - k)| = 3$ 10. $|y + y + y| = \frac{1}{3}$ 11. $|t + 1| = 9$ 12. $|7x - 5| = \frac{1}{2}$
13. $|\frac{1}{4}(5t - 2)| = 6$ 14. $|3d - 2| = \frac{1}{2}$ 15. $|4k + 6 + 2k| = 5$
16. $15 = |w + 2|$ 17. $|\frac{2}{3}y| = \frac{1}{12}$ 18. $|n| + 6 = 2$
19. $|3m + 6| = 4$ 20. $|-3m| = 14$ 21. $6 - 2 = |x| + 3$
22. $|\frac{1}{2}w + \frac{1}{2}w| = 1$ 23. $|2w + w| - 2 = 8$ 24. $|6r + 2| + 6 = 9$
B
25. $|3y - 2| - 4 = 0$ 26. $|\frac{1}{4}x + 6| - 2 = 3$ 27. $\left|\frac{k - 1}{3}\right| = 7$

28. $\left|\frac{3 - n}{5}\right| = 9$ 29. $|3(t - 1) - 4| = 5$ 30. $|8 - 2(y - 1)| = 6$

C   Solve and graph each inequality.

31. $|x| \geq 5$ 32. $|x| \leq 5$ 33. $|n - 2| < 3$ 34. $|y + 4| > 6$
35. $|2x - 1| \leq 9$ 36. $|3y - 2| \geq 8$ 37. $|2(n - 3)| \leq 4$ 38. $|3(2 - k)| < 2$

────── **REVIEW CAPSULE FOR SECTION 7-6** ──────

In Exercises 1–5, write the equation of the line described in words.
(Pages 181–184, 194–196)

1. A line parallel to the y axis and 5 units to its left
2. The y axis
3. A line with slope equal to -3 and y intercept at the origin
4. A line parallel to the x axis and 5 units above it
5. A line with slope equal to $\frac{1}{2}$ and y intercept of 2

Complete the table of ordered pairs for each equation. *(Pages 181–184)*

6. $y = -5x$

x	−3	−1	0	1	3
y	?	?	?	?	?

7. $x + y = 4$

x	−3	−1	0	1	3
y	?	?	?	?	?

7–6 Graphing Absolute Value Relations

On a number line, the graph of $|x| = 3$ consists of two points whose coordinates are 3 and −3.

On the coordinate plane, however, the graph of $|x| = 3$ consists of two parallel lines.

EXAMPLE 1 Graph $|x| = 3$ on the coordinate plane.

Solution: 1. Write the equation with "or."
$|x| = 3$ means $x = 3$ <u>or</u> $x = -3$.

2. Draw the graphs of $x = 3$ and $x = -3$ on the coordinate plane.

The graph consists of two parallel lines, one three units to the right of the y axis, and the other three units to its left.

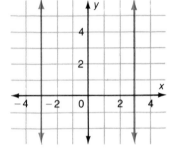

To graph absolute value relations on the coordinate plane, make a table using both positive and negative values of x.

EXAMPLE 2 Graph $y = |x|$.

Solution: 1. Make a table.

x	−5	−3	−1	0	1	3	5
y	5	3	1	0	1	3	5

2. Graph the points in the coordinate plane. Join the points.

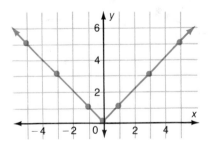

The graph consists of two rays with their initial point at the origin.

CLASSROOM EXERCISES

Complete each table.

1. $y = |2x|$

x	−2	−1	0	1	2
y	?	?	?	?	?

2. $y = -|x|$

x	−2	−1	0	1	2
y	?	?	?	?	?

3. $y = |x| - 2$

x	−3	−2	−1	0	1	2
y	?	?	?	?	?	?

WRITTEN EXERCISES

A Graph each equation on the coordinate plane.

1. $|x| = 2$
2. $|x| = 5$
3. $|y| = 3$
4. $|y| = 1$

5. $y = |2x|$
6. $y = |5x|$
7. $y = -|x|$
8. $y = -|2x|$

9. $y = |x| - 4$
10. $y = |2x| - 5$
11. $y = |-3x| + 7$
12. $x = |2y| - 4$

13. $x = |y|$
14. $x = |-2y|$
15. $x = -|2y| - 6$
16. $x = |-4y| + 3$

17. $x = -|3y|$
18. $x + |y| = 4$
19. $x - |y| = 6$
20. $y + |x| = 10$

B

Example: Graph $|x| + |y| = 5$.

Solution: Solve for $|y|$. $\longrightarrow$ $|y| = 5 - |x|$

x	−5	−4	−3	−2	−1	0	1	2
y	0	±1	±2	?	?	?	?	?

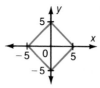

21. $|x| - |y| = 5$
22. $|y| = |x| + 5$
23. $|x| = |y|$
24. $|x + 2| = 5$

25. $|y - 4| = 1$
26. $|x| = -|y|$
27. $|y| = -|x|$
28. $|y - 1| = 4$

C Graph each inequality in the coordinate plane.

29. $|x| \leq 1$
30. $|x| \geq 4$
31. $|y| \geq 4$
32. $y \geq |x|$

33. $y \leq |x|$
34. $y \geq |x - 3|$
35. $y \leq |x + 3|$
36. $|y| \leq |x| + 3$

Review

Solve and check each equation. *(Section 7–5)*

1. $|x + 2| = 5$
2. $|\frac{1}{4}y| = 3$
3. $|-3m| = 1$

4. $|q + 3q| = 8$
5. $|2s - 3 + s| = 0$
6. $|2n - 4\frac{1}{2}| = \frac{1}{2}$

7. $|3z| - 6 = -3$
8. $|4(w + 1) - 3| = 5$
9. $|3(t - 1) + t| = 4$

Graph each equation on the coordinate plane. *(Section 7–6)*

10. $|x| = 4$
11. $y = |-3x|$
12. $y = -|3x|$

13. $y = |-x| + 5$
14. $|y| = 2|x|$
15. $|y - 3| = 1$

BASIC: SOLVING ABSOLUTE VALUE EQUATIONS

Problem: *Write a program which solves equations of the form $|Ax + B| = C$. Include the possibilities that the solution set may be all real numbers or may be the empty set.*

```
100 PRINT "FOR THE EQUATION !AX + B! = C,"
110 PRINT "WHAT ARE A, B, AND C";
120 INPUT A, B, C
130 IF C < 0 THEN 250
140 IF C = 0 THEN 200
150 IF A = 0 THEN 230
160 LET X1 = (C - B)/A
170 LET X2 = (-C - B)/A
180 PRINT "SOLUTIONS ARE ";X1;" AND ";X2
190 GOTO 280
200 LET X = -B/A
210 PRINT "SOLUTION IS ";X
220 GOTO 280
230 IF B = C THEN 270
240 IF B = -C THEN 270
250 PRINT "NO SOLUTION"
260 GOTO 280
270 PRINT "ALL REAL NUMBERS ARE SOLUTIONS."
280 PRINT
290 PRINT "ANY MORE EQUATIONS TO SOLVE (1=YES, 0=NO)";
300 INPUT Z
310 IF Z = 1 THEN 120
320 END
```

The following is the output from a sample run of the program above.

Output:
```
RUN
FOR THE EQUATION !AX + B! = C,
WHAT ARE A, B, AND C? -3,9,15
SOLUTIONS ARE -2   AND   8

ANY MORE EQUATIONS TO SOLVE (1=YES, 0=NO)? 1
? 2,8,0
SOLUTION IS -4

ANY MORE EQUATIONS TO SOLVE (1=YES, 0=NO)? 1
?0,6,8
NO SOLUTION
```

```
ANY MORE EQUATIONS TO SOLVE (1=YES, 0=NO)? 1
? 0,-8,8
ALL REAL NUMBERS ARE SOLUTIONS.

ANY MORE EQUATIONS TO SOLVE (1=YES, 0=NO)? 0
READY
```

Analysis

Statements *130, 250:*	An absolute value expression cannot equal a negative number. Thus if $C < 0$, there is no solution.
Statements *140, 200–210:*	If $C = 0$, the equation has only one solution.
Statements *150, 230–250:*	If $A = 0$, the formulas in statements 160 and 170 cannot be used. Instead, if $|B| = C$, any real number is a solution. But if $|B| \neq C$, no real number is a solution.
Statements *160–180:*	If the computer reaches statement 160, then $C > 0$ and $A \neq 0$. The equation has two solutions, as the following steps show.

$$|Ax + B| = C$$

$Ax + B = C \quad$ or $\quad Ax + B = -C$

$Ax = C - B \quad$ or $\quad Ax = -C - B \quad$ ⟵ **Subtract B from both sides.**

$x = \dfrac{C - B}{A} \quad$ or $\quad x = \dfrac{-C - B}{A} \quad$ ⟵ **Divide both sides by A.**

EXERCISES

A   Write each equation in the form $|Ax + B| = C$. Then use the program on page 268 to solve the equation.

1. $|x - 1| = 5$
2. $|x + 3| - 7 = 0$
3. $|2x| = 24$
4. $35 = |4x - 1|$
5. $|4 - x| = 44$
6. $|15 + 5x| = 55$
7. $0 = |6 - 2x|$
8. $100 = |-5x|$
9. $|4x + 2| + 8 = 0$
10. $|10 + 8x| = 0$
11. $0 = |80 - 10x| - 8$
12. $9 = |3x - 1| + 9$

     Write a BASIC program for each problem.

13. Given the coordinates of a point, decide whether the point is in the solution set of the following system of inequalities.

$$\begin{cases} x \leq 0 \\ 2x + y \geq 6 \\ 4x + y < 3 \end{cases}$$

B

14. Solve inequalities of the form $|Ax + B| < C$.

15. Solve inequalities of the form $|Ax + B| > C$.

Chapter Summary

IMPORTANT IDEAS

1. The compound sentence $x \leq a$ means $x = a$ <u>or</u> $x < a$. The solution set is the union of the solution sets of $x = a$ and $x < a$. Similarly, the compound sentence $x \geq b$ means $x = b$ <u>or</u> $x > b$. The solution set is the union of the solution sets of $x = b$ and $x > b$.

2. The compound sentence $a < x < b$ means $a < x$ <u>and</u> $x < b$. The solution set is the intersection of the solution sets of $a < x$ and $x < b$.

3. The graph of a linear equation separates the coordinate plane into three sets of points — the points in the two half-planes and the points on the line.

4. The maximum or minimum value, if any, of a linear expression evaluated over a polygonal region occurs at one of the vertices of the polygon.

5. A sentence involving absolute value can be written as a compound sentence. For example, $|y| = 8$ means $y = 8$ <u>or</u> $y = -8$.

Chapter Objectives and Review

Objective: *To solve linear inequalities and graph them on a number line (Section 7–1)*

Write each compound sentence as two simple sentences joined by <u>or</u> or <u>and</u>.

1. $5x \geq -10$
2. $b + 3 \leq 0$
3. $-5 < y < 0$
4. $-12 < 3z < -3$
5. $6s - 8 \geq 4$
6. $-1 < \frac{1}{4}f + 1 < 3$

Solve and graph each inequality.

7. $-2 < c < 5$
8. $-4h \geq 0$
9. $-3 < m - 2 \leq 3$
10. $x + 4 \leq -1$
11. $-7 \leq 2y + 3 \leq -5$
12. $3(2 - d) \leq 9$

Objective: *To graph linear inequalities on the coordinate plane (Section 7–2)*

Graph each inequality on the coordinate plane.

13. $y > -4x$
14. $y \leq x - 1$
15. $x + y < -2$
16. $-x + y \geq 5$
17. $y \leq 0$
18. $x < -1$
19. $y \geq -2x - 3$
20. $3x + 2y > 6$

Objective: *To solve systems of linear inequalities by graphing (Section 7–3)*

Match each graph in Exercises 21–24 with one of the systems given in a–d.

21.   22.   23.   24.

a. $\begin{cases} y \le x \\ y \le -x \end{cases}$ b. $\begin{cases} y \le -x \\ y \ge 0 \end{cases}$ c. $\begin{cases} x \le 0 \\ y \ge x \end{cases}$ d. $\begin{cases} y \le x \\ y \ge -x \end{cases}$

Solve each system by graphing.

25. $\begin{cases} y < x + 3 \\ y < -5x \end{cases}$ 26. $\begin{cases} y \ge 2x \\ y \ge x - 1 \end{cases}$ 27. $\begin{cases} 3x - y > -2 \\ x + 2y < 4 \end{cases}$ 28. $\begin{cases} x + y \ge 2 \\ x - y \le 6 \\ y \le 0 \end{cases}$

Objective: *To solve problems containing constraints, using linear programming methods (Section 7–4)*

In Exercises 29–34, find the maximum and minimum values for k, given the constraints shown in the graph.

29. $k = x + y$

30. $k = 3x + y$

31. $k = x + 4y$

32. $k = 2x - y$

33. $k = 3x - 2y$

34. $k = x - 3y$

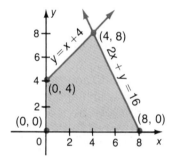

Each of three old machines can stamp out 4 parts per minute. Each of four newer machines can stamp out 6 parts per minute. Only 5 workers are available at any one time to operate the machines.

Use this information in Exercises 35–39.

35. Let x represent the number of old machines used and let y represent the number of newer machines used. Write an expression to represent the total number of parts made per minute.

36. Write a system of inequalities that shows the constraints on x and y.

37. Graph the system of inequalities you wrote in Exercise 36.

38. Write the coordinates of the vertices of the polygonal region graphed in Exercise 37.

39. What is the maximum number of parts that can be made per minute?

Objective: *To solve equations involving absolute value (Section 7-5)*

Solve and check each equation.

40. $|y - 1| = 7$

41. $|4x| - 3 = 1$

42. $|-\frac{1}{2}n| = 3$

43. $12 = |p| + 4$

44. $|6 - q| = 5$

45. $|2(a + 3) - a| = 5$

Objective: *To graph absolute value relations on the coordinate plane (Section 7-6)*

Graph each equation on the coordinate plane.

46. $|y| = 6$

47. $|x| = 1$

48. $y = -|4x|$

49. $y = |-x|$

50. $y = |-2x| + 2$

51. $x = |3y|$

52. $|x| - |y| = 2$

53. $|y + 1| = 3$

_____ Chapter Test _____

Write each compound sentence as two simple sentences joined by <u>or</u> or <u>and</u>.

1. $x - 3 \geq 9$

2. $3x + 2 \leq 10$

3. $-8 < 2n + 6 < -2$

Solve and graph each inequality on a number line.

4. $4x \leq 12$

5. $-3 < y + 1 < 5$

6. Graph the inequality $2x + y \leq 4$ on the coordinate plane.

7. Solve by graphing: $\begin{cases} y < x \\ y < 3x + 6 \end{cases}$

A manufacturer makes two models of a watch. The profit on Model A is $5 per watch and the profit on Model B is $12 per watch. The manufacturer can produce no more than 300 watches per week. To meet the market demand, at least 110 Model A watches and 60 Model B watches must be available each week. Use this information for Exercises 8–12.

8. Let x represent the number of Model A watches and let y represent the number of Model B watches produced per week. Write an expression to represent the total weekly profit.

9. Write a system of inequalities that shows the constraints on x and y.

10. Graph the system of inequalities you wrote in Exercise 9.

11. State the coordinates of the vertices of the polygonal region graphed in Exercise 10.

12. What is the maximum profit possible?

Solve and check each equation.

13. $|4x| = 20$

14. $|y - 2| = 4$

15. Graph $y = |-3x|$ on the coordinate plane.

Additional Practice

Skills

Write each compound sentence as two simple sentences joined by <u>or</u> or <u>and</u>. *(Section 7–1)*

1. $2y \geq 5$ **2.** $\frac{1}{3}n - 2 \geq 3$ **3.** $-6 < 4a + 6 < -2$

Solve and graph each inequality on a number line. *(Section 7–1)*

4. $3n \leq 12$ **5.** $-5 < 2p + 3 \leq 3$ **6.** $3(n + 1) \leq -6$

Graph each inequality on the coordinate plane. *(Section 7–2)*

7. $y > x - 1$ **8.** $y \leq -2x$ **9.** $x + y < -4$ **10.** $2x - y \geq 1$

Solve each system by graphing. *(Section 7–3)*

11. $\begin{cases} x - y < 4 \\ x + y > 0 \end{cases}$ **12.** $\begin{cases} y \geq 3x \\ y \geq -x + 1 \end{cases}$ **13.** $\begin{cases} 3x - y > 2 \\ 2x + y < -3 \end{cases}$ **14.** $\begin{cases} y > -x + 4 \\ y > x \end{cases}$

Solve and check each equation. *(Section 7–5)*

15. $|x - 1| = 3$ **16.** $|3a - 4| - 6 = 0$ **17.** $|2(x - 2) + x| = 8$

Graph each equation on the coordinate plane. *(Section 7–6)*

18. $y = |-4x|$ **19.** $|2y + 1| = 3$ **20.** $|x| + |y| = 4$

Applications

21. A garden supply company had a sale on seedlings. Each customer had to buy at least 15, but no more than 100, seedlings. Represent this as an inequality, where s is the number of seedlings per customer. *(Section 7–1)*

22. Members of the swim team at the town pool must be at least 7 years old and younger than 18. Represent the permissible ages of the swim team members as an inequality, where a is the age in years. *(Section 7–1)*

A group of 360 people is to be bused to the state fair. The bus company has four 60–passenger buses and six 40–passenger buses available. The cost of renting a 60–passenger bus is $200; the cost of renting a 40–passenger bus is $140. Use this information in Exercises 23–25. *(Section 7–4)*

23. Let x represent the number of 60–passenger buses rented and let y represent the number of 40–passenger buses. Write an expression to represent the total cost.

24. Write and graph a system of inequalities showing the constraints on x and y.

25. Write the coordinates of the vertices of the polygonal region graphed in Exercise 24 and find the minimum cost possible.

Review of Word Problems: Chapters 1–7

1. A family's phone bill for December was $32.50 more than the phone bill for November. Phone service for the two months cost a total of $89.30. How much was the December bill? *(Section 4–3)*

2. Two trains 700 kilometers apart start at the same time and travel toward each other. One travels at a rate of 80 kilometers per hour and the other at a rate of 95 kilometers per hour. In how many hours will they meet? *(Section 5–2)*

> The sales tax rate for a certain state is 6%. Use this information in Exercises 3–5. *(Section 5–6)*

3. Make a table to show the amount of tax, t, for sales, s, of $100, $200 and $300.

4. Use the ordered pairs from the table in Exercise 3 to graph the function. Assume that the graph is linear.

5. Use the graph in Exercise 4 to determine the tax on $250.

6. The distance between two cities on a map varies directly with the actual distance between the cities. If 2.5 centimeters on the map represent 50 kilometers, what distance does 6 centimeters represent? *(Section 5–10)*

7. Robert drove from Dallas to Chicago and then from Chicago to Nashville. He drove 1387 miles in all. The distance from Dallas to Chicago is 34 miles greater than twice the distance from Chicago to Nashville. How far is it from Dallas to Chicago? *(Section 6–4)*

8. The sum of the digits of a two-digit number is 10. When 54 is added to the number, the result is the original number with its digits reversed. Find the number. *(Section 6–5)*

9. The regular admission price at the movies is $4.50. Admission for senior citizens is $3.50. One evening, 284 tickets were sold for a total of $1226. How many tickets were sold to senior citizens? *(Section 6–7)*

10. A 3% salt solution is mixed with an 8% salt solution. How many milliliters of each are needed to obtain 800 milliliters of a 5% solution? *(Section 6–8)*

> A wholesale bakery makes large and small loaves of rye bread. The profit on a large loaf is 10 cents, and the profit on a small loaf is 8 cents. No more than 300 loaves of rye bread are baked daily. To meet the demand at the stores, at least 150 small loaves and at least 75 large loaves must be made each day. Use this information in Exercises 11–14. *(Section 7–4)*

11. Let x represent the number of small loaves and let y represent the number of large loaves of rye bread produced each day. Write an equation to represent the total daily profit.

12. Write a system of inequalities that shows the constraints on x and y.

13. Graph the system of inequalities you wrote in Exercise 12 and write the coordinates of the vertices of the polygonal region.

14. What is the maximum possible daily profit on rye bread?

Cumulative Review: Chapters 5–7

Choose the best answer. Choose *a, b, c,* or *d.*

1. Solve for l: $P = 2l + 2w$

   a. $l = P - w$ **b.** $l = \dfrac{P}{2} - w$ **c.** $l = \dfrac{(2w - P)}{2}$ **d.** $l = P - 2w - 2$

2. Two cars leave the same place at the same time. One is traveling east at an average rate of 80 kilometers per hour and the other is traveling west at an average rate of 60 kilometers per hour. In how many hours will they be 1120 kilometers apart?

   a. 8   **b.** 16   **c.** 4   **d.** 3

3. In which quadrant is the graph of $P(-6, 8)$ located?

   a. I   **b.** II   **c.** III   **d.** IV

4. Which point is <u>not</u> on the line parallel to the x axis and 3 units below it?

   a. $A(-3, 0)$ **b.** $B(0, -3)$ **c.** $C(-3, -3)$ **d.** $D(18, -3)$

5. Pencils cost 10¢ each or 3 for 25¢. Which number <u>cannot</u> be in the range of this function?

   a. 30¢   **b.** 50¢   **c.** 60¢   **d.** $1.00

6. Which of the following is a correct description of this set of ordered pairs:
   $$\{(0, 7)\,(-8, 6)\,(9, -7)\,(0, -8)\}$$

   a. Function   **b.** Relation, not a function

   c. Function, not a relation   **d.** Neither a function nor a relation

7. What is the slope of the line containing the points $A(-2, 7)$ and $B(3, -8)$?

   a. 3   **b.** -3 **c.** -1 **d.** 1

8. What is the slope of the graph of $2x + y = 7$?

   a. -2 **b.** 2   **c.** 7   **d.** $\dfrac{7}{2}$

9. If y varies directly as x and $y = 8$ when x is 16, find y when $x = 2$.

   a. -4 **b.** 4   **c.** 1   **d.** -1

10. Seventeen liters of gasoline cost $4.76. How much will 32 liters cost?

    a. $28.00   **b.** $9.52   **c.** $13.72   **d.** $8.96

11. Which points are <u>not</u> on the graph of either line? $\quad \begin{cases} x + y = 10 \\ x - y = 5 \end{cases}$

    a. $A(17, -7)$ **b.** $B(12, 7)$ **c.** $C(12, -7)$ **d.** $D(-20, 30)$

12. Which point is a solution of this system? $\quad \begin{cases} 2x + y = 17 \\ x - 3y = 5 \end{cases}$

    a. $A(8, 1)$ **b.** $B(-8, 1)$ **c.** $C(-8, -1)$ **d.** $D(8, -1)$

13. Which system has no solutions?

    a. $\begin{cases} 3x + y = 7 \\ y - 3x = 9 \end{cases}$ **b.** $\begin{cases} 2x - 3y = 8 \\ 3y = 5x + 7 \end{cases}$ **c.** $\begin{cases} 8y - 5x = 7 \\ y = \frac{5}{8}x - 15 \end{cases}$ **d.** $\begin{cases} x - y = 15 \\ 2x + 7y = 92 \end{cases}$

14. Which of the following systems is equivalent to this system? $\begin{cases} y - 3x = 15 \\ 12y + x = 24 \end{cases}$

a. $\begin{cases} y - 3x = 15 \\ 36y + 3x = 72 \end{cases}$ b. $\begin{cases} y - 3x = 15 \\ 12y + 3x = 24 \end{cases}$ c. $\begin{cases} 4y - 3x = 15 \\ 4y + x = 8 \end{cases}$ d. $\begin{cases} 4y - 3x = 15 \\ 4y + 3x = 24 \end{cases}$

15. The sum of two numbers is 40. Twice the smaller is 8 more than the larger. What are the numbers?

   a. 14 and 26   b. 20 and 32   c. 48 and 88   d. 16 and 24

16. The hundreds, tens, and units digits of a number are h, t, and u, respectively. What is the value of the number if the digits are reversed?

   a. $100h + 10t + u$ b. $h + 10t + 100u$ c. $h + t + u$ d. $100(h + t + u)$

17. Jim has $1.15 in nickels and dimes. He has one more dime than nickels. How many dimes does he have?

   a. 8   b. 7   c. 11   d. 5

18. Cashews at $5.00 per pound are mixed with peanuts at $2.00 per pound to make a mixture worth $4.00 a pound. There are 15 pounds of the mixture. How many pounds of cashews are there?

   a. 10   b. 5   c. 8   d. 12

19. Mr. Skidmore sold a adult tickets and c children's tickets to the school play. The cost of an adult's ticket is $5.75 and the cost of a child's ticket is $2.50. What expression shows the total cost of all the tickets?

   a. $(a + c)8.25$ b. $5.75a + c$ c. $5.75a + 2.50c$ d. $2.50a + 5.75c$

20. Which of the following is equivalent to $8n \leq 11$?

   a. $11 > 8n$ b. $8n = 11$

   c. $8n < 11 \text{ or } 8n = 11$ d. $8n < 11 \text{ and } 8n = 11$

21. Which point is <u>not</u> on the graph of $y < 3x - 4$?

   a. $A(10, 0)$ b. $B(0, -5)$ c. $C(-10, 10)$ d. $D(10, -10)$

22. Points on the graph of $y = 2x - 5$ are <u>not</u> included in the graph of which of the following?

   a. $2x - y > 5$ b. $y \geq 2x - 5$ c. $y \leq 2x - 5$ d. $2x - y \geq 5$

23. What is the solution set of $|2(x - 1) - 8| = 4$?

   a. $\{7\}$ b. $\{3\}$ c. $\{-7, 3\}$ d. $\{7, 3\}$

24. Which point is <u>not</u> on the graph of $y = |x|$?

   a. The origin   b. $B(-8, 8)$ c. $C(17, 17)$ d. $D(-9, -9)$

25. Which point lies on the graph of the system $\begin{cases} x \geq 3 \\ y \geq -2 \\ x + y \leq 5 \end{cases}$?

   a. $A(6, 0)$ b. $B(3, 7)$ c. $C(0, 0)$ d. $D(5, 0)$

26. Find the maximum value of $k = 3x - y$ given these constraints: $\begin{cases} x \geq 0 \\ y \geq 0 \\ x + y \leq 4 \end{cases}$

   a. 12   b. 0   c. -4 d. 16

Preparing for College Entrance Tests

When comparing two quantities or expressions, it is sometimes helpful to choose real numbers that satisfy the conditions of the problem and substitute them in the given expressions.

REMEMBER: If you can find at least one number that makes a statement false, then you have shown that the statement is not always true.

EXAMPLE: If n is a real number and $n < 0$, which of the following statements must be true?

(a) $n > \dfrac{1}{n}$ (b) $(n^2 - 1) > (1 - n^2)$ (c) $(n - 1) > (1 - n)$ (d) $n^2 > n$

Think: Two choices involve n^2, and n^2 is always positive. Thus, check the choices involving n^2 first.

Solution:

(b) $(n^2 - 1) > (1 - n^2)$ ◄——— **Not true when $n = -\frac{1}{2}$**

(d) $n^2 > n$ ◄——— **Always true, since $n < 0$ and $n^2 > 0$**

(a) $n > \dfrac{1}{n}$ ◄——— **Not true when $n = -2$**

(c) $(n - 1) > (1 - n)$ ◄——— **Never true, since $(n - 1) < 0$ and $(1 - n) > 0$**

Answer: d

Choose the best answer. Choose a, b, c, or d. (Assume that all variables represent real numbers.)

1. If $y > 0$, which of the following must be true?

   (a) $y^2 > y$ (b) $y > \dfrac{1}{y}$ (c) $(y + 1) > (y - 1)$ (d) $\dfrac{1}{y} > \dfrac{1}{y^2}$

2. If $y < 0$, which of the following must be true?

   (a) $y^4 > y^2$ (b) $y^3 > y$ (c) $y^3 > y^2$ (d) $y^4 > y$

3. If $p > 2$, which of the following must be true?

   (a) $\dfrac{p - 2}{2} > \dfrac{p}{2}$ (b) $\dfrac{p + 2}{2} > \dfrac{p}{2}$ (c) $\dfrac{2}{p + 2} > \dfrac{2}{p}$ (d) $\dfrac{2}{p} > \dfrac{2}{p - 2}$

4. If $q \neq 0$, which of the following must be true?

   (a) $\dfrac{q - (q + q)}{q} > 1$ (b) $\dfrac{q - (q - q)}{q} > 1$ (c) $\dfrac{q + (q + q)}{q} > 1$ (d) $\dfrac{q + (q - q)}{q} > 1$

5. If $w > 1$, which of the following must be true?

   (a) $\dfrac{1}{w - 1} > \dfrac{1}{1 - w}$ (b) $\dfrac{1}{w - 1} > \dfrac{-1}{1 - w}$ (c) $\dfrac{1}{1 - w} > \dfrac{-1}{w - 1}$ (d) $\dfrac{1}{1 - w} > \dfrac{-1}{1 - w}$

6. If $n > 2$, which of the following must be true?

(a) $\dfrac{2n}{2} < \dfrac{2n}{n}$

(b) $\dfrac{2+n}{2} < \dfrac{2n}{n}$

(c) $\dfrac{2+n}{n} > \dfrac{2+n}{2}$

(d) $\dfrac{2n}{n} > \dfrac{2+n}{n}$

7. If $x > 0$, which of the following must be true?

(a) $-(2x - x) < -(x - 2x)$

(b) $-(2x - x) < (x - 2x)$

(c) $x - 2x < -(x + 2x)$

(d) $2x - x < -(2x - x)$

8. If $x > 0$ and $y < 0$, which of the following must be true?

(a) $x + y > 0$

(b) $x - y > 0$

(c) $xy > 0$

(d) $\dfrac{x}{y} > 0$

9. If $a > 0$ and $b > 0$, which of the following must be true?

(a) $-(a - b) < 0$

(b) $-(a + b) < 0$

(c) $-(b - a) < 0$

(d) $-(-b - a) < 0$

10. If $p < 0$ and $r < 0$, which of the following must be true?

(a) $(p - r) > 0$

(b) $(p^2 - r^2) > 0$

(c) $pr > 0$

(d) $p(p - r) > 0$

11. If $c > 0$ and $d > c$, which of the following must be true?

(a) $(c + d) > 1$

(b) $(d - c) > 1$

(c) $cd > 1$

(d) $\dfrac{d}{c} > 1$

12. If $m < 0$ and $p < m$, which of the following must be true?

(a) $(p - m) < (m - p)$ (b) $\dfrac{p}{m} < 1$

(c) $\dfrac{m}{p} < 0$

(d) $p^2 < m^2$

13. If $ab > 0$, which of the following must be true?

(a) $a > 0$

(b) $b > 0$

(c) $\dfrac{a}{b} > 0$

(d) $(a - b) > 0$

14. If $s > t$ and $s + t > 0$, which of the following must be true?

(a) $t > 0$

(b) $s > 0$

(c) $-s > t$

(d) $(t - s) > 0$

15. If $a < 0$ and $ab > 0$, which of the following must be true?

(a) $0 < b$

(b) $b < a$

(c) $(a + b) < 0$

(d) $(a - b) < 0$

16. If $|k| > 1$, which of the following must be true?

(a) $k > 1$

(b) $|k| > k$

(c) $|k| > k^2$

(d) $k^2 > 1$

17. If $x < 0$, which of the following must be true?

(a) $|x - 2| < |x| - 2$

(b) $|2x| < 2|x|$

(c) $|x + 2| < |x| + 2$

(d) $|2 - x| < 2 - |x|$

18. If $n > 0$ and $p < n$, which of the following must be true?

(a) $|p - n| > p - n$

(b) $|n| > |p|$

(c) $|n| + |p| > |n + p|$

(d) $n + p > n - p$

19. If $c < d$ and $|c| > |d|$, which of the following must be true?

(a) $d > 0$

(b) $d < 0$

(c) $c < 0$

(d) $c > -d$

CHAPTER **8** # Exponents and Polynomials

8-1 Exponents

Suppose that you were offered a position that paid 1¢ on the first day of work. Then, for each day after the first, you receive double the preceding day's wage. Here is a partial list of each day's wages.

Day	Wages in Cents	Powers of Two	
		Factor Form	**Exponent Form**
1	1		2^0
2	2	2	2^1
3	4	2×2	2^2
4	8	$2 \times 2 \times 2$	2^3
5	16	$2 \times 2 \times 2 \times 2$	2^4
6	32	$2 \times 2 \times 2 \times 2 \times 2$	2^5
⋮	⋮	⋮	⋮
29	268,435,456	$\underbrace{2 \times 2 \times 2 \cdots \times 2 \times 2}_{\textbf{28 factors}}$	2^{28}
30	536,870,912	$\underbrace{2 \times 2 \times \cdots \times 2 \times 2}_{\textbf{29 factors}}$	2^{29}

Each day's wages can be expressed as a power of 2. For example, the sixth day's wages can be written

$$2^5 = \underbrace{2 \cdot 2 \cdot 2 \cdot 2 \cdot 2}_{\textbf{5 factors of 2}} = \textbf{32}$$

The wages on day 30 are 2^{29}¢, or over 5 million dollars!

Note how powers are read.

For 2^2, read "two squared" or "the second power of 2."

For 2^3, read "two cubed" or "the third power of 2."

For 2^4, read "two to the fourth" or "the fourth power of 2."

For 2^n, read "two to the nth" or "the nth power of 2."

Examples of exponents used with other bases are given below.

Expression	Base	Exponent	Meaning
3^2	3	2	$3 \cdot 3$
5^4	5	4	$5 \cdot 5 \cdot 5 \cdot 5$
15^1	15	1	15
$(-3)^2$	-3	2	$(-3)(-3)$
x^7	x	7	$x \cdot x \cdot x \cdot x \cdot x \cdot x \cdot x$
x^a	x	a	$\underbrace{x \cdot x \cdot x \cdots \cdot x}_{a \text{ factors}}$

Definitions	If x is a real number and a is an integer greater than 1, then

$$x^a = \underbrace{x \cdot x \cdot x \cdot \cdots \cdot x.}_{a \text{ factors}}$$

When $a = 1$, $x^a = x$. That is, $x^1 = x$.

Example 1 shows how the definition is used to write a number in exponential form.

EXAMPLE 1   Write 10,000 in exponential form.

Solution: $10,000 = 10 \cdot 10 \cdot 10 \cdot 10$ ◄——— **Write as factors of 10.**

$= 10^4$ ◄——— **By definition**

The definition can also be used to write certain products as a base with a single exponent.

EXAMPLE 2   Write $2^5 \cdot 2^3$ as a base with a single exponent.

Solution: $2^5 \cdot 2^3 = \underbrace{2 \cdot 2 \cdot 2 \cdot 2 \cdot 2}_{\text{Five factors}} \cdot \underbrace{2 \cdot 2 \cdot 2}_{\text{Three factors}}$

$\underbrace{}_{\text{Eight factors}}$

$= 2^8$

Example 3 shows how the definition is applied when evaluating expressions.

EXAMPLE 3   Find the value of x^3y^2 when $x = -2$ and $y = 3$.

Solution: Replace x with -2 and y with 3.

$x^3y^2 = (-2)^3(3)^2$

$= \underbrace{(-2)(-2)(-2)}\underbrace{(3)(3)}$ ◄——— **By definition**

$= (-8) \cdot 9 = -72$

CLASSROOM EXERCISES

Complete.

	Expression	Base	Exponent	Meaning
1.	10^6	?	?	?
2.	7^4	?	?	?
3.	?	3	4	?
4.	?	?	?	$2 \cdot 2 \cdot 2 \cdot 2 \cdot 2$
5.	?	?	?	$x \cdot x \cdot x \cdot x \cdot x \cdot x$

WRITTEN EXERCISES

A   Complete.

	Expression	Base	Exponent	Meaning
1.	5^6	?	?	?
2.	10^3	?	?	?
3.	2^6	?	?	?
4.	a^5	?	?	?
5.	?	10	5	?
6.	?	2	3	?
7.	?	?	?	$10 \cdot 10 \cdot 10 \cdot 10$
8.	?	?	?	$x \cdot x \cdot x \cdot x \cdot x \cdot x \cdot x$
9.	?	?	?	x

Evaluate.

10. 10^2 **11.** 10^4 **12.** 10^1 **13.** 10^5 **14.** 10^7 **15.** 10^{10}

16. How many zeros follow the "1" in the decimal numeral for 10^{13}?

17. How many zeros follow the "1" in the decimal numeral for 10^a?

Evaluate.

18. $(-1)^3$ **19.** $(-1)^7$ **20.** $(-1)^9$ **21.** $(-1)^5$ **22.** $(-1)^{11}$ **23.** $(-1)^{99}$

24. $(-1)^2$ **25.** $(-1)^6$ **26.** $(-1)^4$ **27.** $(-1)^{10}$ **28.** $(-1)^{30}$ **29.** $(-1)^{100}$

Write in exponential form.

30. 1000   **31.** 100,000   **32.** 1,000,000   **33.** 1 million   **34.** 1 billion

35. 1 thousand   **36.** 10 billion   **37.** 1,000,000,000   **38.** 10   **39.** 1 trillion

Write each product as a base with a single exponent.

40. $10^3 \cdot 10^2$ **41.** $2^3 \cdot 2^4$ **42.** $5^2 \cdot 5^3$ **43.** $10 \cdot 10^4$

44. $5^3 \cdot 5^2$ **45.** $2^3 \cdot 2^3$ **46.** $15^2 \cdot 15^4$ **47.** $2^{15} \cdot 2^2$

48. $x^2 \cdot x^3$ **49.** $a^4 \cdot a^2$ **50.** $y^5 \cdot y^4$ **51.** $m^6 \cdot m^2$

Find the value when $a = 1$, $b = 2$, and $c = -3$.

52. a^5 **53.** $(-b)^2$ **54.** c^3 **55.** a^2b

56. ab^2 **57.** a^2c^2 **58.** b^2c^2 **59.** abc

60. $a^2b^2c^2$ **61.** abc^2 **62.** $a^{25}b^2$ **63.** $a^{100}b^3c$

64. Evaluate $(a^2b^3c)^2$ for $a = 3$, $b = -2$, and $c = 5$.

Multiply. *(Pages 64–67)*

1. $(-40)(-5)$ **2.** $18(-21)$ **3.** $2(-3)(-3)(-3)$ **4.** $(-1)(-1)(-1)(-1)$

5. $(-18)(-20)0$ **6.** $(-6)(15)(20)(-2)$ **7.** $4(-1)(-7)(-10)$ **8.** $(-1)(-1)(-1)(-1)(-1)$

8–2 Multiplying Monomials

When exponential expressions have the *same base*, their product can be expressed using the same base and a single exponent by applying the definition of exponent.

a. $4^3 \cdot 4^2 = 4 \cdot 4 \cdot 4 \cdot 4 \cdot 4$ **b.** $x^4 \cdot x^4 = x \cdot x \cdot x \cdot x \cdot x \cdot x \cdot x \cdot x$

$= 4^5$ $= x^8$

Note in **a** and **b** that the *sum* of the exponents equals the *single exponent* in the answer. This suggests the following theorem.

Theorem 8–1

| **Multiplication Theorem for Exponents** |
| If x is a real number and a and b are positive integers, then |
| $x^a \cdot x^b = x^{a+b}.$ |

Theorem 8–1 can be used to find products such as $(-3x^2)(2x)$.

EXAMPLE 1   Find each product.

   a. $(-3x^2)(2x)$ **b.** $(-3ab^2)(-2a^3b^5)$

Solutions:

a. $(-3x^2)(2x) = (-3 \cdot 2)(x^2 \cdot x)$ **b.** $(-3ab^2)(-2a^3b^5) = (-3 \cdot -2)(a \cdot a^3)(b^2 \cdot b^5)$

$= -6x^{2+1}$ $= 6a^{1+3}b^{2+5}$

$= -6x^3$ $= 6a^4b^7$

Expressions such as $-3x^2$ and $2x$ are *monomials*.

Definition

| A **monomial** is a term that is the product of numbers and variables with nonnegative integral exponents. |

Monomial	**Not a Monomial**	
$\sqrt{3}x^2$	$3x^{-2}$	⟵ **Negative exponent**
$\frac{1}{4}x^2y^2$	$3y^2 + 7y + 7$	⟵ **Sum of monomials**
8	$4x^{\frac{1}{2}}$	⟵ **Rational number exponen**

Exponents and Polynomials   **283**

Theorem 8-1 can also be used to write a product in exponential form.

EXAMPLE 2 Write in exponential form: $(4 \times 10^5)(2 \times 10^8)$

Solution: $(4 \times 10^5)(2 \times 10^8) = (4 \times 2)(10^5 \times 10^8)$

$= 8 \times 10^{5+8}$ ⟵——— **By Theorem 8-1**

$= 8 \times 10^{13}$

CLASSROOM EXERCISES

Find each product.

1. $x^8 \cdot x^2$
2. $4^5 \cdot 4^3$
3. $-x^2 \cdot x^3$
4. $(-2)^2(-2)^{10}$

5. $(-a)^6 \cdot a^3$
6. $(3x^2)(-4x^2y)$
7. $(-2a^2b^3)(5ab)^0$
8. $x^2y^5 \cdot 3x^9y^4$

WRITTEN EXERCISES

A   Find each product.

1. $(x \cdot x \cdot x \cdot x)(x \cdot x \cdot x)$
2. $(3 \cdot 3)(3 \cdot 3 \cdot 3 \cdot 3)$
3. $(-y)(y \cdot y)$
4. $-1(m \cdot m \cdot m)(m)$

5. $x^4 \cdot x^5$
6. $x^2 \cdot x^4$
7. $m \cdot m^6$
8. $a^2 \cdot a^3$

9. $n^3 \cdot n^4$
10. $b \cdot b^2$
11. $a(a)$
12. $b^3 \cdot b$

13. $b^2 \cdot b^3$
14. $(-b)(-b)$
15. $b(-b)$
16. $-a^5(a^2)$

17. $x(-x^2)$
18. $(-y^2)(y^2)$
19. $-y^2(-y^2)$
20. $a(a^2)(a^3)$

21. $p^3 \cdot p^2$
22. $-x(-x^2)$
23. $3^6 \cdot 3^4$
24. $5(5^4)$

25. $2(2^3)(2^4)$
26. $3(3^2)(3^4)$
27. $5^2(-5^2)(5^3)$
28. $(-2x^4)(-3x^2)$

29. $(-4x^2y)(-5xy)$
30. $(-3a^2b)(ab)(-2ab)^0$
31. $(8mn^2)(-3m^2y^4)$
32. $(-x^5)(3x^2)(7x^4)$

33. $(2x)(3x^4)(-6x^3)$
34. $(4c^2d)(5cd)(cd^2)$
35. $-1(x^3)(-x)$
36. $(-x^2y)(5xy^2)(9x^3y^2)$

37. $10^3 \cdot 10^2 \cdot 10^4$
38. $10^5 \cdot 10^8 \cdot 10$
39. $10 \cdot 10^5 \cdot 10^9$
40. $10^{10} \cdot 10^{15} \cdot 10^0$

Write each product in exponential form.

41. $(2 \times 10^2)(3 \times 10^4)$
42. $(7 \times 10)(9 \times 10^5)$
43. $(1.5 \times 10^3)(2 \times 10^6)$

44. $(2.4 \times 10^7)(3.9 \times 10)$
45. $(2.8 \times 10^9)(a \times 10^2)$
46. $(a \times 10^x)(b \times 10^y)$

B   Identify the number named by each product as positive, P, or negative, N.

47. $(-1)^4(-1)^3$
48. $(-1)^{10}(-1)^8$
49. -10^4
50. -3^{15}
51. $(-3)^{15}$
52. $(-4)^{25}$

C   Write each product in exponential form. All exponents are positive integers.

53. $x^a \cdot x^2$
54. $y^2 \cdot y^b$
55. $x^a \cdot x^b$

56. $a^{x-2} \cdot a^5$
57. $x^{3a} \cdot x^{2a}$
58. $(x^{2a+7})(x^{2a-8})^0$

59. $3^x \cdot 3^2$
60. $2^{4a} \cdot 2^{3a}$
61. $(2^{2a+7})(2^{7a-6})$

62. $(x+2)^2 \cdot (x+2)^4$
63. $(x+2)^a \cdot (x+2)^6$
64. $(x+2)^{2a} \cdot (x+2)^{b-a}$

8-3 Powers of Monomials

The Multiplication Theorem for Exponents can be used to write expressions such as $(5^4)^2$ with a single exponent.

a. $(5^4)^2 = 5^4 \cdot 5^4$

$\qquad = 5^{4+4}$

$\qquad = 5^8$

b. $(t^3)^4 = t^3 \cdot t^3 \cdot t^3 \cdot t^3$

$\qquad = t^{3+3+3+3}$

$\qquad = t^{12}$

The examples suggest this theorem.

Theorem 8-2

> **Power Theorem for Exponents**
>
> If x is a real number and a and b are positive integers, then
>
> $$(x^a)^b = x^{ab}.$$

Example 1 shows you how to apply Theorem 8-2.

EXAMPLE 1 Simplify: **a.** $(6^3)^9$ $\qquad\qquad$ **b.** $(z^5)^{10}$

Solutions: **a.** $(6^3)^9 = 6^{3 \cdot 9}$ ◄── **By Theorem 8-2** ──► **b.** $(z^5)^{10} = z^{5 \cdot 10}$

$\qquad\qquad = 6^{27}$ $\qquad\qquad\qquad\qquad\qquad\qquad\qquad = z^{50}$

The following examples suggest a method for multiplying an exponential expression having a monomial base.

c. $(3r)^3 = (3r)(3r)(3r)$

$\qquad = (3 \cdot 3 \cdot 3)(r \cdot r \cdot r)$

$\qquad = 3^3 r^3$, or $27r^3$

d. $(xy)^5 = (xy)(xy)(xy)(xy)(xy)$

$\qquad = (x \cdot x \cdot x \cdot x \cdot x)(y \cdot y \cdot y \cdot y \cdot y)$

$\qquad = x^5 y^5$

Thus, a power of a product of two or more factors equals the product of the powers of each factor.

Theorem 8-3

> **Power of a Product Theorem for Exponents**
>
> If x and y are real numbers and a is a positive integer, then
>
> $$(xy)^a = x^a y^a.$$

Recall that $-a = -1 \cdot a$. Thus, two factors of $-a$ are -1 and a.

EXAMPLE 2 Simplify: **a.** $(-x)^6$ $\qquad\qquad$ **b.** $\left(-\dfrac{2}{3}x^5 y^2\right)^3$

Solutions: **a.** $(-x)^6 = (-1 \cdot x)^6$

$\qquad\qquad = (-1)^6 (x)^6$

$\qquad\qquad = x^6$

b. $\left(-\dfrac{2}{3}x^5 y^2\right)^3 = \left(-\dfrac{2}{3}\right)^3 (x^5)^3 (y^2)^3$

$\qquad\qquad\qquad\qquad = -\dfrac{8}{27} x^{15} y^6$

NOTE: Raising a negative number to an *even-numbered* exponent gives a *positive* number. Raising a negative number to an *odd-numbered* exponent gives a *negative* number.

CLASSROOM EXERCISES

Simplify. No denominator equals zero.

1. $(x^2)^3$ **2.** $(-y^3)^2$ **3.** $(3x^4)^2$ **4.** $(-2x^2)^3$

5. $(-a^3b^2)^3$ **6.** $\left(\dfrac{2}{3}\right)^2$ **7.** $\left(-\dfrac{3}{4}\right)^2$ **8.** $\left(\dfrac{x}{y}\right)^3$

WRITTEN EXERCISES

A   Simplify. No denominator equals zero.

1. $(x^3)^2$ **2.** $(x^2)^6$ **3.** $(x^4)^2$ **4.** $(y^5)^3$ **5.** $(a^3)^4$

6. $(x^3)^5$ **7.** $(x^7)^3$ **8.** $(x^5)^2$ **9.** $(x^3)^{12}$ **10.** $(x^2)^5$

11. $(y^3)^3$ **12.** $(a^5)^6$ **13.** $(b^4)^6$ **14.** $(a^2)^7$ **15.** $(y^4)^8$

16. $(ab)^3$ **17.** $(xy)^2$ **18.** $(2x)^2$ **19.** $(5x)^2$ **20.** $(2xy)^2$

21. $(xyz)^4$ **22.** $(-5)^2$ **23.** $(-6)^2$ **24.** $(-3)^3$ **25.** $(-x)^4$

26. $(-x)^5$ **27.** $(-y)^2$ **28.** $(-4x)^2$ **29.** $(3b)^3$ **30.** $(-ab)^3$

31. $(3a^2b)^2$ **32.** $(6a^2)^3$ **33.** $(-3b)^3$ **34.** $(2x^5)^2$ **35.** $(2x^3y^2)^3$

36. $(3^2a^2b^4)^2$ **37.** $(4x^3y^2)^3$ **38.** $(2m^3n^2)^4$ **39.** $(x^2y)^4$ **40.** $(2a^2b)^3$

41. $(4a^4c^2d^3)^3$ **42.** $(16x^3y^2)^2$ **43.** $(2x^3y^2)^6$ **44.** $(a^2b)^3$

45. $(-x^4y^3)^2$ **46.** $(-x^4y^2)^3$ **47.** $(2 \times 10^3)^2$ **48.** $(3 \times 10^5)^4$

49. $(1.1 \times 10^6)^3$ **50.** $(2.5 \times 10^{10})^2$ **51.** $\left(\dfrac{x}{y}\right)^2$ **52.** $\left(\dfrac{1}{2}\right)^2$

53. $\left(\dfrac{2}{3}\right)^3$ **54.** $\left(\dfrac{1}{3}\right)^4$ **55.** $\left(\dfrac{c}{d}\right)^7$ **56.** $\left(\dfrac{ab}{c}\right)^5$ **57.** $\left(\dfrac{x^2}{y^3}\right)^2$ **58.** $\left(\dfrac{x^2}{y^2}\right)^4$

59. $\left(\dfrac{b^2}{a}\right)^2$ **60.** $\left(\dfrac{c^2}{d}\right)^3$ **61.** $\left(\dfrac{a^2}{b^3}\right)^3$ **62.** $\left(\dfrac{a^3}{b}\right)^6$ **63.** $\left(\dfrac{x^3}{y^2}\right)^2$ **64.** $\left(\dfrac{c^3}{d^2}\right)^7$

B   Match each expression in Column I with an equivalent expression in Column II.

Column I | Column II

65. $(x^2)^n$ **66.** $(-3x^a)^3$ **a.** x^{n^2} **b.** $-27x^{3a}$

67. $(x^n)^n$ **68.** $(3x^a)^3$ **c.** $\dfrac{3m^c}{2n^c}$ **d.** $\dfrac{x^b}{y^{ab}}$

69. $(xy^a)^b$ **70.** $\dfrac{3}{2}\left(\dfrac{m}{n}\right)^c$ **e.** $27x^{3a}$ **f.** x^by^{ab}

71. $\left(\dfrac{x}{y^a}\right)^b$ **72.** $\left(\dfrac{3m}{2n}\right)^c$ **g.** $\dfrac{3^cm^c}{2^cn^c}$ **h.** $\dfrac{x^b}{y^a}$

i. x^{2n} **j.** xy^{ab}

C Simplify. All variables represent positive integers.

73. $\left(\dfrac{a^2}{bc^3}\right)^4$ **74.** $\left(\dfrac{r^3}{s^2t}\right)^5$ **75.** $\left(\dfrac{a^3b^2}{c^4}\right)^3$ **76.** $\left(\dfrac{xy^6}{z^2}\right)^2$

77. $(-2a^3b^2)(3a^4b^6)$ **78.** $x \cdot x^2(x^3)^2$ **79.** $\left(\dfrac{-3x^2}{4y^2}\right)^3$ **80.** $(a^n)^m$

81. $(x^n)^n$ **82.** $(a^6)^m$ **83.** $\left(\dfrac{m}{n}\right)^k$ **84.** $\left(\dfrac{x^2}{y}\right)^c$

85. $\left(\dfrac{3x^n}{5y^m}\right)^c$ **86.** $\left(\dfrac{3x^3}{4y^2}\right)^m$ **87.** $\left(\dfrac{3a^mb^n}{2xy}\right)^k$ **88.** $\left(\dfrac{2ab}{4xy}\right)^d$

CALCULATOR APPLICATIONS

Evaluating Expressions with Exponents

A calculator with a power key, $\boxed{x^y}$, allows you to evaluate expressions with exponents quickly. You can usually work from left to right.

EXAMPLE 1 Find the value of x^4y^3 when $x = -2$ and $y = 16$.

SOLUTION 2 $\boxed{+/-}$ $\boxed{x^y}$ 4 $\boxed{\times}$ 1 6 $\boxed{x^y}$ 3 $\boxed{=}$ $\boxed{65536.}$

EXAMPLE 2 Evaluate: $(4 \times 10^2)(3 \times 10^4)$

SOLUTION 4 $\boxed{\times}$ 1 0 $\boxed{x^y}$ 2 $\boxed{\times}$ 3 $\boxed{\times}$ 1 0 $\boxed{x^y}$ 4 $\boxed{=}$ $\boxed{12000000.}$

EXAMPLE 3 Find the value of $(-2a^2b)^5$ when $a = 0.25$ and $b = 4$.

SOLUTION 2 $\boxed{+/-}$ $\boxed{\times}$. 2 5 $\boxed{x^y}$ 2 $\boxed{\times}$ 4 $\boxed{=}$ $\boxed{x^y}$ 5 $\boxed{=}$ $\boxed{-0.03125}$

EXERCISES

Find the value of each expression when $x = 5$ and $y = -3$.

1. x^2y^2 **2.** x^3y^2 **3.** x^2y^4 **4.** x^3y^3 **5.** xy^6 **6.** x^4y^3

Evaluate.

7. $(5 \times 10^3)(2 \times 10^2)$ **8.** $(3 \times 10^2)(2 \times 10^5)$ **9.** $(1.4 \times 10^3)(2.6 \times 10^4)$

Find the value of each expression when $a = 8$ and $b = -0.4$.

10. $(a^2)^3$ **11.** $\left(\dfrac{a}{b}\right)^4$ **12.** $(2a^2b)^3$ **13.** $(10a^3b^3)^2$ **14.** $(a^5b^7)^3$ **15.** $(a^2b^2)^7$

──── REVIEW CAPSULE FOR SECTION 8–4 ────

Find each quotient. *(Pages 68–71)*

1. $-8 \div (-8)$ **2.** $0 \div 21$ **3.** $-1 \div 1$ **4.** $-1 \div \left(-\dfrac{1}{4}\right)$

5. $\dfrac{1}{4} \div (-1)$ **6.** $z \div (-1)$ **7.** $-8 \div \dfrac{1}{x}, x \neq 0$ **8.** $-r \div (-r), r \neq 0$

8-4 Dividing Monomials

The quotient of two exponential expressions can be written with a single exponent *if the expressions have the same base.*

a. $\dfrac{2^5}{2^3} = \dfrac{2 \cdot 2 \cdot 2 \cdot 2 \cdot 2}{2 \cdot 2 \cdot 2}$ ← **By definition** → **b.** $\dfrac{x^6}{x^4} = \dfrac{x \cdot x \cdot x \cdot x \cdot x \cdot x}{x \cdot x \cdot x \cdot x}$

$= \left(\dfrac{2 \cdot 2 \cdot 2}{2 \cdot 2 \cdot 2}\right)(2 \cdot 2)$ ← **By the associative postulate** → $= \left(\dfrac{x \cdot x \cdot x \cdot x}{x \cdot x \cdot x \cdot x}\right)(x \cdot x)$

$= 1 \quad \cdot \quad 2^2$

$= 2^2$ ← $2^2 = 2^{5-3}$

$= 1 \quad \cdot \quad x^2$

$= x^2$ ← $x^2 = x^{6-4}$

NOTE: In **a** and **b**, subtracting the exponent of the denominator from the exponent of the numerator gives the single exponent in the answer. This suggests the following theorem.

Theorem 8-4

> **Division Theorem for Exponents**
>
> If x is a real number, $x \neq 0$, and a and b are positive integers such that $a \geq b$, then
>
> $$\frac{x^a}{x^b} = x^{a-b}.$$

Theorem 8-4 can be used to simplify quotients such as $\dfrac{x^4 y^3}{x^2 y}$.

EXAMPLE Simplify: **a.** $\dfrac{x^4 y^3}{x^2 y}$ **b.** $\dfrac{-6a^5 b^3 c^2}{2a^3 b^2 c}$

Solutions: **a.** $\dfrac{x^4 y^3}{x^2 y} = \left(\dfrac{x^4}{x^2}\right)\left(\dfrac{y^3}{y}\right)$

$= x^{(4-2)} y^{(3-1)}$

$= x^2 y^2$

b. $\dfrac{-6a^5 b^3 c^2}{2a^3 b^2 c} = \left(\dfrac{-6}{2}\right)\left(\dfrac{a^5}{a^3}\right)\left(\dfrac{b^3}{b^2}\right)\left(\dfrac{c^2}{c}\right)$

$= -3a^{(5-3)} b^{(3-2)} c^{(2-1)}$

$= -3a^2 bc$

NOTE: When $a = b$, it follows from Theorem 8-4 that

$$\frac{x^a}{x^b} = x^{a-b} = x^0 = 1.$$

Thus, $\dfrac{c}{c} = c^0 = 1,$ $\dfrac{a^2}{a^2} = a^0 = 1,$ and $\dfrac{x^3 y^5}{x^3 y^5} = x^0 y^0 = 1.$

CLASSROOM EXERCISES

Simplify. No denominator equals zero.

1. $\dfrac{x^{12}}{x^6}$
2. $\dfrac{a^{10}}{a^{10}}$
3. $\dfrac{-x^3 y^5}{x^2 y^3}$
4. $\dfrac{-56c^6}{-7c^2}$
5. $\dfrac{8^{21}}{8^{19}}$
6. $\dfrac{-42a^2 b^5 c^3}{3a^0 b^3 c^2}$

WRITTEN EXERCISES

A   Simplify. No denominator equals zero.

1. $\dfrac{2^3}{2}$ **2.** $\dfrac{3^5}{3^2}$ **3.** $\dfrac{5^6}{5^3}$ **4.** $\dfrac{x^5}{x^5}$ **5.** $\dfrac{a^6}{a}$ **6.** $\dfrac{a^9}{a^7}$

7. $\dfrac{x^8}{x^7}$ **8.** $\dfrac{x^3y^2}{xy}$ **9.** $\dfrac{a^3y^3}{a^2y}$ **10.** $\dfrac{y^3}{y^2}$ **11.** $\dfrac{a^3b^5}{ab^2}$ **12.** $\dfrac{2x^7}{3x^7}$

13. $\dfrac{k^5m^3}{k^3m^2}$ **14.** $\dfrac{18x^3y^4}{2xy^2}$ **15.** $\dfrac{-15x^7y^5}{-3x^2y^4}$ **16.** $\dfrac{-36a^2b^2c^4}{4abc^3}$

17. $\dfrac{-27r^5s^8}{-3r^3s^6}$ **18.** $\dfrac{-2k^4m^3}{4k^2}$ **19.** $\dfrac{8 \times 10^2}{2 \times 10^2}$ **20.** $\dfrac{8 \times 10^{11}}{4 \times 10}$

Classify each quotient as positive, *P*, or negative, *N*.

21. $\dfrac{(-1)^8}{(-1)^2}$ **22.** $\dfrac{(-5)^{15}}{(-5)^5}$ **23.** $\left(\dfrac{-8}{-4}\right)^2$ **24.** $\dfrac{(-3)^{19}}{(-3)^9}$

Classify each quotient as positive, *P*, or negative, *N*, when $x=-1$ and $y=-3$.

25. $\dfrac{x^5}{x^2}$ **26.** $\dfrac{y^{10}}{y^3}$ **27.** $\dfrac{x^2y}{x^2y}$ **28.** $\dfrac{x^{95}}{x^3}$

B   Simplify. No denominator equals zero.

Example: $\dfrac{9xy(-4x^2y^3)}{-18x^2y^2} = \dfrac{-36x^3y^4}{-18x^2y^2} = \mathbf{2xy^2}$

29. $\dfrac{4ab(7a^2b^3)}{-14a^3b^3}$ **30.** $\dfrac{4ab^2(-5ab^3)}{10a^2b^2}$ **31.** $\dfrac{(-3ab^2)^2}{6ab}$ **32.** $\dfrac{(3ab^2)^2(-6a^3b)}{(3a^2b^2)^2}$

33. $\dfrac{(5ab)^2(-20a^3b)}{4a^2b^3}$ **34.** $\dfrac{(5a^2b)^2(-100b^3)}{(5^2b)^2}$ **35.** $\dfrac{(5 \times 10^2)^3}{5 \times 10^2}$ **36.** $\dfrac{(11 \times 10)^5}{(11 \times 10^2)^2}$

C   Simplify. All exponents are positive integers. No denominator equals zero.

37. $\dfrac{a^xb^2y}{a^xby}$ **38.** $\dfrac{a^xb^4}{a^y}$ **39.** $\dfrac{a^tb^w}{a^vb^{25}}$ **40.** $\dfrac{x^{u-v}y^{w-z}}{x^{2v-u}y^w}$

41. $\dfrac{x^{3u-2v}y^3}{x^{2u+2v}y^2}$ **42.** $\dfrac{a^{3x}}{a^{2x}}$ **43.** $\dfrac{a^{2x}b^{3y}c^k}{abc}$ **44.** $\dfrac{ab^2c^4d^{2-k}}{ac^3d^k}$

45. $\dfrac{(x^{2a+1})^2}{x^{a-1}}$ **46.** $\dfrac{(y^{3a-9})^6}{y^{2a-4}}$ **47.** $\left(\dfrac{(x^{2a-4})^2}{x^{a+5}}\right)^3$ **48.** $\dfrac{(1.69 \times 10^3)^a}{(1.3 \times 10^a)^2}$

——— **REVIEW CAPSULE FOR SECTION 8-5** ———

Evaluate each expression. *(Pages 9–11, 280–282)*

1. 10^3 **2.** 10^5 **3.** 10^6 **4.** 10^1 **5.** 10^4 **6.** 10^7

7. $\dfrac{1}{10^2}$ **8.** $\dfrac{1}{10^3}$ **9.** $\left(\dfrac{1}{10}\right)^0$ **10.** $\left(\dfrac{1}{10}\right)^3$ **11.** $\dfrac{1}{10^5}$ **12.** $\dfrac{1}{10^4}$

8-5 Scientific Notation

Suppose that the division theorem (Theorem 8–4) holds for positive integers a and b when $a < b$. That is, for any real number x, $x \neq 0$,

$$\frac{x^a}{x^b} = x^{a-b}, \text{ for } a < b.$$

Suppose the Division Theorem Holds	You Already Know	Reasonable Definition
$\dfrac{10^8}{10^{10}} = 10^{8-10} = 10^{-2}$	$\dfrac{10^8}{10^{10}} = \dfrac{10^8}{10^8} \cdot \dfrac{1}{10^2} = \dfrac{1}{10^2}$	$10^{-2} = \dfrac{1}{10^2}$
$\dfrac{10^7}{10^8} = 10^{7-8} = 10^{-1}$	$\dfrac{10^7}{10^8} = \dfrac{10^7}{10^7} \cdot \dfrac{1}{10^1} = \dfrac{1}{10}$	$10^{-1} = \dfrac{1}{10}$
$\dfrac{x^5}{x^8} = x^{5-8} = x^{-3}$	$\dfrac{x^5}{x^8} = \dfrac{x^5}{x^5} \cdot \dfrac{1}{x^3} = \dfrac{1}{x^3}$	$x^{-3} = \dfrac{1}{x^3}$
$\dfrac{y}{y^5} = y^{1-5} = y^{-4}$	$\dfrac{y}{y^5} = \dfrac{y}{y} \cdot \dfrac{1}{y^4} = \dfrac{1}{y^4}$	$y^{-4} = \dfrac{1}{y^4}$

The examples in the table suggest this definition.

Definition

> If x is any real number except zero and a is a positive integer, then
>
> $$x^{-a} = \frac{1}{x^a}.$$

You can use this definition to simplify expressions having negative exponents. To **simplify such an expression** means to rewrite it without exponents or with positive exponents only.

EXAMPLE 1 Simplify: **a.** $(-5)^{-3}$ **b.** $3y^{-2}$ **c.** $\dfrac{x^2}{y^{-2}}$

Solutions: Write each expression with positive exponents. Simplify the result when possible.

a. $(-5)^{-3} = \dfrac{1}{(-5)^3}$

$\qquad = \dfrac{1}{-125}$

$\qquad = -\dfrac{1}{125}$

b. $3y^{-2} = 3 \cdot y^{-2}$

$\qquad = 3 \cdot \dfrac{1}{y^2}$

$\qquad = \dfrac{3}{y^2}$

c. $\dfrac{x^2}{y^{-2}} = x^2 \cdot \dfrac{1}{y^{-2}}$

$\qquad = x^2 \cdot \dfrac{1}{\dfrac{1}{y^2}}$

$\qquad = x^2 \cdot y^2 = x^2 y^2$

Very large and very small numbers are used in many scientific areas. For convenience, these numbers are expressed as the *product of some power of 10 and a number from 1 to 10*. This representation is called **scientific notation.**

Decimal Notation	Scientific Notation
Number	$(1 \leq x < 10) \times 10^a$

	Decimal Notation	Scientific Notation	
Numbers greater than 1	95,672	9.5672×10^4	Numbers greater than 1
	9567.2	9.5672×10^3	
	956.72	9.5672×10^2	
	95.672	9.5672×10^1	
	9.5672	9.5672×10^0	
Numbers less than 1	0.95672	9.5672×10^{-1}	Numbers less than 1
	0.095672	9.5672×10^{-2}	
	0.0095672	9.5672×10^{-3}	
	0.00095672	9.5672×10^{-4}	

NOTE: When the given number *is greater than 10*, the power of 10 at the right in the table has a *positive exponent*.

When the given number *is less than 1*, the power of 10 at the right in the table has a *negative exponent*.

When the given number *is between 1 and 10*, the power of 10 has a *zero exponent*.

EXAMPLE 2 Write each number in scientific notation.

a. 867,000,000,000   **b.** 0.00000305

Solutions: **a.** 867,000,000,000. ◄——— The number is greater than 10.

11 places ◄——— Count the number of places the decimal point must be moved to get a number between 1 and 10.

8.67×10^{11} ◄——— Write as a product.

b. 0.00000305 ◄——— The number is less than 1.

6 places ◄——— Count the number of places the decimal point must be moved to get a number between 1 and 10.

3.05×10^{-6} ◄——— Write as a product.

CLASSROOM EXERCISES

Simplify.

1. $(4)^{-2}$ **2.** $5x^{-1}$ **3.** $(-4)^{-1}$ **4.** $\left(-\frac{2}{3}\right)^{-3}$ **5.** $(3b)^{-2}$

Write in scientific notation.

6. 84,000,000   **7.** 7,000,000,000   **8.** 0.0003   **9.** 0.000063

10. 1,556,000   **11.** 789   **12.** 0.159   **13.** 21.07

WRITTEN EXERCISES

A   Simplify. No variable equals zero.

1. 4^2
2. 3^{-2}
3. 10^0
4. 10^{-1}

5. 10^3
6. 10^{-4}
7. 6^0
8. $(-2)^3$

9. $(-2)^{-3}$
10. $(\frac{1}{2})^{-4}$
11. $(\frac{3}{4})^{-3}$
12. 157^0

13. $(\frac{1}{4})^{-2}$
14. $(-\frac{3}{4})^3$
15. $(-\frac{3}{4})^{-3}$
16. $(-4)^{-3}$

17. 10^{-3}
18. $(-\frac{1}{2})^{-2}$
19. $(-\frac{2}{3})^{-2}$
20. $(-\frac{1}{2})^{-5}$

21. a^{-3}
22. x^{-2}
23. $3x^{-5}$
24. $2y^{-4}$

25. m^{-1}
26. $3x^{-2}$
27. $(4y)^{-1}$
28. ac^{-4}

29. $a^{-3}b^2$
30. $(2x)^{-2}$
31. $(3y)^{-3}$
32. $c^{-3} \cdot c^2$

Write each number in scientific notation.

33. 4600
34. 20,500,000
35. 67,000,000

36. 100,000
37. 24,000,000,000,000
38. 0.0043

39. 0.00057
40. 0.0000008
41. 0.00002

42. 0.07
43. 0.0008
44. 0.005

45. $\dfrac{2}{10,000}$
46. $\dfrac{7}{10,000,000}$
47. 6 million

48. 4 billion
49. 3 thousand
50. 2.6 billion

51. 40 million
52. 400 billion
53. 5 thousandths

APPLICATIONS: Using Scientific Notation

Write each number in scientific notation.

54. The star Alpha Centauri is 40,000,000,-000,000 kilometers from the earth.

55. The speed of light is about 297,600 kilometers per second.

56. In one year, light travels about 10 trillion kilometers.

57. The diameter of our galaxy is 100,000 light years.

58. The center of our galaxy is 30,000 light years away.

59. Our galaxy has about a hundred billion stars.

60. It is about 150,000,000 kilometers to our sun — a mere 8 light minutes away.

61. The sun is about 150,000,000 kilometers from the earth.

62. A teaspoon of neutron star material weighs 1 billion tons.

63. Special balances can weigh something as small as 0.00000001 gram.

64. Astronomers have detected objects so far away that the light from these objects has taken 10 billion years to reach us.

65. When a neutron star collapses, the crust which has a thickness of one kilometer is 1,000,000,000,000,000 times stiffer than steel.

B Write each number in decimal notation.

66. The sun has a mass of 2.2×10^{27} tons.

67. The temperature of the sun is 6×10^3 degrees Celsius.

68. If one foot of copper wire is heated $1°$ Celsius, it expands 1.6×10^{-5} feet.

69. A helium atom has a diameter of 2.2×10^{-8} centimeters.

C Simplify. No variable equals zero.

70. $m^{-2} \cdot m^{-3}$

71. $(a^4)^{-2}$

72. $(x^{-3})^{-1}$

73. $\left(\dfrac{a}{b}\right)^{-2}$

74. $\left(\dfrac{d}{c}\right)^{-1}$

75. $\dfrac{x^3}{x^{-1}}$

76. $\dfrac{y^{-2}}{y^3}$

77. $(x^{-1})^{-1}$

Review

Find the value when $a = -1$, $b = 3$, and $c = -4$. *(Section 8–1)*

1. ab^2

2. a^2b

3. abc^2

4. a^3c^3

5. a^3b^2c

Find each product. *(Section 8–2)*

6. $n \cdot n^3$

7. $x^2(-x^3)$

8. $-(3a^3)(4a^4)$

9. $(2d)(3c^2d)(cd^2)$

Simplify. No denominator equals zero. *(Section 8–3)*

10. $(y^2)^4$

11. $(-a^2b)^4$

12. $(2 \times 10^4)^2$

13. $\left(\dfrac{r^2}{st}\right)^3$

Simplify. No denominator equals zero. *(Section 8–4)*

14. $\dfrac{a^8}{a^6}$

15. $\dfrac{xy^4}{xy^3}$

16. $\dfrac{-12b^2c^2}{4b}$

17. $\dfrac{4a(-2ab^2)}{2a^2}$

Simplify. No variable equals zero. *(Section 8–5)*

18. 3^{-4}

19. $(-4)^3$

20. $\left(-\dfrac{2}{3}\right)^{-3}$

21. $3y^{-2}$

22. $(-3)^{-3}$

Write each number in scientific notation. *(Section 8–5)*

23. 6 million

24. 4 hundredths

25. 0.0007

26. 15,555

REVIEW CAPSULE FOR SECTION 8–6

Write the additive inverse of each polynomial. *(Pages 47–50)*

1. $2n$

2. $(-2n)$

3. $2x - 5$

4. $-3x^2 - 4x$

5. $-7a^2 - 3a + 4$

Write an addition problem for each subtraction problem. Do *not* subtract. *(Pages 56–58)*

6. $2x - (3x - 5)$

7. $3a - (2a - 3b)$

8. $-3y - (-6y - 3y + 4)$

9. $3a - (4a + 3b)$

10. $t - 4 - (2t - 1)$

11. $9 - r - (7r - 6)$

Career Applications: Physics

Astrophysicists study the structure of the universe. Speeds and distances are so great in space that astrophysicists use scientific notation to represent them and do computations with them.

Here are some approximate distances and speeds.

Minimum Distance from the Sun to:
Earth: 147,000,000 (1.47×10^8) kilometers
Mercury: 46,700,000 (4.67×10^7) kilometers
Mars: 206,000,000 (2.06×10^8) kilometers
Saturn: 1,350,000,000 (1.35×10^9) kilometers

Speed of Light or of a Radio Signal:
300,000 (3.0×10^5) kilometers per second.

The Earth as Seen From 400,000 Kilometers in Space

EXAMPLE 1   Find the approximate time in seconds needed for a radio signal to reach the sun from the earth.

Solution: Use $d = rt$.

$$1.47 \times 10^8 = (3.0 \times 10^5) \times t$$

$$t = \frac{1.47 \times 10^8}{3.0 \times 10^5}$$

$$= 0.49 \times 10^3 \text{ or } \textbf{490 seconds}$$

Physicists also study very small quantities and distances. They use scientific notation to represent and calculate with these numbers, also.

EXAMPLE 2   The ink used to print the word "Einstein" has a mass of 1×10^{-9} kilograms (1 **microgram**). In Einstein's formula, $E = mc^2$, the **joule** is the unit for measuring energy, E. Find how many joules of energy would be released if all the mass in kilograms, m, of the ink were converted to energy (c is the speed of light in meters per second).

Solution: $E = mc^2$
$E = (1 \times 10^{-9})(3 \times 10^8)^2$
$= (1 \times 10^{-9})(9 \times 10^{16})$
$= \textbf{9} \times \textbf{10}^7 \textbf{ joules}$

This is enough energy to lift a 6000-kilogram bus holding 44 students, each of mass 50 kilograms, 1.13 kilometers straight up in the air.

EXERCISES

In Exercises 1–4, refer to the speeds and distances given on page 294 to find each of the following. Round each answer to the nearest whole number.

1. The approximate time in seconds for light from the sun to reach Mercury

2. The approximate time in seconds for light from the sun to reach Mars

3. The approximate time in minutes for a radio signal to reach the sun from Saturn

4. The approximate time in minutes for a radio signal to travel from the earth to the sun and back again

Kepler's Third Law of Planetary Motion says that for any planet in the solar system, the cube of its average distance from the sun, R^3, divided by the square of its time for one revolution, T^2, is a constant. Show that this is true in Exercises 5–10. Round each answer to the nearest hundredth.

Planet	Average Radius of Orbit (m)	Time of One Revolution (sec)	$\frac{R^3}{T^2} \left(\frac{m^2}{sec^2} \right)$
5. Mercury	5.79×10^{10}	7.60×10^6	?
6. Venus	1.08×10^{11}	1.94×10^7	?
7. Earth	1.49×10^{11}	3.16×10^7	?
8. Mars	2.28×10^{11}	5.94×10^7	?
9. Jupiter	7.78×10^{11}	3.74×10^8	?
10. Saturn	1.43×10^{12}	9.30×10^8	?

In Exercises 11–12, use the formula $E = mc^2$ to find the number of joules of energy that would be released if the total mass given were converted to energy. Round each answer to the nearest hundredth.

11. The mass of an electron: 9.11×10^{-31} kilograms

12. A particle of mass 0.5 grams: 5×10^{-4} kilograms

13. What is the volume of a droplet of water in a fog? The formula for the volume of a sphere is

$$V = \frac{4}{3}\pi r^3,$$

$r = 2.73 \times 10^{-3}$ centimeters (use $\pi \approx 3$).

14. An atom of gold has a diameter of about 2.5×10^{-10} meters. A thin square of gold foil, 1 centimeter on a side, is 1×10^{-6} meters thick. Find the approximate number of gold atoms in the foil.

Physicists use microscopes and electron microscopes in their work.

8-6 Addition and Subtraction of Polynomials

To find the *perimeter of a polygon,* you add the lengths of its sides.

Polygon	Perimeter
5x² − 6 (top), 2x² (left), 2x² (right), 5x² − 6 (bottom)	$5x^2 - 6$ $5x^2 - 6$ $2x^2$ $\underline{2x^2}$ $14x^2 - 12$
3y² (left), 4y² (right), 6y² − 2 (bottom)	$3y^2$ $4y^2$ $\underline{6y^2 - 2}$ $13y^2 - 2$

The length of each side of each polygon is expressed as a *monomial* or as the sum of monomials. Recall from the definition on page 283 that expressions such as $13y^2$ and -2 are *monomials.*

A **polynomial** is a monomial or the sum of monomials. A polynomial with two terms is called a **binomial;** a polynomial with three terms is called a **trinomial.**

Polynomials

Monomial	Binomial	Trinomial
$7x^2y^2$	$4a + 3$	$3x^2 - 6x + 9$
-9	$9x^2 - 25z^2$	$6a - 7b - 3c$

To add polynomials, you add monomials that are *like terms.*

EXAMPLE 1 Add: $(4a + 6b) + (2a - 3b)$

Solution: First group the like terms. Then apply the distributive postulate.

$(4a + 6b) + (2a - 3b) = (4a + 2a) + (6b - 3b)$

$= (4 + 2)a + (6 - 3)b$ ◄——— By the distributive postulate

$= \mathbf{6a + 3b}$

It is often convenient to arrange like terms in the same column before adding or subtracting.

EXAMPLE 2 Add: $(-3x^2 + 7xy - 6y^2) + (5xy + 3y^2 - 4x^2)$

Solution:
$-3x^2 + 7xy - 6y^2$
$\underline{-4x^2 + 5xy + 3y^2}$ ◄——— Arrange like terms in the same column.
$-7x^2 + 12xy - 3y^2$ ◄——— Add like terms.

To subtract a polynomial, you add its additive inverse.

EXAMPLE 3   Subtract: $(x^3 + 2x^2 - 8x) - (-2x^2 + 7x - 5)$

Solution:
$$
\begin{array}{l}
x^3 + 2x^2 - \ 8x + 0 \longleftarrow \text{Arrange like terms in the same column.} \\
\underline{\ 2x^2 - \ 7x + 5} \longleftarrow \text{Additive inverse of } -2x^2 + 7x - 5. \\
x^3 + 4x^2 - 15x + 5 \longleftarrow \text{Add like terms.}
\end{array}
$$

CLASSROOM EXERCISES

Add or subtract as indicated.

1. $(4a - 3b) + (8a + 5b)$
2. $(4a^2 - 5ab - 6b^2) + (10ab - 6a^2 - 6b^2)$
3. $(6r + 9s) - (4r + 3s)$
4. $(h^2 + 6h + 9) - (25 - 10h + h^2)$
5. $(-3x^3 - 4) - (-6x^2 - 5x - 6)$
6. $(8x^2 - 4x + 5) - (10x^2 - 9x - 8)$

WRITTEN EXERCISES

A   Add.

1. $\begin{array}{l} 4a - 3b + 5c \\ \underline{8a + 5b - 9c} \end{array}$

2. $\begin{array}{l} 4r + 3s + \ t \\ \underline{6r + 9s + 5t} \end{array}$

3. $\begin{array}{r} 6p - 4t + \ x \\ \underline{-7p + 8t + 6x} \end{array}$

4. $5b + 4c + 8d,\ 8b - 7c - 6d,\ 3b - 4c$
5. $7x - 2y + 5z,\ 8y - 9z,\ 7x - 5y$
6. $5x + 7y - 10,\ 8y - 2x + 3,\ 2x - 10y + 4$
7. $4a^2 - 5ab - 6b^2,\ 10ab - 6a^2 - 8b^2,\ 10b^2 - 3a^2 - 7ab$
8. $a - b + c,\ b - c - a,\ c - a + b,\ a - 2b - c$
9. $4ab - 5bc + 6ac,\ 6bc - 7ab - 8ac,\ 10ab - bc - ac$
10. $x^2 + y^2 - z^2,\ 3z^2 - 2x^2 - 4y^2,\ 4y^2 + x^2 + z^2$
11. $x^2 - 6x + 7,\ 8x - 15 - x^2,\ 4x^2 + 6x - 9,\ 7x + 10$
12. $a^2 - 2ab + b^2,\ 2ab + a^2 + b^2,\ 4a^2 - 4ab - b^2,\ a^2 - b^2$
13. $a + 2b,\ 3b - 4c,\ 5a - 7c,\ 3b + 2d$

APPLICATIONS: Using Addition of Polynomials

Find the perimeter of each polygon.

14.

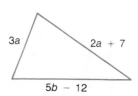

$3a$ $2a + 7$ $5b - 12$

15.

$2y + 3$ $x - 2$ $x - 2$ $2y + 3$

16.

$3x$ $5m - 1$ $5m - 2$ $9x - 2$

Find the perimeter of each polygon.

17.

18.

19.

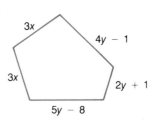

Subtract.

20. $3a + 4$
　$2a + 9$

21. $7b - 5$
　$10b - 8$

22. $r + 8s$
　$r - 5s$

23. $7x - 3$
　$-2x - 9$

24. $3x^2 + 8y^2$
　$x^2 - 8y^2$

25. $5m^2 - 9n$
　$8m^2 - 10n$

26. $8a - 9xy$
　$-a + 9xy$

27. $a - b + c$
　$a + b - c$

28. $x^2 + 2x + 1$
　$x^2 - 2x + 1$

29. $2a + 0$
　$a - b$

30. $2x^2 \quad - 4$
　$\quad x + 2$

31. $x^3 + 0 + 0 + 8$
　$x^3 + x^2 - 2x + 0$

32. $\quad x^2 + 6$
　$x^3 \quad - 3$

33. $3x^2 - 6x$
　$2x^2 \quad + 7$

34. $\quad -4x^2 - x + 9$
　$3x^3 \quad + x$

35. $(5x + y) - (2x - y)$

36. $(a + 5b) - (4a - 3b)$

37. $(3x^2 - 4y^2) - (2x^2 + 5y^2)$

38. $(4x^2 - 2x - 3) - (-5x - 4)$

39. $(5x^2 - 10y^2) - (3x^2 + 2xy - 6y^2)$

40. $(-4x^3 - 6x^2 + 3x - 1) - (8x^3 + 4x^2 - 2x + 3)$

41. $(-5a + 2b - 3c + 8d) - (4a - b + 3c + 5d)$

B

42. From $3a - 2b + 5c$, take $-2a + 5b - c$.

43. Subtract $6x^2 - 3xy + y^2$ from $8x^2 + 5xy - y^2$.

44. From $6ab - 2ac + 5bc$, take $10ab - 2bc + 3ac$.

45. Subtract $x^2 - 2xy + y^2$ from $x^2 + 2xy + y^2$.

46. From $x^2 - 2xy + y^2$, take $x^2 + 4xy + y^2$.

C

47. From the sum of $x + 3y$ and $-3x - y$, subtract $x - y$.

48. Subtract $x^2 - y^2 - z^2$ from the sum of $2x^2 + 3y^2 - z^2$ and $4x^2 - 3y^2 + 5z^2$.

49. Take $a - b + 1$ from the sum of $a + c + 1$ and $a + b + 1$.

50. Subtract the sum of $(4x^3 + 2x^2 - 5)$ and $(15x - x^3 - x^2)$ from the difference of $(9 + 6x - 2x^2)$ and $(4x - 1 - 5x^3 + x^2)$.

51. If x is 3 meters, which is greater: the perimeter of a square whose sides are each $(3x - 1)$ units long or the perimeter of a rectangle whose length is $x + 9$ and whose width is $2x - 3$? How much greater?

Multiply. *(Pages 30–33, 283–284)*

1. $3(2a + 5b - 4)$ **2.** $-7(2x - y + 5)$ **3.** $(-1)(2a - 6b + 1)$

4. $-5(-4k + 3s - 2)$ **5.** $(-1)(21 - 5t - 3r)$ **6.** $(-1)(-6u + 10w - 11z)$

7. $a^4 \cdot a^5$ **8.** $q \cdot q^2$ **9.** $(-t^4)(t^3)$ **10.** $-a^5(-a^5)$ **11.** $3x^2y(-9xy^5)$

Simplify. *(Pages 61–63)*

12. $7a - (6a - 3 + b)$ **13.** $9b + (3c + 2) - b$ **14.** $5n - (-n + 2 - 3n)$

8-7 Products of Polynomials

To find the **area of a rectangle,** you multiply its length and its width.

Rectangle	Area
3x [rectangle] $7x - 9$	$3x(7x - 9) = 3x[7x + (-9)]$ $= 3x(7x) + 3x(-9)$ $= 21x^2 + (-27x)$ $= \mathbf{21x^2 - 27x}$
$4y + 2$ [square] $4y + 2$	$(4y + 2)(4y + 2) = (4y + 2)4y + (4y + 2)2$ $= 4y(4y) + 2(4y) + 4y(2) + 2(2)$ $= 16y^2 + 8y + 8y + 4$ $= \mathbf{16y^2 + 16y + 4}$

You can see from the table that you use the distributive postulate and the properties of exponents to multiply polynomials.

EXAMPLE 1   Multiply: $7y(-6y - 9)$

    Solution: $7y(-6y - 9) = 7y[-6y + (-9)]$

                     $= 7y(-6y) + 7y(-9)$ ⟵ **By the distributive postulate**

                     $= (7)(-6)(y \cdot y) + (7)(-9)y$

                     $= \mathbf{-42y^2 - 63y}$

Example 1 shows how to multiply a monomial and a binomial.

Examples 2 and 3 show how to multiply two binomials. To find the product of two binomials, you use the distributive postulate twice.

Exponents and Polynomials   **299**

EXAMPLE 2 Multiply: $(x + 2)(x - 5)$

Solution:
$$(x + 2)(x - 5) = [x + 2][x + (-5)]$$
$$= (x + 2)x + (x + 2)(-5) \longleftarrow \text{By the distributive post.}$$
$$= (x)(x) + (x)(2) + (x)(-5) + (2)(-5) \longleftarrow \begin{array}{l}\text{By the}\\\text{distributive post.}\end{array}$$
$$= x^2 + 2x - 5x - 10$$
$$= x^2 - 3x - 10$$

It is often easier to use a vertical format to multiply.

EXAMPLE 3 Multiply: $(5n + 2t)(7n + 2t)$

Solution: Arrange the polynomials vertically. Write like terms in the same column.

$$
\begin{array}{r}
5n + 2t \\
7n + 3t \\
\hline
15nt + 6t^2 \\
35n^2 + 14nt \\
\hline
35n^2 + 29nt + 6t^2
\end{array}
$$

$15nt + 6t^2 \longleftarrow 3t(5n + 2t)$

$35n^2 + 14nt \longleftarrow 7n(5n + 2t)$

$35n^2 + 29nt + 6t^2 \longleftarrow 35n^2 + (15nt + 14nt) + 6t^2$

CLASSROOM EXERCISES

Multiply.

1. $3x(x + 9)$
2. $4x(-2x - 6)$
3. $(x + 3)(7x + 4)$
4. $(2y^2 - 5)(3y^2 + 6)$
5. $(-2n^3 - 5n)6n$
6. $-5y(3y^3 - 4y^2 + 6)$
7. $(a + 2)(a + 9)$
8. $(a^3 - 1)2a$
9. $-s(r^2 - 2r + 7)$
10. $a + 2(a + 9)$
11. $(x + y)(x - y)$
12. $x + y(x - y)$

WRITTEN EXERCISES

A Multiply.

1. $a(2a + 3)$
2. $x^2(3x + 4)$
3. $3y(y - 8)$
4. $2y(3y - 4)$
5. $-2y(y + 6)$
6. $-3x(x + 9)$
7. $m(5m - 2)$
8. $r(r^2 - 9)$
9. $s(7s - 8)$
10. $3x^2(2x - 6)$
11. $-4a(3a - 5b)$
12. $5mn(7m - 2n)$
13. $2a(a^2 - 4a + 3)$
14. $-3x(x^2 + 5x + 2)$
15. $y^2(y^2 - 6y + 3)$
16. $-2ab(6a^2 - 4ab + 5b^2)$
17. $3xy(-x^4 - 4x^2y + 5xy^2)$
18. $(3a^2 - 2a - 9)(-a)$
19. $(a + 7)(a + 3)$
20. $(x + 9)(x + 5)$
21. $(2a + 4)(a + 5)$
22. $(7x + 3)(x + 1)$
23. $(a + 3)(a - 4)$
24. $(2a + 3b)(a - b)$
25. $(2a - 5)(3a + 2)$
26. $(a + 3)(a + 2)$
27. $(2a + 3)(3a - 2)$

28. $(a - 3b)(2a + 3b)$

29. $(a + b)(c + d)$

30. $(a - b)(c + d)$

31. $(a - b)(c - d)$

32. $(a + b)(c - d)$

33. $(3b - 4c)(3b + 4c)$

34. $(3b - 4c)(2c + 3d)$

35. $(4x - 5)(4x + 5)$

36. $(7n - 3)(7n + 3)$

37. $(3x - 4)(3x - 4)$

38. $(2a - 3b)(a - 4b)$

39. $(5x - 3y)(3x + 4y)$

40. $(a + b)(a - b)$

41. $(\frac{1}{2}x - y)(2x + y)$

42. $(\frac{1}{3}t - 5)(\frac{1}{3}t + 6)$

43. $(1.6n - 9)(0.2n - 5)$

44. $(a^2 + b)(a^2 - 2b)$

45. $(x^2 - y^2)(x^2 + y^2)$

46. $(m^2 - 2n^2)(m^2 - 2n^2)$

47. $(4s - 3)(2s^2 + 3)$

48. $(a^3 + b^3)(3a^3 - b^3)$

49. $(2x^2 + 3y^2)(3x^2 + 2y^2)$

50. $(x - 3)^2$

51. $(2x + 3y)^2$

52. $(x + 5)(x + 7)$

53. $x + 5(x + 7)$

54. $y - 6(2y + 8)$

55. $(y - 6)(2y + 8)$

56. $2x + y(8x - 4y)$

57. $(2x + y)(8x - 4y)$

B

58. $(7x - 9)(3x - 4)$

59. $4 - (5x + 2)$

60. $5 - 2(8x + 3)$

APPLICATIONS: Using Multiplication of Polynomials

Find the area of each region outlined in red.

61.

62.

63.

64.

65.

66.

67. Which has the greater area, a square with sides x units long or a rectangle with length $(x + 1)$ units and width $(x - 1)$ units. How much greater is it?

68. Which has the greater area, a square with sides x units long, or a rectangle with length $(x + 2)$ units and width $(x - 2)$ units? How much greater is it?

69. Which has the greater area, a square with sides $(x + 1)$ units long or a rectangle with length $(x + 2)$ units and width x units? How much greater is it?

70. Which has the greater area, a square with sides $(x + 1)$ units long or a rectangle with length x units and width $(x - 2)$ units? How much greater is it?

C   Multiply.

71. $(x^2 + 2x + 1)(x + 1)$

72. $(x^2 + 2x + 1)(x - 1)$

73. $(n^3 - 5n^2 + 2)(n^2 - 2n)$

74. $(x^2 - xy + y^2)(x + y)$

75. $(x^2 - 6xy + 9y)(x - 3y)$

76. $(2 - 3a^2 - a)(a - 1)$

77. $(c - 2c^2 + 3)(2 + c)$

78. $(x^3 + 3x^2 + 2x - 1)(x - 1)$

79. $(x^3 - 3x^2 + 3x - 1)(x - 1)$

Find each product. *(Pages 283–284)*

1. $(3c)(3c)$ **2.** $(3x^4)(5x)$ **3.** $(4ab)(3ab)$ **4.** $(2x^2)(3x^2)$

5. $(2a^3)(4a^2)$ **6.** $(4bc^2d)(9b^2c^2d^2)$ **7.** $(xy^2z^3)(3x^3yz^4)$ **8.** $(-x^2y^5)(x^4y^7z)$

8-8 Products of Binomials

Study the pattern in finding the product of two binomials. This is called the *FOIL method*.

Product of first terms	+	Sum of product of outer and inner terms	+	Product of last terms

$$(2x - 7)(3x + 9)$$

$$= (2x)(3x) + (2x)(9) + (-7)(3x) + (-7)(9)$$
$$= \quad 6x^2 \quad + \quad 18x \quad + \quad -21x \quad + \quad -63$$
$$= 6x^2 - 3x - 63$$

You can use the FOIL method to multiply two binomials.

EXAMPLE   Multiply by inspection: **a.** $(4x + 1)(2x.- 3)$ **b.** $(5x - 4)(2x + 7)$

                                          F   O   I   L

Solutions: **a.** $(4x + 1)(2x - 3) = 8x^2 - 12x + 2x - 3 = 8x^2 - 10x - 3$

                                          F   O   I   L

   b. $(5x - 4)(2x + 7) = 10x^2 + 35x - 8x - 28 = 10x^2 + 27x - 28$

CLASSROOM EXERCISES

Match each pair of factors in Column 1 with its corresponding product in Column 2.

Column 1

1. $(x + 5)(x - 3)$

2. $(5a - 3)(2a - 2)$

3. $(4a - 5)(5a - 1)$

4. $(8x - 3)(4x + 5)$

5. $(2ab - 3)(3ab + 3)$

6. $(5a - 3b)(2a + 3b)$

7. $(6a + 2b)(9a - b)$

8. $(3x - 2y)(2x - 5y)$

9. $(a - b)(a + b)$

10. $(x - 5)(x + 5)$

Column 2

a. $6a^2b^2 - 3ab - 9$

b. $20a^2 - 29a + 5$

c. $x^2 - 25$

d. $10a^2 - 16a + 6$

e. $10a^2 + 9ab - 9b^2$

f. $6x^2 - 19xy + 10y^2$

g. $a^2 - b^2$

h. $x^2 + 2x - 15$

i. $32x^2 + 28x - 15$

j. $54a^2 + 12ab - 2b^2$

WRITTEN EXERCISES

A   Find each product.

1. $(x+5)(x+3)$
2. $(x-5)(x+7)$
3. $(x+2)(x-2)$
4. $(x+3)(x+2)$
5. $(a-2)(a+3)$
6. $(y-5)(y+1)$
7. $(b-7)(b+3)$
8. $(d+4)(d-5)$
9. $(p+9)(p+11)$
10. $(2x+5)(5x+6)$
11. $(d-4)(d+5)$
12. $(m+n)(m-n)$
13. $(3y+2)(4y+3)$
14. $(2x+5)(3x+1)$
15. $(x+3)(2x+7)$
16. $(p-9)(p-11)$
17. $(3x-4)(3x+4)$
18. $(m-n)(p-q)$
19. $(b+4)(b+4)$
20. $(n-2)(n+2)$
21. $(m+7)(m-11)$
22. $(a+b)(2a-b)$
23. $(a-2c)(a+2c)$
24. $(3x-2y)(3x+2y)$
25. $(3x+2)(x-1)$
26. $(x^2+2y)(x^2-2y)$
27. $(y^2+3)(y^2+3)$
28. $(2b+3)(4b-7)$
29. $(4y-3)(4y-3)$
30. $(4y-3)(4y+3)$
31. $(2a+5)(2a+3)$
32. $(4c-7)(5c+9)$
33. $(5x+3)(x+1)$
34. $(2f+9)(3f+7)$
35. $(7b+2)(5b-1)$
36. $(10p+3)(6p-1)$
37. $(8x+3)(3x-4)$
38. $(8r-5)(7r+5)$
39. $(2c-9)(3c-8)$
40. $(4x+7)(5x-3)$
41. $(x^2-4)(x^2+4)$
42. $(y^2-2)(y^2+2)$
43. $(7a-2)(a+8)$
44. $(a^2-3b)(a^2+2b)$
45. $(3x-5y)(2x+3y)$

B

46. $(\frac{1}{2}x+5)(6x-10)$
47. $(\frac{1}{2}x-3)(7x+8)$
48. $(5a+1)(\frac{1}{2}a+4)$
49. $(\frac{1}{3}t+8)(\frac{1}{4}t+6)$
50. $(5x+\frac{2}{3})(6x+\frac{3}{2})$
51. $(\frac{1}{5}x-7)(\frac{1}{7}x-5)$
52. $(0.3u-0.4)(0.5u-0.1)$
53. $(1.8w-2.4)(0.2w+0.5)$
54. $(0.4m+0.3n)(1.1m+1.2n)$

APPLICATIONS: Using Products of Binomials

55. Each side of a square has length $(s+4)$. Write a polynomial for the area of the square.

56. A box has length $(5t - 9)$, width $(t + 7)$, and height, t. Write a polynomial for the volume of the box.

57. Which has the greater area, a rectangle with length $(a + 2)$ units and width $(a + 1)$ units, or a rectangle with length $(a + 4)$ units and width $(a - 1)$ units? How much greater is it?

58. Which has the greater area, a rectangle with length $(2a + 1)$ units and width $(a - 5)$ units, or a rectangle with length $(2a + 3)$ units and width $(a - 6)$ units? How much greater is it?

———— **REVIEW CAPSULE FOR SECTION 8–9** ————

Raise to the indicated power. *(Pages 285–287)*

1. $(-2)^2$
2. $(-x)^2$
3. $-(x)^2$
4. $(-xyz)^2$
5. $(a^2)^2$
6. $(-a^2)^2$
7. $-(a^2)^2$
8. $(-2a)^2$
9. $-(-2a)^2$
10. $-(-2a^4)^2$

8-9 Squaring Binomials

Study the table to find the pattern for squaring binomials.

Square of a Sum	Square of a Difference
$(x + 4)^2 = (x + 4)(x + 4)$	$(x - 4)^2 = (x - 4)(x - 4)$
$= x^2 + 4x + 4x + 16$	$= x^2 - 4x - 4x + 16$
$2(4x)$	$2(-4x)$
$= x^2 + 8x + 16$	$= x^2 - 8x + 16$
$(m + 3n)^2 = (m + 3n)(m + 3n)$	$(m - 3n)^2 = (m - 3n)(m - 3n)$
$= m^2 + 3mn + 3mn + 9n^2$	$= m^2 - 3mn - 3mn + 9n^2$
$2(3mn)$	$2(-3mn)$
$= m^2 + 6mn + 9n^2$	$= m^2 - 6mn + 9n^2$
$(a + b)^2 = (a + b)(a + b)$	$(a - b)^2 = (a - b)(a - b)$
$= a^2 + ab + ab + b^2$	$= a^2 - ab - ab + b^2$
$= a^2 + 2ab + b^2$	$= a^2 - 2ab + b^2$

The following procedure summarizes the steps for squaring a binomial.

Procedure

> **To square a binomial:**
> 1. Square the first term.
> 2. Add to this twice the product of the first and last terms when the binomial is of the form $(a + b)$.
>
>   Subtract twice the product of the first and last terms when the binomial is of the form $(a - b)$.
> 3. Add to this the square of the last term.

You can use this procedure to write the square of a binomial as a trinomial.

EXAMPLE 1 Write the square of each binomial as a trinomial.

a. $(5x + 2y)^2$ b. $(2y - 3)^2$

Solutions:

a. $(5x + 2y)^2 = (5x)^2 + 2(5x)(2y) + (2y)^2$
$$= 25x^2 + 20x + 4y^2$$

b. $(2y - 3)^2 = (2y)^2 - 2(2y)(3) + 3^2$
$$= 4y^2 - 12y + 9$$

You can square a number by writing it as the sum or as the difference of two numbers.

EXAMPLE 2 Square each number: **a.** $(32)^2$ **b.** $(49)^2$

Solutions: **a.** $(32)^2 = (30 + 2)^2$ **b.** $(49)^2 = (50 - 1)^2$

$\qquad\qquad\quad = (30)^2 + 2(30)(2) + 2^2 \qquad\qquad = (50)^2 - 2(50)(1) + 1^2$

$\qquad\qquad\quad = 900 + 120 + 4 \qquad\qquad\qquad\quad = 2500 - 100 + 1$

$\qquad\qquad\quad = \mathbf{1024} \qquad\qquad\qquad\qquad\qquad = \mathbf{2401}$

You will find it useful to memorize these special binomial products.

> **Square of a Binomial Sum:** $(a + b)^2 = a^2 + 2ab + b^2$
>
> **Square of a Binomial Difference:** $(a - b)^2 = a^2 - 2ab + b^2$

CLASSROOM EXERCISES

Write the square of each binomial as a trinomial.

1. $(x - 10)^2$ **2.** $(5x + 3)^2$ **3.** $(x - 2y)^2$ **4.** $(n + 5t)^2$

5. $(2p - q)^2$ **6.** $(2x + 3y)^2$ **7.** $(m^2 - 6)^2$ **8.** $(2x^2 + 1)^2$

WRITTEN EXERCISES

A   Write the square of each binomial as a trinomial.

1. $(a + 3)^2$ **2.** $(a - 2)^2$ **3.** $(a + 5)^2$ **4.** $(x - 3)^2$

5. $(a - 5)^2$ **6.** $(n - 6)^2$ **7.** $(x - y)^2$ **8.** $(2a + 3)^2$

9. $(2a + 1)^2$ **10.** $(4a - 1)^2$ **11.** $(5m - 1)^2$ **12.** $(7m - 4)^2$

13. $(n + 3)^2$ **14.** $(5m + 3)^2$ **15.** $(3x - y)^2$ **16.** $(x + 2)^2$

17. $(2x - 3)^2$ **18.** $(2x - 5)^2$ **19.** $(2x + y)^2$ **20.** $(y + 10)^2$

21. $(2x - 3y)^2$ **22.** $(3a - 2b)^2$ **23.** $(10a + 2)^2$ **24.** $(5c + 3d)^2$

25. $(2x^2 + 3y^2)^2$ **26.** $(5c^2 + 4y^3)^2$ **27.** $(a^2 - 3b^2)^2$ **28.** $(x^2y - 5)^2$

29. $(a^2 - 3)^2$ **30.** $(2a^2 + 3)^2$ **31.** $(11a^2 + c^2)^2$ **32.** $(8x^2 - 5d^2)^2$

Square each number.

33. $(20 - 1)^2$ **34.** $(100 - 1)^2$ **35.** $(50 + 2)^2$ **36.** $(100 + 5)^2$

37. $(21)^2$ **38.** $(29)^2$ **39.** $(999)^2$ **40.** $(98)^2$ **41.** $(101)^2$ **42.** $(19)^2$

B   Write the square of each binomial as a trinomial.

43. $(x + \frac{1}{2})^2$ **44.** $(x + \frac{1}{3})^2$ **45.** $(x - \frac{1}{6})^2$ **46.** $(2y + \frac{1}{2})^2$ **47.** $(6b + \frac{1}{2})^2$

48. $\left(9a + \frac{1}{6}\right)^2$ **49.** $\left(x - \frac{a}{2}\right)^2$ **50.** $\left(y - \frac{1}{2}p\right)^2$ **51.** $\left(x + \frac{y}{2}\right)^2$ **52.** $\left(\frac{x}{2} + 4\right)^2$

8–10 Product of $(a + b)$ and $(a - b)$

Study the table to find the pattern for finding the product of the sum and difference of the same two numbers.

$(a + b)(a - b)$	Multiply by inspection.	Simplify.
$(x + 7)(x - 7)$	$x^2 + 7x - 7x - 49$	$x^2 - 49$
$(y + 10)(y - 10)$	$y^2 + 10y - 10y - 100$	$y^2 - 100$
$(2x + 5)(2x - 5)$	$4x^2 + 10x - 10x - 25$	$4x^2 - 25$

The following procedure summarizes the steps for finding the product.

Procedure

> To find the product of the sum and difference of the same two numbers:
>
> [1] Square the first term of either binomial.
>
> [2] Subtract the square of the second term of either binomial.

You can use this procedure to write the product of the sum and difference of the same two numbers as a binomial.

EXAMPLE 1   Write each product as a binomial.

a. $\left(\dfrac{1}{3} + y\right)\left(\dfrac{1}{3} - y\right)$ b. $(3r + 7t)(3r - 7t)$

Solutions: a. $\left(\dfrac{1}{3} + y\right)\left(\dfrac{1}{3} - y\right) = \left(\dfrac{1}{3}\right)^2 - y^2$ ⟵ **(First term)² − (Second term)²**

$$= \dfrac{1}{9} - y^2$$

b. $(3r + 7t)(3r - 7t) = (3r)^2 - (7t)^2$ ⟵ **(First term)² − (Second term)²**

$$= 9r^2 - 49t^2$$

This procedure is useful in finding certain products.

EXAMPLE 2   Find the product: 42×38

Solution: $42 \times 38 = (40 + 2)(40 - 2)$ ⟵ **Write 42 and 38 as the sum and difference of the same two numbers.**

$$= (40^2) - (2)^2$$

$$= 1600 - 4 = \mathbf{1596}$$

You will find it useful to memorize this special binomial product.

> **Product of a Sum and Difference**
>
> $(a + b)(a - b) = a^2 - b^2$

CLASSROOM EXERCISES

Write each product as a binomial.

1. $(x + 1)(x - 1)$ **2.** $(a + 3)(a - 3)$ **3.** $(2r - 5)(2r + 5)$

4. $(1 - 6q)(1 + 6q)$ **5.** $(3h + 4s)(3h - 4s)$ **6.** $(0.2s - 0.1t)(0.2s + 0.1t)$

WRITTEN EXERCISES

A Write each product as a binomial.

1. $(p + 7)(p - 7)$ **2.** $(p - 5)(p + 5)$ **3.** $(p + 8)(p - 8)$

4. $(2p + 5)(2p - 5)$ **5.** $(b + c)(b - c)$ **6.** $(c - 2)(c + 2)$

$(2p + 3)(2p - 3)$ **8.** $(3p + 5)(3p - 5)$ **9.** $(R - r)(R + r)$

$(2x + y)(2x - y)$ **11.** $(5x + 4y)(5x - 4y)$ **12.** $(7x - 6y)(7x + 6y)$

$x^2 - 7y)(6x^2 + 7y)$ **14.** $(a^2 + b^2)(a^2 - b^2)$ **15.** $(ab - c)(ab + c)$

$- x^2)(x^2 + y)$ **17.** $(\frac{1}{2} - 2x)(\frac{1}{2} + 2x)$ **18.** $(y + 0.5)(y - 0.5)$

$+ d)(2c - d)$ **20.** $(3c + 2d)(3c - 2d)$ **21.** $(5y - 4)(4 + 5y)$

. $- y^2)(x^2 - y^2)$ **23.** $(x^3 - y^3)(x^3 + y^3)$ **24.** $(x^4 - y^4)(x^4 + y^4)$

Find each product.

25. $(20 + 1)(20 - 1)$ **26.** $(30 + 1)(30 - 1)$ **27.** $(100 + 2)(100 - 2)$

28. $(50 + 4)(50 - 4)$ **29.** $(10 + 5)(10 - 5)$ **30.** $(1000 + 1)(1000 - 1)$

31. $18 \cdot 22$ **32.** $101 \cdot 99$ **33.** $51 \cdot 49$

APPLICATIONS: Using Binomial Products

B Find the area of the region bounded by the red closed curve.

34.

35.

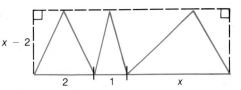

36. Which has the greater area, a square each of whose sides is x units long or a rectangle having the same perimeter but with width 5 units shorter than the width of the square?

37. Which has the greater area, a square each of whose sides is y units long or a rectangle having the same perimeter but with length 4 units longer than the side of the square? How much greater is it?

C Write each product as a binomial.

38. $(x^n + 1)(x^n - 1)$ **39.** $(1 - y^{2a})(1 + y^{2a})$ **40.** $(x^a - y^b)(x^a + y^b)$

41. $(a^2b^8 - 5)(a^2b^8 + 5)$ **42.** $(0.2 + x^3y^5)(0.2 - x^3y^5)$ **43.** $(b^n + c^{2n})(b^n - c^{2n})$

BASIC: SQUARING BINOMIALS

You can write a BASIC program to compute the square of a given binomial.

Problem: *Write a program which squares binomials of the form Ax + B.*

```
100 PRINT "FOR THE BINOMIAL TO BE SQUARED, AX + B,"
110 PRINT "WHAT ARE A AND B";
120 INPUT A, B
130 LET C = 2 * A * B
140 IF C < 0 THEN 170
150 PRINT A*A;"X↑2 +";C;"X +";B*B
160 GOTO 180
170 PRINT A*A;"X↑2 -";ABS(C);"X +";B*B
180 PRINT
190 PRINT "ANY MORE BINOMIALS TO SQUARE (1=YES, 0=NO)";
200 INPUT Z
210 IF Z = 1 THEN 120
220 END
```

The following is the output from a sample run of the program above.

Output:
```
RUN
FOR THE BINOMIAL TO BE SQUARED, AX + B,
WHAT ARE A AND B? 2,3
 4 X↑2 + 12 X + 9

ANY MORE BINOMIALS TO SQUARE (1=YES, 0=NO)? 1
? 1,-3
 1 X↑2 - 6 X + 9

ANY MORE BINOMIALS TO SQUARE (1=YES, 0=NO)? 1
? -6,4
 36 X↑2 - 48 X + 16

ANY MORE BINOMIALS TO SQUARE (1=YES, 0=NO)? 1
? -5,-7
 25 X↑2 + 70 X + 49

ANY MORE BINOMIALS TO SQUARE (1=YES, 0=NO)? 1
? 2,0
 4 X↑2 + 0 X + 0

ANY MORE BINOMIALS TO SQUARE (1=YES, 0=NO)? 0
READY
```

Analysis

Statement 130: When a binomial is squared, the result is a trinomial. The coefficient of the middle term of the square of the binomial is computed.

Statement 140: The first and last terms of the trinomial must have positive coefficients. For printing the trinomial, then, the only question is whether the middle term is positive or negative.

Statement 150: If C is positive, the trinomial is printed with a "+" in front of the middle term as well as a "+" in front of the last term (B^2).

Statement 170: If C is negative, the trinomial is printed with a "−" in front of the middle term and a "+" in front of the last term.

As the output from the second set of input data in the sample run shows, the program does not eliminate the printing of 1 or −1 coefficients. (See Exercise 14 below.) Also the program does not detect whether A or B = 0. (See Exercise 15 below.)

EXERCISES

A   Run the program on page 308 for the following values of *A* and *B*.

1. $A = 3; B = 4$

2. $A = 2; B = 9$

3. $A = 6; B = -3$

4. $A = -5; B = 2$

5. $A = -4; B = -4$

6. $A = -8; B = 0$

Write each binomial in the form $Ax + B$. Then use the program on page 308 to square each binomial.

7. $5 + x$

8. $10 + 3x$

9. $11 - 2x$

10. $21x$

11. $-32x$

12. $15 - 23x$

Rewrite the program on page 308 to do each of the following.

13. Square binomials of the form $Ax + By$.

14. Eliminate the printing of coefficients equal to 1 or −1.

15. Test whether A or B (or both) equals 0 and change the printing of the trinomial accordingly. For example, for the binomial 5 X + 0, print the square simply as 25 X↑2 and not 25 X↑2 + 0 X + 0.

B   Write a BASIC program for each problem. As in the program on page 308 and in Exercises 14 and 15 above, print answers as "neatly" as possible. For example, print 5 X↑2 − 9 X − 2 and not 5 X↑2 + −9 X + −2; print X↑2 + 5 X + 6 and not 1 X↑2 + 5 X + 6; print −X↑2 + 3 X − 2 and not −1 X↑2 + 3 X + −2. Also, do not print terms with 0 coefficients.

16. Multiply $(Ax + B)$ and $(Cx + D)$.

17. Add $(Ax + B)$ and $(Cx + D)$.

18. Subtract $(Cx + D)$ from $(Ax + B)$.

Review

Add or subtract as indicated. *(Section 8–6)*

1. $(3a + 4b) + (2a - 6b)$

2. $(5x^2y + 4xy^2) - (x^2y - 3xy^2)$

3. $(4d^2 + 2d - 4) - (5d + d^2)$

4. $(2x^3 + x^2 - 4x) - (x^3 + x^2)$

Multiply. *(Section 8–7)*

5. $3(4x - 1)$

6. $2y^2(2y + 4)$

7. $(c - 4)(2c + 1)$

8. $(2c + 3)(2c + 3)$

9. $(4a^2 - 2c)(a^2 - c)$

10. $4b - 3(b - 1)$

Find each product by inspection. *(Section 8–8)*

11. $(y + 2)(y - 3)$

12. $(2b + 3)(3b + 1)$

13. $(m^2 - 3n)(3m^2 + n)$

14. $(x^2 + 5)(x^2 - 2)$

15. $(a^2 - b)(a^2 + b)$

16. $(3ab - 4)(ab - 1)$

Write the square of each binomial as a trinomial. *(Section 8–9)*

17. $(a - 2)^2$

18. $(3y + 5)^2$

19. $(2b - 6d)^2$

20. $(r^2s + t)^2$

Write each product as a binomial. *(Section 8–10)*

21. $(b + 2)(b - 2)$

22. $(r + s)(r - s)$

23. $(1 - p)(1 + p)$

24. $(3y + 2)(3y - 2)$

25. $(3c + 2d)(3c - 2d)$

26. $(x^2 + 6)(x^2 - 6)$

Chapter Summary

IMPORTANT TERMS
Binomial (p. 296)
Monomial (p. 283)
Polynomial (p. 296)

Scientific notation (p. 290)
Trinomial (p. 296)

IMPORTANT IDEAS

1. If x is a real number and a is an integer greater than 1, then

$$x^a = \underbrace{x \cdot x \cdot x \cdot \cdots \cdot x.}_{a \text{ factors}}$$

When $a = 1$, $x^a = x$, that is, $x^1 = x$.

2. **Multiplication Theorem for Exponents**   If x is a real number and a and b are positive integers, then

$$x^a \cdot x^b = x^{a+b}.$$

3. **Power Theorem for Exponents**   If x is a real number and a and b are positive integers, then

$$(x^a)^b = x^{ab}.$$

4. **Power of a Product Theorem for Exponents**   If x and y are real numbers and a is a positive integer, then

$$(xy)^a = x^a y^a.$$

5. **Division Theorem for Exponents** If x is a real number, $x \neq 0$, and a and b are positive integers such that $a \geq b$, then

$$\frac{x^a}{x^b} = x^{a-b}.$$

6. If x is any real number except zero and a is a positive integer, then

$$x^{-a} = \frac{1}{x^a}.$$

7. To add polynomials, add monomials that are like terms. To subtract a polynomial, add its additive inverse.

8. **The FOIL Method for Finding the Product of Two Binomials**
Add the product of the **first** terms, the product of the **outer** terms, the product of the **inner** terms, and the product of the **last** terms.

9. **Steps in Squaring a Binomial**
   1 Square the first term.
   2 Add to this twice the product of the first and last terms when the binomial is of the form $(a + b)$.

   Subtract twice the product of the first and last terms when the binomial is of the form $(a - b)$.
   3 Add to this the square of the last term.
$$(a + b)^2 = a^2 + 2ab + b^2$$
$$(a - b)^2 = a^2 - 2ab + b^2$$

10. **Steps in Finding the Product of the Sum and Difference of the Same Two Numbers**
   1 Square the first term of either binomial.
   2 Subtract the square of the second term of either binomial.
$$(a + b)(a - b) = a^2 - b^2$$

Chapter Objectives and Review

Objective: *To evaluate expressions with exponents (Section 8-1)*

Evaluate.

1. $(-2)^3$
2. $(-3)^2$
3. 5^0
4. 10^8
5. $(-1)^{13}$

Find the value when $a = 2$, $b = -4$, and $c = 5$.

6. a^2c
7. a^3b^2
8. abc^2
9. ab^3
10. a^3b^2c

Objective: *To multiply monomials (Section 8-2)*

Find each product.

11. $a^2(a^6)$
12. $x^2 \cdot x^7$
13. $p^4 \times p$
14. $(-h)(-y)$
15. $10^3 \cdot 10^3$
16. $(3x^2)(-4x^3)$
17. $(-3mn)(-m^2)$
18. $(-st)(s^2t^3)$

Objective: *To raise an expression to a power (Section 8–3)*

Raise to the indicated power. No denominator equals zero.

19. $(x^3)^5$

20. $(x^5)^3$

21. $(3y)^3$

22. $(-ab^2)^3$

23. $(3cd^4)^3$

24. $(-3 \times 10^3)^2$

25. $\left(\dfrac{m^2}{pn^3}\right)^3$

26. $\left(\dfrac{q^2r}{s^3}\right)^2$

Objective: *To divide monomials (Section 8–4)*

Simplify. All exponents are positive integers and no denominator equals zero.

27. $\dfrac{3c^3}{c^3}$

28. $\dfrac{m^3n^2}{m^2n}$

29. $\dfrac{-18a^2b^4}{-6ab}$

30. $\dfrac{6p(3p^3)}{9p^2}$

31. $\dfrac{(-6x^3y)(-xy)^2}{-2x^2y^2}$

32. $\dfrac{q^{c+1}}{q^c}$

33. $\dfrac{s^{2x}t^{3y}}{st^2}$

34. $\dfrac{(y^{3k+4})^3}{y^{2k+12}}$

Objective: *To write numbers in scientific notation (Section 8–5)*

Simplify. No variable equals zero.

35. 3^{-4}

36. $(-4)^3$

37. y^{-6}

38. $\left(-\dfrac{2}{3}\right)^{-3}$

39. $3n^{-2}$

Write each number in scientific notation.

40. 800,000,000

41. 29,000,000,000

42. 0.0000038

Objective: *To add and subtract polynomials (Section 8–6)*

Add or subtract as indicated.

43. $(6x + 3y) - (2x + 5y)$

44. $(2a^2b - ab^2) + (ab^2 - 4a^2b)$

45. $(m^2 + 6m) + (2m^2 - m)$

46. $(2cd + c + 5) - (d - cd - 6)$

Objective: *To multiply polynomials (Section 8–7)*

Multiply.

47. $5(6y + 3)$

48. $-6a(3a^2 - 2)$

49. $(2x - y)(x + 4y)$

50. $(\tfrac{1}{2}x - 1)(2x + 4)$

51. $(x - y)(y - x)$

52. $(c^2 + 2d)(2c^2 + d)$

Objective: *To find the product of two binomials by inspection (Section 8–8)*

Find each product by inspection.

53. $(p - 4)(p + 1)$

54. $(3y - 4)(y - 2)$

55. $(2a + 3b)(3a - 4b)$

56. $(2x^2 + 1)(x^2 + 4)$

57. $(2d - h)(d + 3h)$

58. $(0.5r + s)(1.4r - s)$

Objective: *To square binomials (Section 8–9)*

Write the square of each binomial as a trinomial.

59. $(c + 6)^2$

60. $(6p - 1)^2$

61. $(x^2 + 3)^2$

62. $(4a - 3b)^2$

Objective: *To find the product of the sum and difference of the same two numbers*
(Section 8–10)

Write each product as a binomial.

63. $(d-5)(d+5)$

64. $(8+a)(8-a)$

65. $(f-g)(f+g)$

66. $(4w-5)(4w+5)$

67. $(5m+2n)(5m-2n)$

68. $(2b^2-7)(2b^2+7)$

--- **Chapter Test** ---

Find the value when $a=-1$, $b=2$, and $c=-4$.

1. a^2b

2. bc^3

3. abc^2

Simplify. No denominator equals zero.

4. $\dfrac{n^4}{n}$

5. $\dfrac{-15a^2bc^2}{3ab}$

6. $\dfrac{x^2(4xy)^2}{4x^2y}$

Write each number in scientific notation.

7. 650,000,000

8. 0.00003

9. 7 million

Add or subtract as indicated.

10. $(3m-4n)-(2n+m)$

11. $(x^2+x-4)+(3x-1-x^2)$

12. $(3a^2+4ab-4b^2)-(ab-6b^2)$

13. $(6m-n-2p)+(p+1-5m)$

Raise to the indicated power.

14. $(-cd^2)^3$

15. $(x-4)^2$

16. $(3a+4b^2)^2$

Multiply.

17. $w^3(-w^4)$

18. $(-4x^2)(-2x^5)$

19. $3b(2b-1)$

20. $3t(t^2-5t+2)$

21. $(3y+2x)(y-3x)$

22. $(4y^2-3)(y^2+1)$

23. $(3c-2d)(c-d)$

24. $(y+4)(y-4)$

25. $(2a-b)(2a+b)$

Additional Practice

Skills

Find the value when $a=1$, $b=-2$, and $c=5$. *(Section 8–1)*

1. a^2b

2. b^2c

3. abc

4. a^2b^3c

5. $a^3b^4c^2$

Find each product. *(Section 8–2)*

6. $c^2(c^3)$

7. $(-3x)(4x)$

8. $-(-4b^2)(-3)$

9. $3n(2mn)(3n^2)$

Exponents and Polynomials **313**

Raise to the indicated power. No denominator equals zero. *(Section 8–3)*

10. $(x^3)^2$

11. $(ab^4)^3$

12. $\left(\dfrac{n^2p}{2m^3}\right)^4$

13. $\left(\dfrac{ab^3}{c^4}\right)^5$

Simplify. All exponents are positive integers and no denominator equals zero. *(Section 8–4)*

14. $\dfrac{x^7}{x^4}$

15. $\dfrac{a^2b^4}{ab^2}$

16. $\dfrac{(2mn^2)(5m^3n^2)}{(2mn^2)^2}$

17. $\dfrac{p^{5k-1}}{p^{3k-4}}$

Write in scientific notation. *(Section 8–5)*

18. 0.0000024

19. 320,000,000

20. 2500

21. 0.0000652

Add or subtract as indicated. *(Section 8–6)*

22. $(3x + y^2) + (x + y - 2y^2)$

23. $(5m^2n^3 - 2mn) - (-2m^2n^3 + mn)$

Multiply. *(Section 8–7)*

24. $3x(2x - 1)$

25. $(a + 1)(a - 5)$

26. $(3n - 4)(5n - 1)$

Find each product by inspection. *(Section 8–8)*

27. $(y + 8)(y + 3)$

28. $(3x - 4)(x + 1)$

29. $(n^2 - 3)(3n^2 - 5)$

Write the square of each binomial. *(Section 8–9)*

30. $(x + 7)^2$

31. $(2n - 3)^2$

32. $(2m + 5n)^2$

33. $(6y - \frac{2}{3})^2$

Write each product as a binomial. *(Section 8–10)*

34. $(2y - 9)(2y + 9)$

35. $(xy + 1)(xy - 1)$

36. $(6s - \frac{1}{2})(6s + \frac{1}{2})$

Applications

37. Find the perimeter of a square if the length of each of its four equal sides is $(2b + 3)$ units. *(Section 8–6)*

38. Find the perimeter of a rectangle if its length is $(4c - 8)$ units and its width is $(c + 3)$ units. *(Section 8–6)*

39. Which has the greater area, a square with sides each $(x + 2)$ units long or a rectangle with length $(x + 4)$ units and width x units? How much greater is it? *(Section 8–7)*

40. Which has the greater area, a rectangle with length $(a - 2)$ units and width $(a - 3)$ units or one with length $(a - 1)$ units and width $(a - 4)$ units? How much greater is it? *(Section 8–8)*

41. Which has the greater area, a rectangle with length $(2a + 1)$ units and width $(2a - 1)$ units or a rectangle with length $(4a + 4)$ units and width $(a - 1)$ units? How much greater is it? *(Section 8–10)*

42. Which has the greater area, a rectangle with length $(n + 1)$ units and width $(n - 1)$ units or a square with the same perimeter as the rectangle? How much greater is it? *(Section 8–10)*

CHAPTER **9** **Factoring Polynomials**

9-1 Factoring Integers

To *factor* a number or a polynomial means to write it as a product.

Factors of 174

$$174 = 2 \cdot 3 \cdot 29$$

Each number below has only two whole-number factors, the number itself and 1. These numbers are called *prime numbers*.

2, 3, 5, 7, 11, 13, 17, 19, 23, 29, 31

Definition

> A **prime number** is an integer greater than 1 that has exactly two positive integral factors, itself and 1.

Numbers such as 4, 9, 10, 16, 25, and so on, are *composite numbers*.

Definition

> A **composite number** is any integer greater than 1 that is not prime.

Every composite number can be expressed as a product of prime factors.

When a composite number is written as a product of prime-number factors or of powers of prime-number factors, the number is in **prime-factorization form.**

EXAMPLE   Write each number in prime-factorization form.

a. 500   **b.** 756

Solutions: Divide by the prime numbers in order.

Divide by each prime number as many times as possible, before dividing by the next prime number.

a. $500 = 2 \cdot 250$ ←——— **Divide by 2 again.**

$= 2 \cdot 2 \cdot 125$ ←——— **125 is not divisible by 3 or 4. Try 5.**

$= 2 \cdot 2 \cdot 5 \cdot 25$ ←——— **Divide by 5 again.**

$= 2 \cdot 2 \cdot 5 \cdot 5 \cdot 5$ ←——— **Stop! All factors are prime factors.**

$= 2^2 \cdot 5^3$ ←——— **Prime factorization.**

b. $756 = 2 \cdot 378$ ←——— **Divide by 2 again.**

$= 2 \cdot 2 \cdot 189$ ←——— **Divide by 3.**

$= 2 \cdot 2 \cdot 3 \cdot 63$ ←——— **Divide by 3 again.**

$= 2 \cdot 2 \cdot 3 \cdot 3 \cdot 21$

$= 2 \cdot 2 \cdot 3 \cdot 3 \cdot 3 \cdot 7$ ←——— **Stop! All factors are prime factors.**

$= 2^2 \cdot 3^3 \cdot 7$ ←——— **Prime factorization**

The *Unique Factorization Theorem*, also called the *Fundamental Theorem of Arithmetic*, states that there is *one and only one way* to factor positive integers such as 500 and 756 into primes. The order in which the prime factors are written may vary.

Theorem 9–1

> **Unique Factorization Theorem**
>
> The factorization of any positive integer into primes is unique, disregarding the order of the factors.

When you are asked to find the factors of a number, you must know whether you are to find the whole-number, integral, rational, or real-number factors. For example,

$$\frac{1}{2} \text{ and } 36 \text{ are } rational\text{-}number \, factors \text{ of } 18.$$

Unless told otherwise in this text, assume that you are factoring over the set of integers.

CLASSROOM EXERCISES

Determine whether the second number is a factor of the number in parentheses. Answer *Yes* or *No*.

1. $(3^3 \cdot 5)$; $3 \cdot 5$
2. $(2 \cdot 5 \cdot 7)$; 3
3. $(8 + 2)$; 8

Identify each number as prime, *P*, or composite, *C*.

4. 15   **5.** 9   **6.** 13   **7.** 29   **8.** 31   **9.** 51

Write each number in prime-factorization form.

10. 24   **11.** 20   **12.** 70   **13.** 200   **14.** 350   **15.** 41

WRITTEN EXERCISES

A

Determine whether the second number is a factor of the number in parentheses. Answer *Yes* or *No*.

1. $(5 \cdot 6^2 \cdot 8)$; 6
2. $(3 \cdot 4 \cdot 7)$; $3 \cdot 4$
3. $(8^2 \cdot 7 \cdot 4)$; $8 \cdot 7 \cdot 4$

4. $(5^2 \cdot 6^2 \cdot 8)$; $5^2 \cdot 8$
5. $(3^2 + 1)$; 3
6. $(9^2 + 1)$; 9

7. $(8^2 \cdot 9 \cdot 6)$; $8^3 \cdot 9$
8. $(5^2 \cdot 7^2)$; 12^2
9. $(8 \cdot 7 \cdot 6 \cdot 5 \cdot 4)$; $3 \cdot 8$

10. $(6 \cdot 5 \cdot 4)$; 8
11. $(8 \cdot 7 \cdot 6 \cdot 5)$; $3 \cdot 5$
12. $(8 \cdot 7 \cdot 6 \cdot 5 \cdot 4)$; $2 \cdot 4$

Identify each number as prime, *P*, or composite, *C*.

13. 29   **14.** 33   **15.** 18   **16.** 43   **17.** 49   **18.** 11

19. 13   **20.** 100   **21.** 23   **22.** 17   **23.** 48   **24.** 101

Write each number in prime-factorization form.

25. 18   26. 36   27. 21   28. 15   29. 42   30. 32

31. 45   32. 49   33. 25   34. 28   35. 33   36. 44

37. 500   38. 625   39. 300   40. 1000   41. 960   42. 72

B   Write each number as the product of two rational-number factors.

43. 4   44. 6   45. 3   46. 10   47. 7   48. 9

49. 8   50. 11   51. $\frac{1}{8}$ 52. $\frac{1}{16}$ 53. $\frac{1}{10}$ 54. $\frac{1}{2}$

APPLICATIONS: Using Factors

55. A marching band has 72 members. What rectangular formations are possible if each row and each column must have at least 6 players?

56. The Cobb City marching band has 100 members. What rectangular formations are possible if each row and each column must have at least 5 players?

57. Ann sets out 100 tomato plants in her garden. In what ways can she arrange them so that she has the same number in each row and there are at least 5 rows and 5 columns?

58. In how many ways could 150 apple trees be planted so that each row has the same number of trees and there are at least 5 rows and 5 columns?

CALCULATOR APPLICATIONS

Finding Prime Numbers

You can use a calculator to find certain prime numbers p by using the formula $p = 2^n - 1$ for some values of the variable n.

EXAMPLE Use the formula $p = 2^n - 1$ to find p when $n = 7$.

SOLUTION If your calculator does not have an exponent key, $\boxed{x^y}$, you may be able to use the method on page 121 or the method shown below.

2   — 1 = $127.$

EXERCISES

Use the formula $p = 2^n - 1$ to find a prime number p for each value of n.

1. 2   2. 3   3. 5   4. 13   5. 17   6. 19

REVIEW CAPSULE FOR SECTION 9-2

Multiply. *(Pages 97–99)*

1. $x(x + 3)$ 2. $-2(a - 4)$ 3. $ab(a - 2)$ 4. $x^2y(xy + 7)$

5. $a(b + c - d)$ 6. $-2x(y^2 - 6y + 3)$ 7. $(x + y)4$ 8. $-p(-qr + sq)$

9. $a(a - 2) + b(a - 2)$ 10. $z(x + 2) + 3(x + 2)$ 11. $t(y - 1) + 5(y - 1)$

9-2 Common Factors

The distributive postulate is used to find products. It is also used to find factors of polynomials.

Multiplying	**Factoring**
$6(x+y) = 6x + 6y$	$6x + 6y = 6(x+y)$
$a(b+c) = ab + ac$	$ab + ac = a(b+c)$
$5x(3x^2 - 4x - 1) = 15x^3 - 20x^2 - 5x$	$15x^3 - 20x^2 - 5x = 5x(3x^2 - 4x - 1)$
$(x+2)(x+3) = x(x+3) + 2(x+3)$	$x(x+3) + 2(x+3) = (x+2)(x+3)$

Thus, since $6(x + y) = 6x + 6y$, then $6x + 6y = 6(x + y)$.

When you factor **over the integers,** you rewrite the polynomial as the product of factors that have integral coefficients only.

EXAMPLE 1   Factor over the integers.

   a. $3x + 3y$ **b.** $x^2 - x$ **c.** $7x^3 - 21x$ **d.** $2y^3 + 4y^2 + 6y$

Solutions: Look for common monomial factors in each term of the polynomial.

   a. $3x + 3y = 3(x + y)$ ⟵——— **The common monomial factor is 3.**

   b. $x^2 - x = x(x - 1)$ ⟵——— **The common monomial factor is x.**

   c. $7x^3 - 21x = 7x(x^2 - 3)$ ⟵——— **The common monomial factor is 7x.**

   d. $2y^3 + 4y^2 + 6y = 2y(y^2 + 2y + 3)$ ⟵——— **The common monomial factor is 2y.**

When a polynomial has no polynomial factors with integral coefficients except itself and 1, it is a **prime polynomial with respect to the integers.** For example, the polynomial

$$6x + 5y$$

is a prime polynomial over the integers because $6x$ and $5y$ have *no common factors with integral coefficients other than 1.*

Some polynomials have a common binomial factor.

EXAMPLE 2   Factor over the integers: $a(r + t) + b(r + t)$

Solution: Think of $(r + t)$ as a monomial.

   $a(r + t) + b(r + t) = ax + bx$ ⟵——— **Let x = (r + t).**

   $= x(a + b)$ ⟵——— **The common factor is x.**

   $= (r + t)(a + b)$ ⟵——— **Replace x with (r + t).**

Sometimes you have to group terms in order to find the common binomial factor.

EXAMPLE 3 Factor over the integers: $ax + cy + xy + ac$

Solution: The terms of the polynomial can be grouped in two ways.

Method I: $ax + cy + xy + ac = (ax + xy) + (cy + ac)$ ← Group terms with a common factor.

$= x(a + y) + c(y + a)$ ← Common monomial factors: x and c

$= x(a + y) + c(a + y)$ ← $y + a = a + y$

$= (a + y)(x + c)$ ← $(a + y)$ is the common factor.

Method II: $ax + cy + xy + ac = (ax + ac) + (cy + xy)$ ← Group terms with a common factor.

$= a(x + c) + y(c + x)$ ← Common monomial factors: a and y

$= a(x + c) + y(x + c)$ ← $c + x = x + c$

$= (x + c)(a + y)$ ← $(x + c)$ is the common factor.

CLASSROOM EXERCISES

One factor is given for each polynomial. Write the other factor.

1. $8a + 8b = \underline{\ ?\ }(a + b)$
2. $xy + y^2 = \underline{\ ?\ }(x + y)$
3. $3x^3 + 3x = \underline{\ ?\ }(x^2 + 1)$
4. $8x^3 - 4xy^2 = \underline{\ ?\ }(2x^2 - y^2)$
5. $15a^2 + 15ab^2 = 15a(\underline{\ ?\ })$
6. $x^3y - y = y(\underline{\ ?\ })$
7. $-2ab + 8bc - 4ac = -2(\underline{\ ?\ })$
8. $pq + qr + q^2 = q(\underline{\ ?\ })$
9. $3(x - y) + a(x - y) = (\underline{\ ?\ })(3 + a)$
10. $t(x - 4) + w(x - 4) = (\underline{\ ?\ })(x - 4)$

Factor over the integers.

11. $14p + 14q$
12. $12a - 12d$
13. $xt + yt$
14. $4s^2t + 4sw$
15. $13st - 26t$
16. $10x^2y - 15xy + 5$
17. $a(t + w) + b(t + w)$
18. $fg + f + 2g + 2$
19. $4d + 4 + de + e$

WRITTEN EXERCISES

A   One factor is given for each polynomial. Write the other factor.

1. $3x + 6y = 3(\underline{\ ?\ } + 2y)$
2. $4n - 2 = 2(2n - \underline{\ ?\ })$
3. $3b^2 - 24b = 3b(\underline{\ ?\ } - 8)$
4. $15ab^2 - 3b^2 = 3b^2(\underline{\ ?\ } - \underline{\ ?\ })$
5. $-3ax + 6ay = -3a(\underline{\ ?\ } - \underline{\ ?\ })$
6. $p^2 - p = p(\underline{\ ?\ } - \underline{\ ?\ })$
7. $8y - 24 = 8(y - \underline{\ ?\ })$
8. $8x^2y^2 - xy^2 = xy^2(\underline{\ ?\ } - \underline{\ ?\ })$
9. $x^2 - 3x^2y = x^2(\underline{\ ?\ } - \underline{\ ?\ })$
10. $6a^2b - 3ab^2 = 3ab(\underline{\ ?\ } - \underline{\ ?\ })$
11. $5x + 20 = \underline{\ ?\ }(x + 4)$
12. $3x^2 - 6xy + 9y = 3(\underline{\ ?\ } - \underline{\ ?\ } + \underline{\ ?\ })$
13. $16m - 4m^2 = \underline{\ ?\ }(4 - m)$
14. $-xy + 6x^2y - 4xy = -xy(\underline{\ ?\ } - \underline{\ ?\ } + \underline{\ ?\ })$
15. $16x^2 - 2x = 2x(\underline{\ ?\ } - \underline{\ ?\ })$
16. $8x + 8y + 2xy = 2(\underline{\ ?\ } + \underline{\ ?\ } + \underline{\ ?\ })$

17. $4ab + b = b(\underline{\quad?\quad} + \underline{\quad?\quad})$

18. $-5x^2 - 10y^2 = -5(\underline{\quad?\quad} + \underline{\quad?\quad})$

19. $2mn - n = n(\underline{\quad?\quad} - \underline{\quad?\quad})$

20. $4xy - 2x - 3x^2y = x(\underline{\quad?\quad} - \underline{\quad?\quad} - \underline{\quad?\quad})$

21. $12y - 4 = \underline{\quad?\quad}(3y - 1)$

22. $a^3 + 2a^2b = a^2(\underline{\quad?\quad} + \underline{\quad?\quad})$

23. $400x - x^2 = \underline{\quad?\quad}(400 - x)$

24. $1000x^3 - x = x(\underline{\quad?\quad} - \underline{\quad?\quad})$

25. $4ab - b = b(\underline{\quad?\quad} - \underline{\quad?\quad})$

26. $8x^2 - 28x - 4 = \underline{\quad?\quad}(2x^2 - 7x - 1)$

27. $25x^2 - 20y^2 = \underline{\quad?\quad}(5x^2 - 4y^2)$

28. $5m - 10mn - 15 = \underline{\quad?\quad}(m - 2mn - 3)$

29. $7x + 49xy = 7x(\underline{\quad?\quad} + \underline{\quad?\quad})$

30. $4x^3 + 6x^2 - 2x = 2x(\underline{\quad?\quad} + \underline{\quad?\quad} - \underline{\quad?\quad})$

31. $a(x + y) + b(x + y) = (x + y)(\underline{\quad?\quad} + \underline{\quad?\quad})$

32. $t(a + 3) - y(a + 3) = (a + 3)(\underline{\quad?\quad} - \underline{\quad?\quad})$

33. $10 + 2t + 5s + st = (\underline{\quad?\quad} + \underline{\quad?\quad})(5 + t)$

34. $tx - wx + ty - wy = (\underline{\quad?\quad} - \underline{\quad?\quad})(x + y)$

Factor over the integers.

35. $7x + 7y$

36. $3a + 9b$

37. $8x - 4y$

38. $ax + bx$

39. $3x - awx$

40. $9x^2 - 6y^2$

41. $4c + ac + bc$

42. $ay + by + 3y$

43. $d^2 + 2d + ad$

44. $ax - ay + a^2$

45. $5x - 10y + 15z^2$

46. $5t + 10t^2 + t^3$

47. $2\pi r^2 + 2\pi rh$

48. $a^2b + ab^2 + a^3b^3$

49. $cdh^3 + c^2dh + c^3d^2h^2$

50. $d(e + f) + g(e + f)$

51. $a(b - c) + d(b - c)$

52. $3(x + y) - g(x + y)$

53. $a(q - r) - s(q - r)$

54. $(vx + xz) + sv + sz$

55. $kp - kn + (pr - rn)$

B

56. $6w - 15 - 14hw + 35h$

57. $2ax^2 + bx^2 - 2ay^2 - by^2$

Factor over the integers. If a polynomial cannot be factored over the integers, write *Prime*.

58. $3a + b$

59. $7a^2b - 7ab$

60. $18r^2 - 6 + 24r$

61. $8x^2 - 3y^2$

62. $64ab - 16b^2$

63. $10a^2 + 33ab + 17b^2$

64. $12n^2 - 4 + 16n$

65. $9p^2 - 5q^2$

66. $36x^2 - 18xy$

67. $14x^2 + 7xy + 21y^2$

68. $7n^2 - 8mn + 3n^2$

69. $9ab + a^2 + 2b^2$

70. $39a^3 - 52ab^2 + 65ac^2$

71. $27x^4 + 3x^3 + 9ax$

72. $9s - 13s^2 + 5t$

73. $25xy - 50xz + 100x$

74. $4x^2 - 8x + 6$

75. $3x^2 + 6xy - 2x^3$

76. $a^3 + 3a^2b + 3ab^2$

77. $14 - 42p + 7$

78. $3ab^2 - ab + 2a^2$

79. $8x^2 - 12xy - 16xz$

80. $ay^2 + ab + 3a$

81. $3x^3 - 15x^2 - 6x$

82. $8a^3 - 4ax^2 - 12a^2x^2$

83. $3a^2 + 4a^3 - 5a^4b$

84. $6x^3 - 2x^2y + z^3$

C   Find the missing factor.

85. $x^{n+3} + x^n = x^n(\underline{\quad?\quad})$

86. $2y^{n+1} + 4y^n = 2y^n(\underline{\quad?\quad})$

87. $4w^{n-1} + 6w^{n+1} = (\underline{\quad?\quad})(2w^{n-2} + 3w^n)$

88. $9z^{2n} + 21z^{2n+1} = (\underline{\quad?\quad})(3z^n + 7z^{n+1})$

Multiply. *(Pages 302–303)*

1. $(b + 5)(b - 5)$ **2.** $(2a + 1)(2a - 1)$ **3.** $(3x - 2)(3x + 2)$

4. $(x^2 + y^2)(x^2 - y^2)$ **5.** $(\frac{1}{2}x + y)(\frac{1}{2}x - y)$ **6.** $(9 - pq)(9 + pq)$

9-3 Factoring the Difference of Two Squares

A polynomial that represents the *difference of two squares* can be readily factored.

Finding Products	Finding Factors
$(x + 7)(x - 7) = x^2 - 49$	$x^2 - 49 = (x + 7)(x - 7)$
$(4x + y)(4x - y) = 16x^2 - y^2$	$16x^2 - y^2 = (4x + y)(4x - y)$

You will find it useful to memorize this formula for factoring the difference of two squares.

> **Factoring the Difference of Two Squares**
>
> $$a^2 - b^2 = (a + b)(a - b)$$

EXAMPLE 1   Factor over the integers: $25x^2 - 36y^2$

Solution: **Think!** $25x^2 = (5x)^2$ and $36y^2 = (6y)^2$.

$25x^2 - 36y^2 = (5x)^2 - (6y)^2$ ◄——— **Write as the difference of squares.**

$\qquad\qquad = (5x + 6y)(5x - 6y)$ ◄——— **Write as the product of a sum and difference.**

Some polynomials that *cannot be factored over the integers can be factored over the set of rational numbers.*

EXAMPLE 2   Factor over the rational numbers: $\frac{1}{4}p^2 - 9q^2$

Solution: $\frac{1}{4}p^2 - 9q^2 = (\frac{1}{2}p)^2 - (3q)^2$ ◄——— **Write as the difference of squares.**

$\qquad\qquad = (\frac{1}{2}p + 3q)(\frac{1}{2}p - 3q)$ ◄——— **Write as the product of a sum and difference.**

CLASSROOM EXERCISES

Factor over the integers.

1. $m^2 - 1$ **2.** $x^2 - 16$ **3.** $4r^2 - 1$ **4.** $9 - y^2$

5. $a^2 - 144$ **6.** $4t^2 - 121$ **7.** $-4 + y^2$ **8.** $-x^2 + 81$

Factor over the rational numbers.

9. $b^2 - \dfrac{1}{25}$ **10.** $\dfrac{1}{100} - r^2$ **11.** $16t^2 - \dfrac{1}{49}$ **12.** $\dfrac{n^2}{4} - \dfrac{1}{9}$

WRITTEN EXERCISES

Factor each polynomial over the integers. When a polynomial cannot be factored over the integers, write *Prime.*

1. $y^2 - 9$ **2.** $x^2 - 4$ **3.** $x^2 - 25$ **4.** $y^2 - 36$

5. $4x^2 - 9$ **6.** $9x^2 - 4$ **7.** $16y^2 - 36$ **8.** $-64 + 4x^2$

9. $x^2y^2 - a^2$ **10.** $y^6 - 100$ **11.** $9x^4y^2 - b^2$ **12.** $1 - 81y^2$

13. $x^2y^2 - z^2$ **14.** $-25 + 4x^2y^2$ **15.** $x^2 + y^2$ **16.** $x^2 - y^4$

17. $4x^2 + 16y^2$ **18.** $81x^2 - 64y^2$ **19.** $25x^2 - 49$ **20.** $49 - 25x^2$

Factor each polynomial over the rational numbers.

21. $\dfrac{1}{9}x^2 - 16$ **22.** $\dfrac{25}{36}a^2 - b^2$ **23.** $\dfrac{4}{9}x^2 - \dfrac{25}{36}y^2$ **24.** $\dfrac{121}{9}r^2 - s^2$

25. $-\dfrac{1}{49} + x^2$ **26.** $-\dfrac{1}{16} + r^2$ **27.** $-25 + \dfrac{1}{64}b^2$ **28.** $\dfrac{a^2}{9} - \dfrac{b^4}{16}$

APPLICATIONS: Using Factoring

29. Within a large square whose side is a units is a small square whose side is b units. What is the area of the large square? What is the area of the small square? What is the area of the shaded surface between the two squares? Factor the expression for the shaded area.

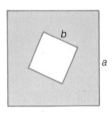

30. A small circle whose radius is r units is drawn within a large circle whose radius is R units. What is the area of the large circle? What is the area of the shaded part? Factor the expression for the shaded area.
(HINT: First, factor out the common monomial factor, π. Then factor the binomial.)

31. If four circular holes (radius r) are cut in a large circular plate of radius R, what is the area of the remaining surface in terms of R and r? Factor the expression for the shaded area. (See the hint for Exercise 30.)

Factor over the integers.

32. $(a + b)^2 - c^2$ **33.** $c^2 - (a + b)^2$

34. $(r + s)^2 - t^2$ **35.** $(r + s)^2 - (t + u)^2$

36. $(x - a)^2 - (y - b)^2$ **37.** $4(x - a)^2 - 9(y + b)^2$ **38.** $4(x - a)^2 - 9(y - b)^2$

Review

Determine whether the second number is a factor of the number in parentheses. Answer *Yes* or *No*. *(Section 9–1)*

1. $(2 \cdot 5^2 \cdot 7)$; 5

2. $(2^2 \cdot 3^2 \cdot 4^3)$; 16

3. $(9 \cdot 7 \cdot 6 \cdot 5 \cdot 4)$; $2 \cdot 8$

Write each number in prime-factorization form. *(Section 9–1)*

4. 45   **5.** 48   **6.** 56   **7.** 78   **8.** 250   **9.** 720

Factor over the integers. If a polynomial cannot be factored over the integers, write *Prime*. *(Section 9–2)*

10. $5a + 10b$

11. $3x + ax + dx$

12. $pr^2 - p^2r$

13. $y^2 + 3y$

14. $3m^2 + 13n^2$

15. $s^3t^2 + s^2t^3 - s^2t$

16. $a(b + c) - 2(b + c)$

17. $kx + wy + wx + ky$

18. $2y + xy + 2x + 4$

Factor over the integers. If a polynomial cannot be factored over the integers, write *Prime*. *(Section 9–3)*

19. $1 - m^2$

20. $-9 + a^2$

21. $9b^2 - 16$

22. $81x^2 - 1$

23. $5m^2 - p^2$

24. $4a^2 - b^4$

25. $x^2y^2 - 9$

26. $p^6 - q^8$

Factor each polynomial over the rational numbers. *(Section 9–3)*

27. $x^2 - \dfrac{1}{4}$

28. $4t^2 - \dfrac{1}{9}$

29. $\dfrac{4}{25}p^2 - 1$

30. $\dfrac{n^2}{16} - \dfrac{m^2}{4}$

Puzzle

Here are some brain teasers for you to solve.

1. Two riders race on a circular track. Rider A can circle the track in 6 minutes, and Rider B in 4 minutes. From the beginning of the race, how many minutes will it be before Rider B overtakes Rider A?

2. If a hen and a half lays an egg and a half in a day and a half, how many eggs will six hens lay in six days?

3. It takes a clock 2 seconds to strike 3 o'clock. How long will it take to strike 12 o'clock?

REVIEW CAPSULE FOR SECTION 9–4

Square each binomial. *(Pages 304–305)*

1. $(a - 3)^2$

2. $(x + 4)^2$

3. $(2x - 5)^2$

4. $(9 + b)^2$

5. $(2a + 5t)^2$

6. $(3p^2 - 2)^2$

7. $(0.1 + z)^2$

8. $(\frac{1}{2} - bc)^2$

Consumer Applications: Nutrition

The average man or woman who is eating a balanced diet requires 16 or 19 calories per pound of body weight, per day, respectively, to maintain current body weight.

The following function is used to predict the weight of an average adult after a given number of days of dieting.

$$W(t) = \frac{1}{a}\left[N + (aW_0 - N)\left(\frac{3500 - a}{3500}\right)^t\right]$$

where

a = calories per pound for constant weight

N = number of calories consumed daily

W_0 = initial weight

t = time in days

$W(t)$ = weight in t days.

EXAMPLE Harry's doctor recommended that he go on a 2000-calorie diet. He weighs 200 pounds at present. Find his weight after 50 days.

A balanced diet consists of food from the four basic food groups: protein products (upper left), carbohydrates (upper right), dairy products (lower left), and fruits and vegetables (lower right).

Solution: $a = 16$; $N = 2000$; $W_0 = 200$; $t = 50$

$$W(50) = \frac{1}{16}\left[2000 + (16 \cdot 200 - 2000)\left(\frac{3500 - 16}{3500}\right)^{50}\right]$$

$$= \frac{1}{16}\left[2000 + 1200\left(\frac{3484}{3500}\right)^{50}\right] \longleftarrow \text{Use a calculator.}$$

$$= 184.64395$$

After 50 days, Harry will weigh about **185 pounds.**

EXERCISES

In Exercises 1–4, find the weight after the given number of days.

1. Janine's doctor told her to go on an 1800–calorie diet for 60 days. She now weighs 145 pounds.

2. Samuel's doctor told him to go on a 2100–calorie diet for 90 days. He now weighs 240 pounds.

3. Frank's doctor advised him to go on a 2000–calorie diet for 45 days. He now weighs 190 pounds.

4. Louise's doctor advised her to go on a 1600–calorie diet for 30 days. She now weighs 135 pounds.

9-4 Factoring a Perfect Square Trinomial

A **perfect square trinomial** is the square of a binomial. That is, since

$$(x + 7)(x + 7) = (x + 7)^2 = x^2 + 14x + 49$$

and $\qquad (x - 7)(x - 7) = (x - 7)^2 = x^2 - 14x + 49,$

both $x^2 + 14x + 49$ and $x^2 - 14x + 49$ are perfect square trinomials. To determine whether a trinomial is a perfect square, follow this procedure.

Procedure

> To determine whether a trinomial is a perfect square, check these two conditions:
>
> 1. The first and last terms must be squares of monomials.
> 2. The middle term must be twice the product of the monomials.

EXAMPLE 1 Determine whether each of the following is a perfect square trinomial.

    a. $x^2 - 14x + 49$ **b.** $4p^2 + 10pq + 9q^2$

Solutions:

a. $x^2 - 14x + 49$ ⟵ **Check Condition 1.** ⟶ **b.** $4p^2 + 10pq + 9q^2$

    $x^2 = (x)^2; 49 = (7)^2$ ⟵ **Check Condition 2.** ⟶ $4p^2 = (2p)^2; 9q^2 = (3q)^2$

    $14x = 2(x)(7)$ $10pq \neq 2(2p)(3q)$

The trinomial in **a** is a perfect square; the trinomial in **b** is not.

To factor a perfect square trinomial, you reverse the procedure for squaring a binomial. First, you find the first and last monomial terms. The sign between these terms is the *same as the sign of the middle term* of the trinomial.

EXAMPLE 2 Factor over the integers: **a.** $4x^2 + 12x + 9$ **b.** $25y^2 - 20y + 4$

Solutions:

a. $4x^2 = (2x)^2; 9 = (3)^2; 12x = 2(2x)(3)$ ⟵ Check for a perfect square trinomial.

    $4x^2 + 12x + 9 = (2x \quad 3)(2x \quad 3)$ ⟵ Write the monomial terms.

                $= (2x + 3)(2x + 3)$ ⟵ Write the same sign as the middle term of the trinomial.

                $= (2x + 3)^2$

b. $25y^2 = (5y)^2; 4 = (2)^2; 20y = 2(5y)(2)$ ⟵ Check for a perfect square trinomial.

    $25y^2 - 20y + 4 = (5y \quad 2)(5y \quad 2)$ ⟵ Write the monomial terms.

                $= (5y - 2)(5y - 2)$ ⟵ Write the same sign as the middle term of the trinomial.

                $= (5y - 2)^2$

Memorizing these formulas will help you to factor perfect square trinomials.

Factoring Perfect Square Trinomials

$$a^2 + 2ab + b^2 = (a + b)(a + b) = (a + b)^2$$
$$a^2 - 2ab + b^2 = (a - b)(a - b) = (a - b)^2$$

CLASSROOM EXERCISES

Determine whether each of the following is a perfect square trinomial. Answer *Yes* or *No*.

1. $x^2 - 2xy + y^2$

2. $x^2 - 5x + 16$

3. $1 - 6x + 9x^2$

4. $b^2 - 20b + 20$

5. $4a^2 - 4ab + b^2$

6. $y^2 + \frac{2}{5}y + \frac{1}{25}$

Write each perfect square trinomial as the square of a binomial. One term of the binomial is written for you.

7. $a^2 + 4ab + 4b^2 = (a + \underline{\ ?\ })^2$

8. $x^2 + 2xy + y^2 = (\underline{\ ?\ } + y)^2$

9. $4x^2 - 4x + 1 = (2x - \underline{\ ?\ })^2$

10. $b^2 - 8bc + 16c^2 = (b - \underline{\ ?\ })^2$

11. $s^2 + 6st + 9t^2 = (s + \underline{\ ?\ })^2$

12. $n^2 - 12n + 36 = (\underline{\ ?\ } - 6)^2$

WRITTEN EXERCISES

A Determine whether each of the following is a perfect square trinomial. Answer *Yes* or *No*.

1. $x^2 - 4x + 4$

2. $a^2 + 2a + 1$

3. $x^2 - 8x + 8$

4. $y^2 - 30y + 225$

5. $z^2 - 16z + 64$

6. $t^2 - 2t + 1$

Write each perfect square trinomial as the square of a binomial. One term of the binomial is written for you.

7. $4x^2 + 20x + 25 = (2x + \underline{\ ?\ })^2$

8. $64x^2 - 16xy + y^2 = (\underline{\ ?\ } - y)^2$

9. $25 - 10y + y^2 = (\underline{\ ?\ } - y)^2$

10. $9a^2 - 24a + 16 = (\underline{\ ?\ } - 4)^2$

11. $1 + 8b + 16b^2 = (\underline{\ ?\ } + 4b)^2$

12. $a^2 - 6ab + 9b^2 = (\underline{\ ?\ } - 3b)^2$

Replace $\underline{\ ?\ }$ with $+$ or $-$ to make the square of the binomial equal the trinomial.

13. $x^2 - 16x + 64 = (x \underline{\ ?\ } 8)^2$

14. $p^2 - 10pq + 25q^2 = (p \underline{\ ?\ } 5q)^2$

15. $n^2 - 12n + 36 = (n \underline{\ ?\ } 6)^2$

16. $4x^2 - 12x + 9 = (2x \underline{\ ?\ } 3)^2$

Factor over the integers.

17. $x^2 + 6x + 9$

18. $x^2 - 6x + 9$

19. $n^2 + 14n + 49$

20. $4x^2 - 12xy + 9y^2$

21. $4x^2 + 12xy + 9y^2$

22. $x^2 - 10x + 25$

23. $1 + 8x + 16x^2$

24. $1 - 8x + 16x^2$

25. $a^2 + 8a + 16$

26. $4x^2 - 4x + 1$

27. $4x^2 + 4x + 1$

28. $a^2 - 16a + 64$

29. $9y^2 + 12y + 4$

30. $9y^2 - 12y + 4$

31. $b^2 - 6b + 9$

32. $4a^2 - 4a + 1$

33. $9a^2 - 12a + 4$

34. $9 + 12x + 4x^2$

35. $49a^2 - 84a + 36$

36. $4m^2 - 12m + 9$

37. $x^2 - 18x + 81$

38. $a^2 + 14a + 49$

39. $1 - 6b + 9b^2$

40. $4 - 20b + 25b^2$

B Factor over the integers.

Example: $x^2 + 2xy + y^2 - z^2 = (x + y)^2 - z^2$
$$= (x + y + z)(x + y - z)$$

41. $(a^2 + 2ab + b^2) - c^2$

42. $c^2 - (a^2 + 2ab + b^2)$

43. $(x^2 - 2xy + y^2) - 9$

44. $16 - (x^2 - 2xy + y^2)$

45. $a^2 - 9 + 2ab + b^2$

46. $x^2 - 16 - 2xy + y^2$

CALCULATOR APPLICATIONS

Finding A Sum

The formula for the sum of the first n natural numbers is $\mathbf{S = \dfrac{n^2 + n}{2}}$. If $n = 4$, $S = \dfrac{4^2 + 4}{2} = 10$, which is the sum of the first four natural numbers, $1 + 2 + 3 + 4$.

EXAMPLE Find the sum of the first 478 natural numbers.

SOLUTION It may be easier to solve this problem with the calculator by factoring the formula,
$$S = \frac{n^2 + n}{2} = \frac{n(n + 1)}{2}.$$

When $n = 478$, $\qquad S = \dfrac{478(478 + 1)}{2} = \dfrac{478(479)}{2}$

$$4\ 7\ 8 \boxed{\times} 4\ 7\ 9 \boxed{\div} 2 \boxed{=} \qquad\qquad \boxed{114481.}$$

EXERCISES

Find the sum of the first n natural numbers for the given value of n.

1. 7   **2.** 13   **3.** 21   **4.** 35   **5.** 58   **6.** 92   **7.** 501   **8.** 1001

_____ **REVIEW CAPSULE FOR SECTION 9-5** _____

Multiply. *(Pages 302–303)*

1. $(a + 1)(a + 2)$

2. $(x - 3)(x - 2)$

3. $(y + 4)(y - 3)$

4. $(2 - t)(5 + t)$

5. $(y - 5z)(y + 2z)$

6. $(d - 8g)(d + 11g)$

7. $(r - 3s)(r + 7s)$

8. $(x - 9y)(x + 2y)$

9. $(w + 2z)(w - z)$

9-5 Factoring $x^2 + bx + c$

Since $(x + 2)(x + 3) = x^2 + 5x + 6$, it should be possible to factor $x^2 + 5x + 6$ as $(x + 2)(x + 3)$. The procedure lies in identifying two integers such that their product is 6 and their sum is 5.

EXAMPLE 1 Factor over the integers: $x^2 + 5x + 6$

Solution:
   1   $x^2 + 5x + 6 = (x \quad)(x \quad \cdot)$ ⟵——— **The factors of x^2 are x and x.**

   2   Write the integral factors of 6.

       $(1, 6); \quad (-1, -6); \quad (2, 3); \quad (-2, -3)$

   3   Test the sum of the factors. Stop when you find two whose sum is 5.

$$\begin{array}{ccc} 1 & -1 & 2 \\ \dfrac{6}{7} \text{ No} & \dfrac{-6}{-7} \text{ No} & \dfrac{3}{5} \text{ Yes} \end{array}$$
⟋   Thus, $x^2 + 5x + 6 = (x + 2)(x + 3)$.

Example 1 illustrates that when the product of the two integral factors is *positive* and their sum is positive, the two factors will both be positive.

EXAMPLE 2 Factor over the integers: $t^2 - 7t + 12$

Solution:
   1   $t^2 - 7t + 12 = (t \quad)(t \quad)$ ⟵——— **The factors of t^2 are t and t.**

   2   Integral factors of 12:

       $(1, 12); \quad (-1, -12); \quad (2, 6); \quad (-2, -6); \quad (3, 4); \quad (-3, -4)$

   3   Test the sum of the factors to find two whose sum is -7.

$$-3 + (-4) = -7$$

Thus, $t^2 - 7t + 12 = (t - 3)(t - 4)$.

Example 2 illustrates that when the product of the two integral factors is *positive* and their sum is negative, the two factors will both be negative.

EXAMPLE 3 Factor over the integers: $x^2 - 5x - 14$

Solution:
   1   $x^2 - 5x - 14 = (x \quad)(x \quad)$

   2   Integral factors of -14: $(1, -14); \quad (-1, 14); \quad (2, -7); \quad (-2, 7)$

   3   Determine which two factors have a sum of -5.

$$2 + (-7) = -5$$

Thus, $x^2 - 5x - 14 = (x + 2)(x - 7)$.

Example 3 illustrates that when the product of two integral factors is negative *and* their sum is negative, one factor will be positive and one will be negative.

With practice, you will be able to apply these procedures more quickly.

EXAMPLE 4 Factor over the integers.

        a. $x^2 - 6x + 8$ **b.** $t^2 - 10t - 24$ **c.** $t^2 + 6rt - 27r^2$

Solutions: **a.** $x^2 - 6x + 8 = (x - 4)(x - 2)$ ⟵ **Since** $-4(-2) = 8$ **and** $-4 + (-2) = -6$

           b. $t^2 - 10t - 24 = (t - 12)(t + 2)$ ⟵ **Since** $-12(2) = -24$ **and** $-12 + 2 = -10$

           c. $t^2 + 6rt - 27r^2 = (t - 3r)(t + 9r)$ ⟵ **Since** $-3(9) = -27$ **and** $-3 + 9 = 6$

CLASSROOM EXERCISES

For each of the following, identify two integers such that their sum equals the first number and their product equals the second number.

1. 7; 12   **2.** -5; 6   **3.** 5; -24 **4.** -6; 5   **5.** -6; 9   **6.** -2; -15

7. -9; 18   **8.** 4; -32 **9.** -4; -32 **10.** -1; -72 **11.** 1; -72 **12.** -13; 36

WRITTEN EXERCISES

A   Factor each trinomial over the integers.

1. $x^2 + 7x + 12$ **2.** $x^2 + 6x + 8$ **3.** $y^2 + 8y + 15$

4. $m^2 + 10m + 21$ **5.** $a^2 + 3a - 4$ **6.** $x^2 + 3x - 10$

7. $y^2 + 7y - 8$ **8.** $b^2 + 2b - 8$ **9.** $x^2 - 5x + 6$

10. $x^2 - 6x + 5$ **11.** $x^2 - 13x + 36$ **12.** $x^2 - 9x + 18$

13. $x^2 - 2x - 15$ **14.** $x^2 - 4x - 32$ **15.** $x^2 - x - 72$

16. $x^2 - 5x - 14$ **17.** $x^2 + 5x - 24$ **18.** $x^2 + 6x + 5$

19. $x^2 + 4x - 32$ **20.** $x^2 + x - 72$ **21.** $x^2 - 10x + 21$

22. $x^2 - 6x + 8$ **23.** $x^2 + 14x + 48$ **24.** $x^2 - 8x + 15$

25. $x^2 + 9x + 8$ **26.** $x^2 + 10x + 16$ **27.** $x^2 + 2x - 8$

28. $y^2 + 9y + 18$ **29.** $y^2 - 17y + 66$ **30.** $x^2 + 2x - 15$

31. $y^2 - y - 156$ **32.** $x^2 + x - 56$ **33.** $y^2 + 6y - 72$

34. $3 - 4t + t^2$ **35.** $20 + 12v + v^2$ **36.** $-30 + 13w + w^2$

37. $51 - 20k + k^2$ **38.** $x^2 + 5xy + 4y^2$ **39.** $r^2 - 6rt + 8t^2$

40. $16p^2 - 8pq + q^2$ **41.** $a^2 - 14ab + 24b^2$ **42.** $y^2 - 6yz - 16z^2$

43. $x^2 - 5xy - 6y^2$ **44.** $48c^2 - 16cd + d^2$ **45.** $x^2 + 7xy - 18y^2$

46. $15r^2 + 2rs - s^2$ **47.** $a^2 + 8ab + 12b^2$ **48.** $66w^2 + 17wz + z^2$

49. $r^2 + 8rt + 15t^2$ **50.** $y^2 - 7xy + 10x^2$ **51.** $x^2 - 11xy - 60y^2$

APPLICATIONS: **Using Factoring**

52. Find the length of the rectangle.

Area is
$x^2 + 5x + 6.$

$x + 2$

?

53. Find the missing factor.

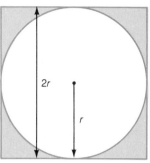

$2r$

r

Area shaded $= (2r)^2 - \pi r^2$
$= 4r^2 - \pi r^2$
$= (4 - \pi)(?)$

For Exercises 54–56, find the dimensions of each rectangle if the lengths of the sides are expressed as binomials with integral coefficients.

54.

Area $= x^2 - 169$

55.

Area $= x^2 + 13x + 12$

56.

Area $= x^2 - 4x + 4$

--- Puzzle ---

Complete the magic square below. The sum of each row, column, and diagonal is $3a^2 + 12a$. Each entry must be given in factored form.

$(a+3)(a+4)$	?	$(a+4)(a+1)$
?	?	?
?	$(a+4)(a+4)$	$(a-3)(a+4)$

_____ **REVIEW CAPSULE FOR SECTION 9–6** _____

Multiply. *(Pages 302–303)*

1. $(2x+3)(3x+4)$
2. $(b-5)(3b+7)$
3. $(y-2)(5y+8)$
4. $(5a+7b)(5a+3b)$
5. $(3a+b)(2a-3b)$
6. $(7c-2d)(c+5d)$
7. $(5y-4)(3y-1)$
8. $(4p+3)(11p-2)$
9. $(3x-y)(4x-3y)$

9-6 Factoring $ax^2 + bx + c$

In the previous lesson, you factored trinomials such as $x^2 + 5x + 6$. The x^2-term of all these trinomials had a coefficient of 1. You can also factor some trinomials in which the x^2-term has a coefficient that is not 1.

EXAMPLE 1 Factor over the integers: $2x^2 - 5x - 3$

Solution:
$\boxed{1}$ $2x^2 - 5x - 3 = (2x\quad)(x\quad)$ ⟵ **Write the factors of $2x^2$. The only possibilities are 2x and x.**

$\boxed{2}$ Integral factors of -3: $(-1, 3)$; $(1, -3)$

$\boxed{3}$ Write all possible binomials. Test the sum of the outer and inner products to find those with a sum of $-5x$.

Binomials	Outer Product + Inner Product
$(2x - 1)(x + 3)$	$6x - x = 5x$ **No**
$(2x + 3)(x - 1)$	$-2x + 3x = x$ **No**
$(2x - 3)(x + 1)$	$2x - 3x = -x$ **No**
$(2x + 1)(x - 3)$	$-6x + x = -5x$ **Yes** ✓ Thus, $2x^2 - 5x - 3 = (2x + 1)(x - 3)$.

In Example 2, all three terms of the trinomial have positive coefficients. Thus, its binomial factors will also have positive coefficients. This reduces the number of possible binomial factors to be tested.

EXAMPLE 2 Factor over the integers: $6x^2 + 7x + 2$

Solution:
$\boxed{1}$ $6x^2 + 7x + 2 = (6x\quad)(x\quad)$ ⟵ **Write the factors of $6x^2$.**

$(3x\quad)(2x\quad)$

$\boxed{2}$ Integral factors of 2: $(2, 1)$

Binomials	Outer Product + Inner Product
$(6x + 1)(x + 2)$	$12x + x = 13x$ **No**
$(6x + 2)(x + 1)$	$6x + 2x = 8x$ **No**
$(3x + 1)(2x + 2)$	$6x + 2x = 8x$ **No**
$(3x + 2)(2x + 1)$	$3x + 4x = 7x$ **Yes** ✓ Thus, $6x^2 + 7x + 2 = (3x + 2)(2x + 1)$.

As the Examples show, you may have to write several pairs of binomial factors before you find the pair that works. As you gain experience, you will be able to find the pair that works after only a few trials.

EXAMPLE 3 Factor over the integers: $8x^2 - 35x + 12$

Solution: $\boxed{1}$ $8x^2 - 35x + 12 = (8x\quad)(x\quad)$ ◄──────── **Write the factors of 8x².**

$\qquad\qquad\qquad = (4x\quad)(2x\quad)$

Since the middle term of the trinomial is preceded by − and the third term is preceded by +, both factors of 12 will be negative.

$\boxed{2}$ Integral factors of 12: $(-1, -12)$; $(-2, -6)$; $(-3, -4)$

$\boxed{3}$ Test the possible binomials.

Binomials	Outer Product + Inner Product
$(8x - 1)(x - 12)$	$-96x - x = -97x$ **No**
$(8x - 12)(x - 1)$	$-8x - 12x = -20x$ **No**
$(8x - 2)(x - 6)$	$-48x - 2x = -50x$ **No**
$(8x - 6)(x - 2)$	$-16x - 6x = -22x$ **No**
$(8x - 3)(x - 4)$	$-32x - 3x = -35x$ **Yes** ✔

Thus, $8x^2 - 35x + 12 = (8x - 3)(x - 4)$.

In Example 3, the correct binomial factors were found on the fifth trial. Thus, the five possibilities involving $4x$ and $2x$ did not have to be checked.

CLASSROOM EXERCISES

Match each trinomial in Column I with its corresponding factorization in Column II.

Column I

1. $2a^2 + 7ab - 15b^2$
2. $3a^2 + 10a - 8$
3. $12a^2 + 17a + 6$
4. $6a^2 - 43a + 72$
5. $4a^2 - 4ab - 15b^2$

Column II

a. $(3a - 2)(a + 4)$
b. $(2a - 9)(3a - 8)$
c. $(2a - 5b)(2a + 3b)$
d. $(2a - 3b)(a + 5b)$
e. $(3a + 2)(4a + 3)$

Factor over the integers. One factor is written for you.

6. $3a^2 + 5a + 2 = (3a + 2)(a + \underline{\ ?\ })$

7. $2x^2 - 13x + 15 = (x - \underline{\ ?\ })(2x - 3)$

8. $4y^2 - 23y - 35 = (y + 5)(4y - \underline{\ ?\ })$

9. $9b^2 + 9b - 4 = (3b - 1)(3b + \underline{\ ?\ })$

10. $8a^2 + 18a - 5 = (2a + 5)(\underline{\ ?\ } - 1)$

11. $7d^2 - 23d + 6 = (d - \underline{\ ?\ })(7d - 2)$

WRITTEN EXERCISES

A Factor over the integers. One factor is written for you.

1. $5x^2 + 9x - 18 = (5x - 6)(x + \underline{\ ?\ })$

2. $2a^2 + 13a - 7 = (2a - \underline{\ ?\ })(a + 7)$

3. $18n^2 + 21n - 4 = (6n - \underline{\ ?\ })(3n + 4)$

4. $14x^2 - 13x - 12 = (7x + 4)(\underline{\ ?\ } - 3)$

5. $40n^2 + n - 6 = (\underline{\ ?\ } - 3)(\underline{\ ?\ } + 2)$

6. $2a^2 + 7ab - 15b^2 = (2a - \underline{\ ?\ })(a + \underline{\ ?\ })$

7. $5a^2 + 2a - 7 = (5a + \underline{\ ?\ })(a - \underline{\ ?\ })$

8. $x^2 + x - 72 = (x + \underline{\ ?\ })(x - \underline{\ ?\ })$

9. $5x^2 + 9x - 2 = (5x - \underline{\ ?\ })(x + \underline{\ ?\ })$

10. $6x^2 + x - 12 = (3x - \underline{\ ?\ })(2x + \underline{\ ?\ })$

Factor over the integers.

11. $2x^2 + 6x + 4$

12. $3x^2 + 11x + 10$

13. $9y^2 + 3y - 2$

14. $15y^2 - y - 2$

15. $6y^2 - 17y + 12$

16. $21x^2 + 5x - 6$

17. $6x^2 + 5x - 4$

18. $9x^2 + 6x - 8$

19. $5x^2 - 16x + 3$

20. $8y^2 - 2y - 1$

21. $3y^2 + 4y - 7$

22. $x^2 - 4x - 32$

23. $2y^2 + 7y + 5$

24. $12y^2 + 7y + 1$

25. $3x^2 - 11x + 6$

26. $2b^2 + 13b + 15$

27. $3a^2 - 10a - 25$

28. $2n^2 + 9n - 5$

29. $2t^2 + 5t - 3$

30. $3z^2 + 13z - 10$

31. $2x^2 - 11x - 40$

32. $2n^2 - 3n - 14$

33. $5q^2 - 42q - 27$

34. $2d^2 - 7d - 4$

B

35. $8x^2 - 10xy + 3y^2$

36. $14x^2 - 57xy - 27y^2$

37. $18 - 9y - 35y^2$

38. $-21x^2 - 3x - 8$

39. $2x^2 + 7x + 6$

40. $40c^2 + 39cd - 40d^2$

41. $12x^2 - 29xy + 14y^2$

42. $56x^2 + 15x - 56$

43. $16a^2 + 56ab + 49b^2$

44. $3x^2 - 8xy - 3y^2$

45. $64a^2 + 112ab + 49b^2$

46. $18x^2 - 57x + 35$

REVIEW CAPSULE FOR SECTION 9-7

State the greatest common monomial factor for each expression.
(Pages 319–321)

1. $sr - st$

2. $3x^2 - 6x - 30$

3. $rs^2 - 2r$

4. $10x - 15x^3$

5. $18a - 27b$

6. $21a^3b^2 - 14a^2b$

7. $2x^2 + 8x + 4$

8. $t^3 - t^2 + t$

Classify each of the following as a difference of squares, *D*, a perfect square trinomial, *P*, or neither of these, *N*. *(Pages 322–324, 326–328)*

9. $a^2 + b^2$

10. $y^2 - 9$

11. $a^2 - 2a + 1$

12. $t^2 + t - 20$

13. $25 - r^2t^2$

14. $x^2 + xy + y^2$

15. $b^2 + 16b + 64$

16. $n^2 - 30n + 225$

9-7 Factoring Completely

A polynomial is **factored completely** when it is expressed as the product of prime polynomials. The following procedure will help you to factor polynomials completely.

Procedure

> To factor polynomials completely:
>
> $\boxed{1}$ Look for common monomial factors.
>
> $\boxed{2}$ Look for a difference of squares.
>
> $\boxed{3}$ Look for a perfect square trinomial.
>
> $\boxed{4}$ Look for a factorable trinomial of the form $x^2 + bx + c$ or $ax^2 + bx + c$.
>
> $\boxed{5}$ When a polynomial has four or more terms, look for a way to group the terms in pairs to find a common binomial factor. Also, look for a group of three terms to find a perfect square trinomial.
>
> $\boxed{6}$ Check each factor to be sure that it is prime. Check your work by multiplying the factors.

EXAMPLE 1 Factor completely over the integers.

   a. $2x^2 - 10x + 12$ **b.** $5k^2 + 55kn + 90n^2$

Solutions: **a.** $2x^2 - 10x + 12 = 2(x^2 - 5x + 6)$ ⟵——— **Common monomial factor: 2**

$\qquad\qquad\qquad = 2(x - 3)(x - 2)$

   b. $5k^2 + 55kn + 90n^2 = 5(k^2 + 11kn + 18n^2)$ ⟵——— **Common monomial factor: 5**

$\qquad\qquad\qquad\qquad = 5(k + 9n)(k + 2n)$

Remember to check whether the factors in your final answer are prime over the integers.

EXAMPLE 2 Factor over the integers.

   a. $4x^2 - 4x^4$ **b.** $4x^3 + x^2 - x$ **c.** $8a^2 + 16a + 8$

Solutions: **a.** $4x^2 - 4x^4 = 4x^2(1 - x^2)$ ⟵——— **The common factor is $4x^2$.**

$\qquad\qquad\quad = 4x^2(1 + x)(1 - x)$ ⟵——— $(1 - x^2) = (1 + x)(1 - x)$

   b. $4x^3 + x^2 - x = x(4x^2 + x - 1)$ ⟵——— **The common factor is x.**

   Since $4x^2 + x - 1$ is a prime polynomial over the integers,

   $4x^3 + x^2 - x = x(4x^2 + x - 1)$.

   c. $8a^2 + 16a + 8 = 8(a^2 + 2a + 1)$ ⟵——— **The common factor is 8.**

$\qquad\qquad\qquad = 8(a + 1)(a + 1)$ ⟵——— $a^2 + 2a + 1 = (a + 1)(a + 1)$

$\qquad\qquad\qquad = 8(a + 1)^2$

CLASSROOM EXERCISES

Factor completely over the integers.

1. $2x^2 + 4x + 2$
2. $3y^2 + 9y + 6$
3. $6t^2 + 30t - 36$
4. $r^3 - rz^2$
5. $ax + bx + cx$
6. $3b^2 - 12b + 12$

WRITTEN EXERCISES

Ⓐ   Factor completely over the integers.

1. $5b^2 + 20b - 60$
2. $2x^2 + 10x - 28$
3. $6x^2 - 21x - 12$
4. $4b^2 + 26b - 14$
5. $12x^2 - 10x - 12$
6. $18a^2 + 21a - 9$
7. $3x^2 - 3y^2$
8. $24a^2 - 54b^2$
9. $3b^2 - 3b$
10. $2y^3 - 4y^2 - 48y$
11. $2m^3 - 20m^2 + 18m$
12. $6z^3 - 3z^2 - 30z$
13. $2a^3 - 2a$
14. $4b^2 - 24b + 20$
15. $12m^2 + 33m - 9$
16. $3t^3 - 27t$
17. $3x^2 + 6x - 24$
18. $4x^2 - 32x + 60$
19. $2x^2 + 12x - 80$
20. $5y^2 - 45y - 110$
21. $2t^2 - 28t + 98$
22. $3x^3 - 33x^2 + 84x$
23. $x^4 - 9x^2$
24. $5x^2 + 60x - 140$
25. $2a^2 + 14a + 24$
26. $5y^2 - 45$
27. $st^2 - st - 20s$
28. $7a^2 - 14a - 105$
29. $3x^2 + 12x + 45$
30. $x^2 - 6x + 9$
31. $6t^2 - 15t^3$
32. $2 - 128t^2$
33. $ab^2 - ab - 72a$
34. $n^2 + 5n + 7$
35. $3a^2 + a - 2$
36. $2a^2 - 5a + 3$
37. $a^2 + 25$
38. $q^2 - 12q - 28$
39. $2x^2 - 14x + 24$
40. $y^4 - 6y^2 - 16$
41. $49c^2 + 70c + 25$
42. $5a^2 - 80$
43. $x^3 - x$
44. $a^4 - 16$
45. $1 - 4y^2$
46. $x^2 + 4y^2$
47. $2xy + 2yz + z^2 - y^2$
48. $2 - 2y^2$

Ⓑ

49. $x^2a + x^2b - 16a - 16b$
50. $y^2x + 2y^2 - 100x - 200$
51. $5r(r + 1)(r - 6) + 8(r - 6)$
52. $p(p - 5)(p + 1) + 9(p + 1)$
53. $x^2 - 2xy + y^2 - 3x + 3y$
54. $a^3 - 4a^2b + 2a^2 - 8b^2$

Ⓒ

55. $z^4 - 81z^2q^2 - 4z^2 + 324q^2$
56. $y^3 - y^2 - 4y + 4$
57. $(x^2 - 25)^2 - (5 - x)^2$
58. $16x^2y^2 - (x^2 + y^2 - g^2)^2$
59. $(x + y)^2 - (x - y)^2$
60. $(4x^2 - 12x + 9) - x^4$
61. $k^3 + k^2 - k - 1$
62. $p^3 - p^2 - 8p + 8$
63. $t^4 + t^2 - 2$
64. $b^4 - 10b^2 + 9$
65. $h^2 - (a^2 - 6a + 9)$
66. $p^2 - 10p + 25 - q^2$
67. $(2a + 3)^2 - (a - 1)^2$
68. $16d^8 - 8d^4 + 1$
69. $(x + y)^4 - 16(x + y)^2 + 63$
70. $(a + b)^2 - (x^2 - 2xy + y^2)$

9-8   Using Factoring to Solve Equations

Some equations can be solved by factoring. The factoring method applies the Zero Product Theorem.

Theorem 9-2

> **Zero Product Theorem**
>
> **If the product of two real numbers a and b is zero, then**
>
> $a = 0$ or $b = 0$ or   **both a and b equal 0.**

Thus, by the Zero Product Theorem, if

$(x + 9)(x - 4) = 0$, then $x + 9 = 0$ or $x - 4 = 0$.   That is,

$x = -9$ or $x = 4$.

Example 1 shows how this theorem is applied in solving equations.

EXAMPLE 1   Solve by factoring: $x^2 - 7x + 12 = 0$

Solution:

$x^2 - 7x + 12 = 0$ ⟵ **Factor $x^2 - 7x + 12$.**

$(x - 3)(x - 4) = 0$

$x - 3 = 0$ or $x - 4 = 0$ ⟵ **By the Zero Product theorem**

$x = 3$ or $x = 4$

Check:

$x^2 - 7x + 12 = 0$ ⟵ **Replace x with 3.** $x^2 - 7x + 12 = 0$ ⟵ **Replace x with 4.**

$(3)^2 - 7(3) + 12 \overset{?}{=} 0$ $(4)^2 - 7(4) + 12 \overset{?}{=} 0$

$9 - 21 + 12 \overset{?}{=} 0$ $16 - 28 + 12 \overset{?}{=} 0$

$0 \overset{?}{=} 0$ Yes ✓ $0 \overset{?}{=} 0$ Yes ✓

Solution set: {3, 4}

When an equation is not in the form $ax^2 + bx + c = 0$, rewrite it in that form before using the factoring method.

EXAMPLE 2   Solve by factoring: $2x^2 = -4x$

Solution:

$2x^2 = -4x$ ⟵ **Add 4x to each side.**

$2x^2 + 4x = 0$ ⟵ **Factor $2x^2 + 4x$.**

$2x(x + 4) = 0$

$2x = 0$ or $x + 4 = 0$ ⟵ **By the Zero Product Theorem**

$x = 0$ or $x = -4$ The check is left for you.

Solution set: {-4, 0}

CLASSROOM EXERCISES

Solve for the variable.

1. $b(b-1)=0$ **2.** $z(z+6)=0$ **3.** $(q-3)(q-7)=0$

Solve by factoring.

4. $x^2-4=0$ **5.** $t^2+2t-3=0$ **6.** $z^2-2z-24=0$

7. $4x^2=36$ **8.** $y^2=8y$ **9.** $2y^2=9y-9$

WRITTEN EXERCISES

Ⓐ Solve by factoring.

1. $x^2-5x-6=0$ **2.** $x^2-5x+6=0$ **3.** $x^2-3x-10=0$ **4.** $x^2=100$

5. $n^2+n=0$ **6.** $y^2+7y=0$ **7.** $y^2-8y-9=0$ **8.** $a^2-36=0$

9. $c^2-49=0$ **10.** $3x^2=75$ **11.** $y^2=4y+12$ **12.** $y^2=-7y-10$

13. $5a^2+3a-2=0$ **14.** $3a^2-10a-8=0$ **15.** $6a^2+a-2=0$

16. $9x^2-36x=0$ **17.** $n^2=7n$ **18.** $y^2=8y$

19. $3n^2+7n=0$ **20.** $15a^2=13a+20$ **21.** $4a^2-9a=0$

22. $3x^2-2=x^2+6$ **23.** $24a^2+26a-63=0$ **24.** $5x^2-2x=3$

25. $0=9w^2+6w-27w^3$ **26.** $23p-6=-4p^2$ **27.** $4y^2+4y=-1$

Ⓑ

28. $p^3-13p^2+36p=0$ **29.** $y^3-16y^2=0$ **30.** $3z^3+2z^2=z$

31. $3r^3-3r^2-3r+3=0$ **32.** $a^3+a^2=4a+4$ **33.** $w^3-2w^2=15w$

34. $(b-2)(b+3)=6$ **35.** $(b+2)(b-3)=6$ **36.** $(x-2)(x-1)=6$

37. $(z+1)(z+8)=-12$ **38.** $(t-5)(t-2)=4$ **39.** $3x^5=27x^3$

40. $(x-5)^2=16$ **41.** $(a+9)^2=25$ **42.** $(2a-4)^2=81$

Ⓒ

43. $(a-1)^2-5(a-1)+6=0$ **44.** $(t+3)^2-(t+3)-12=0$

45. $16(z-1)^2-16(z-1)=0$ **46.** $6(r+2)^2-5(r+2)=6$

47. $(2a-1)(3a+4)-3(a-1)(a+2)=18$

48. $(3r-1)(3r+1)-(2r-1)(2r+1)=45$

Puzzle

What follows next in the sequence a–f below? (HINT: Factor each numerator.)

a. $\dfrac{x^2-16x+60}{x-6}$ **b.** $\dfrac{2x^2+17x+30}{x+6}$ **c.** $\dfrac{3x^2-22x+40}{x-4}$

d. $\dfrac{4x^2+21x+20}{x+4}$ **e.** $\dfrac{25x^2-100}{5x+10}$ **f.** $\underline{\quad?\quad}$

Problem Solving and Applications

9–9 Using Factoring to Solve Problems

Some problems can be represented by equations that can be solved by factoring. However, some solutions of an equation may not satisfy the conditions of the problem. For example, the length of a rectangle cannot be a negative number. In such cases, you disregard these solutions.

EXAMPLE 1 The Calhoun Marching Band uses a rectangular formation with 8 rows and 10 columns as shown at the right. When 40 new members joined the band, an equal number of rows and columns were added to the formation. How many rows and how many columns were added?

Columns

x x x x x x x x x x
x x x x x x x x x x
x x x x x x x x x x
x x x x x x x x x x **Rows**
x x x x x x x x x x
x x x x x x x x x x
x x x x x x x x x x
x x x x x x x x x x

Solution:

$\boxed{1}$ Represent the unknowns.

Let x = the number of rows added.
Then x = the number of columns added.

$\boxed{2}$ Write an equation for the problem.

$(8 + x)(10 + x) = 120$ ◀——— $\left(\begin{array}{c}\textbf{Number of}\\\textbf{Rows}\end{array}\right)\left(\begin{array}{c}\textbf{Number of}\\\textbf{Columns}\end{array}\right) = \textbf{Total}$

$\boxed{3}$ Solve the equation.

$(8 + x)(10 + x) = 120$
$80 + 18x + x^2 = 120$
$x^2 + 18x - 40 = 0$ ◀——— **Factor.**
$(x - 2)(x + 20) = 0$
$x - 2 = 0 \quad$ or $\quad x + 20 = 0$
$x = 2 \quad$ or $\quad x = -20$ ◀——— **The number of rows cannot be negative.**

Check: Does $10(12) = 120$? Yes ✓   **Two rows** and **two columns** were added.

Remember that equations with an x^2–term must be written in the form $x^2 + bx + c = 0$ or $ax^2 + bx + c = 0$ before factoring.

EXAMPLE 2 A photograph is 14 centimeters long and 11 centimeters wide. A white border of uniform width is placed around the photo. The area of the border is 116 square centimeters. What is the width of the border?

Solution:

$\boxed{1}$ Let w = the width of the border.
Then the new length is $14 + 2w$.
The new width is $11 + 2w$.

$\boxed{2}$ $(14 + 2w)(11 + 2w) = 270$ ←— Area of + Area of = 11(14) + 116 = 270
  Photo   Border

$\boxed{3}$ $154 + 50w + 4w^2 \quad = 270$

$\quad 4w^2 + 50w - 116 \quad = 0$

$\quad 2(2w^2 + 25w - 58) \quad = 0$ ←——— Factor.

$\quad 2(2w + 29)(w - 2) \quad = 0$ ←——— $2 \neq 0$

$\quad 2w + 29 = 0 \qquad$ or $\quad w - 2 = 0$

$\qquad w = -14.5 \quad$ or $\qquad w = 2$ ←——— **The width cannot equal − 14.5.**

Check: Total area: $(11 + 4)(14 + 4) = 14(11) + 116$? Yes ✔

The width of the border is **2 centimeters.**

CLASSROOM EXERCISES

In Exercises 1–4:
a. Represent the unknowns.
b. Write the equation you would use to solve the problem.

1. The length of a hallway is four times its width. The area is 144 square meters. Find the length and the width.

2. A living room is 3 feet longer than it is wide. Its area is 180 square feet. Find its length and width.

3. Find two consecutive integers whose product is 182.

4. The sum of an integer and its square is 156. Find the integer.

WORD PROBLEMS

A   Solve each problem.

1. The sum of two numbers is 12. The sum of their squares is 74. What are the numbers?

2. The difference of two numbers is 3. The sum of their squares is 117. What are the numbers?

3. Find two consecutive integers whose product is 210.

4. Find two consecutive even integers whose product is 80.

5. Find two consecutive negative integers such that the sum of their squares is 113.

6. The square of a certain positive integer is 30 more than the integer. Find the integer.

7. Twice the square of a certain number equals 144 more than twice the number. What is the number?

8. The square of a certain number is 4 more than three times the number. What is the number?

9. A rectangular parking lot is 20 meters longer than it is wide. The area of the lot is 1056 square meters. Find the dimensions (length and width).

10. The area of a rectangular flower garden is 192 square meters. The length of the garden is 4 meters more than its width. Find the length and width.

11. Find two consecutive odd integers such that the square of the second decreased by the first is 14.

12. Find two consecutive odd integers such that the square of the first decreased by the second is 28.

13. A farmer planted 360 apple trees so that there were 9 more trees in a row than the number of rows. How many rows were there?

14. 55 band members are arranged in a formation so that there are 6 more rows than the number of persons per row. How many rows are there?

15. A fife-and-drum band has 120 members. When they are arranged in a rectangular formation, the number of players in each row is 7 less than the number of rows. How many players are there in each row?

16. A brass band uses a marching formation of 10 rows and 10 columns. When 54 new members joined the band, the new marching formation had 3 more rows than columns. How many rows were added to the old formation?

17. The length of a rectangle is 3 times its width. Increasing the width by 2 centimeters and the length by 4 centimeters doubles the area of the original rectangle. What are the dimensions of the original rectangle?

18. The length of a square lot is increased by 10 meters and the width is increased by 5 meters. The area of the resulting rectangular lot is 3 times the area of the square. What was the area of the square?

B

19. A real estate agency wishes to double the size (area) of its ad in a telephone directory by adding the same amount to the length and width of its present ad. The present ad is 4 centimeters wide and 6 centimeters long. What will be the new dimensions of the ad?

20. A billboard is 7 meters long and 5 meters high. An advertiser wishes to increase its size by adding the same amount to its length and width. The new area will be 63 square meters. How much must be added to the length and width of the billboard to do this?

21. The perimeter of a picture frame is 80 centimeters. The area is 396 square centimeters. Find the dimensions of the frame.

22. The area of a rectangular heating panel is 192 square centimeters. Its perimeter is 56 centimeters. Find the length and width of the panel.

23. A city lot is 12 meters wide and 42 meters long. How wide a strip must be cut off one end and one side to make the area of the lot 400 square meters?

24. A creek runs along one side of a rectangular lot with an area of 4800 square feet. A fence on three sides requires 200 feet of fencing. What are the length and width of the lot?

25. A courtyard is designed so that the central rectangle with an area of 1000 square feet is surrounded by a walk which is 4 feet wide. The area of the walk is 624 square feet. Find the dimensions of the central rectangle.

26. Squares 4 inches wide are cut out of a square sheet of metal at each corner. The sides are then turned up to form an open box. If the volume of the box is 1024 cubic inches, what was the original length of each side?

———— Review ————

Factor over the integers. *(Section 9-4)*

1. $x^2 + 8x + 16$ **2.** $64 - 16a + a^2$ **3.** $9x^2 + 6x + 1$

(Section 9-5)

4. $x^2 + 4x + 3$ **5.** $b^2 - 6b + 8$ **6.** $r^2 - 4r - 12$

(Section 9-6)

7. $5x^2 - 9x - 2$ **8.** $7y^2 - 8y + 1$ **9.** $6y^2 + 13y + 6$

10. $3b^2 - 5b + 2$ **11.** $2a^2 - 5a - 12$ **12.** $30t^2 + 41t - 6$

Factor completely over the integers. *(Section 9-7)*

13. $4a^2 - 4$ **14.** $3d^2 + 24d + 48$ **15.** $4n^2 - 8n + 4$

16. $x^3 - 7x^2 - 8x$ **17.** $4y^3 + 10y^2 - 6y$ **18.** $6b^4 - 10b^3 - 4b^2$

Solve by factoring. *(Section 9-8)*

19. $x^2 + 4x = 0$ **20.** $2y^2 = 14y$ **21.** $n^2 - n - 6 = 0$

22. $a^2 = 16$ **23.** $p^2 + 6p + 9 = 0$ **24.** $6r^2 + r = 12$

Solve each problem. *(Section 9-9)*

25. Six times a negative integer is 16 less than the square of the integer. Find the integer.

26. A store has 360 square meters of floor space. The length of the store is 9 meters greater than its width. Find the length and the width.

BASIC: FACTORING THE DIFFERENCE OF TWO SQUARES

The radical sign ($\sqrt{}$) does not usually appear on computer keyboards. Therefore, in BASIC the SQR function is used to obtain a square root. LET Y = SQR(X) means that Y will equal the square root of X (provided $X \geq 0$). Another BASIC function needed in the following program is the INT ("integer") function. INT(X) gives the largest integer less than or equal to X. Thus, INT(3.5) = 3; INT(2.9) = 2; INT(-1.8) = -2; INT(81) = 81.

Problem: *Write a program which factors, if possible, the difference of two squares.*

```
100 PRINT "FOR AX↑2 - B, WHAT ARE A AND B";
110 INPUT A, B
120 IF A <= 0 THEN 140
130 IF B > 0 THEN 160
140 PRINT "A AND B MUST BE POSITIVE. TRY AGAIN."
150 GOTO 110
160 LET S = INT(SQR(A) + .5)
170 IF ABS(SQR(A)-S) >= .001 THEN 200
180 LET S = INT(SQR(B) + .5)
190 IF ABS(SQR(B)-S) < .001 THEN 220
200 PRINT "CANNOT BE FACTORED"
210 GOTO 240
220 PRINT "FACTORS ARE (";SQR(A);"X +";SQR(B);")";
230 PRINT "(";SQR(A);"X -";SQR(B);")"
240 PRINT "ANY MORE BINOMIALS TO BE FACTORED (1=YES, 0=NO)";
250 INPUT Z
260 IF Z = 1 THEN 110
270 END
```

The following is the output from a sample run of the program above.

```
RUN
FOR AX↑2 - B, WHAT ARE A AND B? 16,1
FACTORS ARE ( 4 X + 1 )( 4 X - 1 )

ANY MORE BINOMIALS TO BE FACTORED (1=YES, 0=NO)? 1
? 25, 4
FACTORS ARE ( 5 X + 2 )( 5 X - 2 )

ANY MORE BINOMIALS TO BE FACTORED (1=YES, 0=NO)? 1
? 1,288
CANNOT BE FACTORED

ANY MORE BINOMIALS TO BE FACTORED (1=YES, 0=NO)? 0
READY
```

Analysis

Statements 120–150: This section of the program is known as a "bad data trap." If either A or B is not positive, the binomial is not in the right form and cannot be factored.

Statements 160–190: The key questions the program must answer are whether A and B are perfect squares. One way to decide this is to test whether $SQR(A) = INT(SQR(A))$ and $SQR(B) = INT(SQR(B))$. For example, if $A = 16$ (a perfect square), $SQR(A) = 4$ and $INT(SQR(A)) = 4$. However, if $A = 17$ (not a perfect square), $SQR(A) = 4.12311$ but $INT(SQR(A)) = 4$. The problem with this approach is that computers can only *approximate* most square roots. Thus, $SQR(225)$ might equal 14.999 instead of 15. In this case $INT(SQR(225)) = 14$ and not 15. To avoid this problem, 0.5 is added to the square root before the INT function is applied. This is the purpose of S in statements 160 and 180. Then 14.999 becomes 15.499 and $INT(SQR(225))$ does equal 15. But $SQR(225)$ would still not exactly equal $INT(SQR(225) + .5)$ since $14.999 \neq 15$. Hence a **tolerance** (allowance) of 0.001 is used. Thus, if $SQR(A)$ is within 0.001 of S, the square root is considered an integer, and the small difference is due to the inaccuracy of the computer's calculation. Notice that the square roots in the sample output are correctly rounded to the nearest integer before being printed. On most computers, however, this does not necessarily mean that the square roots exactly equalled integers inside the machine.

EXERCISES

A

1. As the last set of data in the sample output on page 343 shows, the program prints "1 X" instead of just "X". Add statements to the program to eliminate printing "1" as a coefficient.

B   Write a BASIC program for each problem.

2. The INT function can be used to decide whether one integer is a factor of another integer. For example, if $A/B = INT(A/B)$, then B is a divisor of A. Given a positive integer A, print all the factors of A. For example, for $A = 36$, print 1 2 3 4 6 9 12 18 36.

3. Given two positive integers a and b, print all common factors of a and b.

4. For binomials of the form $Ax + B$, given integers A and B, decide whether A and B have a common factor other than 1 or -1. If they do, factor out the largest common factor of A and B. For example, for 3 X + 12, print 3 (X + 4).

5. Given nonzero integers b and c, factor trinomials of the form $x^2 + bx + c$ over the integers, if possible.

6. Given integers a, b, and c, factor $ax^2 + bx + c$ over the integers, if possible.

7. Given a positive integer x, determine whether x is prime. NOTE: 1 is not prime.

Chapter Summary

IMPORTANT TERMS

Composite number (p. 316)
Factor (p. 316)
Factor completely (p. 335)
Perfect square trinomial (p. 326)

Prime-factorization form (p. 316)
Prime number (p. 316)
Prime polynomial with respect
   to the integers (p. 319)

IMPORTANT IDEAS

1. **Unique Factorization Theorem (Fundamental Theorem of Arithmetic)** The factorization of any positive integer into primes is unique, disregarding the order of the factors.

2. **Formula for Factoring the Difference of Two Squares**
$$a^2 - b^2 = (a + b)(a - b)$$

3. **Conditions Under Which a Trinomial Is a Perfect Square**

   a. The first and last terms must be squares of monomials.

   b. The middle term must be twice the product of the monomials.

4. **Formulas for Factoring Perfect Square Trinomials**
$$a^2 + 2ab + b^2 = (a + b)(a + b) = (a + b)^2$$
$$a^2 - 2ab + b^2 = (a - b)(a - b) = (a - b)^2$$

5. **Steps for Factoring Polynomials Completely**

   $\boxed{1}$ Look for common monomial factors.

   $\boxed{2}$ Look for a difference of squares.

   $\boxed{3}$ Look for a perfect square trinomial.

   $\boxed{4}$ Look for a factorable trinomial of the form $x^2 + bx + c$ or $ax^2 + bx + c$.

   $\boxed{5}$ When a polynomial has four or more terms, look for a way to group the terms in pairs to find a common binomial factor. Also, look for a group of three terms to find a perfect square trinomial.

   $\boxed{6}$ Check each factor to be sure that it is prime. Check your work by multiplying the factors.

6. **Zero Product Theorem** If the product of two real numbers a and b is zero, then $a = 0$, or $b = 0$, or both a and b equal 0.

Chapter Objectives and Review

Objective: *To write a number in prime factorization form and to write all of its whole number factors. (Section 9–1)*

Write each number in prime factorization form.

1. 27 **2.** 75 **3.** 94 **4.** 180 **5.** 360 **6.** 630

Write all the whole–number factors of each expression. Do not include 1.

7. $3^2 \cdot 5$ **8.** $2 \cdot 3 \cdot 11$ **9.** $2 \cdot 7^2$ **10.** $2 \cdot 3^2 \cdot 5$

Objective: *To factor polynomials by finding common monomial or binomial factors (Section 9–2)*

Factor over the integers. If a polynomial cannot be factored over the integers, write *Prime*.

11. $3a - 6b$

12. $2c^3 - 4c$

13. $5p^3 - 8p^3$

14. $x^2y^3 + x^3y$

15. $4n + mn - n^2$

16. $xy^3 - x^2y^4 + x^3y^3$

Objective: *To factor the difference of two squares (Section 9–3)*

Factor over the integers. If a polynomial cannot be factored over the integers, write *Prime*.

17. $9 - x^2$

18. $4a^2 - 36$

19. $-1 + n^2$

20. $4c^2 + d^2$

21. $100 - 16x^2$

22. $9x^4 - y^2$

23. $m^2n^2 - c^2$

24. $d^6 - 1$

Factor each polynomial over the rational numbers.

25. $\frac{9}{16} - y^2$

26. $9s^2 - \frac{4}{9}$

27. $25 - \frac{1}{25}r^2$

28. $\frac{x^2}{36} - \frac{4y^2}{9}$

Objective: *To factor a perfect square trinomial (Section 9–4)*

Factor over the integers.

29. $y^2 - 10y + 25$

30. $100 + 20b + b^2$

31. $16x^2 - 24x + 9$

32. $9c^2 + 24cd + 16d^2$

33. $4m^2 - 4mn + n^2$

34. $144 - 48a + 4a^2$

Objective: *To factor a polynomial of the form $x^2 + bx + c$ (Section 9–5)*

Factor over the integers.

35. $a^2 + 6a + 8$

36. $c^2 - 9c + 8$

37. $s^2 - 3s - 10$

38. $t^2 + 4t - 45$

39. $-16 + 6y + y^2$

40. $w^2 - w - 2$

41. $-36 + 5n + n^2$

42. $6a^2 - 5ab + b^2$

43. $t^2 + 2st - 15s^2$

Objective: *To factor a polynomial of the form $ax^2 + bx + c$ (Section 9–6)*

Factor over the integers.

44. $3x^2 - x - 2$

45. $5y^2 - 13y + 6$

46. $12y^2 + 16y + 5$

47. $8x^2 - 25x + 3$

48. $8c^2 - 43c - 30$

49. $16n^2 - 2n - 3$

50. $4d^2 + d - 5$

51. $-10 + t + 24t^2$

52. $-12h^2 + 11h - 2$

Objective: *To factor a polynomial completely over the integers (Section 9–7)*

Factor completely over the integers.

53. $2h^2 + 4h + 2$

54. $3b^2 - 27$

55. $4p^2 - 16p + 16$

56. $6r^2 + 18r + 12$

57. $5c^2 - 125$

58. $8r^2 - 56r - 64$

59. $y^3 + 2y^2 - 8y$

60. $6a^3 - 30a^2 + 24a$

61. $8n^4 + 6n^3 - 9n^2$

Objective: *To solve equations by factoring (Section 9–8)*

Solve by factoring.

62. $x^2 = x$

63. $3y^2 + 12y = 0$

64. $m^2 + 2m - 8 = 0$

65. $b^2 = 9$

66. $9q^2 + 4 = 12q$

67. $t^2 + 10t = 24$

68. $3d^2 + 5d - 2 = 0$

69. $y^3 = 36y$

70. $2a^3 - 2a^2 - 12a = 0$

Objective: *To solve word problems using equations that can be solved by factoring (Section 9–9)*

71. Find three consecutive positive integers such that the square of the greatest of the three is equal to the sum of the squares of the other two.

72. Find three consecutive even integers such that the square of the greatest of the three is 148 more than the product of the other two.

73. There are 396 seats in a theater. The number of seats in each row is 4 more than the number of rows. How many seats are there in each row?

74. A patio is twice as long as it is wide. Its area can be doubled by adding 3 meters to its length and 1 meter to its width. Find the patio's dimensions.

75. A marching band has 154 members. When they are arranged in a rectangular formation, the number of players in each row is 3 more than the number of rows. How many players are there in each row?

76. A rectangular lot is 6 meters wide and 10 meters long. When the length and width are increased by the same amount, the area of the lot is increased by 80 square meters. How much must be added to the length and width to do this?

——— **Chapter Test** ——————————————————

Write each number in prime-factorization form.

1. 96   **2.** 300   **3.** 13   **4.** 55   **5.** 220

Factor completely over the integers.

6. $2x^2 + 6xy$

7. $9b^2 - 1$

8. $a^2 + 12a + 36$

9. $y^2 + 11y + 24$

10. $2x^2 - 4x + 2$

11. $a^2b^3 - a^3b$

12. $4 - 4n + n^2$

13. $n^2 + n - 56$

14. $x^4 - 4$

15. $6b^2 + 4b - 2$

16. $4x^2 - 20xy + 25y^2$

17. $a^2b^2 - 16c^2$

18. $2m^2 + 20m + 50$

19. $a^3 - a^2 - 6a$

20. $m^3 - m$

Solve by factoring.

21. $x^2 + 2x - 15 = 0$

22. $2a^2 = 72$

23. $4p^2 + 8p - 12 = 0$

24. Four times the square of an integer is 6 more than twice the integer. What is the integer?

25. A rectangle is three times as long as it is wide. Its area is 48 square centimeters. Find its length and width.

Additional Practice

Skills

Write each number in prime factorization form. *(Section 9–1)*

1. 63   **2.** 44   **3.** 60   **4.** 273   **5.** 375   **6.** 612

Factor over the integers. *(Section 9–2)*

7. $15a - 12a^2$ **8.** $x^2y - x^2y^3 + 2x^3y$ **9.** $9a^2 - 18a^3$

(Section 9–3)

10. $a^2 - 1$ **11.** $16m^2 - 49n^2$ **12.** $a^2b^2 - 100$ **13.** $x^{10} - y^2$

(Section 9–4)

14. $x^2 - 18x + 81$ **15.** $4x^2 + 12x + 9$ **16.** $9a^2 - 24ab + 16b^2$

(Section 9–5)

17. $x^2 - 5x - 14$ **18.** $x^2 - 10x + 9$ **19.** $a^2 + ab - 12b^2$

(Section 9–6)

20. $3n^2 - 11n - 4$ **21.** $4x^2 + 6x - 10$ **22.** $8x^2 - 19x + 6$

Factor completely over the integers. *(Section 9–7)*

23. $5x^2 - 45$ **24.** $3x^2 - 3x - 18$ **25.** $18n^3 - 6n^2 - 4n$

Solve by factoring. *(Section 9–8)*

26. $y^2 - 9y = 0$ **27.** $n^2 - 2n - 24 = 0$ **28.** $2y^2 - y - 36 = 0$

Applications

29. Two hundred forty folding chairs are arranged in a rectangular array for an outdoor concert. What formations are possible, if there must be at least 10 rows and at least 10 chairs in each row? *(Section 9–1)*

30. Each side of a square picture is $2m$ units long. The picture is centered over a square mat with each side $3n$ units long. Express the uncovered area of the mat in terms of m and n. Factor the expression. *(Section 9–3)*

31. The area of a rectangle is $(x^2 - 5x - 36)$ square units. Express the length and width of the rectangle as binomials. *(Section 9–5)*

32. It takes 170 one-foot square tiles to cover a floor. The length of the floor is 3 feet less than twice the width. What are its dimensions? *(Section 9–9)*

33. The names of 108 donors to the library fund are to be displayed in a rectangular array. There are to be 12 fewer columns than there are names in each column. How many columns will there be? *(Section 9–9)*

34. The length of a rectangle is twice its width. Increasing the width by 2 centimeters and the length by 6 centimeters doubles the area of the original rectangle. What are the dimensions of the original rectangle? *(Section 9–9)*

CHAPTER **10** Rational Expressions

Problem Solving and Applications

10–1 Ratio and Proportion

A **ratio** is a comparison of two numbers by division. Ratios can be expressed in several ways.

Example	Ratio			
	Using a Colon	As a Fraction	As a Decimal	As a Per Cent
Batting Average: 30 hits out of 100 times at bat	30:100 (Read: "30 is to 100.")	$\dfrac{30}{100}$, or $\dfrac{3}{10}$	0.3, or 0.30	30%
Chances of rain: 3 out of 4	3:4	$\dfrac{3}{4}$	0.75	75%

A statement such as $\dfrac{40}{100} = \dfrac{2}{5}$ is a *proportion*.

Definition

> A **proportion** is a statement that two ratios are equal.

Proportions can be used to solve many kinds of problems.

EXAMPLE 1 A recipe for 60 cookies uses 3 cups of flour. How many cups of flour will be needed to make 135 cookies?

Solution: $\boxed{1}$ Let x = the number of cups needed. ◄——— **Represent the unknown.**

Known Ratio	Unknown Ratio
$\dfrac{3}{60}$ ◄——— Cups ◄——— Cookies	$\dfrac{x}{135}$ ◄——— Cups ◄——— Cookies

$\boxed{2}$ $\dfrac{3}{60} = \dfrac{x}{135}$ ◄——— **Use the table to write a proportion.**

$\boxed{3}$ $135\left(\dfrac{3}{60}\right) = 135\left(\dfrac{x}{135}\right)$ ◄——— **Solve for x.**

$\dfrac{405}{60} = x$

$6\dfrac{3}{4} = x$ Thus, **$6\dfrac{3}{4}$ cups** of flour will be needed.

Proportions are so useful in problem solving that a special property is often used to solve them.

First term ──────┐   ┌────── Third term

$$\frac{3}{60} = \frac{x}{135}$$

Second term ─────┘   └────── Fourth term

The first and fourth terms are called the **extremes**.

The second and third terms are called the **means**.

Property of Proportions	In a proportion, the product of the means equals the product of the extremes. That is, $$\text{if } \frac{a}{b} = \frac{c}{d} \ (b \neq 0,\ d \neq 0), \text{ then } ad = bc.$$ Also, $\qquad$ if $ad = bc$, then $\frac{a}{b} = \frac{c}{d} \ (b \neq 0,\ d \neq 0).$

EXAMPLE 2 A car travels 490 kilometers on 70 liters of gas. How far can it travel on a full tank of 100 liters?

Solution: $\boxed{1}$ Let x = the number of kilometers.

Known Ratio	Unknown Ratio
$\dfrac{490}{70}$ ◄──── Kilometers ◄──── Liters	$\dfrac{x}{100}$ ◄──── Kilometers ◄──── Liters

$\boxed{2} \qquad \dfrac{490}{70} \diagdown \dfrac{x}{100}$ ◄──────── **Write a proportion.**

$\boxed{3} \quad (490)(100) = 70x$ ◄──────── **Solve for x.**

$$\frac{49{,}000}{70} = x$$

$$700 = x \qquad \text{The car can travel } \textbf{700 kilometers.}$$

In Examples 1 and 2, the check is left for you.

CLASSROOM EXERCISES

1. The directions on a can of orange juice concentrate call for adding three cans of water to one can of concentrate. Write the ratio of concentrate to water as a per cent.

A fabric is made up of 15% rayon, 45% polyester and 40% wool.

2. Write the ratio of rayon to polyester as a fraction in lowest terms.
3. Write the ratio of rayon to wool as a fraction in lowest terms.
4. Write the ratio of polyester to wool as a decimal.
5. Write the ratio of polyester to rayon as a fraction in lowest terms.
6. Write the ratio of wool to rayon as a decimal.

One gallon of white paint, one quart of yellow paint, and one pint of red paint are mixed to make orange paint.

7. Write the ratio of yellow paint to white paint as a per cent.

8. Write the ratio of red paint to yellow paint as a decimal.

9. Write the ratio of red paint to white paint as a fraction.

WRITTEN EXERCISES

A   Solve each proportion.

1. $\dfrac{7}{8} = \dfrac{x}{40}$ **2.** $\dfrac{9}{2} = \dfrac{63}{x}$ **3.** $\dfrac{11}{x} = \dfrac{132}{24}$ **4.** $\dfrac{x}{13} = \dfrac{10}{65}$ **5.** $\dfrac{7}{x} = \dfrac{1}{9}$

6. $\dfrac{5}{13} = \dfrac{x}{65}$ **7.** $\dfrac{21}{5} = \dfrac{x}{2.5}$ **8.** $\dfrac{29}{7} = \dfrac{x}{1.75}$ **9.** $\dfrac{17}{2} = \dfrac{8.5}{x}$ **10.** $\dfrac{12}{3.1} = \dfrac{18}{x}$

11. $\dfrac{b+3}{5} = \dfrac{14}{20}$ **12.** $\dfrac{3}{z} = \dfrac{8}{z+5}$ **13.** $\dfrac{r+4}{2} = \dfrac{r-3}{1}$ **14.** $\dfrac{t-4}{1} = \dfrac{t+3}{2}$

15. $s = \dfrac{s+5}{-9}$ **16.** $\dfrac{44-r}{r} = 21$ **17.** $\dfrac{a-2}{3} = \dfrac{2a+7}{5}$ **18.** $\dfrac{1}{x} = \dfrac{-6}{5-x}$

WORD PROBLEMS

In Exercises 19–22:
a. Represent the unknown.
b. Write a proportion that can be used to solve the problem.

19. A train traveled 90 miles in $1\frac{1}{2}$ hours. How many miles will it travel in 6 hours going at the same rate?

20. Fifty feet of copper wire weigh 2 pounds. How much will 325 feet of the same wire weigh?

21. The distance between two cities is 1500 kilometers. Find how far apart they are on a map with a scale that reads: "1 cm represents 500 km."

22. In a mixture of concrete, the ratio of sand to cement is 1:4. How many bags of cement are needed to mix with 100 bags of sand?

Solve each problem.

23. A recipe for a two-pound cake calls for $1\frac{1}{2}$ cups of butter. How many cups of butter will be needed for a five-pound cake?

24. A nurse, checking the heartbeat of a patient, counted 19 beats in 15 seconds. What would be the patient's heartbeat for 60 seconds?

25. On a map, 1.5 centimeters represents 60 kilometers. What distance does 6 centimeters represent?

26. A car travels 110 kilometers in 3 hours. How far will it travel in 5 hours at the same rate?

27. In a certain city, 0.7 centimeters of rain fell in 3 hours. How many centimeters of rain would fall in 9 hours at the same rate?

28. A chef uses 5 pounds of meat to make 22 meat patties. How many patties of the same size can be made from $17\frac{1}{2}$ pounds of meat?

29. A pitcher allowed 10 earned runs in 15 innings. At this rate, how many runs would the pitcher allow in 9 innings? (The answer to Exercise 29 is called **earned run average,** or **ERA.**)

30. What is the ERA of a pitcher who allows 21 earned runs in 58 innings? (See Exercise 29.) Round the answer to the nearest hundredth.

31. A 747-jumbo jet has a cruising speed of 595 miles per hour. How long will it take to travel at this rate from the east to the west coast, a distance of about 3300 miles?

32. The space shuttle Enterprise has an orbiting speed of 16,540 miles per hour. How long will it take to travel at this rate from the east to the west coast? (See Exercise 31.)

33. A printing press runs 500 copies of a brochure in 8 minutes. How long will it take to run 200,000 copies at the same rate?

34. A 2-meter stick casts a shadow 1.3 meters long at the same time as a tree casts a 21–meter shadow. How tall is the tree?

35. Wallpaper to cover 55 square feet costs $16. How much will it cost to buy wallpaper to cover a wall with an area of 330 square feet?

36. A rate of 30 miles per hour is equivalent to 44 feet per second. How many feet per second are equivalent to a rate of 55 miles per hour?

B

37. Sally and Tom will do a job for $120. They agree to share the money in the ratio 3:2. How much will each receive? (HINT: Let $3y$ = Sally's share and $2y$ = Tom's share. Thus, $3y + 2y = 120$.)

38. Henry and Alice decide to divide a profit of $400 in the ratio 5:3. If Alice receives the larger amount, how much does each receive?

39. The perimeter of a rectangle is 360 meters and the ratio of the length to the width is 11:4. Find the length and width of the rectangle.

40. The measures of two angles of a triangle are in the ratio 2:3. The sum of the measures of the angles is 90°. How many degrees are there in each angle?

C   Solve each proportion.

41. $\dfrac{x-3}{x+3} = \dfrac{x+5}{x-7}$

42. $\dfrac{x+1}{x-2} = \dfrac{x+3}{x-1}$

43. $\dfrac{x}{x+4} = \dfrac{x+1}{x+6}$

44. $\dfrac{3x+1}{5x-7} = \dfrac{3x+6}{5x-3}$

45. $\dfrac{x-2}{3} = \dfrac{4}{x+2}$

46. $\dfrac{-2}{x-2} = \dfrac{x-8}{4}$

47. If $7a - 4b = 0$, find $a{:}b$.

48. If $6a - 5b = 0$, find $b{:}a$.

49. If $5p = q$, find $(p+q){:}q$.

50. If $6(r + s) = 11s$, find $r{:}s$.

_____ **REVIEW CAPSULE FOR SECTION 10–2** _____

Complete. *(Pages 103–106)*

1. 22% of 600 = __?__

2. 16.4% of 900 = __?__

3. $33\frac{1}{3}$% of 192 = __?__

4. 40% of 95 = __?__

5. $12\frac{1}{2}$% of 104 = __?__

6. 12% of 500 = __?__

Problem Solving and Applications

10-2 Investment Problems/Mixture Problems

In Chapter 6, you used a system of equations in two variables to solve investment (money) problems and mixture problems. These can also be solved by writing equations in one variable to represent the problem.

When money is invested, the rate of interest is expressed as a per cent.

The simple interest, i, on p dollars invested at r per cent per year for t years is given by this formula.

$$i = prt$$

EXAMPLE 1 Sandra has $12,000 invested, part at a yearly interest rate of 8% and part at a yearly interest rate of 13% (Condition 1). How much is invested at each rate if the total yearly interest from both investments equals $1310 (Condition 2)?

Solution: **1** Use Condition 1 to express the amount invested at each rate.

Let a = the amount invested at 8%.
Then $12,000 - a$ = the amount invested at 13%.

Organize the information in a table.

Principal	Yearly Rate	Yearly Interest $i = prt$ $(t = 1)$
a	8%	$0.08a$
$(12,000 - a)$	13%	$0.13(12,000 - a)$

2 Use the table and Condition 2 to write an equation.

$0.08a + 0.13(12,000 - a) = 1310$ ◀——— $\dfrac{\text{Interest}}{\text{at 8%}} + \dfrac{\text{Interest}}{\text{at 13%}} = \dfrac{\text{Total}}{\text{Interest}}$

3 Solve the equation.

$$0.08a + 1560 - 0.13a = 1310$$
$$-0.05a + 1560 = 1310$$
$$-0.05a = -250$$
$$a = 5000 \quad ◀——— \text{Don't forget to find (12,000 − a).}$$
$$12,000 - a = 12,000 - 5000 = 7000$$

Check: **4** **Condition 1**   Does $5000 + $7000 = $12,000?   Yes ✔

Condition 2   Does $0.08($5000) + 0.13($7000) = $1310?   Yes ✔

Thus, **$5000** was invested at 8%; **$7000** was invested at 13%.

Many mixture problems use per cent to give the amount of each ingredient. For example, the amount of salt in 25 grams of a 20% solution of salt and water is

$$20\% \text{ of } 25 = 0.20(25), \text{ or } 5 \text{ grams}.$$

EXAMPLE 2 How many grams of salt must a chemist add to 40 grams of a 15% salt solution to obtain a 20% salt solution?

Solution: $\boxed{1}$ Let $x =$ the number of grams of salt to be added.

	Number of Grams	Per Cent of Salt	Number of Grams of Salt
Original solution	40	15%	$0.15(40)$
Salt to be added	x	100%	$1.00x$
New solution	$40 + x$	20%	$0.20(40 + x)$

$\boxed{2}$ Write an equation. Refer to the table.

Amount of Salt in Original Solution	$+$	Amount of Salt Added	$=$	Amount of Salt in New Solution
$0.15(40)$	$+$	x	$=$	$0.20(40 + x)$

$\boxed{3}$ Solve the equation.

$$0.15(40) + x = 0.20(40 + x)$$
$$6 + x = 8 + 0.20x$$
$$0.80x = 2$$
$$x = 2.5$$

Check: $\boxed{4}$ Does $0.15(40) + 2.5 = 0.20(42.5)$? Yes ✔

The chemist must add **2.5 grams** of salt.

CLASSROOM EXERCISES

In Exercises 1–4, represent the total annual income from each investment.

1. $8000 invested at 12% per year

2. y invested at 13% per year

3. $(y + 8000)$ invested at $11\frac{1}{2}\%$ per year

4. $(12,000 - y)$ invested at 9% per year

5. Represent the amount of butterfat in 20 pounds of milk testing 4% butterfat.

6. Represent the amount of salt in $(15 + n)$ grams of a salt solution that is 10% salt.

7. Represent the amount of iodine in $(30 - d)$ grams of a solution of alcohol and iodine that is 60% iodine.

8. Represent the amount of alcohol in 32 grams of a solution of alcohol and water that is 20% alcohol.

WORD PROBLEMS

A   Solve each problem.

1. Tom Billings invested $8000, part at 6% per year and the rest at 9% per year. The total yearly interest was $660. How much did he invest at each rate?

2. Laurie invested an amount of money at 8% per year and twice as much at 9% per year. The total yearly interest was $260. How much did she invest at each rate?

3. How many grams of salt must be added to 600 grams of a 20% salt solution to obtain a 25% salt solution?

4. How many ounces of salt must be added to 60 ounces of a 10% salt solution to obtain a 46% salt solution?

5. An investment club plans to invest in two types of bonds which yield 10% per year and 12% per year. The club has $12,500 to invest and wishes to earn at least $1450 on the investments. How much should be invested at each rate?

6. Claude borrowed money from his parents and twice as much from a bank. The yearly rate of interest on his parents' loan was 6%; the rate of interest on the bank loan was 15%. The total interest for one year was $1080. How much did he borrow from the bank?

7. How many liters of sulfuric acid must be added to 63 liters of a 25% sulfuric acid solution (acid and water) to obtain a 60% sulfuric acid solution?

8. A pharmacist has 10 liters of a 20% peroxide solution. How much peroxide must be added to obtain a 50% peroxide solution?

9. How many quarts of antifreeze must be added to 30 quarts of a 10% antifreeze solution to obtain a 30% antifreeze solution?

10. A 100-gram solution is 4% salt and 96% water. How much water must be evaporated to obtain a solution that is 12% salt?

B

11. Mary has 30 milliliters of a 10% alcohol solution. How many milliliters of a 15% alcohol solution must be added to make a 12% alcohol solution?

12. How many grams of a 30% gold alloy must be mixed with how many grams of a 5% gold alloy to obtain 25 grams of a 12% gold alloy?

13. Jack invested a sum of money at 10% yearly interest, twice this amount at 12% yearly interest, and $500 less at 8% than at 12%. The total yearly income from these investments is $435. How much did he invest at each rate?

14. Carla James invested $30,000 in two business enterprises. In one business, she made a 15% profit; in the other, she had an 8% loss. Her net profit for the year was $1740. How much did she invest in each business?

C

15. Claire has twice as much money invested at 9% as at 12%. Her annual interest on the money at 9% is $1140 more than her annual interest on the money at 12%. How much is invested at each rate?

16. A car radiator is filled with 18 quarts of a 20% antifreeze solution. How much of this solution must be drained and replaced by pure antifreeze to obtain a 50% antifreeze solution?

10-3 Simplifying Rational Expressions

A rational expression is a ratio having polynomials as its terms. The following are rational expressions.

$$\frac{5}{9} \qquad \frac{3}{x} \qquad \frac{x^2 + y^2}{a^2} \qquad \frac{a^2 - b^2}{a + 5b}$$

Definition

> A **rational expression** is an expression of the form $\frac{P}{Q}$, where P and Q are polynomials and $Q \neq 0$.

A rational expression is in **simplest form** when the numerator and denominator of the expression have no common factors other than 1 and -1. Thus, to simplify a rational expression, first factor the numerator and denominator. Then identify any common factors.

EXAMPLE 1   Simplify: $\dfrac{x^2 + xy}{x^2 - xy}$

Solution: Factor the numerator and denominator.

$$\frac{x^2 + xy}{x^2 - xy} = \frac{x(x + y)}{x(x - y)} \qquad \longleftarrow \qquad \textbf{The common factor is x.}$$

$$= \frac{x}{x} \cdot \frac{x + y}{x - y} \qquad \longleftarrow \qquad \frac{\textbf{x}}{\textbf{x}} = \textbf{1}$$

$$= \frac{x + y}{x - y} \qquad \longleftarrow \qquad \textbf{Simplest form}$$

Recall that *division by zero is not defined*. Thus, the values of the variables in a rational expression must be restricted so that the denominator cannot equal zero. In Example 1, x cannot equal zero or y.

EXAMPLE 2   Simplify: $\dfrac{a^2 - 9}{a^2 + 5a + 6}$

Solution: $\dfrac{a^2 - 9}{a^2 + 5a + 6} = \dfrac{(a + 3)(a - 3)}{(a + 3)(a + 2)} \qquad \longleftarrow \qquad$ **The common factor is ($a + 3$).**

$$= \frac{a + 3}{a + 3} \cdot \frac{a - 3}{a + 2} \qquad \longleftarrow \qquad \frac{\overset{1}{\cancel{a + 3}}}{\underset{1}{\cancel{a + 3}}} = \textbf{1}$$

$$= \frac{a - 3}{a + 2} \qquad \longleftarrow \qquad \textbf{Simplest form}$$

NOTE: In Example 2, a cannot equal -2 or -3.

When simplifying rational expressions, watch for factors that are opposites of each other. Recall that

$$-(5y - x) = (-1)(5y - x) = x - 5y.$$

EXAMPLE 3   Simplify: $\dfrac{3x^2 - 15xy + 18y^2}{9y^2 - x^2}$

Solution: $\dfrac{3x^2 - 15xy + 18y^2}{9y^2 - x^2} = \dfrac{3(x^2 - 5xy + 6y^2)}{9y^2 - x^2}$

$= \dfrac{3(x - 3y)(x - 2y)}{(3y - x)(3y + x)}$ ⟵ **(x − 3y) and (3y − x) are opposites.**

$= \dfrac{3(x - 3y)(x - 2y)}{-(x - 3y)(x + 3y)}$ ⟵ **(3y − x) = −(x − 3y)**

$= \dfrac{\overset{1}{\cancel{x - 3y}}}{\underset{1}{\cancel{x - 3y}}} \cdot \dfrac{3(x - 2y)}{-(x + 3y)}$ ⟵ **The common factor is (x − 3y).**

$= \dfrac{3(x - 2y)}{-(x + 3y)}$, or $-\dfrac{3(x - 2y)}{(x + 3y)}$ ⟵ **Simplest form**

NOTE: In Example 3, x cannot equal $3y$ or $-3y$.

CLASSROOM EXERCISES

Simplify. No denominator equals zero.

1. $\dfrac{24}{44}$

2. $\dfrac{6ab}{6}$

3. $\dfrac{6xy}{18x^2}$

4. $\dfrac{x^2 - y^2}{(x + y)(x + y)}$

5. $\dfrac{a^2 + b^2}{a^2 + b^2}$

6. $\dfrac{5 - w}{w - 5}$

7. $\dfrac{4d - 14}{7 - 2d}$

8. $\dfrac{y^2 - y - 2}{y^2 - 4}$

WRITTEN EXERCISES

Ⓐ   Simplify. No denominator equals zero.

1. $\dfrac{3 \cdot 5}{3 \cdot 4}$

2. $\dfrac{3 \cdot 4 \cdot 5}{3 \cdot 4}$

3. $\dfrac{6xy}{6}$

4. $\dfrac{6xy}{6x}$

5. $\dfrac{12}{18}$

6. $\dfrac{9}{12}$

7. $\dfrac{a^2}{ab}$

8. $\dfrac{24a}{36b}$

9. $\dfrac{12x}{15xy}$

10. $\dfrac{25x^2}{30x}$

11. $\dfrac{18x^2y}{24xy}$

12. $\dfrac{3xy}{24y}$

13. $\dfrac{4(x + y)}{7(x + y)}$

14. $\dfrac{5(x - y)}{2(x - y)}$

15. $\dfrac{4(a + b)}{8(a + b)}$

16. $\dfrac{a(x + y)}{b(x + y)}$

17. $\dfrac{24}{15(x + y)}$

18. $\dfrac{m(x - y)^2}{e(x - y)}$

19. $\dfrac{3(x - y)^2}{x - y}$

20. $\dfrac{4(a + 2b)^2}{4(a + 2b)}$

21. $\dfrac{7(x-6y)^2}{7x}$ **22.** $\dfrac{36x}{15(x+2)}$ **23.** $\dfrac{15(a+b)}{6(2a+b)}$ **24.** $\dfrac{8(x-2y)}{18(2x-y)}$

25. $\dfrac{3x-6y}{9x+12y}$ **26.** $\dfrac{a^2b-ab^2}{a^2b^2+ab^2}$ **27.** $\dfrac{2ab+b^2}{a^2-b^2}$ **28.** $\dfrac{4x-4y}{x+y}$

29. $\dfrac{3a+3b}{3(a+b)}$ **30.** $\dfrac{x^2-y^2}{x^2-2xy+y^2}$ **31.** $\dfrac{a+b}{a^2+2ab+b^2}$ **32.** $\dfrac{x-1}{x^2-2x+1}$

33. $\dfrac{x+1}{x^2+2x+1}$ **34.** $\dfrac{5a+5}{a^2+7a+6}$ **35.** $\dfrac{a^2+a}{a}$ **36.** $\dfrac{3a^2-3}{a-1}$

37. $\dfrac{5-v}{v-5}$ **38.** $\dfrac{2(a-1)(a+7)}{(1-a)(a+7)}$ **39.** $\dfrac{b+9}{81-b^2}$ **40.** $\dfrac{c-d}{(d-c)^2}$

41. $\dfrac{(t-1)^2}{1-t^2}$ **42.** $\dfrac{(x-y)^2}{(y-x)}$ **43.** $\dfrac{k-n}{(n-k)^3}$ **44.** $\dfrac{(5a-c)^5}{(c-5a)^5}$

45. $\dfrac{2x^3-12x^2+2x}{x^2-6x+1}$ **46.** $\dfrac{3a+3b}{a^2+2ab+b^2}$ **47.** $\dfrac{2x^2+6x+4}{4x^2-12x-16}$ **48.** $\dfrac{2x^3-2x^2-4x}{3x^3+3x^2+18x}$

49. $\dfrac{6x+12}{x^2-x-6}$ **50.** $\dfrac{x^2y-y}{x+1}$ **51.** $\dfrac{3a^2-3}{1-a}$ **52.** $\dfrac{a^2+1}{a+1}$

B

53. $\dfrac{R^2-r^2}{3r+3R}$ **54.** $\dfrac{6a^2+a-15}{6a^2-13a+6}$ **55.** $\dfrac{2a^2-ab-b^2}{2a^2+ab-b^2}$

56. $\dfrac{6a^2+42a+72}{18-2a^2}$ **57.** $\dfrac{3x^2-27}{24-11x+x^2}$ **58.** $\dfrac{(a+b)^2(a-b)}{a^2-b^2}$

C

59. $\dfrac{(x+y)^2+(x+y)-2}{x+y+2}$ **60.** $\dfrac{(x+y)^2-(r+t)^2}{x+y-r-t}$ **61.** $\dfrac{2+a+2a^2+a^3}{a^3-5a^2+a-5}$

Review

Solve each proportion. *(Section 10-1)*

1. $\dfrac{30}{45}=\dfrac{x}{12}$ **2.** $\dfrac{5}{x}=\dfrac{20}{48}$ **3.** $\dfrac{9}{13}=\dfrac{2.25}{y}$ **4.** $\dfrac{3}{t-4}=\dfrac{6}{10-t}$

5. Out of every 10 columns in one newspaper, 4 columns are advertisements. At this rate, how many columns of advertisements are there in a 16-page newspaper having 6 columns per page? *(Section 10-1)*

6. Bill has $6000 invested, part at a yearly interest rate of 12% and part at a yearly rate of 10%. Total yearly interest amounts to $640. How much is invested at each rate? *(Section 10-2)*

7. How many ounces of salt must be added to 50 ounces of an 8% salt solution in order to obtain a 20% salt solution? *(Section 10-2)*

Simplify. No denominator equals zero. *(Section 10-3)*

8. $\dfrac{16c}{28cd}$ **9.** $\dfrac{2a+b}{4a^2-b^2}$ **10.** $\dfrac{3x+3y}{x^2+2xy+y^2}$ **11.** $\dfrac{6x^2-13xy+6y^2}{6y^2-7xy+2x^2}$

Career Applications: Chemistry

Chemists perform experiments in a laboratory to explore the atomic and molecular nature of the world around them. Many times, in these experiments they prepare solutions of various chemicals. The table below shows the weight of one molecule, **molecular weight,** of some of these chemicals.

Chemical	Molecular Weight
Barium oxide	153.34
Glycerine	92.03
Silver nitrate	169.86
Sodium chloride	58.44
Zinc sulfide	97.44

A **mole** in chemistry is the mass of a substance that equals its molecular weight. A **one molar solution** of glycerine and water would contain 92.03 grams of glycerine in 1 liter of solution.

EXAMPLE 1 Find the number of grams of glycerine needed to make 1500 milliliters of a solution with 5% molarity.

Solution: 1 Find the number of grams of glycerine to make 1 liter (1000 milliliters) of a 5% molarity solution.

5% of 92.03 = (0.05)(92.03) or **4.6 grams**

2 Find the number of grams of glycerine for 1500 milliliters. Solve the following proportion.

$$\frac{4.6}{1000} = \frac{n}{1500} \quad \longleftarrow \quad n = \frac{(4.6)(1500)}{1000}$$

n = **6.9 grams of glycerine**

Sometimes chemists need to work with chemicals in solutions that are already mixed.

EXAMPLE 2 A chemist wants to do an experiment using 75 milligrams of a certain chemical. A solution is available that has 500 milligrams of the chemical in 10 milliliters of solution. How many milliliters of the solution will contain 75 milligrams of the chemical?

Solution: Solve the following proportion for m, the number of milliliters.

$$\frac{75}{m} = \frac{500}{10} \longleftarrow m = \frac{(75)(10)}{500}$$

$$m = 1.5$$

The chemist measures **1.5 milliliters** of solution.

EXERCISES

In Exercises 1–8 use the table on page 360 to help find, to the nearest tenth, the number of grams needed to make a solution of the given number of milliliters and molarity (%).

	Chemical	Milliliters	Molarity
1.	Barium oxide	1200	70%
2.	Silver nitrate	450	20%
3.	Glycerine	600	5%
4.	Zinc sulfide	840	3%

	Chemical	Milliliters	Molarity
5.	Sodium Chloride	1500	1.4%
6.	Glycerine	2000	3.5%
7.	Zinc sulfide	1850	0.3%
8.	Barium oxide	2320	2.8%

9. A chemist needs 30 milligrams of a certain chemical for an experiment. She has a solution of 150 milligrams of the chemical in 40 milliliters of solution. How many milliliters of the solution will contain 30 milligrams of the chemical?

10. Juan Rivera, a chemist, needs 24 milligrams of a certain chemical to complete an experiment. He has a 45-milliliter solution that contains 500 milligrams of the chemical. How much of the solution should Juan use for the experiment?

11. Rosemary Lyons needs to use 25 milligrams of a certain chemical. She has 200 milliliters of a solution that contains 150 milligrams of the chemical. How much solution should she use?

12. Jim Sachs needs 35 milligrams of a certain chemical. He has a solution of 210 milliliters that contains 50 milligrams of the chemical. How much of the solution should he use?

Simplify. *(Pages 283-284, 288-289)*

1. $(4n)(3n)$
2. $(2a^2b)(a^2b^3)$
3. $(\frac{1}{2}c^3)(-4c^7)$
4. $(-4x^2yz^3)(-3xy^2z^5)$

5. $\dfrac{x^{12}}{x^2}$
6. $\dfrac{-8ab}{-32ab^3}$
7. $\dfrac{14r^2st^3}{35rs^2t}$
8. $\dfrac{(3x^5)(2x^4)}{(6x^2)^3}$

9. $\dfrac{36a^2b^3}{8a^5b}$
10. $\dfrac{36a^2b^3}{7ab^9}$
11. $\dfrac{36x^2y^3}{6x^2y^2}$
12. $\dfrac{63x^2y^3}{28a^6b^6}$

Factor over the integers. *(Pages 319-323, 326-336)*

13. $3x^3y^2 - 2x^2y^3$
14. $100z^2 - 1$
15. $16x^3 - 4x$

16. $9t^2 + 18t + 9$
17. $z^2 - 7z - 18$
18. $4q^2 + 11q - 3$

10-4 Multiplying Rational Expressions

Multiplying two rational expressions is similar to multiplying two rational numbers. To multiply rational expressions, you apply this theorem.

Theorem 10-1

> ### Product of Rational Expressions
>
> If $\dfrac{P}{Q}$ and $\dfrac{R}{S}$ are rational expressions, then
>
> $$\frac{P}{Q} \cdot \frac{R}{S} = \frac{P \cdot R}{Q \cdot S}.$$

EXAMPLE 1 Multiply: $\dfrac{3a^2b}{2ab^2} \cdot \dfrac{4abx}{9a^2by}$. Express the product in simplest form.

Solution:

$$\frac{3a^2b}{2ab^2} \cdot \frac{4abx}{9a^2by} = \frac{(3a^2b)(4abx)}{(2ab^2)(9a^2by)} \quad \longleftarrow \quad \textbf{By Theorem 10-1}$$

$$= \frac{12a^3b^2x}{18a^3b^3y} \quad \longleftarrow \quad \textbf{Simplify the product.}$$

$$= \frac{\overset{2}{\cancel{12}}\overset{1}{\cancel{a^3}}\overset{1}{\cancel{b^2}}x}{\underset{3}{\cancel{18}}\underset{1}{\cancel{a^3}}\underset{b}{\cancel{b^3}}y} \quad \longleftarrow \quad \frac{2 \cdot 1 \cdot 1 \cdot x}{3 \cdot 1 \cdot b \cdot y} = \frac{2x}{3by}$$

$$= \frac{2x}{3by} \quad \longleftarrow \quad \textbf{Simplest form}$$

When multiplying rational expressions whose numerators and denominators are not monomials, it is usually easier to simplify first.

Example 2 shows how to do this.

EXAMPLE 2   Multiply: $\dfrac{3a + 3b}{a - b} \cdot \dfrac{a + 2b}{a^2 + 2ab + b^2}$. Express the product in simplest form.

Solution: Factor any polynomials that are not prime over the integers.

$$\frac{3a + 3b}{a - b} \cdot \frac{a + 2b}{a^2 + 2ab + b^2} = \frac{3(a + b)}{a - b} \cdot \frac{(a + 2b)}{(a + b)(a + b)}$$

$$= \frac{3(\overset{1}{\cancel{a + b}})}{a - b} \cdot \frac{a + 2b}{(\underset{1}{\cancel{a + b}})(a + b)} \quad \longleftarrow \quad \textbf{Simplify.}$$

$$= \frac{3(a + 2b)}{(a - b)(a + b)} \quad \longleftarrow \quad \textbf{Multiply.}$$

$$= \frac{3a + 6b}{a^2 - b^2}$$

Unless otherwise indicated, assume throughout the remainder of this text that no denominator equals zero.

CLASSROOM EXERCISES

Multiply. Express each product in simplest form.

1. $\dfrac{a^2}{b^2 c} \cdot \dfrac{ab^2}{a}$

2. $\dfrac{5ab}{3x} \cdot \dfrac{12x^2}{10a^2 b}$

3. $\dfrac{a + b}{a} \cdot \dfrac{a^2}{b}$

4. $\dfrac{m^2 - n^2}{m + n} \cdot \dfrac{m + n}{m - n}$

5. $\dfrac{x^2 - xy}{x - y} \cdot \dfrac{1}{x}$

6. $\dfrac{x - 2}{x^2 - 5x + 6} \cdot \dfrac{x^2 - 9}{x^2 - 3x}$

WRITTEN EXERCISES

A   Multiply. Express each product in simplest form.

1. $\dfrac{x}{y} \cdot \dfrac{my}{nx}$

2. $\dfrac{3}{x} \cdot \dfrac{x^2}{3}$

3. $\dfrac{3x}{d} \cdot \dfrac{c}{3x}$

4. $\dfrac{ab^2}{2} \cdot \dfrac{c}{abd}$

5. $\dfrac{ab}{xy} \cdot \dfrac{x}{a^3 b^2}$

6. $\dfrac{xy^2}{m^3 n} \cdot \dfrac{m^2}{y^3}$

7. $\dfrac{7xy^2}{8x^2 y} \cdot \dfrac{16xz^2}{49y^2 z}$

8. $\dfrac{a}{b} \cdot \dfrac{c}{d} \cdot \dfrac{ax}{by} \cdot \dfrac{y^2}{x^2}$

9. $\dfrac{4 \cdot 6}{2 \cdot 3^2} \cdot \dfrac{27}{2^2 \cdot 3}$

10. $(x + 2) \cdot \dfrac{x + 3}{x + 1}$

11. $(2x + 5) \cdot \dfrac{2x + 3}{2x - 5}$

12. $\dfrac{(x - 5)^2}{3(x - 5)}$

13. $\dfrac{a + 1}{a + 2} \cdot \dfrac{a + 2}{a + 1}$

14. $\dfrac{a + 3}{a - 3} \cdot \dfrac{1}{a + 3}$

15. $(n + 3) \cdot \dfrac{n + 3}{n + 5}$

16. $(2x - 5) \cdot \dfrac{x + 7}{2x - 5}$

17. $x^2 y \cdot \dfrac{8}{2x + 2xy}$

18. $\dfrac{3a - 3b}{10ab} \cdot \dfrac{50a^2 b^2}{a^2 - b^2}$

19. $n(a + b) \cdot \dfrac{1}{m(a + b)}$

20. $\dfrac{a^2 - 4b^2}{a^2 - b^2} \cdot \dfrac{3a^2 b^2}{a + b}$

21. $\dfrac{a^2 + 5a}{a^2 - 16} \cdot \dfrac{a^2 - 4a}{a^2 - 25}$

Multiply. Express each product in simplest form.

22. $\dfrac{3x - 48y^2}{2x^2 - 8y^2} \cdot \dfrac{3x + 6y}{3x + 12y}$

23. $\dfrac{x^2 + 8x + 16}{x^2 - 9} \cdot \dfrac{x - 3}{x + 4}$

24. $\dfrac{a^2 - 3a - 10}{(a - 2)^2} \cdot \dfrac{a - 2}{a - 5}$

25. $\dfrac{9 - x^2}{x + 3} \cdot \dfrac{x}{3 - x}$

26. $\dfrac{24x^2}{3(x^2 - 4x + 4)} \cdot \dfrac{3x - 6}{2x}$

27. $\dfrac{x^2 - 6x + 5}{x - 1} \cdot \dfrac{x - 1}{x - 5}$

28. $\dfrac{c^2 - 6c}{c - 6} \cdot \dfrac{c + 3}{c}$

29. $\dfrac{x^2 - 24 - 2x}{x^2 - 30 - x} \cdot \dfrac{x + 5}{x^2 - 16}$

30. $\dfrac{9 - y^2}{r^3 - r} \cdot \dfrac{r - 1}{y + 3}$

B

31. $\dfrac{a^2 + 7ab + 10b^2}{a^2 + 6ab + 5b^2} \cdot \dfrac{a + b}{a^2 + 4ab + 4b^2} \cdot \dfrac{a + 2b}{1}$

32. $\dfrac{x^2 - y^2}{x^2 - 3xy + 2y^2} \cdot \dfrac{xy - 2y}{y^2 + xy} \cdot \dfrac{x(x - y)}{(x - y)^2}$

33. $\dfrac{2a - 3b}{a^2 + 4ab + 4b^2} \cdot \dfrac{4a^2 - 4b^2}{4a^2 - 9b^2} \cdot \dfrac{5a^2 + 10ab}{3ab - 3b^2}$

34. $\dfrac{6x - 3y}{4x^2 + 4xy + y^2} \cdot \dfrac{2x + y}{4x^2 - 4xy + y^2}$

35. $\dfrac{5m + 5n}{m^2 - n^2} \cdot \dfrac{m^2 - mn}{(m + n)^2}$

36. $\dfrac{x^2 - 3x - 18}{x^2 - x - 2} \cdot \dfrac{3x + 3}{x^2 - 2x - 15}$

37. $\dfrac{a^2 + 6a + 5}{a - 3} \cdot \dfrac{5a - 15}{a^2 + 4a - 5}$

38. $\dfrac{3a + 9}{3a^2 - 5a + 2} \cdot \dfrac{6a^2 - 7a + 2}{2a^2 + 3a - 18}$

39. $\dfrac{4x^2 - 9y^2}{6x^2 - 9xy} \cdot \dfrac{6xy}{4xy + 6y^2}$

40. $\dfrac{x^2 + 6x + 8}{x^2 + 4x + 14} \cdot \dfrac{x^2 + 5x + 6}{x^2 + 7x + 12}$

41. $\dfrac{a^2 + a - 2}{a^2 - 3a - 10} \cdot \dfrac{a^2 - 2a - 8}{a^2 - 7a + 12}$

42. $\dfrac{x^2 - 2xb + b^2}{b - 1} \cdot \dfrac{b^2 - 5b + 4}{x^2 - b^2}$

43. $\dfrac{x^2 - x - 1}{x - 1} \cdot \dfrac{x^2 - 1}{x} \cdot \dfrac{x^2 - x - 1}{x - 1}$

C

44. $\dfrac{a^2 - 5a + 6}{6a^2 - 17a + 5} \cdot \dfrac{6a^2 + 7a - 3}{2a^2 - 7a + 3} \cdot \dfrac{2a^2 - 7a + 5}{a^2 - 3a + 2}$

45. $\dfrac{4x^2 + x - 14}{6xy - 14y} \cdot \dfrac{4x^2}{x^2 - 4} \cdot \dfrac{x - 2}{4x - 7} \cdot \dfrac{3x^2 - x - 14}{2x^2 - 14}$

46. $\dfrac{(a + b)^2 - c^2}{a^2 + ab - ac} \cdot \dfrac{a}{(a + c)^2 - b^2} \cdot \dfrac{(a - b)^2 - c^2}{ab - b^2 - bc}$

47. $\dfrac{4b^2 - 16b + 15}{2b^2 + 3b + 1} \cdot \dfrac{b^2 - 6b - 7}{2b^2 - 17b + 21} \cdot \dfrac{4b^2 - 1}{4b^2 - 20b + 25}$

REVIEW CAPSULE FOR SECTION 10–5

Factor completely over the integers. *(Pages 322–323, 326–336)*

1. $9y^2 - 4$

2. $m^3 - 7m^2 - 18m$

3. $6z^2 + z - 40$

4. $h^4 - 18h^2 + 81$

5. $2z^4 - 162$

6. $2a^2 - 8b^2 + 16b - 8$

7. $x^2y - x^2z + 2x^2$

8. $5x^2 - 2xy - 3y^2$

9. $3x^2y + 6xy + 3y$

10. $4x^2 + 28x + 49$

11. $2ax + 4ay + 2a$

12. $2ax^4 + 2ax^2 - 4a$

10–5 Division of Rational Expressions

To divide by a real number, you multiply by the reciprocal of the divisor.

$$\frac{2}{3} \div \frac{1}{4} = \frac{2}{3} \cdot \frac{4}{1} = \frac{8}{3}, \text{ or } 2\frac{2}{3}.$$

The procedure for dividing by a rational expression is similar. It applies the following theorem.

Theorem 10–2

> **Division of Rational Expressions**
>
> To divide a rational expression $\frac{P}{Q}$ by a rational expression $\frac{R}{S}$, multiply $\frac{P}{Q}$ by the multiplicative inverse, or reciprocal, of $\frac{R}{S}$. That is, for $R \neq 0$,
>
> $$\frac{P}{Q} \div \frac{R}{S} = \frac{P}{Q} \cdot \frac{S}{R}.$$

EXAMPLE 1   Divide: $\dfrac{5y}{9xz^3} \div \dfrac{15y^3}{18x^2z^3}$. Express the answer in simplest form.

Solution: Multiply by the reciprocal of the divisor.

$$\frac{5y}{9xz^3} \div \frac{15y^3}{18x^2z^3} = \frac{5y}{9xz^3} \cdot \frac{18x^2z^3}{15y^3} \qquad \longleftarrow \text{ By Theorem 10–2}$$

$$= \frac{\overset{1}{\cancel{5y}}}{\underset{1}{\cancel{9xz^3}}} \cdot \frac{\overset{2x}{\cancel{18x^2z^3}}}{\underset{3 \cdot y^2}{\cancel{15y^3}}} \qquad \longleftarrow \text{ Simplify.}$$

$$= \frac{2x}{3y^2} \qquad \longleftarrow \text{ Simplest form}$$

When dividing rational expressions having numerators and denominators that are not monomials, look for polynomials that can be factored.

EXAMPLE 2   Divide: $\dfrac{x^2 - 4x + 4}{3x - 6} \div (x - 2)$

Solution: $\dfrac{x^2 - 4x + 4}{3x - 6} \div (x - 2) = \dfrac{x^2 - 4x + 4}{3x - 6} \cdot \dfrac{1}{x - 2} \qquad \longleftarrow \text{ By Theorem 10–2}$

$$= \frac{\overset{1}{\cancel{(x-2)}}\,\overset{1}{\cancel{(x-2)}}}{3\underset{1}{\cancel{(x-2)}}} \cdot \frac{1}{\underset{1}{\cancel{(x-2)}}} \qquad \longleftarrow \quad \frac{1 \cdot 1 \cdot 1}{3 \cdot 1 \cdot 1} = \frac{1}{3}$$

$$= \frac{1}{3}$$

To simplify an expression such as

$$\frac{\frac{x^2}{y^2}}{\frac{x}{y}} \qquad \text{write it in the form} \qquad \frac{x^2}{y^2} \div \frac{x}{y}.$$

Then divide as shown in Examples 1 and 2.

A second method of simplifying such an expression uses the multiplicative inverse postulate. For example, to simplify the expression above, multiply both numerator and denominator by $\frac{y}{x}$, the multiplicative inverse of $\frac{x}{y}$. This will result in a denominator of 1.

$$\frac{\frac{x^2}{y^2}}{\frac{x}{y}} = \frac{\frac{x^2}{y^2} \cdot \frac{y}{x}}{\frac{x}{y} \cdot \frac{y}{x}} = \frac{\frac{x^2 \cdot y}{y^2 \cdot x}}{1} = \frac{\frac{x^2 y}{xy^2}}{1y} = \frac{x}{y}$$

CLASSROOM EXERCISES

Divide. Express the answers in simplest form.

1. $\dfrac{x^2 y}{x} \div \dfrac{x}{y^2}$

2. $\dfrac{5a^2}{7b} \div \dfrac{15a^3}{14b^2}$

3. $\dfrac{x-y}{x+y} \div \dfrac{x^2-y^2}{2}$

4. $\dfrac{b^2-3b-10}{8b^2} \div \dfrac{2b-10}{16b^2}$

5. $8kn \div \dfrac{24k}{n}$

6. $\dfrac{6r^2 t^2}{8s} \div 3rt$

7. $\dfrac{3c+12}{18} \div \dfrac{c-2}{2}$

8. $\dfrac{9}{t^2-1} \div \dfrac{3}{t+1}$

9. $\dfrac{1}{x} \div \dfrac{1}{x^2}$

10. $\dfrac{(n-1)^2}{4} \div (n-1)$

11. $\dfrac{a-x}{y} \div \dfrac{a^2-x^2}{xy}$

12. $\dfrac{9-z^2}{15} \div \dfrac{3-z}{5}$

WRITTEN EXERCISES

A Divide. Express the answers in simplest form.

1. $\dfrac{x}{2} \div \dfrac{x}{4}$

2. $\dfrac{x}{4} \div \dfrac{x}{a}$

3. $\dfrac{2}{x} \div \dfrac{4}{x}$

4. $\dfrac{4}{x} \div \dfrac{2}{x}$

5. $\dfrac{x}{y} \div \dfrac{3}{y}$

6. $\dfrac{ad}{bc} \div \dfrac{a}{b}$

7. $\dfrac{a}{b} \div \dfrac{c}{d}$

8. $\dfrac{xy}{ab} \div \dfrac{xy}{bc}$

9. $\dfrac{1}{a} \div \dfrac{a}{b}$

10. $\dfrac{a}{x} \div \dfrac{c}{x}$

11. $\dfrac{1}{f} \div \dfrac{1}{g}$

12. $\dfrac{a}{x} \div \dfrac{x}{c}$

13. $\dfrac{8}{3a} \div 16$

14. $\dfrac{9ab^2}{8xy^2} \div \dfrac{3b^2}{2xy}$

15. $\dfrac{14a^2}{10b^2} \div \dfrac{21a^2}{15b^2}$

16. $\dfrac{5x}{12yz^2} \div \dfrac{15x^3}{18y^2z^2}$

17. $\dfrac{4a-16}{3a} \div (3a-12)$

18. $\dfrac{6z-27}{4z} \div (4z-18)$

19. $\dfrac{x^2+x}{a} \div x^2$

20. $\dfrac{(a-b)(a+b)}{(x-y)(x+y)} \div \dfrac{a-b}{x+y}$

21. $\dfrac{a^2-b^2}{x^2-y^2} \div \dfrac{a+b}{x-y}$

22. $\dfrac{(2x)^3}{(4yz)^3} \div \dfrac{16x^2}{8y^2z^3}$

23. $\dfrac{3(x+y)^2}{x-y} \div 6(x+y)$

24. $\dfrac{x-y}{x+y} \div \dfrac{5x^2-5y^2}{3x-3y}$

25. $\dfrac{x^2+2x+1}{3x} \div (x+1)$

26. $\dfrac{a^3-6a^2+8a}{5a} \div \dfrac{2a-4}{10a-40}$

27. $\dfrac{5a^2-5ab}{ab+b^2} \div \dfrac{5a^2-5b^2}{b}$

28. $\dfrac{k}{k^2-6k+9} \div \dfrac{1}{k-3}$

29. $\dfrac{a^2-49}{(a+7)^2} \div \dfrac{3a-21}{2a+14}$

30. $(b^2-9) \div \dfrac{b^2+8b+15}{2b+10}$

Write each expression as a problem in division using the division symbol. (The heavier line shows the main division.) Then divide and simplify.

31. $\dfrac{\dfrac{b}{a}}{\dfrac{}{b}}$

31. $\dfrac{\dfrac{b}{a}}{b}$

32. $\dfrac{\dfrac{x}{4}}{\dfrac{3}{2}}$

33. $\dfrac{\dfrac{ab^2}{x}}{\dfrac{x^2}{ab}}$

34. $\dfrac{\dfrac{3x}{y}}{\dfrac{5y^2}{2x^3}}$

35. $\dfrac{\dfrac{a^2b^2}{r}}{\dfrac{r^2}{ab}}$

36. $\dfrac{\dfrac{x+y}{x}}{\dfrac{x^2-y^2}{x^2y}}$

37. $\dfrac{\dfrac{x^2-25}{x}}{x-5}$

38. $\dfrac{\dfrac{a+2}{2a}}{\dfrac{a-2}{a}}$

Perform the indicated operations. Express the answers in simplest form.

39. $\dfrac{x^2-y^2}{x^2} \cdot \dfrac{x+y}{x-y} \div \dfrac{x^2-y^2}{yx}$

40. $\dfrac{a^2-2ab+b^2}{ab} \cdot \dfrac{a+b}{a-b} \div \dfrac{a^2-b^2}{a^2}$

41. $\dfrac{a^3b^3}{a^3-ab^2} \div \dfrac{abc}{a-b} \cdot \dfrac{ab+bc}{ab}$

42. $\dfrac{xy-xz-x^2}{xyz} \cdot \dfrac{x^2y^2z^3}{xy-xz} \div x^3$

43. $\dfrac{2x^3}{2a+b} \div \dfrac{10a^2}{4a^2+4ab+b^2} \cdot \dfrac{12a+3b}{2a^2+ab}$

44. $\dfrac{k+n}{k^2+n^2} \cdot \dfrac{k}{k-n} \div \dfrac{(k+n)^2}{k^4-n^4}$

CALCULATOR APPLICATIONS

Evaluating Rational Expressions

To evaluate a rational expression with a calculator, rewrite the numerator and denominator so that each exponent is 1.

EXAMPLE Evaluate $\dfrac{2x^3+3x^2-4x+5}{4x^2+5x-10}$ when $x=5$.

SOLUTION Factor using x: $\dfrac{(2x^2+3x-4)x+5}{(4x+5)x-10} = \dfrac{[(2x+3)x-4]x+5}{(4x+5)x-10}$

Evaluate the denominator first. Store its value.

4 5 + 5 = × 5 − 1 0 = M+ 2 × 5 + 3 = × 5

− 4 = 5 + 5 = ÷ MR =

2.6956521

EXERCISES

Evaluate each expression below when the variable equals 6.

1. $\dfrac{3y^2+16y-35}{5y^2+33y-14}$

2. $\dfrac{6d^3-4d^2-8d+2}{3d^2+d-2}$

3. $\dfrac{2a^3+4a^2+3a+7}{a^3+2a^2-9a-18}$

4. $\dfrac{z^3-5z^2-2z+8}{z^3-z^2-4z+4}$

10-6 Least Common Denominator

To find the sum or difference of rational expressions such as

$$\frac{2}{a} + \frac{3}{a^2b} \quad \text{and} \quad \frac{3}{5x-10} - \frac{2}{x^2-4},$$

you replace the rational expressions with equivalent expressions having a *common denominator*. For example, a^3b^2 is a common denominator of a and a^2b because a^3b^2 is divisible by *both* a and a^2b. For convenience, however, the *least common denominator,* or LCD, is most often used. The **LCD** of two or more rational expressions is the smallest positive common multiple (least common multiple) of the denominators of the rational expressions.

Procedure

> **To find the LCD of rational expressions:**
> 1. Express each denominator as a product of prime factors.
> 2. Write a product using each prime factor only once.
> 3. For each factor, write the greatest exponent used in any prime factorization.
> 4. Simplify where necessary. The result is the LCD.

Example 1 applies this procedure when the denominators are natural numbers.

EXAMPLE 1 Find the LCD of two rational expressions having 8 and 36 as denominators.

Solution:
1. Write the prime factorization of each number.

    $8 = 2 \cdot 2 \cdot 2$, or 2^3 $\qquad\qquad$ $36 = 2 \cdot 2 \cdot 3 \cdot 3$, or $2^2 \cdot 3^2$

2. Write a product using each prime factor only once. $\qquad 2 \cdot 3$
3. For each factor, write the greatest exponent used in $\qquad 2^3 \cdot 3^2$
   the prime factorizations.
4. Simplify. $\qquad 2^3 \cdot 3^2 = 8 \cdot 9 = 72$ $\qquad$ **LCD: 72**

The method of Example 1 can be used when the denominators of the rational expressions contain variables.

EXAMPLE 2 Find the LCD of two rational expressions having $6x^5y$ and $9x^2y^2$ as denominators.

Solution:
1. $6x^5y = 2 \cdot 3 \cdot x^5 \cdot y \qquad 9x^2y^2 = 3^2 \cdot x^2 \cdot y^2$ ◄——— **Write each prime factor only once.**
2. $2 \cdot 3 \cdot x \cdot y$ ◄——— **Write the greatest exponent of each prime factor.**
3. $2 \cdot 3^2 \cdot x^5 \cdot y^2$
4. $18x^5y^2$ ◄——— **LCD**

When one or more of the factors is a binomial, you can write the LCD in factored form.

EXAMPLE 3 Find the LCD of rational expressions having the given denominators.

$$a^2 - 9; \qquad 3a^2 + 3a - 18; \qquad a^2 - 4a + 4$$

Solution:
$\boxed{1}$ $a^2 - 9 = (a + 3)(a - 3)$
$3a^2 + 3a - 18 = 3(a^2 + a - 6) = 3(a + 3)(a - 2)$
$a^2 - 4a + 4 = (a - 2)(a - 2)$, or $(a - 2)^2$

$\boxed{2}$ Product using each prime factor once: $\quad 3(a + 3)(a - 3)(a - 2)$
$\boxed{3}$ Product having the greatest exponent for each factor:
$$3(a + 3)(a - 3)(a - 2)^2 \longleftarrow \text{ Factored form}$$
Thus, the **LCD** is $3(a + 3)(a - 3)(a - 2)^2$.

CLASSROOM EXERCISES

In Exercises 1–11, find the LCD of the rational expressions having the given denominators.

1. $8; 12$
2. $3; 7$
3. $2; 3; 5$
4. $6xy; 9x^2$
5. $2a; 3b; 5c$
6. $14; 2s^2t; 4t^3$
7. $8a^2b; 6ab^3; 12abc$
8. $(a + b); (a - b)^2$
9. $2(x + y); 3(x + y)$
10. $a^2 - 4; (a + 2)^2$
11. $5r^2 - 15r; 2r^2 + 6r$

WRITTEN EXERCISES

A Find the LCD of rational expressions having the given denominators.

1. $6; 12$
2. $3; 4$
3. $2; 15$
4. $3; 19$
5. $5; 6$
6. $8; 12$
7. $a; b$
8. $x^2; x$
9. $ab; b^2$
10. $2a^2; 12b^2$
11. $2a; 3a$
12. $6x; 3x$
13. $6p; 4p$
14. $2x; 3y$
15. $ab^2; a^2b$
16. $9; 2; 6$
17. $8; 4; 3$
18. $5; 2; 4$
19. $5; 4; 10$
20. $12; 2; 3$
21. $16; 12; 3$
22. $x^2; y; y^2$
23. $x; y; z$
24. $x^2; xy; y^2$
25. $(x - y); (x + y)$
26. $(x^2 - y^2); (x - y)$
27. $(4a - 8b); (3a - 6b)$
28. $(9a^2 - 6); (15a^2 - 10)$
29. $(2x + 2y); (x + y)$
30. $(x^2 - 4); (x + 2)^2$
31. $(x^2 - 5x + 6); (x^2 - 4x + 3)$
32. $(6a^2 - 5a - 6); (12a^2 + 11a + 2)$
33. $(x^2 - 2x - 8); (x^2 - 6x + 8)$
34. $(a^2 + 12a + 36); (a^2 + 3a - 18)$

B

35. $(4x^2 - 9y^2); (4x + 6y)$
36. $(r^2 - 25t^2); (3r - 15t)$
37. $(2b^2 - b - 3); (3b^2 + 5b + 2)$
38. $(3z^2 - 13z + 4); (2z^2 - 5z - 12)$

10-7 Rational Expressions: Addition/Subtraction

Adding or subtracting rational expressions in algebra is similar to adding or subtracting fractions in arithmetic.

Arithmetic	Algebra
$\dfrac{1}{5}+\dfrac{3}{5}=\dfrac{1+3}{5}=\dfrac{4}{5}$	$\dfrac{2}{a}+\dfrac{4}{a}=\dfrac{2+4}{a}=\dfrac{6}{a}$

Theorem 10-3

> **Addition and Subtraction of Rational Expressions**
>
> If $\dfrac{P}{Q}$ and $\dfrac{R}{Q}$ are rational expressions, then
>
> $$\dfrac{P}{Q}+\dfrac{R}{Q}=\dfrac{P+R}{Q} \quad \text{and} \quad \dfrac{P}{Q}-\dfrac{R}{Q}=\dfrac{P-R}{Q}.$$

EXAMPLE 1 Add or subtract as indicated. Express answers in simplest form.

  a. $\dfrac{a+5}{x}+\dfrac{a-2}{x}$ **b.** $\dfrac{3a}{2}-\dfrac{a+7}{2}$

Solutions: **a.** $\dfrac{a+5}{x}+\dfrac{a-2}{x}=\dfrac{a+5+a-2}{x}$ ◄——— **By Theorem 10-3**

  $=\dfrac{2a+3}{x}$ ◄——— **Simplest form**

  b. $\dfrac{3a}{2}-\dfrac{a+7}{2}=\dfrac{3a-(a+7)}{2}$ ◄——— **By Theorem 10-3**

  $=\dfrac{3a-a-7}{2}$ ◄——— $-(a+7)=(-1)(a+7)=-a-7$

  $=\dfrac{2a-7}{2}$ ◄——— **Simplest form**

Adding or subtracting rational expressions with unlike denominators is similar to adding or subtracting fractions with unlike denominators.

Arithmetic	Algebra
$\dfrac{2}{3}+\dfrac{4}{5}$ ◄——— **LCD: 15**	$\dfrac{a}{3x}+\dfrac{c}{2y}$ ◄——— **LCD: 6xy**
$\dfrac{2}{3}+\dfrac{4}{5}=\left(\dfrac{2}{3}\cdot\dfrac{5}{5}\right)+\left(\dfrac{4}{5}\cdot\dfrac{3}{3}\right)$	$\dfrac{a}{3x}+\dfrac{c}{2y}=\left(\dfrac{a}{3x}\cdot\dfrac{2y}{2y}\right)+\left(\dfrac{c}{2y}\cdot\dfrac{3x}{3x}\right)$
$=\dfrac{10}{15}+\dfrac{12}{15}$	$=\dfrac{2ay}{6xy}+\dfrac{3cx}{6xy}$
$=\dfrac{22}{15}$, or $1\dfrac{7}{15}$	$=\dfrac{2ay+3cx}{6xy}$

> **To add or subtract rational expressions:**
> 1. Find the LCD of the denominators.
> 2. Write equivalent rational expressions having the LCD as denominators.
> 3. Add or subtract as indicated.
> 4. Write the answer in simplest form.

EXAMPLE 2   Add or subtract as indicated: $\dfrac{3}{x^2} + \dfrac{5}{2xy} - \dfrac{4}{3y^2}$

Solution: 1. Find the LCD.   LCD: $6x^2y^2$

2. Write equivalent expressions having $6x^2y^2$ as the denominator. That is,

$$\text{multiply } \frac{3}{x^2} \text{ by } \frac{6y^2}{6y^2} \text{ because } (x^2)(6y^2) = 6x^2y^2;$$

$$\text{multiply } \frac{5}{2xy} \text{ by } \frac{3xy}{3xy} \text{ because } (2xy)(3xy) = 6x^2y^2; \text{ and}$$

$$\text{multiply } \frac{4}{3y^2} \text{ by } \frac{2x^2}{2x^2} \text{ because } (3y^2)(2x^2) = 6x^2y^2.$$

$$\frac{3}{x^2} + \frac{5}{2xy} - \frac{4}{3y^2} = \left(\frac{3}{x^2} \cdot \frac{6y^2}{6y^2}\right) + \left(\frac{5}{2xy} \cdot \frac{3xy}{3xy}\right) - \left(\frac{4}{3y^2} \cdot \frac{2x^2}{2x^2}\right)$$

$$= \frac{18y^2}{6x^2y^2} + \frac{15xy}{6x^2y^2} - \frac{8x^2}{6x^2y^2}$$

3. $$= \frac{18y^2 + 15xy - 8x^2}{6x^2y^2} \longleftarrow \textbf{By Theorem 10-3}$$

NOTE: Recall that multiplying a rational expression by an expression such as $\dfrac{6y^2}{6y^2}$ $(y \neq 0)$ is equivalent to multiplying by 1.

EXAMPLE 3   Add or subtract as indicated: $\dfrac{x + 1}{x^2 - 9} + \dfrac{4}{x + 3} - \dfrac{x - 1}{x - 3}$

Solution: Factor the denominator, $x^2 - 9$. Then find the LCD.

$$\frac{x + 1}{x^2 - 9} + \frac{4}{x + 3} - \frac{x - 1}{x - 3} = \frac{x + 1}{(x + 3)(x - 3)} + \frac{4}{x + 3} - \frac{x - 1}{x - 3} \longleftarrow \textbf{LCD: } (x + 3)(x - 3)$$

$$= \frac{x + 1}{(x + 3)(x - 3)} + \left(\frac{4}{x + 3} \cdot \frac{x - 3}{x - 3}\right) - \left(\frac{x - 1}{x - 3} \cdot \frac{x + 3}{x + 3}\right)$$

$$= \frac{x + 1}{(x + 3)(x - 3)} + \frac{4(x - 3)}{(x + 3)(x - 3)} - \frac{(x - 1)(x + 3)}{(x + 3)(x - 3)}$$

$$= \frac{x + 1 + 4(x - 3) - (x - 1)(x + 3)}{(x + 3)(x - 3)} \longleftarrow \textbf{By Theorem 10-3}$$

$$= \frac{x + 1 + 4x - 12 - (x^2 + 2x - 3)}{(x + 3)(x - 3)} \longleftarrow \text{Simplify.}$$

$$= \frac{5x - 11 - x^2 - 2x + 3}{(x + 3)(x - 3)}$$

$$= \frac{-x^2 + 3x - 8}{(x + 3)(x - 3)} \longleftarrow \text{Simplest form}$$

CLASSROOM EXERCISES

Add or subtract as indicated. Write the answers in simplest form.

1. $\dfrac{2}{9} + \dfrac{5}{9}$

2. $\dfrac{9}{y} - \dfrac{7}{y}$

3. $\dfrac{1 + x}{z} - \dfrac{1 - x}{z}$

4. $\dfrac{4}{x} + \dfrac{6}{y}$

5. $\dfrac{a}{2b} - \dfrac{3c}{b^2 d}$

6. $\dfrac{5}{x} - \dfrac{2}{x + 1} + \dfrac{7}{y}$

WRITTEN EXERCISES

Add or subtract as indicated. Write the answers in simplest form.

1. $\dfrac{7}{b} + \dfrac{9}{b}$

2. $\dfrac{10}{c} - \dfrac{3}{c}$

3. $\dfrac{27}{q} + \dfrac{23}{q} - \dfrac{1}{q}$

4. $\dfrac{3a}{2} + \dfrac{(a + 9)}{2}$

5. $\dfrac{17b}{3} + \dfrac{(2a - 6)}{3}$

6. $\dfrac{(2a + 6)}{4} + \dfrac{(3a - 9)}{4}$

7. $\dfrac{17m}{6} + \dfrac{(3m + 4)}{6}$

8. $\dfrac{(2a - 3)}{2} - \dfrac{(6a + 5)}{2}$

9. $\dfrac{(2a + 9)}{4} - \dfrac{(2a - 6)}{4}$

10. $\dfrac{(3x - 2y)}{6} - \dfrac{(4x - 5y)}{6}$

11. $\dfrac{(2a - 7b)}{12} - \dfrac{(6a + 6b)}{12}$

12. $\dfrac{2a}{x + 5} + \dfrac{3a}{x + 5}$

13. $\dfrac{m}{x - y} + \dfrac{n}{x - y}$

14. $\dfrac{2a}{x - 4} - \dfrac{5a}{x - 4}$

15. $\dfrac{7m}{2y + 5} - \dfrac{6m}{2y + 5}$

16. $\dfrac{q}{r - 7} - \dfrac{s}{r - 7}$

17. $\dfrac{5q}{r + 6} - \dfrac{7q}{r + 6}$

18. $\dfrac{x}{a - b} - \dfrac{y}{a - b}$

19. $\dfrac{x^2}{7} + \dfrac{x^2}{6}$

20. $\dfrac{2x}{3} + \dfrac{5y}{2}$

21. $\dfrac{x^2 y}{6} + \dfrac{xy^2}{5}$

22. $\dfrac{7ab}{10} - \dfrac{3a}{4}$

23. $\dfrac{2a + 3}{6} - \dfrac{5a - 7}{9}$

24. $\dfrac{3x - 5}{4} + \dfrac{5x - 3}{3}$

25. $\dfrac{4n - 1}{5} - \dfrac{n + 2}{4}$

26. $\dfrac{x^2 - y^2}{3} - \dfrac{x^2 + y^2}{8}$

27. $\dfrac{3c}{8} + \dfrac{b + c}{3}$

28. $\dfrac{1}{a} + \dfrac{1}{b}$

29. $\dfrac{2}{a} + \dfrac{3}{b}$

30. $\dfrac{1}{a} - \dfrac{1}{b}$

31. $\dfrac{4}{x} - \dfrac{5}{y}$

32. $\dfrac{a}{b} - \dfrac{c}{d}$

33. $\dfrac{3}{2c} + \dfrac{4}{6c}$

Add or subtract as indicated. Write the answers in simplest form.

34. $\dfrac{5}{4a} - \dfrac{3}{8a}$

35. $\dfrac{7a}{10p} - \dfrac{2b}{5p}$

36. $\dfrac{5r}{4c} + \dfrac{4s}{5d}$

37. $\dfrac{3}{x} + \dfrac{5}{x^2}$

38. $\dfrac{4a}{b^2} - \dfrac{3a}{b}$

39. $\dfrac{3}{x} - \dfrac{5}{x^3} + \dfrac{2}{x^2}$

40. $\dfrac{a}{x^3} + \dfrac{b}{x^2} - \dfrac{c}{x}$

41. $\dfrac{5}{ab^2} - \dfrac{7}{a^2b}$

42. $\dfrac{2}{xy} + \dfrac{3}{yz}$

43. $\dfrac{9}{mn} + \dfrac{3}{mn^2}$

44. $\dfrac{8}{x} + \dfrac{3}{xy}$

45. $\dfrac{1}{6p} - \dfrac{1}{4p} + \dfrac{1}{3p}$

46. $\dfrac{3}{b} + \dfrac{5}{2b} - \dfrac{11}{3b}$

47. $\dfrac{a+b}{b} - \dfrac{a-b}{a}$

48. $\dfrac{x+1}{2x} + \dfrac{2}{x}$

49. $\dfrac{2x-1}{x} - \dfrac{x+3}{3x}$

50. $\dfrac{1}{2a^2} - \dfrac{5}{6ab} + \dfrac{7}{12b^2}$

51. $\dfrac{x}{2b} + \dfrac{2x}{b} - \dfrac{1}{b^2}$

52. $\dfrac{x-1}{3xy} + \dfrac{x^2-x}{9x^2y^2}$

53. $\dfrac{3a+5}{a} - \dfrac{2b-3}{b}$

54. $\dfrac{3x-y}{x} + \dfrac{4x+2y}{x}$

55. $\dfrac{4x+y}{x} - \dfrac{3x-4y}{x^2}$

56. $\dfrac{2y-3}{2y} + \dfrac{y-4}{3y}$

57. $\dfrac{5a-2b}{-a^2} + \dfrac{4a+3b}{-3a^2}$

B

58. $\dfrac{5}{x+2} + \dfrac{3}{x-2}$

59. $\dfrac{5}{x+5} - \dfrac{3}{x-5}$

60. $\dfrac{2}{a+3} + \dfrac{5}{a+5}$

61. $\dfrac{2x}{x-y} - \dfrac{3y}{x+y}$

62. $\dfrac{a}{2a+2b} - \dfrac{b}{3a+3b}$

63. $\dfrac{4a}{6a-2b} + \dfrac{3b}{9a-3b}$

64. $\dfrac{2}{3t+3s} + \dfrac{3}{5t-5s}$

65. $\dfrac{3x}{2y-3} - \dfrac{2x}{3y-2}$

66. $\dfrac{x+3}{x-5} + \dfrac{x-5}{x+3}$

67. $\dfrac{a-2}{a+3} - \dfrac{a-3}{a+5}$

68. $\dfrac{x+3}{x^2-4} + \dfrac{x-5}{x+2}$

69. $\dfrac{3a+2}{3a+6} - \dfrac{a-2}{a^2-4}$

70. $\dfrac{a+b}{ax+ay} - \dfrac{a+b}{bx+by}$

71. $\dfrac{a-b}{a+b} - \dfrac{a}{a^2-b^2}$

72. $\dfrac{x-y}{x+y} + \dfrac{4xy}{x^2-y^2}$

C

73. $\dfrac{4a}{2a+6} - \dfrac{a-1}{a+3}$

74. $\dfrac{x-6y}{2x^2-5xy+2y^2} - \dfrac{7}{x+2y}$

75. $\dfrac{7}{a^2+a-2} - \dfrac{5}{a^2-4a+3}$

76. $\dfrac{2x}{x^2-25} - \dfrac{4(x-5)}{x-5}$

77. $\dfrac{3}{y^2+y-6} + \dfrac{2}{y^2-4y+4}$

78. $\dfrac{5}{a^2-2ab+b^2} + \dfrac{6}{a-b}$

79. $\dfrac{5}{3x-3} + \dfrac{x}{2x+2} - \dfrac{3x^2}{x^2-1}$

80. $\dfrac{x^2}{a^2-b^2} + \dfrac{x}{(a-b)^2}$

81. $\dfrac{r-s}{(r+s)^2} - \dfrac{1}{r-s} + \dfrac{s}{r^2-s^2}$

REVIEW CAPSULE FOR SECTION 10–8

Perform the indicated operations. Simplify. *(Pages 97–99)*

1. $2(x+y) + 2x + 3y$

2. $3r + 7 - 2(r^2-9)$

3. $10(c-3) + c + 2$

4. $18(a-b) - (a-b)$

5. $8 - 6(3x-1)$

6. $(a+1)(a+1) + 1$

10-8 Mixed Expressions: Addition/Subtraction

Recall that numbers such as $4\frac{1}{2}$ and $5\frac{2}{3}$ are called **mixed numbers**. They indicate the sum of a whole number and a fraction.

$$4\frac{1}{2} = 4 + \frac{1}{2} \qquad\qquad 5\frac{2}{3} = 5 + \frac{2}{3}$$

The sum or difference of rational expressions where one rational expression has a denominator of 1 is called a **mixed expression**.

EXAMPLE 1 Add: $t + \dfrac{5}{2t}$

Solution: Write t as $\dfrac{t}{1}$. Then identify the LCD.

$$t + \frac{5}{2t} = \frac{t}{1} + \frac{5}{2t} \quad\longleftarrow\quad \textbf{LCD: } \boldsymbol{2t}$$

$$= \left(\frac{t}{1} \cdot \frac{2t}{2t}\right) + \frac{5}{2t}$$

$$= \frac{2t^2}{2t} + \frac{5}{2t}$$

$$= \frac{2t^2 + 5}{2t} \quad\longleftarrow\quad \textbf{Simplest form} \quad \bullet$$

The method of Example 1 can also be used when the operation is subtraction.

EXAMPLE 2 Subtract: $a + 1 - \dfrac{1}{a-1}$

Solution: $a + 1 - \dfrac{1}{a-1} = \dfrac{a+1}{1} - \dfrac{1}{a-1} \quad\longleftarrow\quad \textbf{LCD: } \boldsymbol{(a-1)}$

$$= \left(\frac{a+1}{1} \cdot \frac{a-1}{a-1}\right) - \frac{1}{a-1}$$

$$= \frac{(a+1)(a-1)}{1(a-1)} - \frac{1}{a-1}$$

$$= \frac{a^2 - 1}{a-1} - \frac{1}{a-1}$$

$$= \frac{a^2 - 1 - 1}{a-1} \quad\longleftarrow\quad \textbf{By Theorem 10-3}$$

$$= \frac{a^2 - 2}{a-1}$$

CLASSROOM EXERCISES

Add or subtract as indicated. Write the answers in simplest form.

1. $1 + \dfrac{1}{b}$ **2.** $1 - \dfrac{1}{b}$ **3.** $x + \dfrac{3}{x}$ **4.** $x - \dfrac{3}{x}$

5. $t + 1 + \dfrac{5}{t}$ **6.** $\dfrac{10}{d} - 3$ **7.** $\dfrac{1}{a} - (a + 1)$ **8.** $\dfrac{1}{a} - (a - 1)$

WRITTEN EXERCISES

A Add or subtract as indicated. Write the answers in simplest form.

1. $3 + \dfrac{1}{a}$ **2.** $s - \dfrac{5}{3s}$ **3.** $3 + \dfrac{a}{b}$ **4.** $1 + \dfrac{3}{x + 1}$

5. $7 - \dfrac{4}{a - b}$ **6.** $7 + \dfrac{2x}{y + z}$ **7.** $a + \dfrac{1}{a + 1}$ **8.** $a - \dfrac{1}{a - 1}$

9. $9 - \dfrac{2r}{r + s}$ **10.** $\dfrac{4}{z - 2} + 4$ **11.** $10 + \dfrac{c + 2}{c - 3}$ **12.** $18 - \dfrac{a + b}{a - b}$

13. $ax + \dfrac{b}{x}$ **14.** $2x - \dfrac{x + y}{y}$ **15.** $a - \dfrac{b}{c}$ **16.** $\dfrac{a}{x} - (a - 1)$

17. $a^2 - \dfrac{1}{a}$ **18.** $\dfrac{4a}{(a - 2)^2} + 1$ **19.** $\dfrac{3r}{r^2 - 9} - 2$ **20.** $2 + \dfrac{2x + 3y}{x + y}$

21. $(a + 1) + \dfrac{1}{a + 1}$ **22.** $6 + \dfrac{5}{4x - 2}$ **23.** $\dfrac{8}{3x - 1} - 6$ **24.** $\dfrac{5}{t - 1} - (t - 1)$

B

25. $(x - 5) - \dfrac{x}{x + 3}$ **26.** $\dfrac{2a - 1}{a + 2} + (2a - 3)$ **27.** $(2t - 1) - \dfrac{4t}{t + 6}$

28. $\dfrac{x - 7}{2x + 5} + (x - 4)$ **29.** $\dfrac{5t + 1}{t - 4} + (t + 4)$ **30.** $(a + 6) + \dfrac{3a - 4}{a + 6}$

31. $(a + 2) + \dfrac{5}{a - 2}$ **32.** $4 - \dfrac{3}{t - 1} - \dfrac{1}{t + 1}$ **33.** $\dfrac{x}{x + 2} + \dfrac{x}{x - 2} - 1$

C

34. $\dfrac{x^2}{x + y} - \dfrac{y^2}{x - y} - (x - y)$ **35.** $\dfrac{7}{x - 5} + (x^2 + 2x - 3)$

36. $(a^2 + 3a + 1) + \dfrac{4}{a - 5}$ **37.** $\dfrac{7}{x - 2} + x^2 + \dfrac{4}{x + 2} + 4$

38. $\dfrac{\dfrac{1}{2} - \dfrac{1}{3}}{\dfrac{1}{2} + \dfrac{1}{3}}$ **39.** $\dfrac{\dfrac{3}{4} + \dfrac{2}{5}}{\dfrac{3}{4} - \dfrac{2}{5}}$ **40.** $\dfrac{\dfrac{1}{a} - \dfrac{1}{2a}}{\dfrac{2}{a}}$ **41.** $\dfrac{1 - \dfrac{9}{x^2}}{x + 3}$

42. $\dfrac{\dfrac{a}{b} + 1}{\dfrac{a}{b} - 1}$ **43.** $\dfrac{\dfrac{3a}{2} + 1}{\dfrac{3a}{4} - \dfrac{1}{3a}}$ **44.** $\dfrac{\dfrac{r^2 + t^2}{rt} + 2}{\dfrac{r^2 - t^2}{2rt}}$ **45.** $\dfrac{1 + \dfrac{2r}{r^2 + 1}}{1 - \dfrac{2r + 2}{r^2 + 1}}$

Divide. *(Pages 288–289)*

1. $8a \div 2$　　　　**2.** $9f \div f$　　　　**3.** $a^3b^2 \div ab^2$　　　　**4.** $t^2y \div ty$

5. $21x^2y \div 7x$　　　**6.** $24z^4 \div 8z^2$　　　**7.** $11x^2y^3 \div 11x^2y^3$　　　**8.** $30z^5 \div 15z^4$

10-9　Division of Polynomials

Division of one polynomial by another is similar to long division in arithmetic.

Arithmetic

$$\boxed{1}\ 28\overline{)537} \qquad \begin{array}{c}1\end{array}$$

$\longleftarrow$ **Think: (28)(_?_) ≤ 53**

$$\begin{array}{r}28 \\ \hline 25\end{array}$$

$\longleftarrow$ **1 · 28**

$\longleftarrow$ **53 − 28**

$$\boxed{2}\ 28\overline{)537} \qquad \begin{array}{c}19\end{array}$$

$$\begin{array}{r}28 \\ \hline 257 \\ 252 \\ \hline 5\end{array}$$

$\longleftarrow$ **Think: (28)(_?_) ≤ 257**

$\longleftarrow$ **Remainder**

Answer: $19 + \dfrac{5}{28}$, or $19\dfrac{5}{28}$

Algebra

$$\boxed{1}\ x+3\overline{)x^2+\ x-1} \qquad \begin{array}{c}x\end{array}$$

$\longleftarrow$ **Think: (x)(_?_) = x²**

$$\begin{array}{r}x^2 + 3x \\ \hline -2x\end{array}$$

$\longleftarrow$ **x(x + 3)**

$\longleftarrow$ **x − 3x**

$$\boxed{2}\ x+3\overline{)x^2+\ x-1} \qquad \begin{array}{c}x-2\end{array}$$

$$\begin{array}{r}x^2 + 3x \\ \hline -2x-1 \\ -2x-6 \\ \hline 5\end{array}$$

$\longleftarrow$ **Think: (x)(_?_) = −2x**

$\longleftarrow$ **Remainder**

Answer: $x - 2 + \dfrac{5}{x+3}$

As these examples show, a division problem can be expressed in general form.

$$\frac{\textbf{Dividend}}{\textbf{Divisor}} = \textbf{Quotient} + \frac{\textbf{Remainder}}{\textbf{Divisor}}, \text{ or}$$

$$\textbf{Dividend} = \textbf{(Divisor)(Quotient)} + \textbf{Remainder}$$

Example 1 shows how to use this general form to check a division problem.

EXAMPLE 1　Divide $x^3 - x^2 - 2x + 10$ by $x + 2$.

Solution:

$$\boxed{1}\ x+2\overline{)x^3-\ x^2-2x+10} \qquad \begin{array}{c}x^2\end{array}$$

$\longleftarrow$ **Think: (x)(_?_) = x³**

$$\begin{array}{r}x^3 + 2x^2 \\ \hline -3x^2 - 2x + 10\end{array}$$

$\longleftarrow$ **x²(x + 2)**

$\longleftarrow$ **x³ − x² − 2x + 10 − (x³ + 2x²)**

$\longleftarrow$ **Think: x(_?_) = −3x²**

$$\boxed{2}\ x+2\overline{)x^3-\ x^2-2x+10} \qquad \begin{array}{c}x^2-3x\end{array}$$

$$\begin{array}{r}x^3 + 2x^2 \\ \hline -3x^2 - 2x + 10 \\ -3x^2 - 6x \\ \hline 4x + 10\end{array}$$

$\longleftarrow$ **(−3x)(x + 2)**

$\longleftarrow$ **(−3x² − 2x + 10) − (−3x² − 6x)**

$$
\begin{array}{r}
x^2 - 3x + 4 \quad\longleftarrow \quad \textbf{Think: } \textbf{(x)(\underline{\ ?\ }) = 4x} \\
\boxed{3}\ x + 2\overline{)\,x^3 - x^2 - 2x + 10} \\
\underline{x^3 + 2x^2} \\
-3x^2 - 2x + 10 \\
\underline{-3x^2 - 6x} \\
4x + 10 \\
\underline{4x + 8} \quad\longleftarrow\quad \textbf{4(x + 2)} \\
2 \quad\longleftarrow\quad \textbf{Remainder}
\end{array}
$$

Thus, $x^3 - x^2 - 2x + 10 \div x + 2 = x^2 - 3x + 4 + \dfrac{2}{x + 2}$.

Check: Dividend = (Divisor)(Quotient) + Remainder

$$x^3 - x^2 - 2x + 10 \overset{?}{=} (x + 2)(x^2 - 3x + 4) + 2$$
$$x^3 - x^2 - 2x + 10 \overset{?}{=} (x^3 - x^2 - 2x + 8) + 2$$
$$x^3 - x^2 - 2x + 10 \overset{?}{=} x^3 - x^2 - 2x + 10 \quad \text{Yes } \vphantom{}✔$$

When you divide polynomials, always be sure that the terms of each polynomial are arranged in descending order of the exponents of the variable. Also, when one of the terms in the dividend is "missing," insert 0 as the coefficient.

EXAMPLE 2 Divide $2a^2 + a^3 - 75$ by $a - 5$.

Solution: Write $2a^2 + a^3 - 75$ as $a^3 + 2a^2 + 0a - 75$. $\longleftarrow$ **Descending order of exponents**

$$
\begin{array}{r}
a^2 + 7a + 35 \\
a - 5\overline{)\,a^3 + 2a^2 + 0a - 75} \\
\underline{a^3 - 5a^2} \\
7a^2 + 0a \\
\underline{7a^2 - 35a} \\
35a - 75 \\
\underline{35a - 175} \\
100
\end{array}
$$

Answer: $a^2 + 7a + 35 + \dfrac{100}{a - 5}$

The check is left for you.

CLASSROOM EXERCISES

Write the missing terms to be inserted in the dividend before dividing.

1. $t + 5\overline{)\,t^2 - 25}$

2. $x - 3\overline{)\,x^2 - 12}$

3. $2a - 1\overline{)\,4a^3 - 8a^2 + 10}$

4. $x + 2\overline{)\,x^3 + 8}$

5. $2x^2 + 2x + 1\overline{)\,4x^4 + 1}$

6. $3x - 1\overline{)\,12x^3 - 9x^2 + 7}$

Write the terms of the dividend in descending order of the exponents of the variable.

7. $2r - 1\overline{)\,10r - 9r^2 + 5 + 2r^3}$

8. $4k - 1\overline{)\,7 + 8k^2 - 30k}$

9. $z - 3\overline{)\,2 - 13z + 6z^2}$

WRITTEN EXERCISES

A   Divide the first polynomial by the second.

1. $x^2 + 10x + 21; x + 3$ **2.** $y^2 + 13y + 22; y + 2$ **3.** $c^2 - 3c - 28; c - 7$

4. $p^2 - p + 32; p + 5$ **5.** $3n^2 + 14n + 8; n + 4$ **6.** $2a^2 - 11a + 14; a - 2$

7. $4y^2 + 19y + 21; y + 1$ **8.** $3c^2 - 24c + 9; c - 3$ **9.** $3x^2 - 8x - 3; x - 3$

10. $2x^2 - 11x - 40; 2x + 5$ **11.** $6a^2 - 13a + 7; 2a - 3$

12. $8x^2 - 14x - 30; 2x - 6$ **13.** $15n^2 + 16n + 10; 3n + 2$

14. $x^2 + xy - 3y^2; x - y$ **15.** $a^3 - 5a^2 + 2a + 8; a - 2$

16. $c^3 + 2c^2 - 2c + 24; c + 4$ **17.** $6x^3 + x^2 - 19x + 6; 2x - 3$

18. $8p^3 - 2p^2 - 5p - 4; 4p + 1$ **19.** $3a^3 + 8a^2b + 7ab^2; 3a + 2b$

20. $6y^3 - 10y^2 + 2y - 10; 3y + 1$ **21.** $x^2 + 25; x + 5$

22. $6a^2 - ab + b^2; 2a + b$ **23.** $a^3 - 8b^3; a - 2b$

B

24. $2x^3 - 5x + 7x^2 - 4; 2x + 1$ **25.** $8x + 13x^2 + 6x^3 + 5; 3x + 5$

26. $8x^2 + 11x + 5x^3 - 6; 5x - 2$ **27.** $x^3 + 4x - 3; x + 5$

28. $x^3 - 6x^2 + 1; x + 2$ **29.** $x^3 - 2x - 21; x - 3$

30. $x^3 - 125; x - 5$ **31.** $x^3 + 27; x + 3$

32. Factor $x^2 - 8x - 9$ completely, given that $(x + 1)$ is a factor.

33. Factor $3y^2 + 8y + 4$ completely, given that $(3y + 2)$ is a factor.

34. One factor of $y^4 - 6y^2 + 8$ is $(y^2 - 4)$. Find the other factor. Then factor completely over the integers.

35. One factor of $2t^3 - t^2 - 4t + 3$ is $(t^2 + 1 - 2t)$. Find the other factor. Then factor completely over the integers.

36. Is $(r - 2)$ a factor of $r^3 - 2r^2 + 4r - 6$? Give a reason for your answer.

37. Is $(2n - 4)$ a factor of $6n^3 - 22n + 1$? Give a reason for your answer.

C

38. Find the value of k for which $(3t + 2)$ is a factor of $15t^2 - 2t + k$.

39. Find the value of k for which $(x - 3)$ is a factor of $2x^3 - x^2 - 17x + k$.

40. A rectangle of width $(4x - 9y)$ units has an area of $(12x^2 - 11xy - 36y^2)$ square units. Find the perimeter of the rectangle.

41. When $6p^3 - 22p + c$ is divided by $2p - 4$, the remainder is 5. Find c.

Puzzle

A four–digit number is divided by a two–digit number to give a two–digit number, as shown.

Find the missing digits. (There is only one solution.)

```
        xx
5x ) 1xxx
     x5x
     xxx
     400
```

BASIC: ADDING FRACTIONS

A computer cannot handle fractions as you do. If you enter $2/5$ into a computer, the machine will divide 2 by 5 and return a decimal, 0.4. To program a computer to compute the sum of two fractions in fractional form, you must include the following algebra in the program.

$$\frac{a}{b} + \frac{c}{d} = \frac{ad}{bd} + \frac{bc}{bd} = \frac{ad + bc}{bd}$$

Problem: *Write a program which adds two fractions.*

Program:

```
100 PRINT "FOR THE FRACTIONS A/B AND C/D, WHAT"
110 PRINT "ARE A, B, C, AND D (NONE 0)";
120 INPUT A, B, C, D
130 IF A*B*C*D <> 0 THEN 160
140 PRINT "NO ZERO VALUES. TRY AGAIN."
150 GOTO 120
160 LET N = A*D + B*C
170 LET D1 = B*D
180 IF N = 0 THEN 310
190 LET N1 = ABS(N)
200 LET D2 = ABS(D1)
210 IF N1 > D2 THEN 240
220 LET S = N1
230 GOTO 250
240 LET S = D2
250 FOR Y = S TO 1 STEP -1
260 IF N1/Y <> INT(N1/Y) THEN 280
270 IF D2/Y = INT(D2/Y) THEN 290
280 NEXT Y
290 LET N = N/Y
300 LET D1 = D1/Y
310 PRINT "(";A;"/";B;") + (";C;"/";D;") = ";
320 IF ABS(D1) = 1 THEN 380
330 IF N * D1 < 0 THEN 360
340 PRINT ABS(N);"/";ABS(D1)
350 GOTO 390
360 PRINT "-";ABS(N);"/";ABS(D1)
370 GOTO 390
380 PRINT N * D1
390 PRINT
400 PRINT "ANY MORE FRACTIONS (1=YES, 0=NO)";
410 INPUT Z
420 IF Z = 1 THEN 120
430 END
```

Output:
```
RUN
FOR THE FRACTIONS A/B AND C/D, WHAT
ARE A, B, C, AND D (NONE 0)? 1,2,1,4
( 1 / 2 ) + ( 1 / 4 ) = 3 / 4

ANY MORE FRACTIONS (1=YES, 0=NO)? 1
? 7,-8,-5,9
( 7 /-8 ) + (-5 / 9 ) = - 103 / 72

ANY MORE FRACTIONS (1=YES, 0=NO)? 0
READY
```

Analysis

Statements 130–150: This is the bad data trap.

Statements 160–170: N and D1 are the numerator and denominator, respectively, for the sum. However, N/D1 must be reduced to lowest terms.

Statements 190–300: This section determines the greatest common factor (GCF) of N and D1. First (statements 190–200), the ABS (absolute value) function serves to make sure that, if either N or D1 is negative, the corresponding positive value (N1 or D2) is used when determining the GCF. Then (statements 210–240), S is set equal to the smaller of N1 and D2. In this way, the loop (statements 250–280) that finds the GCF can start at S and go backwards to 1. For each value of Y in this range, the INT function is used (statements 260–270) to decide whether Y is a factor of both N1 and D2. When such a Y value is found (and notice that, if all larger values fail, 1 will work), the computer jumps to statements 290 and 300, which reduce N/D1 to lowest terms by dividing each value by Y.

Statements 310–380: These steps print the sum in as "neat" a way as possible. Statements 320 and 380 handle cases where D1 is 1 or −1 so that, for example, 8 is not printed as 8 / 1 and −7 is not printed as 7 / −1. Statements 330 and 360 take care of negative sums so that, for instance, −3 / 4 is printed instead of 3 / −4.

EXERCISES

A   Rewrite the program on page 379 so that it does each of the following.

1. Subtract C/D from A/B.   **2.** Multiply A/B and C/D.   **3.** Divide A/B by C/D.

B   Write a BASIC program for each problem.

4. Determine whether $\frac{a}{b}$ equals $\frac{c}{d}$. For example, $\frac{2}{4} = \frac{1}{2}$ but $\frac{2}{5} \neq \frac{1}{2}$.

5. Given two positive integers a and b, print the least common multiple (LCM) of a and b.

Review

Multiply. Write each product in simplest form. *(Section 10-4)*

1. $\dfrac{ah}{4x} \cdot \dfrac{x}{h}$

2. $(x + 1) \cdot \dfrac{x - 3}{x - 1}$

3. $\dfrac{x^2 - 3x - 10}{x^2 - 2x} \cdot \dfrac{x^2 - 3x + 2}{x^2 - 25}$

Divide. Write each answer in simplest form. *(Section 10-5)*

4. $\dfrac{x}{3} \div \dfrac{x}{a}$

5. $\dfrac{4ab}{x} \div \dfrac{8a^2}{x^2}$

6. $\dfrac{a^2 - 2a - 3}{a^2 + a - 2} \div \dfrac{a - 3}{2a^2 + 2a - 4}$

Find the LCD of the rational expressions having the given denominators. *(Section 10-6)*

7. $3; 11$

8. $2ab^2; 4a^2$

9. $(x^2 - 2x - 8); (x^2 - 3x - 4)$

Add or subtract as indicated. Write each answer in simplest form. *(Section 10-7)*

10. $\dfrac{2a + 4}{a + b} + \dfrac{3a - 5}{a + b}$

11. $\dfrac{3}{xy^2} + \dfrac{2}{x^2y}$

12. $\dfrac{x}{x^2 - 4} + \dfrac{1}{x^2 + 2x}$

(Section 10-8)

13. $2 + \dfrac{1}{x}$

14. $y - \dfrac{1}{2y}$

15. $(a + b) - \dfrac{2ab}{a + b}$

16. $\dfrac{1}{x - 1} - (x - 1)$

Divide the first polynomial by the second. *(Section 10-9)*

17. $x^2 - x - 6; x + 2$

18. $9b^2 - 16; 3b - 4$

19. $x^2 + 13x + 36; x + 9$

20. $16y^2 - 6y - 1; 2y - 1$

Chapter Summary

IMPORTANT TERMS

Extremes (p. 351)
Least common denominator,
    or LCD (p. 368)
Means (p. 351)
Mixed expression (p. 374)

Mixed number (p. 374)
Proportion (p. 350)
Ratio (p. 350)
Rational expression (p. 357)
Simplest form (p. 357)

IMPORTANT IDEAS

1. Multiplication Property of Proportions In a proportion, the product of the means equals the product of the extremes. That is,

$$\text{if } ad = bc, \text{ then } \frac{a}{b} = \frac{c}{d} \ (b \neq 0, d \neq 0).$$

Also,

$$\text{if } ad = bc, \text{ then } \frac{a}{b} = \frac{c}{d} \ (b \neq 0, d \neq 0).$$

2. **Product of Rational Expressions Theorem** If $\dfrac{P}{Q}$ and $\dfrac{R}{S}$ are rational expressions, then

$$\frac{P}{Q} \cdot \frac{R}{S} = \frac{P \cdot R}{Q \cdot S}.$$

3. **Division of Rational Expressions Theorem** To divide a rational expression $\dfrac{P}{Q}$ by a rational expression $\dfrac{R}{S}$, multiply $\dfrac{P}{Q}$ by the multiplicative inverse, or reciprocal, of $\dfrac{R}{S}$. That is, for $R \neq 0$,

$$\frac{P}{Q} \div \frac{R}{S} = \frac{P}{Q} \cdot \frac{S}{R}.$$

4. **Steps for finding the LCD of rational expressions**

   1. Express each denominator as a product of prime factors.
   2. Write a product using each prime factor only once.
   3. For each factor, write the greatest exponent used in any prime factorization.
   4. Simplify where necessary. The result is the LCD.

5. **Addition and Subtraction of Rational Expressions Theorem**

   If $\dfrac{P}{Q}$ and $\dfrac{R}{Q}$ are rational expressions, then

   $$\frac{P}{Q} + \frac{R}{Q} = \frac{P + R}{Q} \qquad \text{and} \qquad \frac{P}{Q} - \frac{R}{Q} = \frac{P - R}{Q}.$$

6. **Steps for Adding or Subtracting Rational Expressions**

   1. Find the LCD of the denominators.
   2. Write equivalent rational expressions having the LCD as denominators.
   3. Add or subtract as indicated.
   4. Write the answer in simplest form.

——— Chapter Objectives and Review ———

Objective: *To solve proportions (Section 10–1)*

Solve each proportion.

1. $\dfrac{35}{84} = \dfrac{21}{x}$

2. $\dfrac{17}{1.5} = \dfrac{y}{1.8}$

3. $\dfrac{1}{b-3} = \dfrac{2}{b+6}$

4. $n = \dfrac{n+8}{-3}$

5. In a mixture of green paint, the ratio of blue paint to yellow paint is 4:3. How many gallons of blue paint should be mixed with 2 gallons of yellow paint to produce this shade of green?

6. Two candidates, Alio and Benton, ran for mayor. The voters elected Alio by a ratio of 5 to 3. A total of 2480 votes were cast. How many votes did each receive?

Objective: *To solve investment problems and mixture problems (Section 10-2)*

7. Enrico invested one third of his savings at 9% per year and the rest at 11% per year. The total yearly interest was $496. In all, how much money did he invest?

8. Carol invested the same amount of money at 12% yearly interest and at 10%. She received a total of $330 in interest for the year. How much money did she invest at each rate?

9. How many grams of salt must be added to 400 grams of a 15% salt solution to obtain a 20% salt solution?

10. How many kilograms of a 10% copper alloy must be melted with 20 kilograms of a 20% copper alloy to obtain an 18% copper alloy?

Objective: *To simplify rational expressions (Section 10-3)*

Simplify.

11. $\dfrac{39}{65}$

12. $\dfrac{12ab}{30b^2}$

13. $\dfrac{3(x+y)}{9(x-y)}$

14. $\dfrac{6(c+2d)^2}{8(c+2d)}$

15. $\dfrac{5x}{5x+10}$

16. $\dfrac{2a-4b}{6a+4b}$

17. $\dfrac{4x^2-16y^2}{8y^2-2x^2}$

18. $\dfrac{6a^2-15ab+9b^2}{3b^2-4ab+a^2}$

Objective: *To multiply rational expressions (Section 10-4)*

Multiply. Write each product in simplest form.

19. $\dfrac{x^2}{2a}\cdot\dfrac{a}{x}$

20. $(2x+1)\cdot\dfrac{x+5}{6x+3}$

21. $\dfrac{3a+3}{4a-4}\cdot\dfrac{a-1}{a+1}$

22. $\dfrac{4x}{x^2-y^2}\cdot\dfrac{x-y}{2x^2+2xy}$

23. $\dfrac{2x}{x+2}\cdot\dfrac{x^2+5x+6}{2x+2}$

24. $\dfrac{3a+b}{a^2-b^2}\cdot\dfrac{a-b}{3a^2+4ab+b^2}$

Objective: *To divide rational expressions (Section 10-5)*

Divide. Write each answer in simplest form.

25. $\dfrac{3}{a}\div\dfrac{6}{b}$

26. $\dfrac{ax}{by}\div\dfrac{x}{y}$

27. $\dfrac{6a^2b}{5c}\div\dfrac{3ac}{5b}$

28. $\dfrac{(5xy)^2}{12z}\div\dfrac{10x}{9z^3}$

29. $\dfrac{x^2+xy}{a^2-b^2}\div\dfrac{x+y}{(a-b)^2}$

30. $(x^2-a^2)\div\dfrac{ax-a^2}{x+a}$

Objective: *To find the LCD of rational expressions (Section 10-6)*

Find the LCD of rational expressions having the given denominators.

31. $7;\ 9$

32. $4;\ 10$

33. $3x^2y^2;\ 9xy^2$

34. $(x+3);\ (x-3)$

35. $(a^2-b^2);\ (a+b)$

36. $(y^2+2y+1);\ (y^2-y-2)$

Objective: *To add and subtract rational expressions (Section 10-7)*

Add or subtract as indicated. Write each answer in simplest form.

37. $\dfrac{3x+5}{x+2}-\dfrac{2x+3}{x+2}$

38. $\dfrac{a-1}{6}+\dfrac{a+1}{9}$

39. $\dfrac{a+b}{ab}-\dfrac{3}{2a}$

Add or subtract as indicated. Write each answer in simplest form.

40. $\dfrac{1 - 3y}{3xy} - \dfrac{2x - 1}{6x^2y}$ **41.** $\dfrac{2}{a + 3} - \dfrac{1}{a - 1}$ **42.** $\dfrac{x}{x + 2} - \dfrac{8}{x^2 - 4}$

43. $\dfrac{x - y}{3x + 3y} - \dfrac{x - y}{2x + 2y}$ **44.** $\dfrac{x + 1}{2xy} - \dfrac{2y - 1}{4y^2}$ **45.** $\dfrac{2ab}{a^2 - b^2} + \dfrac{a - b}{a + b}$

Objective: *To add or subtract a polynomial and a rational expression (Section 10–8)*

Add or subtract as indicated. Write each answer in simplest form.

46. $3 + \dfrac{x}{y}$ **47.** $b + \dfrac{3}{2b}$ **48.** $x - \dfrac{2y}{3x}$ **49.** $\dfrac{3}{x} + 2x$

50. $a - \dfrac{ab}{a + b}$ **51.** $x - \dfrac{3}{x + 2}$ **52.** $1 + \dfrac{2x + 1}{x - 1}$ **53.** $(a + 1) + \dfrac{1}{a - 1}$

Objective: *To divide one polynomial by another (Section 10–9)*

Divide the first polynomial by the second.

54. $x^2 + x - 6; \ x + 3$ **55.** $a^2 - 6a + 9; \ a - 3$

56. $4y^2 - 25; \ 2y - 5$ **57.** $4x^2 - 5x - 6; \ 4x + 3$

58. $b^3 + 4b + 5; \ b + 1$ **59.** $2n^3 + 3n^2 + 3n + 1; \ 2n + 1$

60. $y^3 + 3y^2 + 16; \ y + 4$ **61.** $4a^3 - 4a^2 - 15a + 1; \ 2a - 3$

───── **Chapter Test** ──────────────────────────────

Solve each proportion.

1. $\dfrac{17}{26} = \dfrac{x}{78}$ **2.** $\dfrac{2.5}{1} = \dfrac{0.5}{n}$ **3.** $\dfrac{15 - n}{2} = \dfrac{15 + n}{3}$

Perform the indicated operations. Express answers in simplest form.

4. $\dfrac{4x^2}{3y} \div \dfrac{x}{y}$ **5.** $3 - \dfrac{2}{a}$ **6.** $\dfrac{9x^2}{4} \cdot \dfrac{2}{15x}$ **7.** $\dfrac{3b^3}{4} \div \dfrac{26}{8}$

8. $\dfrac{a^2 + ab}{a^2 - b^2} \cdot \dfrac{a - b}{a + ab}$ **9.** $\dfrac{2x + 3y}{x - y} + \dfrac{x - 6y}{x - y}$ **10.** $\dfrac{x^2 - y^2}{3xy} \div \dfrac{x^2 - 2xy + y^2}{6x}$

11. $\dfrac{c - d}{cd} + \dfrac{c + d}{c^2}$ **12.** $\dfrac{3}{2x + 2y} - \dfrac{x}{x^2 - y^2}$ **13.** $\dfrac{x^2 - 9}{x^2 + 2x} \cdot \dfrac{x + 2}{x^2 + 6x + 9}$

14. $\dfrac{3}{a + 1} + 1$ **15.** $\dfrac{y^2 - 3y + 2}{2y + 2} \cdot \dfrac{y + 1}{y - 1}$ **16.** $\dfrac{a + 1}{4a^2} - \dfrac{1 - a}{2a}$

17. Divide $x^2 + 5x + 6$ by $x + 3$. **18.** Divide $y^3 - 7y + 6$ by $y - 2$.

19. A machine can fill 96 bottles of milk in one minute. At this rate, how many bottles can it fill in 60 minutes?

20. How many kilograms of pure lead must be melted with 40 kilograms of a 10% lead alloy in order to make a 20% alloy?

More Challenging Problems

Perform the indicated operations.

1. $(a^{n+1} + 5)(a^{n-1} + 5)$
2. $(a^5 - 243) \div (a - 3)$
3. $(a^{\frac{n}{2}} + b^{\frac{n}{2}} + c^{\frac{n}{2}})^2$
4. $(c - 5)^3 - (c + 5)^2$
5. $(x - y)(x^{n-1} + x^{n-2}y + x^{n-3}y^2 + \cdots + x^2y^{n-3} + xy^{n-2} + y^{n-1})$

Factor each polynomial.

6. $(c^2 + 2cd + d^2) - (9x^2 - 6xy + y^2)$
7. $(x^2 + 6x + 9) - (y - 1)^2$
8. $x^2(2x - 3) - 2x(2x - 3) + (2x - 3)$
9. $4a^2 + 4ab + b^2 - 9c^2 + 12cd - 4d^2$

Perform the indicated operations and simplify.

10. $\dfrac{x + y + \dfrac{y^2}{x}}{x + y + \dfrac{x^2}{y}}$

11. $\dfrac{x + \dfrac{y^3}{x^2}}{\dfrac{y^2}{x^2} - \dfrac{y}{x} + 1}$

12. $\dfrac{\dfrac{x^2}{y^2} - 1}{\dfrac{x^2}{y^2} + \dfrac{2x}{y} + 1}$

13. $\dfrac{\dfrac{1 - 4x^2}{(2x + y)^2}\left[1 + \dfrac{y + 1}{2x - 1}\right]}{\dfrac{1}{2x + y} - \dfrac{1}{2x - y} + \dfrac{1}{4x^2 - y^2}}$

14. $\dfrac{x - 6 + \dfrac{4}{x - 2}}{\left(\dfrac{1}{x + 2} - \dfrac{x}{7x - 4}\right)\left(x - \dfrac{x + 8}{x - 1}\right)}$

Additional Practice

Skills

Solve each proportion. *(Section 10–1)*

1. $\dfrac{14}{91} = \dfrac{63}{x}$

2. $\dfrac{5}{n} = \dfrac{4}{n - 1}$

3. $\dfrac{10}{y + 3} = \dfrac{4}{y - 1}$

Simplify. No denominator equals zero. *(Section 10–3)*

4. $\dfrac{24a^2b}{56a}$

5. $\dfrac{36xy}{60wx}$

6. $\dfrac{3a + 3b}{3a^2 - 3b^2}$

7. $\dfrac{x^2 - x - 6}{x^2 + x - 12}$

Multiply. Write each product in simplest form. *(Section 10–4)*

8. $\dfrac{x + y}{12} \cdot \dfrac{3}{x}$

9. $(2x - 3) \cdot \dfrac{x}{4x - 6}$

10. $\dfrac{a^2 - b^2}{4a + 2b} \cdot \dfrac{2}{a - b}$

Divide. Write each answer in simplest form. *(Section 10–5)*

11. $\dfrac{18}{c} \div \dfrac{36}{c^2}$

12. $\dfrac{9x^2 - 4y^2}{2x^2} \div \dfrac{3x - 2y}{8x}$

13. $\dfrac{n^2 + 2n + 1}{3n - 3} \div \dfrac{n + 1}{3}$

Find the LCD of the rational expressions having the given denominators. *(Section 10–6)*

14. $8a$; $12a$

15. $4xy^2$; $16x^2y$

16. $x^2 - 1$; $2x^2 + 2x$

Add or subtract as indicated. Write each answer in simplest form. *(Section 10–7)*

17. $\dfrac{3a + b}{a + b} - \dfrac{a - b}{a + b}$

18. $\dfrac{x + 1}{6x} + \dfrac{4x}{8x^2}$

19. $\dfrac{x}{x^2 - x - 6} - \dfrac{1}{x^2 - 3x}$

(Section 10–8)

20. $3 + \dfrac{1}{2a}$

21. $x - \dfrac{1}{x + 1}$

22. $\dfrac{2}{y + 3} - (y - 3)$

Divide the first polynomial by the second. *(Section 10–9)*

23. $x^2 - 8x + 15$; $x - 3$

24. $y^3 - 3y^2 - 4y$; $y + 1$

25. $4a^2 - 25$; $2a - 5$

26. $n^3 - 8$; $n - 2$

27. $8y^3 - 12y + 5$; $2y - 1$

28. $8a^3 + b^3$; $2a + b$

29. $2x^3 - 9x^2 + 11x - 3$; $2x - 3$

30. $12b^2 - 11bc - 36c^2$; $4b - 9c$

Applications

31. A vertical meter stick casts a shadow 1.6 meters long at the same time that a flagpole casts a 10.4-meter shadow. How tall is the flagpole? *(Section 10–1)*

32. A recipe for a casserole that serves 6 people calls for $2\frac{1}{2}$ cups of milk. How many cups of milk are necessary if the recipe is to serve 10 people? *(Section 10–1)*

33. A truck travels 80 kilometers in 2 hours. How far will it travel in 5 hours at the same rate? *(Section 10–1)*

34. On a map, 2.5 centimeters represent 50 kilometers. How many centimeters represent 75 kilometers? *(Section 10–1)*

35. How many liters of concentrated plant food must be added to 11 liters of an 8% solution of the concentrate in order to obtain a 12% solution? *(Section 10–2)*

36. How many milliliters of an 18% ammonia solution must be added to 20 milliliters of a 12% ammonia solution to make a 15% solution? *(Section 10–2)*

37. A 150-gram solution is 6% salt and 94% water. How many grams of water must be evaporated to obtain a solution that is 14% salt? *(Section 10–2)*

38. Earl invested $10,000, part at 12% per year and part at 14% per year. He wants to earn at least $1310 on the investments in a year. How much should he invest at each rate? *(Section 10–2)*

39. Juanita invested $12,000, part at 8% per year and the rest at 12% per year. The total yearly interest was $1120. How much did she invest at each rate? *(Section 10–2)*

40. Julian invested an amount of money at 9% per year and three times as much at 11% per year. The total yearly interest was $168. How much did he invest at each rate? *(Section 10–2)*

CHAPTER **11** Applications of Rational Expressions

11-1 Equations with Rational Expressions

To solve equations containing rational expressions, follow these steps.

Procedure

> **Steps for Solving Equations with Rational Expressions**
> 1. Multiply **each side** of the equation by the LCD.
> 2. Follow the usual procedures to solve the resulting equation.

EXAMPLE 1 Solve: $\dfrac{n}{3} + \dfrac{n}{2} = 1$

Solution:

$$\frac{n}{3} + \frac{n}{2} = 1 \qquad \longleftarrow \quad \text{The LCD is 6.}$$
$$\text{Multiply each side by 6.}$$

$$6\left(\frac{n}{3} + \frac{n}{2}\right) = 6(1)$$

$$6 \cdot \frac{n}{3} + 6 \cdot \frac{n}{2} = 6 \cdot 1 \qquad \longleftarrow \quad \text{By the distributive postulate}$$

$$2n + 3n = 6 \qquad \longleftarrow \quad \text{Solve for } n.$$

$$5n = 6$$

$$n = \frac{6}{5}$$

Check:

$$\frac{n}{3} + \frac{n}{2} = 1$$

$$\frac{\frac{6}{5}}{3} + \frac{\frac{6}{5}}{2} \stackrel{?}{=} 1$$

$$\frac{\frac{6}{5}}{3} = \frac{6}{5} \div 3 = \frac{6}{5} \cdot \frac{1}{3} \quad \text{and} \quad \frac{\frac{6}{5}}{2} = \frac{6}{5} \div 2 = \frac{6}{5} \cdot \frac{1}{2}.$$

$$\frac{6}{15} + \frac{6}{10} \stackrel{?}{=} 1$$

$$\frac{2}{5} + \frac{3}{5} \stackrel{?}{=} 1$$

$$1 \stackrel{?}{=} 1 \quad \text{Yes} \ \vee \qquad \text{Solution set: } \left\{\frac{6}{5}\right\}$$

REMEMBER: Multiply each side of an equation containing rational expressions by the LCD.

The equation in Example 2 contains rational expressions that have a variable in the denominator. Recall that values of the variable that could make a denominator equal zero must be excluded. Thus, in Example 2, x cannot equal 2 or 4.

EXAMPLE 2 Solve: $\dfrac{7}{x-4} - \dfrac{5}{x-2} = 0$

Solution: $\dfrac{7}{x-4} - \dfrac{5}{x-2} = 0$ ⟵ **The LCD is $(x-4)(x-2)$, x ≠ 4, x ≠ 2.**
Multiply each side by $(x-4)(x-2)$.

$$(x-4)(x-2)\left(\dfrac{7}{x-4} - \dfrac{5}{x-2}\right) = (x-4)(x-2)(0)$$

$$7(x-2) - 5(x-4) = 0 \quad \longleftarrow \quad \textbf{Simplify.}$$

$$7x - 14 - 5x + 20 = 0$$

$$2x + 6 = 0$$

$$2x = -6$$

$$x = -3 \quad \longleftarrow \quad \textbf{Remember: x ≠ 2 and x ≠ 4}$$

Check: $\dfrac{7}{x-4} - \dfrac{5}{x-2} = 0 \quad \longleftarrow \quad \textbf{Replace x with −3.}$

$$\dfrac{7}{-3-4} - \dfrac{5}{-3-2} \overset{?}{=} 0$$

$$\dfrac{7}{-7} - \dfrac{5}{-5} \overset{?}{=} 0 \quad \longleftarrow \quad -\left(\dfrac{5}{-5}\right) = -(-1) = 1$$

$$-1 + 1 \overset{?}{=} 0 \quad \text{Yes} \; ✓ \qquad \textbf{Solution set:} \; \{-3\}$$

Sometimes the number obtained as a solution to an equation does not check in the original equation. The number is only an **apparent solution** (not a solution at all). This is why it is important to check.

EXAMPLE 3 Solve: $\dfrac{x}{10} + \dfrac{1}{x-1} = \dfrac{x+1}{2x-2}$

Solution:

$$\dfrac{x}{10} + \dfrac{1}{x-1} = \dfrac{x+1}{2x-2} \quad \longleftarrow \quad \textbf{Factor 2x − 2.}$$

$$\dfrac{x}{10} + \dfrac{1}{x-1} = \dfrac{x+1}{2(x-1)} \quad \longleftarrow \quad \textbf{LCD: 10(x − 1),}\\ \textbf{x ≠ 1}$$

$$10(x-1)\left(\dfrac{x}{10} + \dfrac{1}{x-1}\right) = [10(x-1)]\left[\dfrac{x+1}{2(x-1)}\right]$$

$$10(x-1)\left(\dfrac{x}{10}\right) + 10(x-1)\left(\dfrac{1}{x-1}\right) = 5(x+1)$$

$$(x-1)x + 10 = 5(x+1)$$

$$x^2 - x + 10 = 5x + 5 \quad \longleftarrow \quad \textbf{Write in the form}\\ \textbf{x}^2 + \textbf{bx} + \textbf{c} = \textbf{0.}$$

$$x^2 - 6x + 5 = 0 \quad \longleftarrow \quad \textbf{Factor x}^2 - \textbf{6x + 5.}$$

$$(x-5)(x-1) = 0$$

$$x - 5 = 0 \quad \text{or} \quad x - 1 = 0$$

$$x = 5 \quad \text{or} \quad x = 1 \quad \longleftarrow \quad \textbf{Remember:}\\ \textbf{x ≠ 1}$$

Applications of Rational Expressions **389**

Note what happens when you check both solutions.

Check: $\dfrac{x}{10}+\dfrac{1}{x-1}=\dfrac{x+1}{2x-2}$ ← **Replace x with 5.**

$\dfrac{5}{10}+\dfrac{1}{4}\overset{?}{=}\dfrac{6}{8}$

$\dfrac{1}{2}+\dfrac{1}{4}\overset{?}{=}\dfrac{3}{4}$

$\dfrac{3}{4}\overset{?}{=}\dfrac{3}{4}$ **Yes** ✔ **Solution set: {5}**

$\dfrac{x}{10}+\dfrac{1}{x-1}=\dfrac{x+1}{2x-2}$ ← **Replace x with 1.**

$\dfrac{1}{10}+\dfrac{1}{0}\overset{?}{=}\dfrac{2}{0}$

Since division by 0 is not defined, 1 is not a solution.

CLASSROOM EXERCISES

Solve each equation.

1. $\dfrac{2x}{3}-\dfrac{x}{2}=2$

2. $\dfrac{6p}{7}-\dfrac{p}{2}=5$

3. $\dfrac{2}{x}+\dfrac{3}{x}=5$

4. $\dfrac{3}{2a}-\dfrac{1}{4}=\dfrac{7}{8a}$

5. $\dfrac{6}{y-2}=\dfrac{3}{2}$

6. $\dfrac{3}{n+2}=\dfrac{5}{n-1}$

7. $\dfrac{2}{x+3}=\dfrac{4}{x+1}$

8. $\dfrac{x-4}{7}+\dfrac{2}{x-2}=1$

9. $\dfrac{1}{a}-\dfrac{2a}{a+1}=0$

WRITTEN EXERCISES

A   Solve each equation.

1. $\dfrac{a}{3}-\dfrac{a}{4}=2$

2. $\dfrac{b}{4}-\dfrac{b}{5}=2$

3. $\dfrac{3a}{5}+\dfrac{3}{2}=\dfrac{7a}{10}$

4. $\dfrac{4d}{7}+\dfrac{5}{4}=\dfrac{17d}{28}$

5. $\dfrac{3t}{4}+\dfrac{5}{3}=\dfrac{7t}{6}$

6. $\dfrac{3m}{2}+\dfrac{5}{3}=\dfrac{7m}{6}$

7. $\dfrac{2}{x}=3$

8. $\dfrac{3}{a}=-4$

9. $\dfrac{2}{3x}=\dfrac{1}{9}$

10. $\dfrac{3}{2x}-\dfrac{1}{3}=\dfrac{5}{6x}$

11. $\dfrac{5}{6x}+3=\dfrac{1}{2x}$

12. $\dfrac{3}{10x}-\dfrac{3}{5}=\dfrac{2}{5x}$

13. $\dfrac{5}{n}-\dfrac{1}{2}=2$

14. $\dfrac{4}{x}+\dfrac{3}{2x}=\dfrac{11}{6}$

15. $\dfrac{2n+1}{2n}-\dfrac{3n-2}{3n}=\dfrac{7}{12}$

16. $\dfrac{4}{2x}-3=\dfrac{-2}{5x}-\dfrac{3}{5}$

17. $\dfrac{4}{3x}-\dfrac{5}{2x}=5-\dfrac{1}{6x}$

18. $\dfrac{7}{4x}-2=\dfrac{3}{2x}-4$

19. $\dfrac{3}{2}=\dfrac{x}{x+2}$

20. $\dfrac{b-2}{b+3}=\dfrac{3}{8}$

21. $\dfrac{x-7}{x+2}=\dfrac{1}{4}$

22. $\dfrac{5}{a+3}=\dfrac{2}{2}$

23. $\dfrac{a-1}{a-2}=1.5$

24. $\dfrac{y}{y-3}=\dfrac{6}{3}$

25. $\dfrac{2}{x+3}=\dfrac{5}{x}$

26. $\dfrac{t+1}{t-1}=\dfrac{2}{t-1}+\dfrac{t}{8}$

27. $\dfrac{b}{6}+\dfrac{1}{b-1}=\dfrac{b+1}{2b-2}$

B

28. $\dfrac{x}{3} + \dfrac{2x^2}{3x-4} = \dfrac{9x-2}{9}$

29. $\dfrac{2x-1}{2} - \dfrac{x+2}{2x+5} = \dfrac{6x-5}{6}$

30. $\dfrac{7}{x-4} = \dfrac{5}{x-2}$

31. $\dfrac{10}{x-3} = \dfrac{9}{x-5}$

32. $\dfrac{x+5}{x-3} + \dfrac{4}{x-3} = 5$

33. $\dfrac{x+2}{x+4} = \dfrac{x+6}{x-8}$

34. $\dfrac{x-1}{x+1} = \dfrac{x+3}{x+10}$

35. $\dfrac{x-3}{x+5} = \dfrac{x-2}{x+2}$

36. $\dfrac{x}{x-3} + \dfrac{2}{x+4} = 1$

37. $\dfrac{3x}{x-2} - 3 = \dfrac{4}{x+2}$

38. $\dfrac{2x}{x-4} - \dfrac{4}{x+5} = 2$

39. $\dfrac{5x}{x+1} - \dfrac{x}{x+6} = 4$

40. $\dfrac{x-1}{x+1} - \dfrac{2x}{x-1} = -1$

41. $\dfrac{6}{4x} = \dfrac{x+2}{x^2-3x}$

42. $6 + \dfrac{20}{x^2-1} = \dfrac{10}{x-1}$

C

43. $\dfrac{3}{3x^2-3x-28} = \dfrac{5}{5x^2-x-20}$

44. $\dfrac{2x+1}{x-1} - \dfrac{3x}{x+2} = \dfrac{-x^2-2}{x^2+x-2}$

45. $\dfrac{a}{a-2} = \dfrac{a+3}{a+2} - \dfrac{a}{a^2-4}$

46. $\dfrac{3(x-4)}{4x^2-9} = \dfrac{3x}{4x^2-16x+15}$

47. For what value of k will the solution set of $\dfrac{a-2}{5a} = \dfrac{1}{k} - \dfrac{4}{15a}$ be $\{4\}$?

48. For what value of k will the solution set of $\dfrac{k}{3t} = \dfrac{t-5}{t^2-4t}$ be $\left\{\dfrac{5}{2}\right\}$?

Puzzle

A six-digit number is divided by a three-digit number to give a three-digit number, as shown at the right.

Find the missing digits. (There is only one solution.)

```
           xxx
    xxx) xxxxxx
        x0xx
        xxxx
        x50x
         xxx
         x4x
```

REVIEW CAPSULE FOR SECTION 11–2

Determine the slope of the line containing the given points. *(Pages 189–193)*

1. $P(1, 3)$; $Q(4, 9)$
2. $R(-2, 5)$; $T(6, -1)$
3. $N(0, 0)$; $V(-5, 0)$
4. $S(-3, -2)$; $T(4, 3)$
5. $R(12, 8)$; $P(-4, -10)$
6. $H(0, -2)$; $T(-1, -3)$

In Exercises 7–10:
a. Write each equation in the form $y = mx + b$.
b. Give the slope and y intercept of the line. *(Pages 194–196)*

7. $3x + y = 6$
8. $y - 5x = 9$
9. $6x - 3y = 18$
10. $10 - 6y = 21x$

11-2 Using Slope to Write a Linear Equation

When you know the slope and y intercept of a line, you can write the equation of the line. The equation will be in the form $y = mx + b$.

EXAMPLE 1   The slope of a line is 2 and its y intercept is 5. Write the equation of the line.

Solution: $y = \underline{mx} + b$ ←——— **Replace m with 2 and b with 5.**

$y = 2x + 5$

You can also determine the equation of a line when you know its slope and the coordinates of a point on the line.

EXAMPLE 2   A line with slope -3 passes through the point $Q(2, -4)$. Determine the equation of the line.

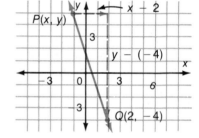

Solution: $\boxed{1}$ Let $P(x, y)$ be any point (other than Q) on the line.

$\boxed{2}$ Write an equation using slope.

$\dfrac{y - (-4)}{x - 2} = m$ ←——— **Replace m with -3.**

$\dfrac{y + 4}{x - 2} = -3$

$\boxed{3}$ Solve the equation for y. Multiply each side by the LCD, $(x - 2)$.

$(x - 2)\left(\dfrac{y + 4}{x - 2}\right) = (x - 2)(-3)$ ←——— **Remember: $x \neq 2$**

$y + 4 = -3x + 6 \quad \text{and} \quad y = -3x + 2$

The equation of a line can also be determined from its graph.

EXAMPLE 3   Determine the equation of the line shown in the graph.

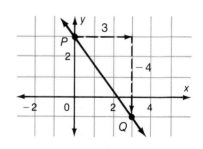

Solution: $\boxed{1}$ Read the y intercept from the graph: $b = 3$

$\boxed{2}$ To find the slope m, choose two convenient points on the graph.

$P(0, 3); Q(3, -1)$

$m = \dfrac{-1 - 3}{3 - 0} = \dfrac{-4}{3}, \text{ or } -\dfrac{4}{3}$

$\boxed{3}$ Write the equation as in Example 1. $y = -\dfrac{4}{3}x + 3$

CLASSROOM EXERCISES

In Exercises 1–6, a point on a line and the slope of the line are given. Write the equation of the line in the form $y = mx + b$.

1. $P(0, 2)$; $m = 4$
2. $Q(-1, 2)$; $m = 3$
3. $R(4, 6)$; $m = \frac{1}{2}$
4. $A(-3, 1)$; $m = -2$
5. $B(0, -3)$; $m = -\frac{1}{4}$
6. $C(1, -1)$; $m = -1$

WRITTEN EXERCISES

A   In Exercises 1–6, the slope and the y intercept of a line are given. Write the equation of the line in the form $y = mx + b$.

1. slope: 3; y intercept: 4
2. slope: 2; y intercept: 1
3. slope: $\frac{1}{2}$; y intercept: -3
4. slope: $\frac{2}{3}$; y intercept: -2
5. slope: -4; y intercept: $\frac{2}{3}$
6. slope: $-\frac{3}{8}$; y intercept: $-\frac{1}{2}$

In Exercises 7–15, one point on a line and the slope of the line are given. Write the equation of the line in the form $y = mx + b$.

7. $D(2, 3)$; $m = 2$
8. $G(0, 4)$; $m = 3$
9. $P(4, 5)$; $m = -3$
10. $T(0, 0)$; $m = 1$
11. $H(-2, 1)$; $m = 1$
12. $S(0, 0)$; $m = -1$
13. $N(-1, 1)$; $m = \frac{1}{2}$
14. $Q(\frac{1}{2}, 3)$; $m = -\frac{2}{3}$
15. $V(-3, 4)$; $m = -\frac{1}{3}$

Determine the equation of each line from its graph.

16.

17.

18.

19.

20.

21.
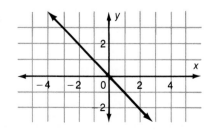

Determine the equation of each line from its graph.

22.

23.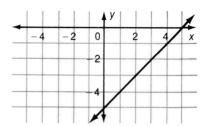

B In Exercises 24–31, determine the equation of each line. Write the equation in the form $y = mx + b$. REMEMBER: Parallel lines have the same slope.

24. The line has -2 as its y intercept and is parallel to the line defined by the equation $3y = x - 9$.

25. The line has 3 as its y intercept and is parallel to the line defined by the equation $3x - y + 6 = 0$.

26. The line passes through the point $(2, 3)$ and is parallel to the line defined by the equation $2y - 3x = 4$.

27. The line passes through the point $(2, 1)$ and is parallel to the line defined by the equation $2x - y = 8$.

28. The line has the same slope as the graph of $y + 3x = 7$ and the same y intercept as the graph of $y - 4x = 9$.

29. The line has the same slope as the graph of $y + 4x = -8$ and the same y intercept as the graph of $2y - 6x = 10$.

C

30. The line passes through the point $(3, 4)$ and is parallel to the x axis.

31. The line passes through the point $(3, 4)$ and is parallel to the y axis.

When two lines are perpendicular (meet at a 90°–angle), their slopes are negative reciprocals of each other.

Example: Determine the slope of a line perpendicular to $y = 2x + 9$.

Solution: Slope of $y = 2x + 9$: 2

Negative reciprocal of 2: $-\frac{1}{2}$ ⟵ $2(-\frac{1}{2}) = -1$

Slope of line perpendicular to $y = 2x + 9$: $-\frac{1}{2}$

In Exercises 32–35, write the equation of each line. Write the equation in the form $y = mx + b$.

32. The line has 4 as its y intercept and is perpendicular to the line defined by the equation $y = 2x - 3$.

33. The line passes through the point $(2, 3)$ and is perpendicular to the line defined by the equation $y + 4x = 5$.

34. The line passes through the point $(-1, 4)$ and is perpendicular to the line defined by $3y - 2x = 9$.

35. The line passes through the point $(3, -2)$ and is perpendicular to the line defined by $4y + 3x = 7$.

36. Show that the equation of a line with x intercept a and y intercept b is $\frac{x}{a} + \frac{y}{b} = 1$, $a \neq 0$, $b \neq 0$.

37. Show that the y intercept of the line with slope m and passing through a given point (x_1, y_1) is $y_1 - mx_1$.

Determine the slope of the line containing the given points. *(Pages 189–193)*

1. $P(7, 5)$; $R(-2, 4)$
2. $S(8, 6)$; $T(-3, 5)$
3. $V(9, -2)$; $S(-3, -4)$
4. $M(-7, -2)$; $Q(-5, -6)$
5. $A(0, -4)$; $B(5, 5)$
6. $Q(5, 0)$; $R(0, 5)$

Solve each equation for y in terms of x. *(Pages 162–164, 350–353)*

7. $\dfrac{y-5}{x+2} = \dfrac{3}{4}$

8. $\dfrac{y-1}{x-3} = -\dfrac{1}{2}$

9. $\dfrac{y+3}{x-1} = -\dfrac{2}{5}$

10. $\dfrac{y-9}{x+3} = \dfrac{7}{8}$

11. $\dfrac{y+2}{x} = -3$

12. $\dfrac{y-2}{x+2} = -\dfrac{5}{6}$

11-3 Using Two Points to Write a Linear Equation

When you know two points on a line, you can use these points to determine the equation of the line by expressing slope in two ways.

EXAMPLE 1 Determine the equation of the line passing through the points $Q(-3, 7)$ and $R(2, -9)$.

Solution:

1 Use the given points to find m.

$$m = \frac{-9 - 7}{2 - (-3)} = \frac{-16}{5}, \text{ or } -\frac{16}{5}$$

2 Let $P(x, y)$ be a third point on the line. Use the coordinates of P or Q to find m.

$$m = \frac{y - 7}{x - (-3)} = \frac{y - 7}{x + 3}$$

3 Since the slope of a line is *everywhere the same*, use the two expressions for m to write an equation.

$$\frac{y - 7}{x + 3} = -\frac{16}{5} \quad \longleftarrow \quad \textbf{LCD: } 5(x + 3),\ x \neq -3$$

$$5(x + 3)\left(\frac{y - 7}{x + 3}\right) = 5(x + 3)\left(-\frac{16}{5}\right)$$

$$5(y - 7) = (x + 3)(-16)$$

$$5y - 35 = -16x - 48$$

$$5y = -16x - 13$$

$$y = -\frac{16}{5}x - \frac{13}{5}$$

Given two points on a line, you can also determine the equation of the line by finding the slope and y intercept.

EXAMPLE 2 Determine the equation of the line passing through the points $R(-3, 4)$ and $T(4, 7)$.

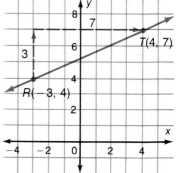

Solution: $\boxed{1}$ Use the given points to find m.

$$m = \frac{7-4}{4-(-3)} = \frac{3}{7}$$

$\boxed{2}$ In $y = mx + b$, replace m with $\frac{3}{7}$.

$$y = \frac{3}{7}x + b$$

$\boxed{3}$ Since $T(4, 7)$ is on the line, replace x with 4 and y with 7.

$$7 = \frac{3}{7}(4) + b$$

$$7 = \frac{12}{7} + b$$

$$\frac{37}{7} = b$$

$\boxed{4}$ Write the equation with $m = \frac{3}{7}$ and $b = \frac{37}{7}$.

$$y = \frac{3}{7}x + \frac{37}{7}$$

By multiplying each side of $y = \frac{3}{7}x + \frac{37}{7}$ by 7, the LCD, the equation can be written as

$$7y = 3x + 37, \quad \text{or} \quad -3x + 7y = 37. \longleftarrow \textbf{General form}$$

A linear equation written in the form

$$Ax + By = C$$

is said to be expressed in **general form**. Recall that the coefficients A, B, and C are real numbers and A and B cannot both equal zero. When writing a linear equation in general form, the coefficient, A, is usually expressed as a positive real number.

CLASSROOM EXERCISES

Determine the equation of the line passing through the given points. Write the equation in the form $y = mx + b$.

1. $P(2, 0)$ and $Q(0, 2)$
2. $E(2, 0)$ and $F(0, -2)$
3. $S(3, 0)$ and $T(-4, 0)$
4. $S(0, 0)$ and $R(3, -4)$
5. $V(6, 0)$ and $N(-1, -2)$
6. $M(-1, 2)$ and $E(-2, -3)$

WRITTEN EXERCISES

A Determine the equation of the line passing through the given points. Write the equation in the form $y = mx + b$.

1. $R(1, 1); S(2, 3)$
2. $T(0, 0); V(-3, 4)$
3. $A(0, 1); B(-1, 1)$
4. $D(0, 0); E(-1, -2)$
5. $F(3, 4); N(-2, 5)$
6. $E(5, -1); H(3, -2)$
7. $K(-3, -4); P(-5, -6)$
8. $R(2, 3); S(-1, 5)$
9. $T(4, -3); N(6, 0)$
10. $C(2, 2); N(3, 7)$
11. $T(1, -4); A(3, -6)$
12. $V(0, 4); Y(4, 0)$

Determine the equation of the line passing through the given points. Write the equation in general form.

13. $P(1, 4); S(3, 9)$
14. $T(1, 0); M(3, -6)$
15. $W(-3, -1); Z(9, 7)$
16. $M(0, -1); V(6, 8)$
17. $Z(1, -6); B(6, 0)$
18. $Q(-2, -5); R(-1, -2)$
19. $V(-3, 11); C(6, 5)$
20. $D(0, 0); F(-3, 5)$
21. $D(0, 3); C(-4, -8)$

B In Exercises 22–27, use the given slope and one point to write an equation of a line. Then determine whether the other point lies on that line.

22. $6; (2, 3); (6, 9)$
23. $\frac{1}{2}; (4, 2); (-2, -1)$
24. $-\frac{3}{5}; (-5, 7); (0, 4)$
25. $-4; (2, 6); (-1, 13)$
26. $2; (-1, -2); (2, 4)$
27. $-3; (-2, 2); (1, 6)$

C In each of Exercises 28–33, the coordinates of the vertices of a triangle are given. Write the equations of the lines forming the sides of each triangle. Write the equations in general form.

28. $A(2, 4); B(6, 2); C(3, -1)$
29. $D(6, 6); E(8, 4); F(1, 2)$
30. $F(3, 2); G(-2, 3); H(1, -2)$
31. $X(-3, 4); Y(-2, -1); Z(1, 1)$
32. $R(3, 3); S(5, -1); T(2, -2)$
33. $V(3, 6); G(5, 4); P(-1, 4)$

34. Show that if $P(x_1, y_1)$ and $Q(x_2, y_2)$ are different points on the graph of the equation $y = 4x - 2$, then $\dfrac{y_2 - y_1}{x_2 - x_1} = 4$.

Review

Solve each equation. *(Section 11–1)*

1. $\dfrac{a}{2} - \dfrac{a}{3} = 2$
2. $\dfrac{9}{x} - 6 = \dfrac{15}{x}$
3. $\dfrac{b + 2}{b + 4} = \dfrac{3}{b}$
4. $\dfrac{x}{2} = \dfrac{x}{x - 1}$
5. $\dfrac{x + 4}{2x + 3} = \dfrac{4}{x}$
6. $\dfrac{x}{2} = \dfrac{1}{x - 2} - \dfrac{x}{2x - 4}$

One point on a line and the slope of the line are given. Write the equation of the line in the form $y = mx + b$. *(Section 11–2)*

7. $A(0, 4); m = 1$
8. $P(0, -1); m = -2$
9. $C\left(0, \frac{1}{2}\right); m = -\frac{2}{3}$

Determine the equation of the line passing through the given points. Write the equation in the form $y = mx + b$. *(Section 11–3)*

10. $A(4, 4)$; $B(-4, -4)$ **11.** $P(1, 2)$; $Q(0, -1)$ **12.** $C(2, 1)$; $D(-3, 0)$

Determine the equation of the line passing through the given points. Write the equation in general form. *(Section 11–3)*

13. $M(0, 4)$; $N(4, 2)$ **14.** $S(2, -2)$; $T(-2, 10)$ **15.** $F(1, -1)$; $G(-3, 0)$

CALCULATOR APPLICATIONS

Checking Equations with Rational Expressions

You can use a calculator to check the solution set of an equation with rational expressions.

EXAMPLE Equation: $\dfrac{n}{3} + \dfrac{n}{2} = 1$ Solution set: $\left\{\dfrac{6}{5}\right\}$ (Example 1 on page 388)

$$\dfrac{\frac{6}{5}}{3} + \dfrac{\frac{6}{5}}{2} = 1 \quad \text{Evaluate the first term and store its value.}$$

$$6 \boxed{\div} 5 \boxed{\div} 3 \boxed{=} \boxed{M+} 6 \boxed{\div} 5 \boxed{\div} 2 \boxed{+} \boxed{MR} \boxed{=} \boxed{\quad 1. \quad}$$

Since both sides of the equation have the same value, the solution checks.

EXERCISES

Use a calculator to check each given "solution set." Correct any incorrect answers.

1. $\dfrac{b}{3} + \dfrac{b}{4} = 21$; $\{36\}$ **2.** $\dfrac{n}{3} - \dfrac{2n}{3} = 1$; $\{3\}$ **3.** $4m - \dfrac{6m + 3}{2} = 8$; $\{\frac{19}{2}\}$

4. $\dfrac{1}{3z} + \dfrac{1}{8} = \dfrac{4}{3z}$; $\{8\}$ **5.** $\dfrac{x}{2} - \dfrac{x}{6} = x - 16$; $\{24\}$ **6.** $\dfrac{10}{d} - 2 = \dfrac{5 - d}{4d}$; $\{-5\}$

—— REVIEW CAPSULE FOR SECTION 11–4 ——

Write the reciprocal of each number. *(Pages 68–71)*

1. $\dfrac{5}{8}$ **2.** $-\dfrac{7}{3}$ **3.** $-\dfrac{1}{9}$ **4.** 12 **5.** $\dfrac{1}{a}$, $a \neq 0$ **6.** $-z$

Solve and check each equation. *(Pages 350–353, 388–391)*

7. $\dfrac{6}{3y - 1} = \dfrac{3}{4}$ **8.** $\dfrac{1 - t}{1 + t} = \dfrac{2}{3}$ **9.** $\dfrac{2}{s} = \dfrac{5}{3s - 1}$ **10.** $\dfrac{n + 1}{3n - 2} = \dfrac{5}{2}$

11. $\dfrac{1}{x} + \dfrac{1}{2} = 5$ **12.** $\dfrac{3}{4} - \dfrac{1}{y} = 4$ **13.** $\dfrac{1}{2y} - \dfrac{1}{3y} = 2$ **14.** $\dfrac{r + 3}{r - 2} = \dfrac{5}{3}$

Consumer Applications

Borrowing Money

It is important for the consumer to know the cost of borrowing money, or **interest**, particularly when buying a car or a home. The following formula can be used to determine the monthly payment for a given loan. With this, you can then compute the interest.

$$m = \frac{A\left(\frac{r}{12}\right)\left(1 + \frac{r}{12}\right)^n}{\left(1 + \frac{r}{12}\right)^n - 1}$$

EXAMPLE   Mr. and Mrs. Jones want to borrow $5000 to buy a car. The annual rate of interest is 14% and the loan is to be paid back over 48 months. Find **a.** the monthly payment **b.** the total interest.

Solution: **a.** $A = \$5000; \; r = 0.14; \; n = 48$

$$m = \frac{5000\left(\frac{0.14}{12}\right)\left(1 + \frac{0.14}{12}\right)^{48}}{\left(1 + \frac{0.14}{12}\right)^{48} - 1} \quad \longleftarrow \quad \frac{0.14}{12} = 0.0117$$

$$= \frac{5000(0.0117)(1.0117)^{48}}{(1.0117)^{48} - 1} \quad \longleftarrow \quad \text{Use a calculator.}$$

$$= \$136.73$$

b. Total Interest = Total of Payments − Cash Price of Car

$$= (48 \times 136.73) - 5000$$
$$= 6563.04 - 5000$$
$$= \$1563.04 \text{ interest}$$

EXERCISES

In Exercises 1–5, compute the missing amounts.

	Amount Borrowed	Rate	Months	Monthly Payments	Total Cost	Total Interest
1.	$ 3,000	12.5%	36	?	?	?
2.	$10,000	13%	48	?	?	?
3.	$15,000	12%	96	?	?	?
4.	$20,000	13.5%	120	?	?	?
5.	$ 2,000	18%	24	?	?	?

Problem Solving and Applications

11–4 Number Problems

Some number problems can be represented by equations involving rational expressions.

EXAMPLE 1 When the same number is subtracted from the numerator and added to the denominator of $\frac{17}{22}$ (Condition 1), the result is $\frac{5}{8}$ (Condition 2). What is the number?

Solution: $\boxed{1}$ Use Condition 1 to represent the unknown. Then represent the original fraction and the new fraction.

Let $x =$ the number to be added and subtracted.

Original fraction: $\dfrac{17}{22}$ New fraction: $\dfrac{17 - x}{22 + x}$

$\boxed{2}$ Use Condition 2 to write an equation for the problem.

$$\frac{17 - x}{22 + x} = \frac{5}{8} \qquad \longleftarrow \quad \textbf{The new fraction equals } \frac{5}{8}.$$

$\boxed{3}$ Solve the equation. The LCD is $8(22 + x)$, $x \neq -22$.

$$8(22 + x)\left(\frac{17 - x}{22 + x}\right) = 8(22 + x)\left(\frac{5}{8}\right)$$

$$8(17 - x) = (22 + x)5 \quad \longleftarrow \quad \textbf{Multiply.}$$

$$136 - 8x = 110 + 5x \quad \longleftarrow \quad \textbf{Solve for x.}$$

$$26 = 13x$$

$$2 = x$$

Check: $\boxed{4}$ $\dfrac{17 - 2}{22 + 2} \overset{?}{=} \dfrac{5}{8}$

$$\frac{15}{24} \overset{?}{=} \frac{5}{8} \quad \textbf{Yes } \blacktriangleright$$

The number is **2**.

Recall that any two numbers whose product is 1 are *reciprocals* or *multiplicative inverses* of each other.

Thus, $\dfrac{2}{3}$ and $\dfrac{3}{2}$ are **reciprocals** because $\dfrac{2}{3} \cdot \dfrac{3}{2} = 1$.

Also, -5 and $-\dfrac{1}{5}$ are **reciprocals** because $-5\left(-\dfrac{1}{5}\right) = 1$.

EXAMPLE 2 One positive number is three times another (Condition 1). The difference of their reciprocals is $\frac{1}{6}$ (Condition 2). Find the numbers.

Solution: $\boxed{1}$ Let a = the smaller positive number.

Then $3a$ = the larger number.

Reciprocals: $\frac{1}{a}$ and $\frac{1}{3a}$, $a \neq 0$

$\boxed{2}$ Since $3a > a$, $\frac{1}{a} > \frac{1}{3a}$. Subtract $\frac{1}{3a}$ from $\frac{1}{a}$.

$$\frac{1}{a} - \frac{1}{3a} = \frac{1}{6} \longleftarrow \quad \textbf{LCD: 6a, } a \neq 0$$

$\boxed{3}$ $6a\left(\frac{1}{a} - \frac{1}{3a}\right) = 6a\left(\frac{1}{6}\right)$

$6 - 2 = a$

$4 = a \longleftarrow \quad$ **Don't forget to find 3a.**

$12 = 3a$

Check: $\boxed{4}$ Does $12 = 3 \cdot 4$?   Yes ✔

Does $\frac{1}{4} - \frac{1}{12} = \frac{1}{6}$?   Yes ✔   The numbers are **4** and **12**.

CLASSROOM EXERCISES

In Exercises 1–4:
a. Use Condition 1 to represent the unknown(s).
b. Use Condition 2 to write an equation for the problem.

1. What number added to both numerator and denominator of the fraction $\frac{3}{7}$ (Condition 1) results in a fraction equal to $\frac{3}{5}$ (Condition 2)?

2. What number added to both the numerator and denominator of the fraction $\frac{4}{9}$ (Condition 1) results in a fraction equal to $\frac{2}{3}$ (Condition 2)?

3. One positive number is 4 times another (Condition 1). The difference of their reciprocals is $\frac{3}{8}$ (Condition 2). Find the numbers.

4. A positive number is twice another (Condition 1). The sum of their reciprocals is $\frac{1}{2}$ (Condition 2). Find the numbers.

WORD PROBLEMS

Ⓐ   Solve each problem.

1. What number must be added to both the numerator and denominator of the fraction $\frac{5}{8}$ to make a fraction equal to $\frac{3}{4}$?

2. What number must be subtracted from both the numerator and denominator of the fraction $\frac{7}{12}$ to make a fraction equal to $\frac{1}{2}$?

3. One positive number is 5 times another number. The difference of their reciprocals is $\frac{2}{5}$. Find the numbers.

4. One positive number is 3 times another number. The sum of their reciprocals is $\frac{2}{3}$. Find the numbers.

5. What number must be added to the numerator and subtracted from the denominator of $\frac{17}{32}$ to make a fraction equal to $\frac{3}{4}$?

6. What number must be subtracted from the numerator and added to the denominator of $\frac{13}{23}$ to make a fraction equal to $\frac{1}{3}$?

7. The numerator of a fraction is 3 less than its denominator. If 2 is added to the numerator, the value of the fraction becomes $\frac{3}{4}$. What is the fraction?

8. The denominator of a fraction is 4 more than its numerator. If 6 is added to the denominator, the value of the fraction becomes $\frac{1}{3}$. What is the fraction?

9. One number is 4 more than another. The quotient of the larger divided by the smaller is $\frac{5}{2}$. Find the numbers.

10. One number is 7 less than another. The quotient of the larger divided by the smaller is $\frac{4}{3}$. Find the numbers.

11. The sum of two fractions is $\frac{11}{16}$ and one of them is $\frac{5}{6}$ of the other. Find the fractions.

12. The difference between two fractions is $\frac{1}{8}$. One fraction is $\frac{2}{3}$ of the other. Find the fractions.

B

13. Two integers are consecutive. If 6 is added to the first and 2 is subtracted from the second, the quotient of the resulting integers is $4\frac{1}{2}$. Find them.

14. Two integers are consecutive. If 5 is added to the first and 3 is subtracted from the second, the quotient of the resulting integers is $2\frac{2}{5}$. Find them.

15. The sum of two numbers is 11. The sum of their reciprocals is $\frac{11}{30}$. Find the numbers.

16. The difference of two numbers is 5. The difference of their reciprocals is $\frac{5}{126}$. Find the numbers.

17. The sum of a positive number and its reciprocal is $\frac{41}{20}$. Find the number.

18. The difference of a positive number and its reciprocal is $\frac{24}{35}$. Find the number.

C

19. The numerator of a fraction is 1 less than the denominator. The reciprocal of the fraction is $\frac{7}{12}$ more than the fraction. Find the fraction.

20. The denominator of a fraction is 3 more than the numerator. The fraction is $\frac{21}{10}$ less than its reciprocal. Find the fraction.

REVIEW CAPSULE FOR SECTION 11–5

Solve and check each equation. *(Pages 388–391)*

1. $\dfrac{210}{y} = \dfrac{195}{y-5}$

2. $\dfrac{1}{3} + \dfrac{1}{x} = \dfrac{1}{2}$

3. $\dfrac{2}{t} = \dfrac{5}{3t-1}$

4. $\dfrac{500}{r} = \dfrac{450}{r-5}$

5. $\dfrac{x}{5} - \dfrac{x}{15} = 4$

6. $\dfrac{48}{12-r} = 2\left(\dfrac{48}{12+r}\right)$

11–5 Motion Problems

Motion problems are based on the distance/rate/time formula.

Distance = rate × time,   or $d = rt$

EXAMPLE 1   David Blaisdell spends 5 hours traveling to and from work each day. If his average rate driving his moped to work is 18 miles per hour and his average rate returning is 12 miles per hour (Condition 1), how far is it from his home to his place of work (Condition 2)?

Solution: $\boxed{1}$ Organize the information in a table.
Use Condition 1 to represent the unknowns.

	Rate (r)	Time (t)	Distance $d = rt$
Going	18 mph	t	$18t$
Returning	12 mph	$5 - t$	$12(5 - t)$

$\boxed{2}$ Use the table and Condition 2 to write an equation.

$\underline{\text{Distance going}} = \underline{\text{Distance returning}} \longleftarrow$ **Condition 2**

$$18t \quad = \quad 12(5 - t)$$

$\boxed{3}$ Solve the equation.
$$18t = 12(5 - t)$$
$$18t = 60 - 12t$$
$$30t = 60$$
$$t = 2 \longleftarrow \text{ It takes 2 hours to drive to work.}$$

Check: $\boxed{4}$ **Condition 1**   Does $2 + 3 = 5$?   Yes ✓
Condition 2   Does $18 \cdot 2 = 12 \cdot 3$?   Yes ✓

The distance from home to work is $2 \cdot 18$, or **36 miles.**

Suppose that a boat travels at a rate of 30 kilometers per hour in still water and that the rate of the current is 4 kilometers per hour.

Then,

rate traveling upstream is 30 − 4,   or   26 km/h,

and

rate traveling downstream is 30 + 4,   or   34 km/h.

EXAMPLE 2 A motorboat can travel at a rate of 25 kilometers per hour in still water. Find the rate of the current of a river if the boat takes $\frac{2}{3}$ as much time to travel 100 kilometers downstream as it takes to travel the same distance upstream.

Solution: $\boxed{1}$ Let x = the rate of the current.

	Rate (r)	Distance (d)	Time $t = d \div r$
Downstream	$25 + x$	100	$\dfrac{100}{25 + x}$
Upstream	$25 - x$	100	$\dfrac{100}{25 - x}$

$\boxed{2}$ **Time downstream** $= \dfrac{2}{3}$ **(Time upstream)**

$$\frac{100}{25 + x} = \frac{2}{3}\left(\frac{100}{25 - x}\right) \longleftarrow \begin{array}{l} \textbf{LCD:} \\ \textbf{3(25 + x)(25 − x)} \end{array}$$

$\boxed{3}$ $3(25 + x)(25 - x)\left(\dfrac{100}{25 + x}\right) = 3(25 + x)(25 - x)\left(\dfrac{2}{3}\right)\left(\dfrac{100}{25 - x}\right)$

$$3(25 - x)(100) = (25 + x)(2)(100)$$
$$300(25 - x) = 200(25 + x)$$
$$7500 - 300x = 5000 + 200x$$
$$2500 = 500x$$
$$5 = x$$

$\boxed{4}$ The check is left for you.   Rate of the current: **5 km/h**

CLASSROOM EXERCISES

The rate of a jet plane in still air is 1100 kilometers per hour. The rate of the wind is 150 kilometers per hour. Use this information in Exercises 1–8.

1. What is the rate of the plane flying with the wind?

2. What is the rate of the plane flying against the wind?

3. What is the rate of the plane flying with the wind if the rate of the wind decreases by w kilometers per hour?

4. What is the rate of the plane flying against the wind if the rate of the wind increases by q kilometers per hour?

5. How far can the plane in Exercise 1 travel in 3 hours?

6. How far can the plane in Exercise 2 travel in 3 hours?

7. How long will it take the plane in Exercise 1 to travel 7500 kilometers?

8. How long will it take the plane in Exercise 2 to travel 7600 kilometers?

A jet had been flying for 2 hours when it encountered headwinds which reduced its speed by 64 kilometers per hour. If the plane took 5 hours to travel 2304 kilometers, what was its rate of speed before meeting the head winds?

Use this information in Exercises 9–11.

9. Complete the table.

	Rate (r)	Time (t)	Distance d = rt
Before headwinds **After headwinds**	x ?	2 ?	? ?

10. Write the equation you would use to find the plane's rate before encountering the headwinds?

11. What was the rate of the plane after encountering the headwinds?

WORD PROBLEMS

A   Solve each problem.

1. A tanker takes $\frac{1}{2}$ hour to go from a refinery to a delivery point and back. If its rate going is 30 mph and its rate returning is 40 mph, how far is it from the refinery to the delivery point?

2. Laurie takes 3 hours to travel from Ahmes to Billings on her moped. Brian covers the same distance in 2 hours, traveling 10 kilometers per hour faster. How far is it from Ahmes to Billings?

3. Jim drove his car 500 kilometers in the same time that Ed drove his car 450 kilometers. Jim drove 5 kilometers an hour faster than Ed. Find the speed of each.

4. A sight-seeing bus travels 90 kilometers to its destination. If the rate returning is twice the rate going and the time for a round trip is 3 hours, find the rate of travel each way.

5. Millan and Sharon work at the same store. Millan drives 30 miles to work and Sharon drives 20 miles. Both take the same time to get there since Millan drives 15 mph faster than Sharon. Find the speed of each person.

6. Karen can row at the speed of 10 kilometers per hour in still water. In a river where the current is 5 kilometers per hour, it takes her 4 hours longer to row x kilometers upstream than the same distance downstream. Find x

7. Tim can average 12 mph with his motor boat in still water. Find the rate of the current of a river if the boat takes twice as long to go 48 miles upstream as it does to travel the same distance downstream.

8. A boat that sails at the rate of 30 kilometers per hour in still water can go 104 kilometers down a river in the same time it takes to travel 91 kilometers up the river. Find the rate of the current of the river.

9. A boat goes 36 kilometers upstream in the same time that it takes to travel 45 kilometers downstream. The current is flowing at 3 kilometers per hour. Find the rate of the boat in still water.

10. A plane can fly 600 kilometers with the wind in the same time that it can fly 520 kilometers against the wind. The wind is blowing at 30 kilometers per hour. Find the rate of the plane in still air.

B

11. Allan can drive his car over a route in 5 hours, and Carla can drive her car over the same route in 4 hours. How long would it take to meet if they started at opposite ends at the same time?

12. On a trip, June drove at a rate of 55 mph. She decided to return by a route that was 5 miles longer. Her rate returning was 45 mph. If it took her 1 hour longer returning, how long was the second route?

13. An airplane flew 200 kilometers with a tailwind of 60 kilometers per hour. Then it returned against the wind. Find the rate of the plane in still air if the trip took 45 minutes.

14. A plane flies 852 kilometers with a tailwind in half the time it takes to fly 1560 kilometers against the same wind. If the rate in still air is 408 kilometers per hour, find the speed of the wind.

C

15. Rhonda can swim in still water at twice the rate of the current in the river near her home. She swam one kilometer upstream and then back in 40 minutes. Find the rate of the current.

16. Two cars race on a 6.4-kilometer track. The faster car gains a lap in 40 minutes. The sum of the rates of the cars is 320 kilometers per hour. Find the rate of each car.

REVIEW CAPSULE FOR SECTION 11–6

Write each fraction in lowest terms.

1. $\dfrac{2}{30}$ 2. $\dfrac{4}{60}$ 3. $\dfrac{9}{54}$ 4. $\dfrac{16}{50}$ 5. $\dfrac{18}{90}$ 6. $\dfrac{27}{81}$

Solve and check each equation. *(Pages 388–391)*

7. $\dfrac{n}{20} + \dfrac{n}{30} = 1$ 8. $\dfrac{1}{2} + \dfrac{w}{6} = 1$ 9. $\dfrac{20}{x} + \dfrac{20}{2x} = 1$

10. $\dfrac{a}{6} + \dfrac{a-2}{9} = 1$ 11. $\dfrac{8}{x} + \dfrac{8}{3x} = 1$ 12. $\dfrac{x+4}{9} + \dfrac{1}{4} = 1$

13. $\dfrac{1}{y} - \dfrac{1}{y-4} = 1$ 14. $\dfrac{-2}{x-2} + \dfrac{x}{x+2} = 1$ 15. $y - \dfrac{2}{y} = 1$

Problem Solving and Applications

11–6 Work Problems

Work problems usually deal with persons or machines working at different rates of speed. The first step in solving these problems involves determining how much of the work an individual or a machine can do in a given unit of time, such as a minute, an hour, and so on.

For example suppose Freida takes 3 hours to type a term paper.

Part of job done in 1 hour: $\dfrac{1}{3}$

Part of job done in 2 hours: $\dfrac{1}{3} \cdot 2$, or $\dfrac{2}{3}$

Part of job done in n hours: $\dfrac{1}{3} \cdot n$, or $\dfrac{n}{3}$

Many work problems involve this formula.

$$\textbf{rate of work} \times \textbf{time} = \textbf{work done,} \qquad \text{or}$$

$$r \quad \cdot \quad t \ = \quad w$$

EXAMPLE 1   Gloria can clear the snow from a sidewalk in 60 minutes. Marsha can clear the same area in 30 minutes. How long will it take them to do the job if they work together?

Solution: $\boxed{1}$ Represent the unknown. Organize the information in a table.

Let $t =$ the number of minutes for both to do the job working together.

Worker	Rate of Work per Minute (r)	Time Spent Working Together (t)	Part of Work Done ($r \cdot t = w$)
Gloria	$\dfrac{1}{60}$	t	$\dfrac{1}{60}t$, or $\dfrac{t}{60}$
Marsha	$\dfrac{1}{30}$	t	$\dfrac{1}{30}t$, or $\dfrac{t}{30}$

$\boxed{2}$ Use the table to write an equation for the problem.

$$\dfrac{\text{Work done by}}{\text{Gloria}} + \dfrac{\text{Work done by}}{\text{Marsha}} = \dfrac{\text{Total}}{\text{job}}$$

$$\dfrac{t}{60} \quad + \quad \dfrac{t}{30} \quad = \quad 1$$

$\boxed{3}$ Solve the equation. The LCD is 60.

$$60\left(\frac{t}{60} + \frac{t}{30}\right) = 60(1)$$

$$60\left(\frac{t}{60}\right) + 60\left(\frac{t}{30}\right) = 60$$

$$t + 2t = 60 \quad \longleftarrow \quad \textbf{Solve for } \textit{t.}$$

$$3t = 60$$

$$t = 20 \quad \longleftarrow \quad \begin{array}{l}\textbf{Number of minutes they}\\ \textbf{work together}\end{array}$$

Check: $\boxed{4}$ Gloria does $\frac{20}{60}$, or $\frac{1}{3}$ of the work in 20 minutes.

Marsha does $\frac{20}{30}$, or $\frac{2}{3}$ of the work in 20 minutes.

Total work done: $\frac{1}{3} + \frac{2}{3} = \frac{3}{3}$, or 1

Working together, Gloria and Marsha can complete the job in **20 minutes.**

REMEMBER: When a job is completed, the sum of the fractional parts of the job done by each worker equals 1.

EXAMPLE 2 Bill can do a certain job in 8 days. After working alone for 4 days, he is joined by Tony. Together they finish the job in 2 more days. How long would it take Tony to do the job alone?

Solution: $\boxed{1}$ Let d = the number of days for Tony to do the job alone.

Then $\frac{1}{d}$ = Tony's rate of work.

Worker	Rate of Work Per Day	Time Working Alone	Time Working Together	Work Done ($r \cdot t = w$)
Bill	$\frac{1}{8}$	4 days	2 days	$\frac{1}{8}(4) + \frac{1}{8}(2) = \frac{3}{4}$
Tony	$\frac{1}{d}$	0 days	2 days	$\frac{1}{d} \cdot 2$, or $\frac{2}{d}$

$\boxed{2}$ $\underset{\text{Bill}}{\underline{\text{Work done by}}} \; + \; \underset{\text{Tony}}{\underline{\text{Work done by}}} \; = \; \underset{\text{job}}{\underline{\text{Total}}}$

$$\frac{3}{4} \quad + \quad \frac{2}{d} \quad = \quad 1 \quad \longleftarrow \quad \textbf{LCD: } \textit{4d}$$

$\boxed{3}$

$$4d\left(\frac{3}{4} + \frac{2}{d}\right) = 4d(1)$$

$$4d\left(\frac{3}{4}\right) + 4d\left(\frac{2}{d}\right) = 4d$$

$$3d + 8 = 4d$$

$$8 = d \quad \longleftarrow \quad \begin{array}{l}\textbf{Number of days if}\\ \textbf{Tony worked alone}\end{array}$$

Check: **4** Work done by Bill: $\frac{3}{4}$

Work done by Tony: $\frac{2}{d} = \frac{2}{8} = \frac{1}{4}$

Total work done: $\frac{3}{4} + \frac{1}{4} = 1$

It will take Tony **8 days** to do the job alone.

CLASSROOM EXERCISES

Clarence can mow a lawn in 80 minutes. Jim can mow the same lawn in 120 minutes. Use this information in Exercises 1–6.

1. What part of the lawn can Clarence mow in 1 minute?

2. What part of the lawn can Jim mow in 1 minute?

3. What part of the lawn can Clarence mow in 30 minutes?

4. What part of the lawn can Jim mow in 90 minutes?

5. What part of the lawn can Clarence mow in m minutes?

6. What part of the lawn can Jim mow in y minutes?

Pipe A can empty a pool in 5 hours. Pipe B can empty the pool in 3 hours. Use this information in Exercises 7–13.

7. What part of the pool can Pipe A empty in 1 hour?

8. What part of the pool can Pipe A empty in 4 hours?

9. What part of the pool can Pipe B empty in 1 hour?

10. What part of the pool can Pipe B empty in 3 hours?

11. What part of the pool is drained in 1 hour by both pipes?

12. What part of the pool can be emptied in x hours by both pipes?

13. Write an equation whose solution would give the number of hours that it would take both pipes to empty the pool.

WORD PROBLEMS

A   Solve each problem.

1. Ken can build a fence in 4 days. His niece Sara can do it in 4.5 days. How long would it take them working together?

2. Jill can paint a house in 2 days. Her brother can paint it in 4 days. How long would it take them to paint the house if they work together?

3. A large pipe can empty a tank in 5 minutes, and a smaller pipe can empty it in 8 minutes. How long would it take both pipes to empty the tank?

4. Marge can do a piece of work in 3 days, Mae in 5 days, and Gina in 8 days. If all three work together, how long will it take them to do the work?

5. To remove the dirt from a building foundation, a contractor is using a large diesel shovel and a small one. If the large shovel can do the entire job in 6 days and the small shovel can do it in 9 days, how long will it take them together?

6. Gwen Hall estimates that she can paint the Smiths' house in 6 days. Her brother Doug can paint it in 8 days and her sister Laura can paint it in 10 days. How long will it take all three working together?

7. Jim can shovel the driveway in 2 hours. Lucy can shovel it in 4 hours. Jim shovels for 1 hour and then Lucy helps him finish the job. How long does it take the two of them to finish?

8. If one pipe can fill a tank in 3 hours, a second pipe in 5 hours and a third pipe in 6 hours, how long will it take to fill the tank if all three pipes are being used?

9. One machine can complete an order for bolts in 7 hours and another machine can do it in 5 hours. How long will it take both machines to finish the job after the slower machine has been working alone for $3\frac{1}{2}$ hours?

10. Juan can paint a room in 3 hours. Anita can paint the same room in 5 hours. Anita paints alone for 2 hours and then Juan helps her finish. How long does it take them to finish painting the room?

B

11. Kate can type a manuscript in 6 hours. If Mark helps her they can type the complete manuscript in 4 hours. How long would it take Mark if he did all the typing?

12. Jacques can spade a garden in 5 hours. After working alone for 2 hours he is joined by Dave. Together they finish the job in 1 hour. How long would it take Dave to spade the garden alone?

13. It takes 10 minutes to fill a certain tank and 15 minutes to empty it when it is full. With the drain open and the tank empty, how long would it take to fill it?

14. Janette can make an afghan in 10 days, Bill in 6 days, and Sue in 15 days. Bill and Janette work for 3 days. How long will it take Janette and Sue to finish the afghan?

15. One card reader can read a deck of computer cards in twice the time it takes another reader. Together they can read the deck in 8 minutes. How long would it take each reader alone to read the deck?

16. An old machine requires 3 times as many hours to complete a job as a new machine. When both machines work together, they require 9 hours to complete a job. How many hours would it take the new machine to finish the job alone?

C

17. A swimming pool can be filled by a large pipe in 4 hours and by a small pipe in 6 hours. A third pipe can empty the pool in 3 hours. How long would it take to fill the pool if all three pipes were open at the same time?

18. Jaime, Brigette, and Tom can prepare the ballots for a school election in 2 hours. If Jaime could prepare the ballots in 5 hours and Brigette could prepare them in 6 hours, how long will it take Tom to prepare the ballots alone?

19. Frank and Liz, working together, can assemble a ham radio kit in 12 hours. Frank requires 18 hours to do it alone. Frank and Liz work together for 4 hours and Liz leaves. How long will it take Frank to finish alone?

20. It takes Louis 12 hours to repair a car's transmission. Tina came to help him after Louis had worked 6 hours alone. Together they finished the job in 3 more hours. How long would it take Tina to repair the transmission alone?

Puzzle

Copy the puzzle at the right. Complete the puzzle by entering the solutions to the equations in the appropriate box(es).

Across

1. $\dfrac{n}{6} - \dfrac{n}{4} = -1$

3. $\dfrac{2}{5} = \dfrac{4}{r-4}$

4. $\dfrac{4}{12} = \dfrac{5}{d}$

5. $b = \sqrt{100}$

8. $x^2 - 12x = -36$

9. $3 = \dfrac{2+b}{6}$

10. $\dfrac{9}{x-3} = \dfrac{7}{x-5}$

11. $\dfrac{4}{y} = \dfrac{7}{y-6}$

12. $\dfrac{m}{28} = \dfrac{1}{4}$

16. $\dfrac{3f}{8} - \dfrac{1}{4} = \dfrac{f}{3} - \dfrac{11}{24}$

Down

2. $\dfrac{2}{k-7} = \dfrac{3}{k}$

6. $\dfrac{2p}{3} + \dfrac{3p}{4} = 51$

10. $\dfrac{2}{5} = \dfrac{w}{45}$

14. $\dfrac{g}{12} = \dfrac{5}{4}$

5. $\dfrac{1}{2} = \dfrac{50}{s}$

7. $\dfrac{3z}{4} - 12 = \dfrac{3(z-12)}{5}$

13. $\dfrac{6}{c-2} = \dfrac{5}{c-3}$

15. $x^2 - 18x = -81$

REVIEW CAPSULE FOR SECTION 11–7

In Exercises 1–4, write a formula to express the direct variation. Use k as the constant of variation. *(Pages 197–200)*

1. The perimeter, P, of an equilateral triangle varies directly as the length of a side, r.

2. The length, r, of a person's shadow at a given time varies directly as the height, h, of the person.

3. The total income, T, at a fixed rate of pay per hour, varies directly as the number of hours worked, h.

4. For a car traveling at a constant rate of speed, the distance covered, d, varies directly as the time, t, that it travels.

5. If s varies directly as n, and $s = 60$ when $n = 2$, find s when $n = 7$.

6. If w varies directly as p, and $w = 5$ when $p = 10$, find p when $w = 12.5$.

11-7 Inverse Variation

The table below and the graph at the right illustrate the rate of speed required to travel 480 kilometers during various periods of time.

r	80	60	40	30	20	10	5
t	6	8	12	16	24	48	96

For a trip of 480 kilometers, the relationship between rate of travel (speed) and time can be defined by the equation $rt = 480$. The equation describes an *inverse variation*. It shows that r varies inversely as t or that t varies inversely as r. That is, as the values of r decrease, the values of t increase. Also, as the values of r increase, the values of t decrease.

Definition

> If the product of two variables is a nonzero constant, the variables are in **inverse variation**. The equation for the inverse variation may be written as
>
> $$xy = k \qquad \text{or} \qquad y = \frac{k}{x},$$
>
> where k is the **constant of variation.**

EXAMPLE 1 Determine whether each equation is an example of inverse variation.

a. $bh = 40$ **b.** $t = \dfrac{100}{r}$

Solution: Compare each equation with $xy = k$ or $y = \dfrac{k}{x}$.

a. $bh = 40$ has the same form as $xy = k$. Thus, it is an example of inverse variation.

b. $t = \dfrac{100}{r}$ has the same form as $y = \dfrac{k}{x}$. Thus, it is an example of inverse variation.

NOTE: In $bh = 40$, the constant of variation is 40. In $t = \dfrac{100}{r}$, the constant of variation is 100.

When you are given that a function is an inverse variation and you know one ordered pair of the function, you can determine k, the constant of variation. Then you can write the equation that shows how x and y are related.

EXAMPLE 2 If x varies inversely as y, and $x = 4$ when $y = 5$, write the equation that shows how x and y are related.

Solution: **1** Find k, the constant of variation.

$$xy = k \longleftarrow \quad \textbf{x varies inversely as y.}$$
$$\textbf{Replace x with 4 and y with 5.}$$
$$4 \cdot 5 = k$$
$$20 = k \longleftarrow \quad \textbf{Write the equation. Use } k = 20.$$

2 Equation: $xy = 20$

The graph of the inverse variation

$$xy = k, \text{ where } k > 0$$

is a **hyperbola.** Its branches are in the first and third quadrants as shown at the right.

$$xy = 4$$

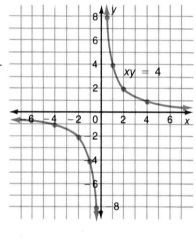

x	y		x	y
-4	-1		$\frac{1}{2}$	8
-2	-2		1	4
-1	-4		2	2
$-\frac{1}{2}$	-8		4	1

When $k < 0$, the branches of the hyperbola are in the second and fourth quadrants. In practical applications, only the branch in the first quadrant usually satisfies all the conditions of the problem.

EXAMPLE 3 The current in an electric circuit varies inversely as the resistance. When the current is 40 amps, the resistance is 12 ohms. Find the current when the resistance is 20 ohms.

Solution: **1** Find the constant of variation.

$$cr = k \longleftarrow \quad \textbf{c varies inversely as r.}$$
$$40 \cdot 12 = k \quad \text{and} \quad k = 480 \qquad \textbf{Equation:} \quad cr = 480$$

2 Find c when $r = 20$.

$$cr = 480$$
$$20c = 480$$
$$c = 24 \qquad \text{The current is \textbf{24 amps.}}$$

CLASSROOM EXERCISES

Determine whether each equation is an example of inverse variation. Answer *Yes* or *No.*

1. $yz = 6$　　　　**2.** $y = x$　　　　**3.** $b + h = 40$　　　　**4.** $ab = \frac{1}{4}$

5. $\frac{x}{y} = \frac{1}{2}$　　　　**6.** $y = \frac{1}{x}$　　　　**7.** $x = \frac{200}{z}$　　　　**8.** $\frac{a}{5} = \frac{3}{b}$

In Exercises 9–12, use the equation $xy = 28$.

9. If x increases, what happens to y?

10. If x decreases, what happens to y?

11. If a certain value of x is doubled, what happens to the value of y?

12. If a certain value of y is multiplied by 4, what happens to the value of x?

WRITTEN EXERCISES

A　　Determine whether each of the following is an example of inverse variation. Answer *Yes* or *No*. Give a reason for each answer.

1. $xy = 6$　　　　**2.** $x + y = 6$　　　　**3.** $x - y = 6$　　　　**4.** $x = 10y$

5. $\frac{x}{y} = 6$　　　　**6.** $x = \frac{10}{y}$　　　　**7.** $y = \frac{42}{x}$　　　　**8.** $x + y = 10$

9. $y = 250x$　　　　**10.** $y = 430x - 5$　　　　**11.** $xy + y = 8$　　　　**12.** $xy - y = 8$

In Exercises 13–18, y varies inversely as x. Write the equation that shows how x and y are related.

13. $y = 7$ when $x = 6$　　　**14.** $y = 4$ when $x = 12$　　　**15.** $y = \frac{3}{4}$ when $x = \frac{2}{3}$

16. $y = -5$ when $x = 2$　　　**17.** $y = -8$ when $x = -5$　　　**18.** $y = -5\frac{1}{4}$ when $x = -8\frac{1}{3}$

19. If x varies inversely as y, and $x = 8$ when $y = 9$, find x when $y = 18$.

20. If p varies inversely as q, and $p = 50$ when $q = 4$, find p when $q = 40$.

21. If r varies inversely as t and $r = 80$ when $t = 0.25$, find r when $t = 2$.

22. If y varies inversely as z and $y = 6$ when $z = -4$, find y when $z = -3$.

23. If a varies inversely as b and $a = 60$ when $b = \frac{1}{2}$, find b when $a = 20$.

24. If c varies inversely as d and $c = 0.40$ when $d = 100$, find d when $c = 1.6$.

WORD PROBLEMS

Solve each problem.

In Exercises 25–26, the current varies inversely as the resistance.

25. When the resistance in a certain electrical circuit is 10 ohms, the current is 24 amps. Find the current when the resistance is 20 ohms.

26. A certain electrical circuit has a resistance of 12 ohms. The current is 15 amps. Find the current when the resistance is decreased to 4 ohms.

27. The number of days needed to finish repairing a sidewalk varies inversely as the number of people working. It takes 12 days for two people to repair the walk. How many people are needed to complete the job in 4 days?

28. The rent for an apartment varies inversely as the number of people sharing the cost. Four people sharing an apartment pay $120 each per month. How many people would be needed so that each would pay $80 per month?

29. The amount of time to make a trip varies inversely as the rate of travel. At 30 miles per hour it takes Jenny 4 hours to travel from her home to her vacation cottage. How long would it take if she drove at 50 miles per hour?

30. A jet traveling at 2200 kilometers per hour took 4 hours to fly from Boston to Paris. The time varies inversely as the rate of speed. How long would it take a plane traveling at 2500 km/hr to make the same trip?

31. The number of tomato plants in a row in George's garden varies inversely as the space between them. If the plants are spaced 15 centimeters apart, 60 plants fit in a row. How many can fit if he places them 25 centimeters apart?

32. The number of days needed to paint the outside of a house varies inversely as the number of people painting the house. It takes 2 people 8 days to paint the house. How many days will it take 4 people to paint the house?

B

33. The number of square tiles on a floor varies inversely as the area of the tiles. It takes 108 tiles with an area of 1 square foot to cover a certain floor. How many tiles with an area of $\frac{9}{16}$ square foot would it take to cover the same floor?

34. When the tension on a wire is kept constant, the number of vibrations per second varies inversely as the length of the wire. A wire 400 centimeters long vibrates 160 times per second. How long should a wire be so that it will vibrate 240 times per second?

If y varies inversely as the square of x, then $y = \dfrac{k}{x^2}$, or $yx^2 = k$. Find the constant of variation and write the equation for each relation.

35. $y = 6$ when $x = 2$

36. $y = 2$ when $x = 1$

37. $y = 8$ when $x = 4$

38. $y = 4$ when $x = -3$

39. $y = -5$ when $x = -4$

40. $y = 3\frac{1}{2}$ when $x = 5\frac{3}{4}$

C

41. The frequency, f, of vibration of a wire (of uniform length and tension) varies inversely as the square root of its weight, w. Express this relation in a formula, using k to represent the constant of variation. Given that k is 508, what is f when w is 4?

42. The intensity, I, of a light varies inversely as the square of the distance, d, from the light. How far should a book be placed from a light to receive four times as much intensity of illumination as it received when it was 2 meters from the light?

In Exercises 43–44, use the formula $fp = v$, where f is the frequency, p is the wavelength and v is the speed of sound (about 335 meters per second in air).

43. An open pipe produces a sound wave whose length is twice that of the pipe. What is the frequency of the sound from a pipe whose length is 1 meter?

44. A stopped pipe produces a sound wave whose length is four times that of the pipe. Find the length of a pipe that produces a sound with a frequency of 220.

11-8 Joint Variation

When one variable varies directly as the product of two or more variables, the variation is called a **joint variation.**

EXAMPLE 1 The volume, V, of a pyramid varies jointly as the area of its base, B, and its altitude h. When $B = 18$ and $h = 4$, $V = 24$. Find V when $B = 7$ and $h = 12$.

Solution: $V = kBh$ ⟵————— V **varies jointly as B and h.**

To find k, replace V with 24, B with 18, and h with 4.

$24 = k(18)(4)$

$24 = 72k$

$\dfrac{1}{3} = k$ ⟵————— **Write the equation for the joint variation. Use $k = \dfrac{1}{3}$.**

Thus, $V = \dfrac{1}{3}Bh$. ⟵————— **Replace B with 7 and h with 12.**

$V = \dfrac{1}{3}(7)(12)$

$V = 28$ **cubic units** ⟵————— **Volume is measured in cubic units.**

When a variable varies directly as one variable and inversely as another, the variation is sometimes called **combined variation.** Thus, if x varies directly as y and inversely as z, then

$$x = ky\left(\frac{1}{z}\right) \quad \text{or} \quad x = \frac{ky}{z}.$$

EXAMPLE 2 Suppose that y varies directly as x and inversely as w. If $y = 2$ when $x = 7$ and $w = 14$, find y when $x = 10$ and $w = 8$.

Solution: $y = \dfrac{kx}{w}$ ⟵————— y **varies directly as x and inversely as w.**

To find k, replace y with 2, x with 7, and w with 14.

$2 = \dfrac{7k}{14}$

$2 = \dfrac{1}{2}k$

$4 = k$ ⟵————— **Write the equation for the variation.**

$y = \dfrac{4x}{w}$ ⟵————— **Replace x with 10 and w with 8.**

$y = \dfrac{4 \cdot 10}{8}$

$y = 5$

CLASSROOM EXERCISES

Write a formula for each statement. Use k as the constant of variation.

1. a varies jointly as b and c.
2. t varies jointly as s and v.
3. m varies directly as n and inversely as p.
4. h varies directly as g and inversely as l.
5. s varies directly as t and inversely as the square of r.
6. x varies directly as the square of y and inversely as the cube of w.

WRITTEN EXERCISES

A

1. If t varies jointly as s and r, and $t = 120$ when $s = 15$ and $r = 4$, find t when $s = 12$ and $r = 9$.

2. If q varies jointly as n and p, and $q = 12$ when $n = 14$ and $p = 6$, find q when $n = 21$ and $p = 8$.

3. If x varies jointly as w, y, and z, and $x = 15$ when $w = 2$, $y = 10$, and $z = 3$, find x when $w = 8$, $y = 5$, and $z = 7$.

4. If a varies jointly as b, c, and d, and $a = 75$ when $b = 1$, $c = 5$, and $d = 5$, find a when $b = 3$, $c = 7$, and $d = 9$.

5. If q varies directly as h and inversely as j, and $q = 14$ when $h = 28$ and $j = 7$, find q when $h = 14$ and $j = 6$.

6. If f varies directly as d^2 and inversely as b, and $f = 3$ when $d = 6$ and $b = 4$, find f when $d = 9$ and $b = 5$.

7. If A varies directly as B and inversely as C^2, and $A = 9$ when $B = 9$ and $C = 4$, find A when $B = 5$ and $C = 2$.

8. If G varies directly as H^3 and inversely as F^2, and $G = 4$ when $H = 2$ and $F = 4$, find G when $H = 6$ and $F = 12$.

9. If m varies jointly as p and r^2, and $m = 28$ when $p = 7$ and $r = 8$, find m when $p = 10$ and $r = 4$.

10. If x varies jointly as y and z and inversely as m, and $x = 60$ when $y = 2$, $z = 5$, and $m = 4$, find x when $y = 3$, $z = 9$, and $m = 6$.

WORD PROBLEMS

11. The area of a triangle varies jointly as the base and the height. A triangle with a base of 5 inches and a height of 6 inches has an area of 15 square inches. Find the area when the base is 7 inches and the height is 4 inches.

12. The mass, m, of a rectangular sheet of wood varies jointly as the length, l, and the width, w. When l is 40 centimeters and w is 20 centimeters, m is 400 grams. Find m when l is 30 centimeters and w is 20 centimeters.

13. The volume of a pyramid, V, varies jointly as the area of the base, B, and the height, h. When B is 12 square centimeters and h is 9 centimeters, V is 36 cubic centimeters. Find V when B is 14 square centimeters and h is 6 centimeters.

14. The volume of a cone varies jointly as the area of the base, B_1 and the height, h. The volume is 50 cubic centimeters when the area of the base is 30 square centimeters and the height is 5 centimeters. Find V when $h = 9$ centimeters and $B = 40$ square centimeters.

15. The glide ability of a hang glider depends on a ratio called the **aspect ratio,** R. R varies directly as the square of the wingspread, S^2, and inversely as the wing area, A. When A is 30 square feet and, S is 9 feet, R is 2.7. Find R when A is 40 square feet and S is 10 feet.

16. The force of attraction, F, of a body varies directly as its mass, m, and inversely as the square of the distance, d, from the body. When $m = 8$ kilograms and $d = 5$ meters, $F = 100$ Newtons. Find F when $m = 2$ kilograms and $d = 15$ meters.

17. The electrical resistance in a wire varies directly as its length, L, and inversely as the square of its diameter, d. A wire 5 kilometers long with a diameter of 6 millimeters has a resistance of 20 ohms. Find the resistance of a wire of the same material with a length of 6 kilometers and a diameter of 4 millimeters.

18. The crushing load, L, of a square wooden post varies directly as the fourth power of its thickness, t^4, and inversely as its length squared, l^2. A post 10 centimeters thick and 4 meters high is crushed by a load of 22.5 tons. What is the crushing load of a post 5 centimeters thick and 3 meters high?

_____ **Review** _____

1. The sum of two fractions is $\frac{10}{3}$ and one of them is $\frac{1}{4}$ of the other. Find the fractions. *(Section 11-4)*

2. One integer is $\frac{2}{3}$ of another integer. The sum of their reciprocals is $\frac{5}{36}$. Find the integers. *(Section 11-4)*

3. It takes 12 hours to drive a truck to its delivery point and back. If the rate going is 50 kilometers per hour and the return rate is 70 kilometers per hour, how long is the round trip? *(Section 11-5)*

4. An airplane flies 99 miles with a tailwind of 20 miles per hour. It returns to its starting point flying against the wind. If the round trip takes one hour, what is the rate of the plane in still air? *(Section 11-5)*

5. One pipe can fill a tank in 20 minutes. A larger pipe can fill it in 12 minutes. If both pipes are used, how long will it take to fill the tank? *(Section 11-6)*

6. Maria can make out the payroll in 6 hours. If Ted helps her, they can finish in 4 hours. How long would it take Ted to do the job alone? *(Section 11-6)*

7. The current in an electrical circuit varies inversely as the resistance. When the resistance in a certain circuit is 12 ohms, the current is 30 amps. Find the current when the resistance is 18 ohms. *(Section 11-7)*

8. The number of days needed to paint a house varies inversely as the number of people working. It takes 10 days for two people to paint the house. How many people are needed to complete the job in 5 days? *(Section 11-7)*

9. The area of a triangle varies jointly as the base and the height. A triangle with a base of 7 inches and a height of 8 inches has an area of 28 square inches. Find the area when the base is 5 inches and the height is 6 inches. *(Section 11-8)*

10. The mass, m, of a rectangular sheet of metal varies jointly as the length, l, and the width, w, When l is 4 meters and w is 2 meters, m is 2 kilograms. Find m when l is 5 meters and w is 3 meters. *(Section 11-8)*

BASIC: EQUATION OF A LINE

Problem: *Given the slope and the coordinates of a point on a line, write a program which prints the equation of the line in slope-intercept form.*

```
100 PRINT "WHAT IS THE SLOPE OF THE LINE AND THE"
110 PRINT "COORDINATES OF A POINT ON THE LINE";
120 INPUT M, X1, Y1
130 LET B = Y1 - M*X1
140 PRINT "EQUATION IS Y = ";
150 IF M = 0 THEN 240
160 IF B = 0 THEN 200
170 IF B < 0 THEN 220
180 PRINT M;"X +";B
190 GOTO 250
200 PRINT M;"X"
210 GOTO 250
220 PRINT M;"X -";ABS(B)
230 GOTO 250
240 PRINT B
250 PRINT
260 PRINT "ANY MORE LINES (1=YES, 0=NO)";
270 INPUT Z
280 IF Z = 1 THEN 120
290 END
```

Output:
```
RUN
WHAT IS THE SLOPE OF THE LINE AND THE
COORDINATES OF A POINT ON THE LINE? 3,1,1
EQUATION IS Y = 3 X - 2

ANY MORE LINES (1=YES, 0=NO)? 1
? -2,4,-7
EQUATION IS Y = -2 X + 1

ANY MORE LINES (1=YES, 0=NO)? 1
? 0,15,-1
EQUATION IS Y = -1

ANY MORE LINES (1=YES, 0=NO)? 1
? 5,1,5
EQUATION IS Y = 5 X

ANY MORE LINES (1=YES, 0=NO)? 0
READY
```

Analysis

Statement 130: In the slope–intercept form of a linear equation $(y = mx + b)$, b represents the y intercept. Statement 130 is derived by solving the equation for b, and substituting the coordinates of the sample point, (x_1, y_1).

$$y = mx + b$$
$$y - mx = b \quad \underline{\text{or}} \quad b = y - mx$$
$$b = y_1 - m(x_1)$$

Statements 140–240: The bulk of the program is concerned with printing the equation as neatly as possible.

Statements 150 and 240: If M = 0, no X term is printed. See the output for the third set of data in the sample run on page 419.

Statements 160 and 200: If B = 0, just the X term is printed. See the output for the last set of data in the sample run on page 419.

Statements 170 and 220: If B < 0, the equation is printed as Y = 3 X - 2 and not as Y = 3 X + -2.

EXERCISES

A   Run the program on page 419, using the following values of slope and coordinates of a point on each line.

1. Slope: 2; Point: $(0, 3)$
2. Slope: 4; Point: $(-2, -1)$
3. Slope: 3; Point: $(1, -3)$
4. Slope: 7; Point: $(3, 6)$
5. Slope: -1; Point: $(4, 0)$
6. Slope: -3; Point: $(1, 3)$
7. Slope: -10; Point: $(6, 2)$
8. Slope: 12; Point: $(0, 8)$
9. Slope: 0; Point: $(2, -5)$
10. Slope: 0; Point: $(-1, -1)$

11. The program on page 419 does not handle vertical lines, since the slope of such lines is undefined. Add statements to the program so that a value of 999 for the slope is the code for a vertical line. Print the equation in the form $x = x_1$.

B   Write a BASIC program for each problem.

12. Given the coordinates of two points on a line, print the equation of the line in slope–intercept form.
13. Given the coordinates of a point on a line and the y intercept, print the equation of the line in slope–intercept form.
14. y varies inversely as x. Given the constant of variation and the smallest and largest x values, print a table of ordered pairs for x and y.
15. Given two ordered pairs, print whether the set of ordered pairs is an example of inverse variation.

Chapter Summary

Apparent solution (p. 389)
Combined variation (p. 416)
General form of a linear
equation (p. 396)

Hyperbola (p. 413)
Inverse variation (p. 412)
Joint variation (p. 416)

IMPORTANT IDEAS

1. **Steps for Solving Equations with Rational Expressions**
   - $\boxed{1}$ Multiply each side of the equation by the LCD.
   - $\boxed{2}$ Follow the usual procedures to solve the resulting equation.
2. You can write the equation of a line if you know
   - **a.** the slope and the y intercept,
   - **b.** the slope and the coordinates of one point on the line, or
   - **c.** the coordinates of two points on the line.
3. **Work formula:** rate of work $\times$ time $=$ work done, or $r \cdot t = w$

Chapter Objectives and Review

Objective: *To solve equations containing rational expressions (Section 11-1)*

Solve each equation.

1. $\dfrac{n}{2} - \dfrac{2n}{9} = 5$

2. $\dfrac{24}{3x} = \dfrac{4}{9}$

3. $\dfrac{12}{5x} - \dfrac{7}{5x} = \dfrac{1}{2}$

4. $\dfrac{y}{6} = \dfrac{y}{2(2-y)}$

5. $\dfrac{a}{3} = \dfrac{4}{a+4}$

6. $\dfrac{1}{y} + \dfrac{1}{2y} = \dfrac{1}{y+2}$

7. $\dfrac{4}{x} = \dfrac{x}{x+1} - \dfrac{1}{x^2+x}$

8. $\dfrac{3}{x-3} + \dfrac{4}{x} = \dfrac{x}{x-3}$

9. $\dfrac{a}{1+3a} = \dfrac{2}{a+5}$

10. $\dfrac{x-1}{x+2} - \dfrac{6}{x^2+2x} = \dfrac{2}{x}$

11. $\dfrac{y}{y+14} = \dfrac{2}{y+5}$

12. $\dfrac{n+1}{n} = \dfrac{2}{2n-3} + \dfrac{2}{n}$

Objective: *To write the equation of a line, given its slope and the coordinates of a point on the line (Section 11-2)*

The slope and the y intercept of a line are given. Write the equation of the line in the form $y = mx + b$.

13. slope: -3; y intercept: 4

14. slope: 5; y intercept: 0

15. slope: $-\dfrac{1}{2}$; y intercept: $-\dfrac{3}{4}$

16. slope: $\dfrac{5}{8}$; y intercept: 8

One point on a line and the slope of the line are given. Write the equation of the line in the form $y = mx + b$.

17. $B(1, 4)$; $m = 2$

18. $P(-2, 3)$; $m = \dfrac{1}{4}$

19. $Y(-4, -4)$; $m = -1$

20. $D(5, 0)$; $m = 6$

21. $Q(3, -3)$; $m = \dfrac{3}{2}$

22. $G(-4, -4)$; $m = 4$

Objective: *To write the equation of a line, given the coordinates of two points on the line (Section 11–3)*

Determine the equation of the line passing through the given points. Write the equation in the form $y = mx + b$.

23. $M(0, 2)$; $N(3, 11)$
24. $P(2, 0)$; $Q(-4, 3)$
25. $X(0, 0)$; $Y(-3, 15)$
26. $A(1, 2)$; $B(-1, -4)$
27. $F(2, -3)$; $G(-2, 5)$
28. $J(3, 0)$; $K(-6, -12)$

Determine the equation of the line passing through the given points. Write the equation in general form.

29. $C(3, 5)$; $D(5, 3)$
30. $X(0, -4)$; $Y(1, -2)$
31. $H(4, -1)$; $I(-6, 3)$

Objective: *To solve number problems involving rational expressions (Section 11–4)*

32. The sum of two fractions is $\frac{11}{12}$. One fraction is $\frac{3}{8}$ of the other. Find the fractions.

33. The sum of two positive integers is 14. The difference of their reciprocals is $\frac{1}{24}$. Find the integers.

Objective: *To solve motion problems (Section 11–5)*

34. Miriam drove 400 kilometers in the same amount of time that it took Ruth to drive 320 kilometers. Miriam drove 15 kilometers per hour faster than Ruth. Find the speed of each.

35. Bob paddles his canoe at a rate of 6 kilometers per hour in still water. Find the rate of the current if it takes Bob twice as long to paddle 20 kilometers upstream as to paddle 20 kilometers downstream.

Objective: *To solve work problems (Section 11–6)*

36. An old machine can produce an order for bottle caps in 7.5 hours. A newer machine can produce the same number of caps in 5 hours. How long would it take to fill the order using both machines together?

37. One outboard motor uses up a tank of fuel in 6 hours. A larger motor uses the same amount of fuel in 4 hours. How long can both motors be run if they are connected to the same tank that is filled to capacity?

Objective: *To solve problems involving inverse variation (Section 11–7)*

y varies inversely as x. Write the equation that shows how x and y are related.

38. $y = 36$ when $x = -3$
39. $y = 7$ when $x = 1$
40. $y = 6$ when $x = 16$
41. $y = 9$ when $x = \frac{1}{2}$
42. $y = -2\frac{1}{2}$ when $x = 3$
43. $y = -\frac{9}{2}$ when $x = \frac{2}{3}$

44. A rectangular garden is to have a given area. When the length is 8 meters, the width is 3.5 meters. What is the width when the length is 5.6 meters?

45. A rectangular box is to have a given volume. When the area of the base of the box is 144 square units, the height is 8 units. What is the height when the area of the base is 256 square units?

Objective: *To solve problems involving joint or combined variation*
(Section 11–8)

46. If c varies jointly as p and q, and $c = 84$ when $p = 3$ and $q = 7$, find c when $p = \frac{1}{2}$ and $q = 9$.

47. If r varies directly as w and inversely as y^2, and $r = 2$ when $w = 6$ and $y = 3$, find r when $w = 10$ and $y = 2$.

48. If b varies jointly as c and d and inversely as f^2, and $b = 80$ when $c = 10$, $d = 2$, and $f = 4$, find b when $c = 5$, $d = 6$, and $f = 2$.

49. If h varies jointly as j^2 and k and inversely as g, and $h = 50$ when $j = 2$, $k = 5$, and $g = \frac{1}{2}$, find h when $j = 4$, $k = 10$, and $g = \frac{1}{4}$.

50. The interest, i, for one year varies jointly as the principal, p, and the rate, r. When p is \$500 and r is 6%, i is \$30. Find i when p is \$800 and r is 9%. (HINT: Write a decimal for 6% and 9%.)

51. The attraction, F, between two objects varies jointly as their masses, a and b, and inversely as the square of the distance, d, between them. When $F = 4$, $a = 3$, $b = 4$, and $d = 6$. Find F when $a = 5$, $b = 15$, and $d = 20$.

_____ Chapter Test _____

Solve each equation.

1. $\dfrac{x}{6} + \dfrac{2x}{9} = 7$

2. $\dfrac{3y}{y+9} + \dfrac{3}{4y} = 1$

3. $\dfrac{a}{a-2} = \dfrac{2}{a-3}$

One point on a line and the slope of the line are given. Write the equation of the line in the form $y = mx + b$.

4. $A(0, 3)$; $m = -1$

5. $P(1, -2)$; $m = \frac{1}{3}$

6. $F(-6, 5)$; $m = 3$

Determine the equation of the line passing through the given points. Write the equation in the form $y = mx + b$.

7. $A(3, 5)$; $B(5, 3)$

8. $X(0, -4)$; $Y(1, -2)$

9. $M(4, -1)$; $N(-6, 3)$

10. Jan drove 160 kilometers in the same time that Karen drove 150 kilometers. Jan drove 5 kilometers per hour faster than Karen. Find the speed of each.

11. It takes David 30 minutes to load a truck. Matthew can do the job in 20 minutes. How long will it take them to load the truck if they work together?

12. The sum of two fractions is $1\frac{1}{2}$. One fraction is $\frac{4}{5}$ of the other fraction. Find the two fractions.

13. If p varies inversely as t, and $p = 3$ when $t = 6$, find p when $t = 9$.

14. If c varies inversely as d, and $c = 4$ when $d = -6$, find c when $d = 2$.

15. Given that c varies jointly as n and p and inversely as t, and $n = 4$, $p = 6$, and $t = 12$ when $c = 1$, find c when $n = 5$, $p = 18$, and $t = 15$.

Applications of Rational Expressions **423**

Additional Practice

Skills

Solve. *(Section 11-1)*

1. $\dfrac{y}{6} + \dfrac{y}{9} = 5$

2. $\dfrac{2}{x} + \dfrac{3}{4} = \dfrac{4x+5}{4x}$

3. $\dfrac{n}{n+1} = \dfrac{3}{n-1} - \dfrac{6}{n^2-1}$

One point on a line and the slope of the line are given. Write the equation of the line in the form $y = mx + b$. *(Section 11-2)*

4. $A(3, 4)$; $m = 4$

5. $B(0, -6)$; $m = -2$

6. $C(-2, -4)$; $m = 1$

7. $D(-1, 5)$; $m = -\dfrac{1}{2}$

8. $E(3, 0)$; $m = \dfrac{2}{3}$

9. $F(0, 0)$; $m = -\dfrac{3}{4}$

Determine the equation of the line passing through the given points. Write the equation in the form $y = mx + b$. *(Section 11-3)*

10. $A(-2, 0)$; $D(0, 4)$

11. $C(0, 0)$; $B(2, -3)$

12. $M(0, 5)$; $N(-1, -4)$

13. $P(3, 2)$; $Q(-2, -3)$

14. $R(4, -1)$; $S(-2, -2)$

15. $J(-1, -1)$; $K(1, 5)$

Determine the equation of the line passing through the given points. Write the equation in general form. *(Section 11-3)*

16. $S(6, -2)$; $T(0, 3)$

17. $F(-4, -1)$; $G(4, -2)$

18. $V(0, -3)$; $W(12, 0)$

(Section 11-7)

19. If y varies inversely as x, and $y = 6$ when $x = 8$, find y when $x = 12$.

20. If b varies inversely as h, and $b = 0.5$ when $h = 4$, find b when $h = 10$.

(Section 11-8)

21. If x varies jointly as y and z, and $x = 60$ when $y = 5$ and $z = 2$, find x when $y = 3$ and $z = 4$.

22. If p varies directly as q^2 and inversely as r, and $p = -4$ when $q = 4$ and $r = -2$, find p when $q = 3$ and $r = 6$.

Applications

23. Two integers are consecutive. If 5 is subtracted from the lesser integer and added to the greater integer, their quotient is equal to $\dfrac{1}{2}$. Find the integers. *(Section 11-4)*

24. Kim drove her car 100 kilometers in the same time that Sue drove her car 110 kilometers. Sue's average rate was 6 kilometers per hour faster than Kim's. Find the average rate for each person. *(Section 11-5)*

25. A plane can fly 1050 kilometers with a tailwind in the same time that it can fly 900 kilometers against the wind. If the wind speed is 25 kilometers per hour, what is the speed of the plane in still air? *(Section 11-5)*

26. Janet can type a manuscript in 6 days. After working alone one day, Ted helps her to complete the job. Together, they finish the typing in 3 more days. How long would it take Ted to do the job alone? *(Section 11-6)*

Review of Word Problems: Chapters 1–11

1. Jill paid $19.53 for 45 liters of gasoline and one liter of oil. If the oil cost $1.93, what was the cost of one liter of gasoline? *(Section 3–4)*

2. The perimeter of a triangle is 75 inches. The first side is $\frac{2}{3}$ of the second side and the third side is $\frac{5}{6}$ of the second side. Find the length of each side of the triangle. *(Section 4–4)*

3. Alex is now four times as old as his sister, Louise. In 2 years, Alex will be three times as old as Louise will be then. How old are Alex and Louise now? *(Section 4–6)*

4. Ronald and Tony left the same place at the same time and drove in opposite directions. Ronald's rate was 8 miles per hour less than Tony's rate. After 2 hours they were 200 miles apart. Find the rate at which each was traveling. *(Section 5–2)*

5. Which has the greater area, a rectangle with length $(a + 6)$ units and width $(a - 4)$ units or a rectangle with length $(a + 5)$ units and width $(a - 3)$ units? How much greater is it? *(Section 8–8)*

6. In how many ways can 126 seedlings be planted so that each row has the same number of seedlings and there are at least 6 rows and 6 columns? *(Section 9–1)*

7. The area of a rectangle is expressed as $(x^2 + 4x - 12)$ square units. Express the length and width of the rectangle as binomials. *(Section 9–5)*

8. The area of the carpet in a large reception room is 96 square meters. The length of the carpet is 4 meters more than its width. Find the length and width of the carpet. *(Section 9–9)*

9. A 3–meter pole casts a 2.4–meter shadow at the same time that a tree casts a 10.4–meter shadow. How tall is the tree? *(Section 10–1)*

10. Patricia Brancato invested some money at different yearly interest rates. Part was invested at 12%, twice that amount at 13%, and $200 less at 10% than at 12%. The total yearly income was $460. How much was invested at each rate? *(Section 10–2)*

11. The sum of two fractions is $\frac{14}{15}$. One fraction is $\frac{3}{25}$ of the other. Find the fractions. *(Section 11–4)*

12. It took Marcia 4 hours to drive from her home to the airport and back. Her average rate going was 50 miles per hour. Her average rate returning was 30 miles per hour, since the traffic was heavy. How far is her home from the airport? *(Section 11–5)*

13. Warren can weed a garden in 2 hours. His younger brother can weed the same garden in 6 hours. How long will it take them to weed the garden if they work together? *(Section 11–6)*

14. The current in an electric circuit varies inversely as the resistance. When the resistance is 8 ohms, the current is 60 amps. Find the resistance when the current is 32 amps. *(Section 11–7)*

Cumulative Review: Chapters 8–11

1. Which expression equals xy^3?

   a. $x \cdot y \cdot y \cdot y$ **b.** $x \cdot x \cdot x \cdot y \cdot y \cdot y$ **c.** $(x \cdot y)(x \cdot y)(x \cdot y)$ **d.** $x \cdot x \cdot x \cdot y$

2. Which expression equals $(y^2)^3$?

   a. $3 \cdot y^2$ **b.** $y^2 \cdot y$ **c.** $y^2 \cdot y^2 \cdot y^2$ **d.** $y^{3 \cdot 3}$

3. For which numbers in the replacement set $\{-5, 0, 5\}$ is it true that $(3y^2)^3 = 27y^6$?

   a. 0 **b.** -5 **c.** -5 and 5 **d.** $-5, 0$ and 5

4. Simplify: $\dfrac{(4m^2d^3)(3md^2)^3}{(3md^3)^2}$

   a. $12m^3d^3$ **b.** $(12md)^3$ **c.** $12m^3d^5$ **d.** $\dfrac{4m^2}{3d^3}$

5. Simplify: $(2)^{-3}$

   a. -6 **b.** $-\dfrac{1}{8}$ **c.** $\dfrac{1}{8}$ **d.** -8

6. Write 84,000,000 in scientific notation.

   a. 8.4×10^6 **b.** 0.84×10^8 **c.** 0.84×10^6 **d.** 8.4×10^7

7. Subtract: $(7xy - 3xy^2 - 6) - (xy^2 - xy - 9)$

   a. $8xy - 4xy^2 - 3$ **b.** $6xy - 2xy^2 - 15$ **c.** $6xy - 4xy^2 - 15$ **d.** $8xy - 4xy^2 + 3$

8. Subtract: $7 - 4(3m - 5)$

   a. $9m + 20$ **b.** $-12m + 27$ **c.** $-12m - 13$ **d.** $9m - 5$

9. Which expression equals $(x - 3y)^2$?

   a. $x^2 - 3xy + 9y^2$ **b.** $x^2 - 6xy + 9y^2$ **c.** $x^2 + 9y^2$ **d.** $x^2 - 9y^2$

10. Multiply: $(3y - 7x)(3y + 7x)$

    a. $9y^2 + 49x^2$ **b.** $3y^2 - 7x^2$ **c.** $9y^2 - 49x^2$ **d.** $9x^2 - 14xy + 49y^2$

11. Write the prime factorization of 72.

    a. $4 \cdot 2 \cdot 3^2$ **b.** $2^3 \cdot 3^2$ **c.** $2 \cdot 6^2$ **d.** $2^3 \cdot 9$

12. Which of the following is *not* a factor of $12(x + y)(x - y)$?

    a. $12(x - y)$ **b.** $x + y$ **c.** $(x - y)^2$ **d.** $12(x + y)$

13. Which of the following is a factor of $8(x + y) - 3(x + y)$?

    a. $x + y$ **b.** 3 **c.** $5(x - y)$ **d.** $5x + 8y$

14. Which of the following is *not* a factor of $\dfrac{n^2}{25} - \dfrac{m^2}{36}$?

    a. $\dfrac{n}{5} + \dfrac{m}{6}$ **b.** $\dfrac{n}{5} - \dfrac{m}{6}$ **c.** $\dfrac{n^2 - m^2}{25 \cdot 36}$ **d.** $\dfrac{36n^2 - 25m^2}{900}$

15. Find a factor of $6y^4 - 10y^3 + 4y^2$.

    a. $3y + 1$ **b.** $2y^2$ **c.** $(3y + 2)(y - 1)$ **d.** $2y^2(y + 1)$

16. Which of the following is a perfect square trinomial?

    a. $6a^2 + 6ab + 4b^2$ **b.** $3a^2 + 12ab + 4b^2$ **c.** $9a^2 + 12ab + 4b^2$ **d.** $9a^2 + 12ab + b^2$

17. Solve: $2x^2 = 18x$

    a. $\{0\}$ **b.** $\{0, 9\}$ **c.** $\{\ \}$ **d.** $\{\pm 3\}$

18. Solve: $2x^2 = x + 3$

    a. $\{1\}$ **b.** $\{3, -1\}$ **c.** $\{\frac{3}{2}, -1\}$ **d.** $\{\frac{2}{3}, -1\}$

19. The length of a rectangle is 2 centimeters more than the width. When the length and the width are each increased by 3 centimeters, the area is 80 square centimeters. Which equation will give the original width of the rectangle, w?

    a. $2(w + 2) = 80$ **b.** $(w + 3)(w + 5) = 80$

    c. $w(w + 2) + 80 = (w + 3)(w + 5)$ **d.** $w^2 + w(w + 2) = 80$

20. Solve for y: $\dfrac{y + 4}{2} = \dfrac{y - 3}{5}$

    a. $y = -8\frac{2}{3}$ **b.** $y = 8$ **c.** $y = -8$ **d.** $y = 0$

21. Carlo has \$6000 invested, part at 6% and the rest at 11%. His total yearly interest is \$460. If x is the amount at 6%, which equation expresses the total interest?

    a. $0.11x + 0.06(6000 - x) = 460$ **b.** $0.11 - 6000 + 0.06x = 460$

    c. $0.06x + 0.11(6000 - x) = 460$ **d.** $(0.06 + 0.11)(6000 - x) = 460$

22. Divide and simplify: $\dfrac{x - 2}{x^2 - 5x + 6} \div \dfrac{x^2 - 3x}{x^2 - 9}$

    a. $\dfrac{x - 1}{x}$ **b.** $\dfrac{x}{(x - 3)(x + 3)}$ **c.** $\dfrac{x + 3}{x(x - 3)}$ **d.** $-\dfrac{6}{x(x^2 + 1)}$

23. Subtract: $\dfrac{3y}{2} - \dfrac{y + 7}{6}$

    a. $\dfrac{8y - 7}{6}$ **b.** $\dfrac{2y - 7}{6}$ **c.** $\dfrac{8y + 7}{6}$ **d.** $8y - 7$

24. Divide: $(x^3 - 6x^2 - x + 30) \div (x + 2)$

    a. $x - 3$ **b.** $x^2 + 8x + 15$ **c.** $x - 5$ **d.** $x^2 - 8x + 15$

25. Solve: $\dfrac{7}{4y} - 2 = \dfrac{3}{2y} - 4$

    a. $y = \frac{5}{8}$ **b.** $y = -\frac{1}{8}$ **c.** $y = 0$ **d.** $y = \frac{1}{8}$

26. What is the equation of the line with slope -4 and containing the point $A(-5, 3)$?

    a. $y - 4x = 17$ **b.** $y = -4x + 17$ **c.** $3y - 5x = -4$ **d.** $4x + y = -17$

27. The numerator of a fraction is 7 less than the denominator. If 2 is added to the numerator, the new fraction equals $\frac{3}{4}$. What is the denominator of the original fraction?

    a. 20   **b.** 13   **c.** 4   **d.** 5

28. y varies directly as the square of x and inversely as z. When x is 3 and z is 1, then y is 63. Find y when x is 4 and z is 2.

    a. 14   **b.** 7   **c.** 56   **d.** 112

Preparing for College Entrance Tests

Given a system of equations (or a compound sentence with "and"), you can sometimes answer questions on College Entrance tests without solving the system. The key is in recognizing a binomial product or the factors of such a product.

EXAMPLE: If $a + b = 5$ and $a - b = 3$, find $a^2 - b^2$.

    (a) 2   (b) 3   (c) 15   (d) 16

Think: $a^2 - b^2 = (a + b)(a - b)$

Solution: $a^2 - b^2 = (a + b)(a - b)$ ⟵ **From the given equations: $a + b = 5$; $a - b = 3$.**

                     $= (5)(3) = 15$ **Answer: c**

Choose the best answer. Choose *a, b, c,* or *d.*

1. If $x - y = 6$ and $x + y = -1$, find $x^2 - y^2$.

  (a) -6 (b) 5   (c) 6   (d) 35

2. If $m + 2p = 4$ and $m - 2p = 6$, find $m^2 - 4p^2$.

  (a) -8 (b) 10   (c) 24   (d) 26

3. If $3c - d = 1$ and $3c + d = \frac{1}{2}$, find $9c^2 - d^2$.

  (a) $\frac{1}{2}$ (b) $\frac{3}{4}$ (c) $1\frac{1}{2}$ (d) 2

4. If $s^2 - t^2 = 6$ and $s + t = 3$, find $s - t$.

  (a) 2   (b) 3   (c) 6   (d) 18

5. If $a - b = 2$ and $a^2 - b^2 = 12$, find $a + b$.

  (a) $\frac{1}{6}$ (b) 6   (c) 14   (d) 24

6. If $4p^2 - 9r^2 = 3$ and $2p + 3r = 3$, find $2p - 3r$.

  (a) -1 (b) 1   (c) 3   (d) 9

7. If $(a + b)^2 = 6$ and $ab = 8$, find $a^2 + b^2$. (**HINT:** $(a + b)^2 = a^2 + 2ab + b^2$.)

  (a) 22   (b) 20   (c) -2 (d) -10

8. If $x + y = 8$ and $xy = 4$, find $x^2 + y^2$.

  (a) 0   (b) 56   (c) 60   (d) 72

9. If $(a - b)^2 = 49$ and $ab = 30$, find $a^2 + b^2$.

  (a) 109   (b) 79   (c) 67   (d) -11

10. If $xy = \frac{1}{2}$ and $x^2 + y^2 = 1\frac{1}{4}$, find $(x + y)^2$.

  (a) $\frac{1}{4}$ (b) $\frac{5}{8}$ (c) $\frac{3}{4}$ (d) $2\frac{1}{4}$

11. If $x^2 + y^2 = 8$ and $xy = 4$, find $(x - y)^2$.

  (a) 0   (b) 2   (c) 12   (d) 16

Preparing for College Entrance Tests

On College Entrance tests, it is important to recognize problems that can be solved by using proportions.

REMEMBER: Write the ratios of a proportion so that they compare the same units in the same order.

EXAMPLE: If c cans of stew make x servings, how many cans are needed to make y servings?

(a) $\dfrac{xy}{c}$ 　　 (b) $\dfrac{cx}{y}$ 　　 (c) $\dfrac{c}{xy}$ 　　 (d) $\dfrac{cy}{x}$

Think: $\dfrac{c \text{ cans}}{x \text{ servings}} = \dfrac{?}{y \text{ servings}}$

Solution: Let $n =$ the number of cans needed for y servings.

$\dfrac{c}{x} = \dfrac{n}{y}$ ⟵——— **Cans**
　　　　 ⟵——— **Servings**

$xn = cy$

$n = \dfrac{cy}{x}$ 　　**Answer: d**

Choose the best answer. Choose *a, b, c,* or *d.*

1. If a machine fills c cans in h hours, how many hours will it take to fill d cans?

   (a) $\dfrac{hd}{c}$ 　　　　 (b) $\dfrac{h}{cd}$ 　　　　 (c) $\dfrac{d}{hc}$ 　　　　 (d) $\dfrac{cd}{h}$

2. If Beth earns d dollars in h hours, how many dollars will she earn in 10 hours?

   (a) $\dfrac{10h}{d}$ 　　　　 (b) $\dfrac{10d}{h}$ 　　　　 (c) $10 + \dfrac{d}{h}$ 　　　　 (d) $\dfrac{10 + d}{h}$

3. A car travels a kilometers in b hours. At that rate, how many hours will it take the car to go 200 kilometers?

   (a) $200\dfrac{a}{b}$ 　　　　 (b) $\dfrac{b}{200a}$ 　　　　 (c) $\dfrac{200}{a} + b$ 　　　　 (d) $\dfrac{200b}{a}$

4. If c cups of flour are used to make p pie crusts, how many cups of flour are needed to make $2p$ pie crusts?

   (a) $2p$ 　　　　 (b) $\dfrac{c}{2}$ 　　　　 (c) $2c$ 　　　　 (d) $\dfrac{2}{p}$

5. If p pounds of potatoes cost d dollars, how many pounds of potatoes can be bought with $3d$ dollars?

   (a) $3p$ 　　　　 (b) $3d$ 　　　　 (c) $\dfrac{3d^2}{p}$ 　　　　 (d) $\dfrac{3p}{d} + 1$

6. A car uses x liters of gasoline every y kilometers it is driven. At that rate, how many kilometers can the car be driven with $x + 10$ liters of gasoline?

(a) $y + \dfrac{10}{x}$ (b) $\dfrac{x^2 + 10x}{y}$ (c) $y(x + 10)$ (d) $\dfrac{y(x + 10)}{x}$

7. During p hours, a total of v vehicles pass through an intersection. At that rate, how many vehicles would pass through the intersection in $p - 1$ hours?

(a) $pv(p - 1)$ (b) $v - \dfrac{1}{p}$ (c) $\dfrac{pv - 1}{p}$ (d) $\dfrac{v(p - 1)}{p}$

8. Maria earns d dollars per hour. How many dollars does she earn in 40 hours?

(a) $\dfrac{40}{d}$ (b) $40d$ (c) $\dfrac{d}{40}$ (d) $d + 40$

9. If c crates can be carried on each boxcar, how many boxcars are needed to carry 500 crates?

(a) $500c$ (b) $500 - c$ (c) $\dfrac{500}{c}$ (d) $\dfrac{c}{500}$

10. An airplane travels m miles in h hours. At that rate, how many miles does it travel in 30 minutes?

(a) $\dfrac{m}{2h}$ (b) $\dfrac{1800h}{m}$ (c) $\dfrac{2m}{h}$ (d) $30mh$

11. Keith types w words per minute. At that rate, how many words does he type in h hours?

(a) $\dfrac{60w}{h}$ (b) $\dfrac{60h}{w}$ (c) $60wh$ (d) $\dfrac{wh}{60}$

12. For nonzero numbers a, b, and c, $2a = 4b$ and $8b = 6c$. Then $\dfrac{a}{c} = $ __?__
(HINT: Since $2a = 4b$, $4a = 8b$. But $8b = 6c$. Then $4a = 6c$.)

(a) $\dfrac{2}{3}$ (b) $\dfrac{3}{2}$ (c) $\dfrac{8}{3}$ (d) $\dfrac{3}{1}$

13. For nonzero numbers x, y, and z, $3x = 2y$ and $6y = 4z$. Then $\dfrac{x}{z} = $ __?__

(a) $\dfrac{9}{4}$ (b) $\dfrac{3}{4}$ (c) $\dfrac{2}{3}$ (d) $\dfrac{4}{9}$

14. For nonzero numbers r, s, and t, $4r = 8s$ and $4s = 5t$. Then $\dfrac{r}{t} = $ __?__

(a) $\dfrac{5}{2}$ (b) $\dfrac{8}{5}$ (c) $\dfrac{5}{4}$ (d) $\dfrac{5}{8}$

15. The ratio of the length of a rectangle to its perimeter is $1 : 3$. What is the ratio of the length of the rectangle to its width?
(HINT: Perimeter of a rectangle $= 2l + 2w$)

(a) $2 : 1$ (b) $3 : 1$ (c) $3 : 2$ (d) $1 : 1$

CHAPTER 12 Radicals

12–1 Roots of Numbers

To square a number, you multiply it by itself. The inverse operation is taking the square root.

$$\text{Since } 5^2 = 25,\ \sqrt{25} = 5. \quad \longleftarrow \quad \textbf{Read: "The square root of 25 is 5."}$$

In the expression $\sqrt{25}$, $\sqrt{\ }$ is the **radical symbol**, 25 is the **radicand**, and $\sqrt{25}$ is the **radical.**

Since $9^2 = 81$ and $(-9)^2 = 81$, the number 81 has two square roots, 9 and -9. Every positive real number has two square roots, one positive and one negative.

Definition

> The **principal square root** of a positive real number is the positive square root of the number. The principal square root is indicated by the radical symbol, $\sqrt{\ }$.

From the definition,

$$\sqrt{\frac{49}{9}} = \frac{7}{3} \qquad \text{and} \qquad \sqrt{0.36} = 0.6.$$

A negative square root is associated with the symbol, $-\sqrt{\ }$. The symbol, $\pm\sqrt{\ }$, indicates both square roots. Thus,

$$-\sqrt{81} = -9 \qquad \text{and} \qquad \pm\sqrt{81} = \pm 9.$$

EXAMPLE 1 Simplify: **a.** $\sqrt{400}$ **b.** $\pm\sqrt{\dfrac{49}{625}}$

Solutions: **a.** $\sqrt{400} = 20$ $\quad\longleftarrow\quad$ **Since** $(20)^2 = 400$

b. $\pm\sqrt{\dfrac{49}{625}} = \pm\dfrac{7}{25}$ $\quad\longleftarrow\quad$ **Since** $\left(\dfrac{7}{25}\right)^2 = \dfrac{49}{625}$ **and** $\left(-\dfrac{7}{25}\right)^2 = \dfrac{49}{625}$

A negative number has no real-number square root.

$$\sqrt{-225} \neq -15 \text{ because } (-15)^2 = 225.$$

Thus, for $\sqrt{a}$ to represent a nonnegative real number, a must be a positive real number or zero. Since $|a| \geq 0$ for all real numbers, absolute value notation can be used to ensure that $\sqrt{a^2}$ is a nonnegative real number.

Definition

> For any real number a,
> $$\sqrt{a^2} = |a|.$$

EXAMPLE 2 Simplify: **a.** $\sqrt{r^2t^2}$ **b.** $\sqrt{81a^4}$

Solutions: **a.** $\sqrt{r^2t^2} = |rt|$ $\quad\longleftarrow\quad$ **By definition**

b. $\sqrt{81a^4} = 9|a^2| = 9a^2$ $\quad\longleftarrow\quad$ **Since** a^2 **cannot be negative**

NOTE: Since squaring a positive number and taking the square root are inverse operations, it follows that
$$(\sqrt{11})^2 = 11, \quad \text{and} \quad (\sqrt{a})^2 = a.$$

CLASSROOM EXERCISES

Write the two square roots of each number.

1. 64 **2.** 121 **3.** $\frac{25}{36}$ **4.** $\frac{1}{4}$ **5.** 10,000 **6.** $\frac{9}{100}$

Simplify.

7. $-\sqrt{36}$ **8.** $\pm\sqrt{144}$ **9.** $-\sqrt{\frac{25}{169}}$ **10.** $-(\sqrt{7})^2$ **11.** $-(\sqrt{18})^2$ **12.** $(\sqrt{y})^2$

WRITTEN EXERCISES

A Simplify.

1. $\sqrt{16}$ **2.** $-\sqrt{25}$ **3.** $\sqrt{49}$ **4.** $\pm\sqrt{144}$

5. $\pm\sqrt{100}$ **6.** $\pm\sqrt{81}$ **7.** $\sqrt{10,000}$ **8.** $\sqrt{40,000}$

9. $-\sqrt{4^2}$ **10.** $\pm\sqrt{8^2}$ **11.** $\pm\sqrt{100^2}$ **12.** $\sqrt{125^2}$

13. $\sqrt{\frac{9}{49}}$ **14.** $\sqrt{\frac{4}{81}}$ **15.** $\pm\sqrt{\frac{25}{36}}$ **16.** $\pm\sqrt{\frac{121}{100}}$

17. $-\sqrt{\frac{64}{25}}$ **18.** $\pm\sqrt{\frac{144}{169}}$ **19.** $\sqrt{\frac{81}{100}}$ **20.** $\sqrt{\frac{196}{49}}$

21. $(\sqrt{17})^2$ **22.** $(\sqrt{13})^2$ **23.** $(\sqrt{25})^2$ **24.** $(\sqrt{46})^2$

25. $\sqrt{b^2}$ **26.** $\sqrt{c^4}$ **27.** $\pm\sqrt{t^{10}}$ **28.** $\pm\sqrt{d^6}$

29. $\sqrt{c^4 d^6}$ **30.** $-\sqrt{f^{10}t^4}$ **31.** $-\sqrt{h^8 s^{12}}$ **32.** $\sqrt{r^{12}t^6}$

33. $\sqrt{9c^2}$ **34.** $\sqrt{81t^8}$ **35.** $-\sqrt{64c^6}$ **36.** $-\sqrt{49b^4}$

37. $\pm\sqrt{25d^4}$ **38.** $\pm\sqrt{100r^{12}}$ **39.** $\sqrt{4x^2 y^2}$ **40.** $\sqrt{9a^2 b^2}$

B

41. $\sqrt{0.49}$ **42.** $\sqrt{0.25}$ **43.** $-\sqrt{2.25}$ **44.** $-\sqrt{1.44}$

45. $\sqrt{0.64b^2}$ **46.** $\sqrt{1.69a^2}$ **47.** $\pm\sqrt{6.25t^4}$ **48.** $\pm\sqrt{4.41a^6}$

49. $\sqrt{25r^8 s^{16} t^{12}}$ **50.** $\pm\sqrt{49c^{10}d^6 f^{12}}$ **51.** $-\sqrt{81a^{12}b^8 d^{16}}$ **52.** $\sqrt{16f^4 g^{10}h^{18}}$

53. $\pm\sqrt{\frac{49t^4}{25b^6}}$ **54.** $\pm\sqrt{\frac{16d^8}{121f^2}}$ **55.** $\sqrt{\frac{49a^4 b^2}{9}}$ **56.** $\sqrt{\frac{25x^2 y^2}{36}}$

57. $\sqrt{(13c^3)^2}$ **58.** $\sqrt{(468d^7)^2}$ **59.** $\sqrt{(2a^2)^4}$ **60.** $\sqrt{(3b^3)^6}$

C Examples: $\sqrt[3]{8} = 2$ ◀── Since $2^3 = 8$ $\sqrt[4]{81} = 3$ ◀── Since $3^4 = 81$

61. $\sqrt[3]{27}$ **62.** $\sqrt[3]{125}$ **63.** $\sqrt[4]{256}$ **64.** $\sqrt[4]{625}$

65. $\sqrt[3]{a^6 b^3}$ **66.** $\sqrt[3]{d^6 t^9}$ **67.** $\sqrt[3]{c^{12}f^{18}g^6}$ **68.** $\sqrt[3]{r^9 s^3 t^6}$

69. $\sqrt[4]{(14b^2)^4}$ **70.** $\sqrt[3]{(23d^4)^3}$ **71.** $(\sqrt[3]{16f^6})^3$ **72.** $\sqrt[4]{(21t^3)^4}$

Classify each number as rational, Q, or irrational, Ir. *(Pages 25–29)*

1. $\sqrt{9}$ **2.** $\sqrt{121}$ **3.** $\sqrt{21}$ **4.** $\sqrt{5}$ **5.** $\sqrt{625}$ **6.** $\sqrt{37}$

Copy this table. Write *Yes* or *No* to identify the sets to which each number belongs. *(Pages 25–29)*

	Integers	Rational Numbers	Irrational Numbers	Real Numbers
7. −9	?	?	?	?
8. 64	?	?	?	?
9. 54	?	?	?	?
10. 1.25	?	?	?	?
11. 3.6	?	?	?	?
12. $\frac{1}{8}$	?	?	?	?

12-2 Rational Approximations of Square Roots

You learned in Chapter 1 that every rational number can be represented by an infinite repeating decimal or by a terminating decimal.

$$\frac{1}{3} = 0.333 \cdots, \text{ or } \mathbf{0.\overline{3}} \qquad 1\tfrac{3}{5} = \frac{8}{5} = \mathbf{1.6}$$

The bar indicates the digits that repeat.

You also learned that any rational number can be represented in the form $\frac{a}{b}$, where a is an integer and b is a natural number.

$$0 = \frac{0}{1} \qquad 5.61 = \frac{561}{100} \qquad 0.001 = \frac{1}{1000}$$

Example 1 shows how to represent an infinite repeating decimal in the form $\frac{a}{b}$.

EXAMPLE 1   Write $0.\overline{3}$ in the form $\frac{a}{b}$.

Solution: Let $n = 0.\overline{3}$ ⟵——— **Multiply each side by 10^1, or 10.**

$10n = 3.\overline{3}$ ⟵——— **Subtract $n = 0.\overline{3}$ from this equation.**

$\underline{n = 0.\overline{3}}$

$9n = 3.0$ ⟵——— **Solve for n.**

$n = \frac{3}{9}$, or $\frac{1}{3}$ Thus, $0.\overline{3} = \frac{1}{3}$.

EXAMPLE 2 Write $9.\overline{18}$ in the form $\frac{a}{b}$.

Solution: Let $n = \quad 9.\overline{18}$ ◄─────── **Multiply each side by 10², or 100.**

$100n = 918.\overline{18}$ ◄─────── **Subtract $n = 9.\overline{18}$ from this equation.**

$$\underline{\quad n = \quad 9.\overline{18}\quad}$$

$$99n = 909.00$$

$$n = \frac{909}{99} = \frac{101}{11} \qquad \text{Thus, } 9.\overline{18} = \frac{101}{11}.$$

Recall that a rational number is a perfect square if it is the square of a rational number. A rational number that is not a perfect square has an **irrational square root.** Thus, the following numbers are irrational.

$$\sqrt{2} \qquad \sqrt{5} \qquad -\sqrt{17} \qquad \sqrt{31}$$

An irrational square root is often left in radical form. However, you can always approximate an irrational square root between consecutive integers.

$$2 < \sqrt{7} < 3 \quad \longleftarrow \quad \textbf{Since } \sqrt{4} < \sqrt{7} < \sqrt{9}$$

$$9 < \sqrt{84} < 10 \quad \longleftarrow \quad \textbf{Since } \sqrt{81} < \sqrt{84} < \sqrt{100}$$

You can use a calculator or the Table of Squares and Square Roots on page 567 to find a closer approximation to the square root of an irrational number.

EXAMPLE 3 The area of a square is 55 square meters. What is the length of each side to the nearest tenth of a meter?

Solution: Let $s =$ the length of each side.

$s^2 = 55$ ◄──────── **Area = s · s**

$s = \pm\sqrt{55}$ ◄──────── **Since $s^2 = 55$, $s = \sqrt{55}$, or $s = -\sqrt{55}$.**

$s = \sqrt{55}$ ◄──────── **s must be positive.**

Use the Table of Square Roots on page 541 to find $\sqrt{55}$.

$s \approx 7.416$ ◄──────── **Round to the nearest tenth.**

$s \approx 7.4$ **meters**

No.	Square	Square Root
55	3025	7.416

CLASSROOM EXERCISES

Determine the consecutive integers x and y between which each square root lies.

1. $x < \sqrt{13} < y$ **2.** $x < \sqrt{26} < y$ **3.** $x < \sqrt{92} < y$ **4.** $x < \sqrt{32} < y$

Use the Table of Square Roots on page 567 to determine an approximation to each square root. Round each answer to the nearest tenth.

5. $\sqrt{8}$ **6.** $\sqrt{21}$ **7.** $\sqrt{13}$ **8.** $\sqrt{26}$ **9.** $\sqrt{92}$ **10.** $\sqrt{59}$

WRITTEN EXERCISES

Write each rational number in the form $\frac{a}{b}$.

1. $0.\overline{4}$ 2. $0.\overline{8}$ 3. $0.\overline{15}$ 4. $0.\overline{81}$

5. $0.7\overline{2}$ 6. $0.2\overline{3}$ 7. $0.1\overline{86}$ 8. $0.2\overline{96}$

9. $0.5\overline{43}$ 10. $0.\overline{262}$ 11. $1.\overline{2}$ 12. $3.\overline{4}$

13. $2.5\overline{1}$ 14. $6.\overline{23}$ 15. $3.1\overline{4}$ 16. $6.3\overline{4}$

17. $1.3\overline{78}$ 18. $4.2\overline{54}$ 19. $3.70\overline{4}$ 20. $2.82\overline{9}$

Determine the consecutive integers x and y between which each square root lies.

21. $x < \sqrt{67} < y$ 22. $x < \sqrt{47} < y$ 23. $x < \sqrt{27} < y$

24. $x < \sqrt{101} < y$ 25. $x < \sqrt{123} < y$ 26. $x < \sqrt{150} < y$

27. $x < \sqrt{136} < y$ 28. $x < \sqrt{46} < y$ 29. $x < \sqrt{56} < y$

30. $x < \sqrt{14} < y$ 31. $x < \sqrt{260} < y$ 32. $x < \sqrt{901} < y$

33. $x < \sqrt{10,001} < y$ 34. $x < \sqrt{1,000,001} < y$ 35. $x < \sqrt{8101} < y$

APPLICATIONS: Using Approximations of Square Roots

Solve each problem.

Use the Table of Squares and Square Roots on page 567 or a calculator. Round answers to the nearest tenth.

36. The area of a square garden is 74 square meters. What is the length of one side of the garden?

37. The area of a square poster is 630 square centimeters. What is the length of a side of the poster?

38. The area of a circle is 67 square centimeters. What is the radius of the circle? (HINT: Area $= \pi r^2$; use $\pi = 3.14$.)

39. The area of a circular rug is 7 square meters. What is the diameter of the rug? (Use $\pi = 3.14$.)

40. The formula $d = 4.9t^2$ gives the approximate distance in meters traveled in t seconds by an object falling from rest. How long will an object take to fall 490 meters from rest?

41. The length of a rectangle is 5 times its width. The area of the rectangle is 204 square inches. Find the length and width of the rectangle.

42. The formula $D = 3.56\sqrt{a}$ gives the approximate distance to the horizon (in kilometers) from the viewpoint of an aircraft a meters above the ground. Find the distance to the horizon from the cockpit of an airplane 2025 meters off the ground. (HINT: Use the "Squares" column in the Table of Squares and Square Roots.)

12-3 Simplifying Radicals

The following illustrates an important property of radicals.

$$\sqrt{9 \cdot 4} = \sqrt{36} = 6 \qquad \sqrt{9} \cdot \sqrt{4} = 3 \cdot 2 = 6$$

This suggests the following theorem.

Theorem 12–1	The square root of the product of two nonnegative numbers is the product of their square roots. That is, if a and b are real numbers and $a \geq 0$, $b \geq 0$, then $$\sqrt{ab} = \sqrt{a} \cdot \sqrt{b}.$$

Theorem 12–1 is used to simplify radicals. A radical is in **simplest form** when the radicand does not contain a perfect square factor other than 1.

EXAMPLE Simplify.

a. $\sqrt{50}$ **b.** $3\sqrt{8}$ **c.** $\sqrt{4d^5}$

Solutions: Identify the perfect square factors in the radicand.

a. $\sqrt{50} = \sqrt{25 \cdot 2}$ ←   **25 is the largest perfect square factor of 50.**

$\quad\quad\quad = \sqrt{25} \cdot \sqrt{2}$ ← $\sqrt{25 \cdot 2} = \sqrt{25} \cdot \sqrt{2}$

$\quad\quad\quad = 5\sqrt{2}$ ←   **Simplest form**

b. $3\sqrt{8} = 3\sqrt{4 \cdot 2}$

$\quad\quad\quad = 3 \cdot \sqrt{4} \cdot \sqrt{2}$ ← $\sqrt{4 \cdot 2} = \sqrt{4} \cdot \sqrt{2}$

$\quad\quad\quad = 3 \cdot 2 \cdot \sqrt{2}$

$\quad\quad\quad = 6\sqrt{2}$ ←   **Simplest form**

c. $\sqrt{4d^5} = \sqrt{4d^4 \cdot d}$ ←   **$4d^4$ is the largest perfect square factor of $4d^5$.**

$\quad\quad\quad = \sqrt{4d^4} \cdot \sqrt{d}$

$\quad\quad\quad = 2d^2\sqrt{d}$ ←   **Simplest form**

CLASSROOM EXERCISES

Write each number as the product of the greatest possible perfect square integer and another factor.

1. $18 = \underline{\quad?\quad} \times 2$ **2.** $27 = \underline{\quad?\quad} \times 3$ **3.** $200 = \underline{\quad?\quad} \times 2$

4. $24 = \underline{\quad?\quad} \times 6$ **5.** $40 = \underline{\quad?\quad} \times 10$ **6.** $75 = \underline{\quad?\quad} \times \underline{\quad?\quad}$

7. $125 = \underline{\quad?\quad} \times \underline{\quad?\quad}$ **8.** $288 = \underline{\quad?\quad} \times \underline{\quad?\quad}$ **9.** $300 = \underline{\quad?\quad} \times \underline{\quad?\quad}$

10. $98 = \underline{\quad?\quad} \times \underline{\quad?\quad}$ **11.** $243 = \underline{\quad?\quad} \times \underline{\quad?\quad}$ **12.** $320 = \underline{\quad?\quad} \times \underline{\quad?\quad}$

WRITTEN EXERCISES

A   Simplify. Assume that all variables represent positive real numbers.

1. $\sqrt{8}$ 2. $\sqrt{40}$ 3. $\sqrt{20}$ 4. $\sqrt{24}$

5. $\sqrt{12}$ 6. $\sqrt{63}$ 7. $\sqrt{75}$ 8. $\sqrt{125}$

9. $\sqrt{100}$ 10. $\sqrt{98}$ 11. $\sqrt{32}$ 12. $2\sqrt{4}$

13. $\sqrt{242}$ 14. $\sqrt{64}$ 15. $\sqrt{196}$ 16. $\sqrt{28}$

17. $4\sqrt{72}$ 18. $2\sqrt{20}$ 19. $3\sqrt{28}$ 20. $4\sqrt{49}$

21. $\sqrt{56}$ 22. $3\sqrt{18}$ 23. $9\sqrt{50}$ 24. $6\sqrt{72}$

25. $8\sqrt{12}$ 26. $-6\sqrt{9}$ 27. $-3\sqrt{16}$ 28. $-2\sqrt{32}$

29. $-5\sqrt{32}$ 30. $4\sqrt{200}$ 31. $3\sqrt{1000}$ 32. $\sqrt{1\text{ million}}$

33. $3\sqrt{1\text{ million}}$ 34. $\sqrt{1{,}000{,}000{,}000{,}000}$ 35. $3\sqrt{1{,}000{,}000{,}000}$ 36. $4\sqrt{10{,}000{,}000{,}000}$

37. $\sqrt{10^2}$ 38. $\sqrt{10^4}$ 39. $\sqrt{10^7}$ 40. $\sqrt{9t^7}$

41. $\sqrt{36b^3}$ 42. $\sqrt{25m^9}$ 43. $\sqrt{18p^5}$ 44. $\sqrt{24c^7}$

45. $\sqrt{75q^{11}}$ 46. $\sqrt{12r^5s^7}$ 47. $\sqrt{32a^9b^3}$ 48. $\sqrt{72c^9d^{13}}$

B   Approximations for $\sqrt{2}$, $\sqrt{3}$, and $\sqrt{5}$ are given below.

$$\sqrt{2} \approx 1.414 \qquad \sqrt{3} \approx 1.732 \qquad \sqrt{5} \approx 2.236$$

Use these three approximations to name the nonnegative square root of each number below to the nearest hundredth.

Example: 300 $\sqrt{300} = \sqrt{100} \cdot \sqrt{3} = 10\sqrt{3} \approx 10(1.732) = \textbf{17.32}$

49. 8   **50.** 12   **51.** 20   **52.** 45   **53.** 98   **54.** 50

55. 147   **56.** 320   **57.** 192   **58.** 216   **59.** 360   **60.** 200

C   Simplify. Assume that all variables represent positive real numbers.

61. $\sqrt{3(x+y)^2}$ 62. $\sqrt{5(t-r)^2}$ 63. $\sqrt{28(c^2+d^2)^3}$

64. $\sqrt{48(a^2-b^2)^5}$ 65. $\sqrt{x^2+2xy+y^2}$ 66. $\sqrt{d^2+6d+9}$

———— **REVIEW CAPSULE FOR SECTION 12-4** ————

Simplify. *(Pages 9–11, 304–305, 432–433)*

1. 10^2 2. 15^2 3. 7^2 4. $(a-1)^2$ 5. $(a+1)^2$ 6. $(2t+5)^2$

7. $(\sqrt{2})^2$ 8. $(\sqrt{5})^2$ 9. $(\sqrt{9})^2$ 10. $(\sqrt{16})^2$ 11. $(\sqrt{7})^2$ 12. $(\sqrt{25})^2$

Solve for a^2. *(Pages 84–85)*

13. $a^2 + 25 = 144$ 14. $18 + a^2 = 225$ 15. $72 - a^2 = 15$ 16. $21 = 169 - a^2$

Solve for a. *(Pages 337–338)*

17. $a^2 = 81$ 18. $a^2 = 36$ 19. $a^2 - 144 = 0$ 20. $121 - a^2 = 0$

12-4 The Pythagorean Theorem

Test each triangle below to determine whether the sum of the squares of the shorter sides equals the square of the longest side. (The symbol ⌐ means that an angle is a right angle.)

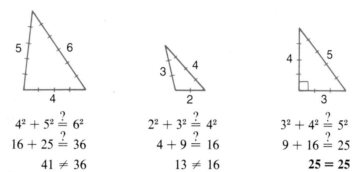

$$4^2 + 5^2 \stackrel{?}{=} 6^2$$
$$16 + 25 \stackrel{?}{=} 36$$
$$41 \neq 36$$

$$2^2 + 3^2 \stackrel{?}{=} 4^2$$
$$4 + 9 \stackrel{?}{=} 16$$
$$13 \neq 16$$

$$3^2 + 4^2 \stackrel{?}{=} 5^2$$
$$9 + 16 \stackrel{?}{=} 25$$
$$\mathbf{25 = 25}$$

The sentence is true for the third triangle only because it is a *right triangle*. A *right triangle* is a triangle with one angle of 90°. The relationship between the two shorter sides (legs) and the longest side (hypotenuse) of every right triangle is known as the *Pythagorean Theorem*.

Theorem 12-2

> **Pythagorean Theorem**
>
> If a, b, and c are the lengths of the sides of a right triangle and c is the length of the **hypotenuse** (longest side), then
> $$a^2 + b^2 = c^2.$$

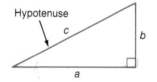

The proof of the Pythagorean Theorem is outlined in Exercises 35–38 on page 442.

EXAMPLE 1 The shorter sides of a right triangle are 12 and 5. Find the length of the hypotenuse.

Solution: Since the triangle is a right triangle, use the Pythagorean Theorem.

$$a^2 + b^2 = c^2 \quad \longleftarrow \textbf{Replace } \boldsymbol{a} \textbf{ with 5 and } \boldsymbol{b} \textbf{ with 12.}$$
$$5^2 + 12^2 = c^2$$
$$25 + 144 = c^2$$
$$169 = c^2 \quad \longleftarrow \textbf{Since } \boldsymbol{c^2 = 169, c = 13} \textbf{ or } \boldsymbol{c = -13.}$$
$$13 = c \quad \longleftarrow \textbf{The length of a side of the triangle must be positive.}$$

The length of the hypotenuse is **13**.

The Pythagorean Theorem is useful in solving problems related to right triangles.

EXAMPLE 2 The top of a 6-meter ladder reaches a window ledge. The ledge is 5 meters above the ground. To the nearest tenth of a meter, how far from the house is the foot of the ladder?

Solution: Since the ladder, the ground, and the side of the house form a right triangle, use the Pythagorean Theorem.

$$c^2 = a^2 + b^2 \quad \longleftarrow \quad \textbf{Replace } c \textbf{ with 6}$$
$$\textbf{and } b \textbf{ with 5.}$$
$$6^2 = a^2 + 5^2$$
$$36 = a^2 + 25 \quad \longleftarrow \quad \textbf{Solve for } a^2.$$
$$11 = a^2$$
$$\pm\sqrt{11} = a \quad \longleftarrow \quad \textbf{The distance, } a \textbf{, cannot be negative.}$$
$$a \approx 3.317 \quad \longleftarrow \quad \textbf{Use the Table of Square Roots or a calculator.}$$

The foot of the ladder is about **3.3 meters** from the house.

When you know the lengths of three sides of a triangle, you can use this theorem to determine whether it is a right triangle.

Theorem 12–3

If the sum of the squares of the lengths of the two shorter sides (legs) of a triangle is equal to the square of the length of the longest side (hypotenuse), then the triangle is a right triangle.

EXAMPLE 3 Determine whether a triangle whose sides are 10, 15, and 20 units long is a right triangle.

Solution:
$$c^2 = a^2 + b^2 \quad \longleftarrow \quad \textbf{Replace } c \textbf{ with 20, } a \textbf{ with 10,}$$
$$\textbf{and } b \textbf{ with 15.}$$
$$20^2 \overset{?}{=} 10^2 + 15^2$$
$$400 \overset{?}{=} 100 + 225$$
$$400 \neq 325 \qquad \text{The triangle is \textbf{not} a right triangle.}$$

CLASSROOM EXERCISES

Use the Pythagorean Theorem to find the unknown side.

1. $a = 3$, $b = 4$, $c = \underline{\ ?\ }$

2. $a = 5$, $b = 12$, $c = \underline{\ ?\ }$

3. $a = 12$, $c = 15$, $b = \underline{\ ?\ }$

4. $b = 2$, $c = \sqrt{13}$, $a = \underline{\ ?\ }$

5. $a = \sqrt{2}$, $b = \sqrt{2}$, $c = \underline{\ ?\ }$

6. $a = 5\sqrt{3}$, $c = 10$, $b = \underline{\ ?\ }$

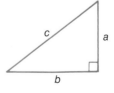

WRITTEN EXERCISES

In Exercises 1–10, refer to the diagram at the right. Use the Pythagorean Theorem to find the unknown side. Use the Square Root Table on page 567 or a calculator. Round answers to the nearest tenth.

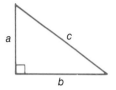

1. $a = 6$, $b = 8$, $c =$ __?__
2. $a = 24$, $b = 10$, $c =$ __?__
3. $a = 14$, $b = 7$, $c =$ __?__
4. $a = 9$, $b = 5$, $c =$ __?__
5. $a = 10$, $b = 12$, $c =$ __?__
6. $a = 8$, $b = 10$, $c =$ __?__
7. $a = 12$, $b =$ __?__ , $c = 17$
8. $a = 10$, $b =$ __?__ , $c = 13$
9. $a =$ __?__ , $b = 16$, $c = 25$
10. $a =$ __?__ , $b = 10$, $c = 19$

In Exercises 11–22, the lengths of three sides of a triangle are given. State whether or not they form a right triangle. Answer *Yes* or *No*.

11. 12, 5, 13
12. 9, 12, 15
13. 4, 5, 7
14. 3, 10, 12
15. 9, 40, 41
16. 16, 20, 24
17. 2, 9, 10
18. 3, 4, 5
19. 7, 10, 12
20. 1, 1, $\sqrt{2}$
21. $\sqrt{3}$, 1, 2
22. $\sqrt{2}$, $\sqrt{2}$, 2

APPLICATIONS: Using the Pythagorean Theorem

In Exercises 23–32, draw a sketch for each problem. Use the Table of Square Roots on page 567 or a calculator. Round answers to the nearest tenth.

23. Find the length of the diagonal of a rectangle whose length is 6 meters and whose width is 4 meters.

24. Find the length of the diagonal of a square whose sides each have a length of 3 meters.

25. A pipeline is built diagonally across a square field. Each side of the field is 7 kilometers long. What is the length of the pipeline?

26. A wire stretches from the top of a pole 22 feet high to a stake in the ground which is 10 feet from the foot of the pole. Find the length of the wire.

27. A ladder 40 feet long leans against a building and reaches a ledge. The foot of the ladder is 16 feet from the building. How high is the ledge?

28. Sean took a homing pigeon 10 kilometers due east of his home and then 5 kilometers north. When he let the pigeon go, it flew straight home. How far did it fly?

29. A diagonal of a square is 10 centimeters long. Find the length of each side of the square.

30. The diagonal of a rectangle is 20 inches long. The rectangle's length is 3 times its width. Find the dimensions of the rectangle.

31. Two telephone poles, 30 feet and 39 feet high, respectively, are 60 feet apart. How long is the wire from the top of one pole to the top of the other pole?

32. In a swimming pool 70 feet long and 25 feet wide, how many feet will be saved by swimming diagonally across the pool instead of along its sides?

Ⓒ

33. A rectangle of height 12 centimeters is inscribed in a circle with a radius of 10 centimeters. Find the area of the rectangle.

34. A man on a wharf 12 meters above the water pulls in a boat on the end of a rope. He had 20 meters of rope out and then pulled in 7 meters of rope. How far did he move the boat?

The figure at the right suggests a proof of the Pythagorean Theorem. Note that each side of the larger square is $(a + b)$ units long. The area of this square is made up of four triangles and a smaller square each of whose sides is c units long.

In Exercises 35–38, give a reason for each statement.

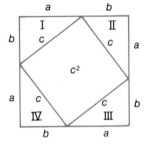

35. $(a+b)^2 = c^2 + 4(\frac{1}{2}ab)$ (Why?)

36. $a^2 + 2ab + b^2 = c^2 + 4(\frac{1}{2}ab)$ (Why?)

37. $a^2 + 4(\frac{1}{2}ab) + b^2 = c^2 + 4(\frac{1}{2}ab)$ (Why?)

38. $a^2 + b^2 = c^2$ (Why?)

39. Derive a formula for the length of the altitude, h, of the equilateral triangle shown at the right.

40. Derive a formula for the area of an equilateral triangle in terms of a side, s.

41. Prove: A triangle with sides $2pq$, $(p^2 - q^2)$, and $(p^2 + q^2)$ is a right triangle.

———— **REVIEW CAPSULE FOR SECTION 12–5** ————

Evaluate. *(Pages 9–11, 47–50, 56–58)*

1. $|-18|$ **2.** $|15 - 12|$ **3.** $|-8 + 6|$ **4.** $|-8 - (-7)|$ **5.** $|9 - (-1)|$

6. $[9 - (-7)]^2$ **7.** $(21 - 8)^2$ **8.** $(1 - 3)^2$ **9.** $[7 - (-5)]^2$ **10.** $[-3 - (-5)]^2$

Evaluate $(x_2 - x_1)^2 + (y_2 - y_1)^2$ for the given values of (x_1, y_1) and (x_2, y_2). *(Pages 9–11, 56–58)*

11. $x_1 = 7$, $y_1 = 0$; $x_2 = 3$, $y_2 = -1$

12. $x_1 = 0$, $y_1 = -1$; $x_2 = 3$, $y_2 = -1$

13. $x_1 = -4$, $y_1 = -5$; $x_2 = -2$, $y_2 = -2$

14. $x_1 = 2$, $y_1 = -5$; $x_2 = 4$, $y_2 = 2$

12-5 The Distance Formula

Two points that lie on a line parallel to the x axis (horizontal line) have the same y coordinate. To find the distance between two such points, determine the absolute value of the difference of their x coordinates. Thus, in Figure 1,

Figure 1

$$AB = |-2 - 1| = |-3| = 3.$$

Similarly, two points that lie on a line parallel to the y axis (vertical line) have the same x coordinate. To find the distance between two such points, determine the absolute value of the difference of their y coordinates. Thus, in Figure 2,

Figure 2

$$CD = |4 - (-2)| = |4 + 2| = |6| = 6.$$

Suppose that you wish to find the distance between the points $A(-2, 3)$ and $B(4, -5)$ shown in Figure 3. First you draw the horizontal and vertical line segments intersecting at C to form right triangle ABC. After finding the lengths of AC and BC, you can use the Pythagorean Theorem to find the length of AB. Thus,

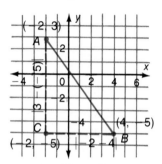

Figure 3

$$BC = |-2 - 4| = |-6| = 6 \quad \text{and} \quad AC = |3 - (-5)| = |8| = 8$$

$$(AB)^2 = (BC)^2 + (AC)^2 \longleftarrow \textbf{By the Pythagorean Theorem}$$

$$(AB)^2 = 6^2 + 8^2$$

$$(AB)^2 = 36 + 64$$

$$(AB)^2 = 100 \quad \text{and} \quad AB = 10 \qquad \text{Thus, } AB \text{ is } \textbf{10 units} \text{ long.}$$

This procedure can be generalized as a formula to find the distance between any two points $P_1(x_1, y_1)$ and $P_2(x_2, y_2)$ in the coordinate plane. You are asked to prove this formula in the Exercises.

Distance Formula

If $P_1(x_1, y_1)$ and $P_2(x_2, y_2)$ are any two points in the coordinate plane, then the distance, d, between the points is given by the formula

$$d = \sqrt{(x_2 - x_1)^2 + (y_2 - y_1)^2}.$$

EXAMPLE   Find the distance between $P(7, 3)$ and $Q(2, -5)$.

    Solution: Use the Distance Formula.

$$d = \sqrt{(x_2 - x_1)^2 + (y_2 - y_1)^2}$$ ←   **Replace x_2 with 2 and x_1 with 7.**
Replace y_2 with -5 and y_1 with 3.

$$d = \sqrt{(2 - 7)^2 + (-5 - 3)^2}$$

$$d = \sqrt{(-5)^2 + (-8)^2}$$

$$d = \sqrt{25 + 64}, \text{ or } \sqrt{89}$$ ←   **Simplest form**

It does not matter which point is considered (x_1, y_1) and which one is considered (x_2, y_2). The distance will be the same.

CLASSROOM EXERCISES

Find the distance between each pair of points.

1. $P(4, 3)$ and $Q(0, 0)$ 2. $A(0, 0)$ and $C(-5, 9)$ 3. $Q(-1, 2)$ and $R(8, -2)$

4. $P(1, 4)$ and $S(6, 9)$ 5. $T(-3, 2)$ and $R(2, -7)$ 6. $S(4, 0)$ and $V(4, 9)$

WRITTEN EXERCISES

A   Find the distance between each pair of points.

1. $A(0, 0)$ and $B(-5, 0)$ 2. $P(0, 0)$ and $Q(0, -5)$ 3. $C(-3, 5)$ and $D(-3, -3)$

4. $H(7, -8)$ and $J(-2, -8)$ 5. $K(9, 4)$ and $L(3, 4)$ 6. $B(5, 13)$ and $C(5, -1)$

7. $D(6, 8)$ and $E(0, 0)$ 8. $M(0, 0)$ and $N(2, 3)$ 9. $S(1, 3)$ and $T(4, 7)$

10. $U(5, 10)$ and $V(2, 6)$ 11. $X(2, 1)$ and $Y(-3, -4)$ 12. $L(-2, 4)$ and $M(-1, 2)$

13. $C(3, 1)$ and $D(-1, 6)$ 14. $A(2, 2)$ and $B(2, -7)$ 15. $P(9, 6)$ and $R(-5, 6)$

16. $N(-2, -3)$ and $T(1, 2)$ 17. $E(3, 2)$ and $F(8, -10)$ 18. $J(-2, 4)$ and $K(7, -8)$

APPLICATIONS: Using the Distance Formula

Use the given figure to answer each question.

19.

$M(-1, 1)$ $N(1, 1)$

What is the distance between the objects on the teeter-totter?

20. $S(90, 90)$

$H(0, 0)$

How far is it from home plate to second base?

21. $T(13, 28)$

$R(6, 4)$

How long is the guy wire of the radio antenna?

Find the perimeter of each triangle.

22.

23.

24.

25.

26.

27.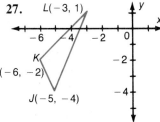

28. Use the Pythagorean Theorem to prove the Distance Formula.

───── **Review** ──────────────────────────────

Simplify. *(Section 12–1)*

1. $\sqrt{64}$ **2.** $-\sqrt{400}$ **3.** $\sqrt{100x^2}$ **4.** $\pm\sqrt{a^8b^4}$

5. The area of a square is 7 square meters. What is the length of one side of the square to the nearest tenth of a meter? *(Section 12–2)*

6. The length of a rectangle is twice its width. The area of the rectangle is 218 square units. Find the dimensions to the nearest tenth. *(Section 12–2)*

Simplify. Variables represent positive numbers. *(Section 12–3)*

7. $\sqrt{28}$ **8.** $\sqrt{80}$ **9.** $-\sqrt{24x^5}$ **10.** $2\sqrt{36d^3}$

The lengths of the legs of a right triangle are *a* and *b*, and *c* is the length of the hypotenuse. Use the Pythagorean Theorem to find the length of the unknown side to the nearest tenth. *(Section 12–4)*

11. $a = 9$, $b = 12$, $c = $ __?__   **12.** $b = 5$, $c = 9$, $a = $ __?__

Find the distance between each pair of points. *(Section 12–5)*

13. $A(4, -6)$ and $B(1, -6)$ **14.** $P(4, -2)$ and $Q(-2, 4)$ **15.** $K(7, 3)$ and $L(-4, -5)$

Career Applications

Space Technology

Reuben Ramos is an Engineer at NASA.

Aerospace engineers develop and design space-craft. These vehicles must be able to travel at great speeds so that they can either enter an orbit around the earth or escape the earth's gravitational field and travel to other parts of the universe.

The speed of the spacecraft determines whether it will come right back to the earth, orbit the earth, or travel into outer space. The following formulas give the orbital and escape speeds of a spacecraft at a specific height above the earth.

$$V_o = R\sqrt{\frac{g}{R+h}} \text{ and } V_e = \sqrt{2} \cdot V_o \quad \longleftarrow \quad \begin{array}{l} V_o = \textbf{orbital speed} \\ V_e = \textbf{escape speed} \end{array}$$

In the formula, R is the radius of the earth, 6.4×10^6 meters, g is the acceleration due to gravity on the earth, 9.8 m/sec^2, and h is the height above the surface of the earth at which the spacecraft is traveling.

EXAMPLE 1   Suppose that the U.S. space shuttle is to orbit the earth at an average height of 12.8×10^6 meters above its surface. Find the orbital speed and the escape speed of the shuttle orbiter.

Solution: $V_o = R\sqrt{\dfrac{g}{R+h}}$

$$= 6.4 \times 10^6 \sqrt{\frac{9.8}{(6.4 \times 10^6) + (12.8 \times 10^6)}}$$

$$= 6.4 \times 10^6 \sqrt{\frac{9.8}{19.2 \times 10^6}} \quad \longleftarrow \quad \text{Use a calculator.}$$

$$= (6.4 \times 10^6) \cdot 0.714 \times 10^{-3}$$

$$\approx 4.6 \times 10^3 \text{ m/sec}$$

$$V_e = \sqrt{2} \cdot 4.6 \times 10^3 \approx 1.4 \cdot 46 \times 10^3 \approx \textbf{6.4} \times \textbf{10}^3 \textbf{ m/sec}$$

     NOTE: If the speed of the spacecraft is less than V_o for a given height, it will return to earth. The vehicle will orbit the earth if its speed is between V_o and V_e. If the spacecraft's speed is greater than or equal to V_e, it will escape the earth's gravity and travel into outer space.

The shuttle orbiter was designed to land like a jet airplane. As the orbiter approaches the earth, the distance to the horizon becomes shorter. The following formula approximates this distance in kilometers.

$D = 3.56\sqrt{A}$ ⟵ **A is the altitude of the orbiter in meters.**

390 km

12,000 m ↑ A

EXAMPLE 2 Find the distance to the horizon from the orbiter when its altitude is 12,000 meters.

Solution:
$$D = 3.56\sqrt{12,000}$$
$$= 3.56\sqrt{400} \cdot \sqrt{30}$$
$$= 3.56 \cdot 20 \cdot \sqrt{30}$$
$$\approx 390 \text{ kilometers}$$

EXERCISES

In Exercises 1–3, use the formulas on page 446 to find the orbital speed and the escape speed of a spacecraft at the given height above the earth.

1. 6.4×10^6 meters

2. 3.2×10^6 meters

3. 9.6×10^6 meters

In Exercises 4–5, state whether a spacecraft with the given speed at the given height would return to earth, orbit the earth, or travel into outer space.

4. Speed: 4.6×10^3 meters per second
   Height: 6.4×10^6 meters

5. Speed: 4.8×10^3 meters per second
   Height: 1.92×10^7 meters

6. On December 3, 1980, Janice Brown made the first solar-powered flight in the Solar Challenger. At one point in the flight the plane was 27 meters above the ground. How far could Janice see to the horizon? (nearest km)

7. On July 7, 1981, Stephen Ptacek flew the Solar Challenger across the English Channel. At one point in the flight, the plane was 50 meters high. Find the distance to the horizon. (nearest km)

8. Find the distance to the horizon from a plane that is 3000 meters above the earth. (nearest km)

9. Find the distance to the horizon from the shuttle when it is 4000 meters above the earth. (nearest km)

12-6 Multiplication of Radicals

To multiply two radicals such as $4\sqrt{2}$ and $3\sqrt{5}$, you use the commutative and associative properties of multiplication.

EXAMPLE 1 Multiply: $-3\sqrt{6} \cdot 4\sqrt{3}$. Express the answer in simplest form.

Solution: $-3\sqrt{6} \cdot 4\sqrt{3} = (-3 \cdot 4) \cdot (\sqrt{6} \cdot \sqrt{3})$ ◄————— **By the commutative and associative postulates**

$= -12 \cdot \sqrt{6 \cdot 3}$

$= -12 \cdot \sqrt{18}$ ◄————— $\sqrt{18}$ **can be simplified.**

$= -12 \cdot \sqrt{9} \cdot \sqrt{2}$ ◄————— $\sqrt{18} = \sqrt{9} \cdot \sqrt{2}$

$= -12 \cdot 3 \cdot \sqrt{2}$

$= -36\sqrt{2}$ ◄————— **Simplest form**

When a radical can be simplified, it is usually easier to do this before multiplying by other factors.

EXAMPLE 2 Multiply: $\sqrt{8} \cdot \sqrt{6}$. Express the answer in simplest form.

Solution: $\sqrt{8} \cdot \sqrt{6} = \sqrt{4 \cdot 2} \cdot \sqrt{6}$ ◄————— $\sqrt{8}$ **can be simplified.**

$= 2 \cdot \sqrt{2} \cdot \sqrt{6}$ ◄————— $\sqrt{2} \cdot \sqrt{6} = \sqrt{12}$

$= 2 \cdot \sqrt{12}$ ◄————— $\sqrt{12}$ **can be simplified.**

$= 2 \cdot \sqrt{4 \cdot 3}$

$= 2 \cdot \sqrt{4} \cdot \sqrt{3}$

$= 2 \cdot 2 \cdot \sqrt{3}$

$= 4\sqrt{3}$ ◄————— **Simplest form**

CLASSROOM EXERCISES

Multiply. Express your answers in simplest form.

1. $\sqrt{2} \cdot \sqrt{7}$
2. $\sqrt{2} \cdot \sqrt{8}$
3. $\sqrt{2} \cdot \sqrt{9}$
4. $\sqrt{15} \cdot \sqrt{3}$
5. $-\sqrt{2} \cdot \sqrt{18}$
6. $3\sqrt{3} \cdot \sqrt{2}$
7. $\sqrt{5} \cdot 5\sqrt{3}$
8. $\sqrt{5} \cdot 5\sqrt{5}$
9. $6\sqrt{8} \cdot 5\sqrt{6}$
10. $\sqrt{300} \cdot \sqrt{3}$
11. $2\sqrt{1000}$
12. $5\sqrt{10} \cdot 4\sqrt{10}$

WRITTEN EXERCISES

A Multiply and simplify.

1. $\sqrt{5} \cdot \sqrt{2}$
2. $\sqrt{3} \cdot \sqrt{5}$
3. $\sqrt{7} \cdot \sqrt{2}$
4. $\sqrt{6} \cdot \sqrt{2}$
5. $\sqrt{3} \cdot \sqrt{6}$
6. $3\sqrt{3} \cdot \sqrt{2}$
7. $\sqrt{5} \cdot \sqrt{10}$
8. $\sqrt{8} \cdot \sqrt{2}$

9. $\sqrt{9} \cdot \sqrt{4}$ **10.** $\sqrt{4} \cdot \sqrt{2}$ **11.** $\sqrt{3} \cdot \sqrt{12}$ **12.** $\sqrt{10} \cdot \sqrt{20}$

13. $\sqrt{25} \cdot \sqrt{3}$ **14.** $\sqrt{50} \cdot \sqrt{2}$ **15.** $\sqrt{7} \cdot \sqrt{7}$ **16.** $\sqrt{30} \cdot \sqrt{3}$

17. $2\sqrt{3} \cdot \sqrt{2}$ **18.** $\sqrt{3} \cdot 5\sqrt{7}$ **19.** $4\sqrt{2} \cdot \sqrt{5}$ **20.** $3\sqrt{2} \cdot 4\sqrt{3}$

21. $5\sqrt{2} \cdot 3\sqrt{5}$ **22.** $4\sqrt{5} \cdot 3\sqrt{2}$ **23.** $7\sqrt{6} \cdot 2\sqrt{2}$ **24.** $8\sqrt{5} \cdot 3\sqrt{6}$

25. $-7\sqrt{12} \cdot 4\sqrt{3}$ **26.** $8\sqrt{6} \cdot -3\sqrt{3}$ **27.** $3\sqrt{6} \cdot -4\sqrt{10}$ **28.** $-2\sqrt{12} \cdot -3\sqrt{2}$

29. $-8\sqrt{6} \cdot -3\sqrt{7}$ **30.** $-6\sqrt{8} \cdot -3\sqrt{6}$ **31.** $-9\sqrt{10} \cdot 7\sqrt{3}$ **32.** $-4\sqrt{14} \cdot 2\sqrt{7}$

B   Multiply. Variables represent positive numbers.

33. $\sqrt{a} \cdot \sqrt{ab}$ **34.** $\sqrt{cd} \cdot \sqrt{c}$ **35.** $\sqrt{8bc} \cdot \sqrt{4bc}$ **36.** $\sqrt{6ax} \cdot \sqrt{9ax}$

37. $\sqrt{6m^4} \cdot \sqrt{3mn^2}$ **38.** $\sqrt{2a^2c} \cdot \sqrt{2c^2x}$ **39.** $\sqrt{a^3b} \cdot \sqrt{bc^3}$ **40.** $\sqrt{c^3} \cdot -\sqrt{5cd}$

41. $\sqrt[3]{4} \cdot \sqrt[3]{2}$ **42.** $\sqrt[3]{9} \cdot \sqrt[3]{3}$ **43.** $\sqrt[3]{4^2} \cdot \sqrt[3]{4}$ **44.** $\sqrt[3]{7} \cdot \sqrt[3]{7^2}$

45. $\sqrt[3]{10} \cdot \sqrt[3]{10^2}$ **46.** $\sqrt[3]{8} \cdot \sqrt[3]{2}$ **47.** $\sqrt[3]{12} \cdot \sqrt[3]{2}$ **48.** $\sqrt[3]{24} \cdot \sqrt[3]{2}$

C

49. $-3a\sqrt{ab} \cdot 2a\sqrt{ab}$ **50.** $-2\sqrt{7y} \cdot 5\sqrt{2y}$ **51.** $y^2\sqrt{xy} \cdot 2x\sqrt{y}$

52. $3b\sqrt{b^2e} \cdot 2e\sqrt{be^2}$ **53.** $5t^2\sqrt{k^3} \cdot 2t\sqrt{k}$ **54.** $2\sqrt{r} \cdot 3\sqrt{r^3} \cdot 3\sqrt{r^5}$

CALCULATOR APPLICATIONS

Evaluating the Product of Two Radicals

If you have a calculator with square root and memory keys, you can use the calculator to evaluate the product of two radicals.

EXAMPLE Multiply: $-3\sqrt{6} \cdot 4\sqrt{3}$ (See Example 1 on page 448.)

SOLUTION Rewrite the problem so that each radical is the first term in each factor.
$$-3\sqrt{6} \cdot 4\sqrt{3} = (\sqrt{6} \cdot -3)(\sqrt{3} \cdot 4)$$

6 [√] [×] 3 [+/−] [=] [M+] 3 [√] [×] 4 [×] [MR] [=] | −50.911687 |

EXERCISES

Multiply.

1. $2\sqrt{5} \cdot 6\sqrt{3}$ **2.** $-4\sqrt{8} \cdot 6\sqrt{2}$ **3.** $-6\sqrt{5} \cdot -3\sqrt{3}$ **4.** $5\sqrt{10} \cdot \sqrt{8}$

5. $4\sqrt{6} \cdot -2\sqrt{5}$ **6.** $-8\sqrt{3} \cdot 4\sqrt{7}$ **7.** $\sqrt{8} \cdot 4\sqrt{3}$ **8.** $-2\sqrt{5} \cdot 9\sqrt{2}$

—————— **REVIEW CAPSULE FOR SECTION 12-7** ——————

Simplify. *(Pages 432–433, 448–449)*

1. $\sqrt{2} \cdot \sqrt{2}$ **2.** $\sqrt{3} \cdot \sqrt{3}$ **3.** $(\sqrt{5})^2$ **4.** $(\sqrt{8})^2$ **5.** $(\sqrt{125})^2$

6. $\dfrac{1}{\sqrt{2}} \cdot \dfrac{\sqrt{2}}{\sqrt{2}}$ **7.** $\dfrac{1}{\sqrt{5}} \cdot \dfrac{\sqrt{5}}{\sqrt{5}}$ **8.** $\dfrac{6}{\sqrt{3}} \cdot \dfrac{\sqrt{3}}{\sqrt{3}}$ **9.** $\dfrac{14}{\sqrt{7}} \cdot \dfrac{\sqrt{7}}{\sqrt{7}}$ **10.** $\dfrac{18}{\sqrt{2}} \cdot \dfrac{\sqrt{2}}{\sqrt{2}}$

12–7 Quotients of Radicals

Since $\sqrt{\dfrac{16}{81}} = \dfrac{4}{9}$ and $\dfrac{\sqrt{16}}{\sqrt{81}} = \dfrac{4}{9}$, $\sqrt{\dfrac{16}{81}} = \dfrac{\sqrt{16}}{\sqrt{81}}$.

Since $\sqrt{\dfrac{4}{25}} = \dfrac{2}{5}$ and $\dfrac{\sqrt{4}}{\sqrt{25}} = \dfrac{2}{5}$, $\sqrt{\dfrac{4}{25}} = \dfrac{\sqrt{4}}{\sqrt{25}}$.

These statements suggest the following theorem.

Theorem 12–4

> **Division Theorem for Square Roots**
>
> If a and b are real numbers where $a \geq 0$ and $b > 0$, then
> $$\sqrt{\dfrac{a}{b}} = \dfrac{\sqrt{a}}{\sqrt{b}}.$$

EXAMPLE 1 Simplify: **a.** $\sqrt{\dfrac{8}{49}}$ **b.** $4\sqrt{\dfrac{5}{16}}$

Solutions: **a.** $\sqrt{\dfrac{8}{49}} = \dfrac{\sqrt{8}}{\sqrt{49}}$ ← **By Theorem 12–4**

$= \dfrac{\sqrt{4 \cdot 2}}{7}$ ← $\sqrt{8} = \sqrt{4 \cdot 2} = \sqrt{4} \cdot \sqrt{2}$

$= \dfrac{2\sqrt{2}}{7}$ ← **Simplest form**

b. $4\sqrt{\dfrac{5}{16}} = 4 \cdot \dfrac{\sqrt{5}}{\sqrt{16}}$ ← **By Theorem 12–4**

$= \overset{1}{\cancel{4}} \cdot \dfrac{\sqrt{5}}{\underset{1}{\cancel{4}}}$ ← $\dfrac{1 \cdot \sqrt{5}}{1}$

$= \sqrt{5}$

The following definition will help you to determine whether a radical is in simplest form.

Definition

> **A radical is in simplest form when:**
> 1. The radicand contains no factor that is a perfect square.
> 2. The radicand does not contain a fraction.
> 3. No radical appears in a denominator.

To simplify a fraction such as $\dfrac{\sqrt{7}}{\sqrt{3}}$, you write an equivalent fraction having a rational denominator. This is called **rationalizing the denominator.**

EXAMPLE 2 Simplify: **a.** $\sqrt{\dfrac{7}{3}}$ **b.** $\dfrac{5\sqrt{2}}{2\sqrt{18}}$

Solutions: **a.** $\sqrt{\dfrac{7}{3}} = \dfrac{\sqrt{7}}{\sqrt{3}}$ ⟵ **By Theorem 12–4**

$= \dfrac{\sqrt{7}}{\sqrt{3}} \cdot \dfrac{\sqrt{3}}{\sqrt{3}}$ ⟵ **Multiplying by $\dfrac{\sqrt{3}}{\sqrt{3}}$ will give an equivalent fraction with no radical in the denominator.**

$= \dfrac{\sqrt{21}}{3}$ ⟵ $\sqrt{3} \cdot \sqrt{3} = (\sqrt{3})^2 = 3$

b. $\dfrac{5\sqrt{2}}{2\sqrt{18}} = \dfrac{5\sqrt{2}}{2\sqrt{18}} \cdot \dfrac{\sqrt{2}}{\sqrt{2}}$ ⟵ **Multiplying by $\dfrac{\sqrt{2}}{\sqrt{2}}$ will give an equivalent fraction with no radical in the denominator.**

$= \dfrac{5\sqrt{4}}{2\sqrt{36}}$

$= \dfrac{5 \cdot 2}{2 \cdot 6}$

$= \dfrac{10}{12}, \text{ or } \dfrac{5}{6}$

Follow the method of Example 2 to rationalize a denominator containing variables.

EXAMPLE 3 Simplify: **a.** $\sqrt{\dfrac{1}{b^5}}$ **b.** $\sqrt{\dfrac{2}{10x}}$

Solutions: **a.** $\sqrt{\dfrac{1}{b^5}} = \dfrac{\sqrt{1}}{\sqrt{b^5}}$ ⟵ **By Theorem 12–4**

$= \dfrac{1}{\sqrt{b^5}} \cdot \dfrac{\sqrt{b}}{\sqrt{b}}$ ⟵ **Multiplying by $\dfrac{\sqrt{b}}{\sqrt{b}}$ will give an equivalent rational expression with no radical in the denominator.**

$= \dfrac{\sqrt{b}}{\sqrt{b^6}}$

$= \dfrac{\sqrt{b}}{b^3}, \text{ or } \dfrac{1}{b^3}\sqrt{b}$

b. $\sqrt{\dfrac{2}{10x}} = \sqrt{\dfrac{1}{5x}}$ ⟵ $\dfrac{2}{10} = \dfrac{1}{5}$

$= \dfrac{1}{\sqrt{5x}}$ ⟵ **By Theorem 12–4**

$= \dfrac{1}{\sqrt{5x}} \cdot \dfrac{\sqrt{5x}}{\sqrt{5x}}$

$= \dfrac{\sqrt{5x}}{5x}$ ⟵ $(\sqrt{5x} \cdot \sqrt{5x}) = (\sqrt{5x})^2 = 5x$

Compare these two methods of approximating $\dfrac{1}{\sqrt{5}}$.

$$\frac{1}{\sqrt{5}} = \frac{\sqrt{5}}{5} \approx \frac{2.236}{5} = 0.447 \qquad\qquad \frac{1}{\sqrt{5}} \approx \frac{1}{2.236} = 0.447$$

You can see that rationalizing the denominator *before dividing* makes it easier to evaluate $\dfrac{1}{\sqrt{5}}$.

CLASSROOM EXERCISES

Simplify.

1. $\sqrt{\dfrac{16}{25}}$　　2. $\pm\sqrt{\dfrac{49}{100}}$　　3. $4\sqrt{\dfrac{32}{81}}$　　4. $-2\sqrt{\dfrac{27}{144}}$　　5. $\pm3\sqrt{\dfrac{5}{49}}$

Rationalize the denominators and simplify.

6. $\dfrac{1}{\sqrt{6}}$　　7. $\sqrt{\dfrac{3}{6}}$　　8. $\dfrac{\sqrt{6}}{\sqrt{5}}$　　9. $\dfrac{1}{\sqrt{8}}$　　10. $\dfrac{\sqrt{2}}{\sqrt{3}}$

11. $\sqrt{\dfrac{2}{9}}$　　12. $\sqrt{\dfrac{1}{7}}$　　13. $\dfrac{4\sqrt{5}}{\sqrt{2}}$　　14. $\dfrac{15\sqrt{3}}{3\sqrt{5}}$　　15. $\sqrt{\dfrac{1}{x^3}}$

WRITTEN EXERCISES

A　　Simplify.

1. $\sqrt{\dfrac{4}{25}}$　　2. $\sqrt{\dfrac{3}{49}}$　　3. $\sqrt{\dfrac{7}{36}}$　　4. $\sqrt{\dfrac{10}{81}}$　　5. $\sqrt{\dfrac{6}{16}}$

6. $2\sqrt{\dfrac{7}{25}}$　　7. $5\sqrt{\dfrac{9}{196}}$　　8. $3\sqrt{\dfrac{6}{100}}$　　9. $7\sqrt{\dfrac{11}{144}}$　　10. $6\sqrt{\dfrac{3}{64}}$

11. $2\sqrt{\dfrac{12}{225}}$　　12. $7\sqrt{\dfrac{18}{49}}$　　13. $5\sqrt{\dfrac{24}{121}}$　　14. $9\sqrt{\dfrac{27}{169}}$　　15. $7\sqrt{\dfrac{75}{625}}$

Rationalize the denominators and simplify. All variables represent positive numbers.

16. $\dfrac{3}{\sqrt{5}}$　　17. $\dfrac{2}{\sqrt{3}}$　　18. $\dfrac{5}{\sqrt{2}}$　　19. $\dfrac{2}{\sqrt{6}}$　　20. $\dfrac{\sqrt{3}}{\sqrt{2}}$

21. $\dfrac{\sqrt{7}}{\sqrt{2}}$　　22. $\dfrac{\sqrt{8}}{\sqrt{3}}$　　23. $\dfrac{\sqrt{7}}{\sqrt{5}}$　　24. $\dfrac{2\sqrt{3}}{\sqrt{2}}$　　25. $\dfrac{3\sqrt{2}}{\sqrt{3}}$

26. $\dfrac{4\sqrt{2}}{\sqrt{5}}$　　27. $\dfrac{3\sqrt{3}}{\sqrt{2}}$　　28. $\dfrac{5\sqrt{8}}{\sqrt{7}}$　　29. $\dfrac{3\sqrt{9}}{\sqrt{2}}$　　30. $\dfrac{2\sqrt{4}}{\sqrt{3}}$

31. $\dfrac{8\sqrt{5}}{\sqrt{15}}$　　32. $\dfrac{3\sqrt{6}}{2\sqrt{2}}$　　33. $\dfrac{2\sqrt{7}}{5\sqrt{3}}$　　34. $\dfrac{5\sqrt{3}}{\sqrt{18}}$　　35. $\dfrac{4\sqrt{2}}{3\sqrt{32}}$

36. $\dfrac{4}{\sqrt{a}}$ **37.** $\dfrac{7}{\sqrt{y}}$ **38.** $\dfrac{21}{\sqrt{2b}}$ **39.** $\dfrac{14}{\sqrt{4c}}$ **40.** $\dfrac{8}{\sqrt{2d}}$

41. $\sqrt{\dfrac{3}{b^3}}$ **42.** $\sqrt{\dfrac{4}{c^5}}$ **43.** $\sqrt{\dfrac{3}{12x^3}}$ **44.** $\sqrt{\dfrac{14}{8x^5}}$ **45.** $\sqrt{\dfrac{21}{27d^3}}$

46. $\dfrac{\sqrt{ax}}{\sqrt{a}}$ **47.** $\dfrac{\sqrt{b^3d^4}}{\sqrt{bd}}$ **48.** $\dfrac{\sqrt{24b^3}}{\sqrt{6b}}$ **49.** $\sqrt{\dfrac{60m^3n}{5m}}$ **50.** $\sqrt{\dfrac{x^2y}{xy^2}}$

B   Simplify.

51. $\sqrt{\dfrac{2}{3}} \cdot \sqrt{\dfrac{3}{4}}$ **52.** $\sqrt{\dfrac{3}{5}} \cdot \sqrt{\dfrac{2}{5}}$ **53.** $\sqrt{\dfrac{7}{2}} \cdot \sqrt{\dfrac{7}{5}}$ **54.** $\sqrt{\dfrac{7}{8}} \cdot \sqrt{\dfrac{3}{8}}$

55. $\sqrt{\dfrac{3}{5}} \cdot \sqrt{\dfrac{6}{7}}$ **56.** $\sqrt{\dfrac{10}{13}} \cdot \sqrt{\dfrac{1}{2}}$ **57.** $\sqrt{\dfrac{6}{7}} \cdot \sqrt{\dfrac{7}{6}}$ **58.** $\sqrt{\dfrac{3}{5}} \cdot \sqrt{\dfrac{3}{5}}$

59. $\sqrt{3 - \dfrac{1}{2}}$ **60.** $\sqrt{7 + \dfrac{3}{4}}$ **61.** $\sqrt{25 - \dfrac{25}{4}}$ **62.** $\sqrt{4^2 - \left(\dfrac{1}{4}\right)^2}$

C   Rationalize the denominators. Then use the values below to find a decimal approximation for each expression.

$$\sqrt{2} \approx 1.414 \qquad \sqrt{3} \approx 1.732 \qquad \sqrt{5} \approx 2.236$$

Example: $\dfrac{3}{\sqrt{2}}$ **Solution:** $\dfrac{3}{\sqrt{2}} = \dfrac{3\sqrt{2}}{\sqrt{2} \cdot \sqrt{2}}$

$$= \dfrac{3\sqrt{2}}{2}$$

$$\approx \dfrac{3 \cdot 1.414}{2} = \mathbf{2.121}$$

63. $\dfrac{4}{\sqrt{3}}$ **64.** $\dfrac{5}{\sqrt{2}}$ **65.** $\dfrac{3}{\sqrt{12}}$ **66.** $\dfrac{4}{\sqrt{8}}$ **67.** $\dfrac{3}{\sqrt{20}}$ **68.** $\dfrac{4}{\sqrt{18}}$

69. $\dfrac{5}{\sqrt{10}}$ **70.** $\dfrac{4}{\sqrt{15}}$ **71.** $\dfrac{7}{\sqrt{18}}$ **72.** $\dfrac{10}{\sqrt{24}}$ **73.** $\dfrac{7}{\sqrt{45}}$ **74.** $\dfrac{11}{\sqrt{30}}$

--------- **REVIEW CAPSULE FOR SECTION 12–8** ---------

Simplify. *(Pages 437–438)*

1. $\sqrt{24}$ **2.** $\sqrt{80}$ **3.** $\sqrt{40}$ **4.** $\sqrt{128}$ **5.** $3\sqrt{32}$ **6.** $3\sqrt{64}$

7. $5\sqrt{28}$ **8.** $-2\sqrt{18}$ **9.** $8\sqrt{50}$ **10.** $3\sqrt{12}$ **11.** $-4\sqrt{96}$ **12.** $7\sqrt{75}$

Multiply. Write the product in simplest form. *(Pages 448–449)*

13. $\sqrt{7} \cdot \sqrt{5}$ **14.** $\sqrt{5} \cdot \sqrt{12}$ **15.** $\sqrt{3} \cdot \sqrt{2}$ **16.** $5\sqrt{2} \cdot \sqrt{2}$

17. $5\sqrt{2} \cdot 6\sqrt{2}$ **18.** $\sqrt{7} \cdot \sqrt{7}$ **19.** $\sqrt{8} \cdot \sqrt{8}$ **20.** $2\sqrt{2} \cdot \sqrt{8}$

12-8 Addition and Subtraction of Radicals

Terms such as $-5x^3y^2$ and $3x^3y^2$ are like terms because their variable factors, x and y, are the same and they have the same exponents. Similarly, $2\sqrt{3}$ and $7\sqrt{3}$ are **like terms** because their radicals are the same.

Like Radicals	Unlike Radicals
$\sqrt{5}$ and $6\sqrt{5}$	$\sqrt{3}$ and $\sqrt{5}$
$3\sqrt{a}$ and $-2\sqrt{a}$	$3\sqrt{a}$ and $2\sqrt{b}$

To add or subtract like radicals, you apply the distributive postulate.

$$5\sqrt{y} + 7\sqrt{y} = (5+7)\sqrt{y} = 12\sqrt{y}$$

EXAMPLE 1 Add or subtract as indicated: $3\sqrt{5} + 6\sqrt{2} - \sqrt{5}$

Solution: Group the like terms.

$$3\sqrt{5} + 6\sqrt{2} - \sqrt{5} = (3\sqrt{5} - \sqrt{5}) + 6\sqrt{2}$$
$$= (3-1)\sqrt{5} + 6\sqrt{2} \quad \longleftarrow \quad \textbf{By the distributive}$$
$$\textbf{postulate}$$
$$= 2\sqrt{5} + 6\sqrt{2}$$

Always express each radical in simplest form before adding or subtracting. This will help you to identify like radicals.

EXAMPLE 2 Add or subtract as indicated: $\sqrt{48} + 6\sqrt{27} - 5\sqrt{12}$

Solution: Simplify the radicals before adding or subtracting.

$$\sqrt{48} + 6\sqrt{27} - 5\sqrt{12} = \sqrt{16 \cdot 3} + 6\sqrt{9 \cdot 3} - 5\sqrt{4 \cdot 3} \quad \longleftarrow \quad \begin{array}{l}\sqrt{16 \cdot 3} = 4\sqrt{3}; \\ \sqrt{9 \cdot 3} = 3\sqrt{3}; \\ \sqrt{4 \cdot 3} = 2\sqrt{3}\end{array}$$
$$= 4\sqrt{3} + 6 \cdot 3\sqrt{3} - 5 \cdot 2\sqrt{3}$$
$$= 4\sqrt{3} + 18\sqrt{3} - 10\sqrt{3}$$
$$= (4 + 18 - 10)\sqrt{3}$$
$$= 12\sqrt{3} \quad \longleftarrow \quad \textbf{Simplest form}$$

You can also use the distributive postulate to simplify products of radical expressions.

EXAMPLE 3 Simplify each expression. **a.** $\sqrt{5}(3 + \sqrt{10})$ **b.** $(3 - \sqrt{5})(3 + \sqrt{5})$

Solutions: **a.** $\sqrt{5}(3 + \sqrt{10}) = \sqrt{5} \cdot 3 + \sqrt{5} \cdot \sqrt{10} \quad \longleftarrow \quad$ **By the distributive postulate**
$$= 3\sqrt{5} + \sqrt{50} \quad \longleftarrow \quad \textbf{Simplify.}$$
$$= 3\sqrt{5} + \sqrt{25 \cdot 2}$$
$$= 3\sqrt{5} + 5\sqrt{2} \quad \longleftarrow \quad \textbf{Simplest form}$$

b. $(3 - \sqrt{5})(3 + \sqrt{5}) = (3)^2 - (\sqrt{5})^2 \quad \longleftarrow \quad \textbf{(a + b)(a - b) = a}^2 \textbf{- b}^2$
$$= 9 - 5 = 4 \quad \longleftarrow \quad \textbf{(}\sqrt{5}\textbf{)}^2 \textbf{= 5}$$

In Example 3b, note that the product of $(3 - \sqrt{5})$ and $(3 + \sqrt{5})$ is a rational number. Expressions of the form $(a + \sqrt{b})$ and $(a - \sqrt{b})$ are called **conjugates.** Since

$$(a + \sqrt{b})(a - \sqrt{b}) = a^2 - b,$$

you can use conjugates to rationalize some binomial denominators. (See the Example for Exercises 48–51.)

CLASSROOM EXERCISES

Add or subtract as indicated.

1. $5\sqrt{3} - 2\sqrt{3} + \sqrt{3}$
2. $-5\sqrt{6} + 2\sqrt{6} + 8\sqrt{6}$
3. $2\sqrt{2} - \sqrt{8} + \sqrt{2}$
4. $5\sqrt{2} + 2\sqrt{18} - 3\sqrt{72}$
5. $\sqrt{12} + \sqrt{3} - 2\sqrt{27}$
6. $6\sqrt{y} - 7\sqrt{y} + 13\sqrt{y}$

Simplify.

7. $\sqrt{2}(9 + \sqrt{5})$
8. $\sqrt{3}(3 - \sqrt{3})$
9. $\sqrt{5}(6 - 2\sqrt{5})$
10. $(1 + \sqrt{2})(1 - \sqrt{2})$

WRITTEN EXERCISES

A   Add or subtract as indicated.

1. $3\sqrt{2} + 2\sqrt{2} - 4\sqrt{2}$
2. $5\sqrt{3} - 2\sqrt{3} - 6\sqrt{3}$
3. $6\sqrt{2} + 8\sqrt{2} - 9\sqrt{2}$
4. $-3\sqrt{3} + 4\sqrt{3} - 10\sqrt{3}$
5. $5\sqrt{7} + 6\sqrt{7} - 11\sqrt{7}$
6. $4\sqrt{3} + 2\sqrt{3} - 2\sqrt{2} + 7\sqrt{2}$
7. $8\sqrt{5} + 6\sqrt{5} + 2\sqrt{3} + 7\sqrt{3}$
8. $10\sqrt{2} + 7\sqrt{3} - 4\sqrt{2} - 5\sqrt{3}$
9. $\sqrt{4} + 3\sqrt{2} + 7 - 5\sqrt{2}$
10. $\sqrt{12} + 3\sqrt{3}$
11. $\sqrt{8} + 5\sqrt{2} - 6\sqrt{2}$
12. $\sqrt{20} - 3\sqrt{5} + 2\sqrt{5}$
13. $-6\sqrt{5} + 7\sqrt{5} - \sqrt{20}$
14. $\sqrt{12} - \sqrt{27} + \sqrt{48}$
15. $3\sqrt{18} - 7\sqrt{32} - 5\sqrt{50}$
16. $10\sqrt{8} - \sqrt{72} + 3\sqrt{98}$
17. $10\sqrt{8} - 3\sqrt{98} + 6\sqrt{72}$
18. $2\sqrt{8} + 4\sqrt{50} + 3\sqrt{18}$
19. $6\sqrt{54} - 3\sqrt{24} - 2\sqrt{6}$
20. $\sqrt{125} + 2\sqrt{80} - 3\sqrt{20}$
21. $2\sqrt{40} + \sqrt{90} + 5\sqrt{160}$

Simplify.

22. $\sqrt{2}(\sqrt{3} + 3)$
23. $\sqrt{7}(\sqrt{2} + 5)$
24. $\sqrt{3}(\sqrt{3} + 2)$
25. $\sqrt{4}(\sqrt{8} + 2)$
26. $\sqrt{8}(2\sqrt{3} - 5)$
27. $\sqrt{5}(\sqrt{2} - \sqrt{3})$
28. $(8 + \sqrt{7})(8 - \sqrt{7})$
29. $(\sqrt{5} - 2)(\sqrt{5} + 2)$
30. $(\sqrt{6} + 9)(\sqrt{6} - 9)$

B   Add or subtract as indicated.

31. $\sqrt{\dfrac{2}{3}} + \sqrt{\dfrac{8}{3}}$
32. $5\sqrt{\dfrac{1}{6}} - 3\sqrt{\dfrac{3}{2}}$
33. $\sqrt{\dfrac{2}{3}} - 3\sqrt{\dfrac{1}{6}}$
34. $\sqrt{\dfrac{2}{36}} - 3\sqrt{\dfrac{2}{49}} - 6\sqrt{\dfrac{2}{25}}$
35. $\sqrt{\dfrac{8}{9}} + 2\sqrt{\dfrac{1}{2}} - 3\sqrt{\dfrac{9}{8}}$
36. $\sqrt{\dfrac{3}{4}} - 2\sqrt{\dfrac{19}{16}} + \sqrt{\dfrac{3}{8}}$
37. $\sqrt{100x} - \sqrt{9x}$
38. $2a\sqrt{ab} + 4\sqrt{a^3b}$
39. $3\sqrt{2b^3} - \sqrt{8b^3}$
40. $4\sqrt{12r^2} + 2\sqrt{75r^2} - 3\sqrt{27r^2}$
41. $\sqrt{12a^3} - 2\sqrt{3a^3} + \sqrt{27a^3}$
42. $x\sqrt{xy^3} + xy\sqrt{xy} + y\sqrt{x^3y}$
43. $2b\sqrt{25b} + b\sqrt{4b} - 3b\sqrt{9b}$

Write the conjugate of each radical expression.

44. $1 + \sqrt{2}$ **45.** $3 - \sqrt{5}$ **46.** $2\sqrt{3} + 5\sqrt{7}$ **47.** $1 - \sqrt{x}$

Rationalize the denominator.

Example: $\dfrac{5}{1 - 2\sqrt{5}} = \dfrac{5}{1 - 2\sqrt{5}} \cdot \dfrac{1 + 2\sqrt{5}}{1 + 2\sqrt{5}} = \dfrac{5 + 10\sqrt{5}}{1 - 4(5)} = \dfrac{5 + 10\sqrt{5}}{-19}$

48. $\dfrac{2}{1 + \sqrt{2}}$ **49.** $\dfrac{4}{\sqrt{7} - 2}$ **50.** $\dfrac{7}{5 - \sqrt{3}}$ **51.** $\dfrac{2}{\sqrt{6} - 3}$

Ⓒ

52. $\dfrac{3\sqrt{5} + 2\sqrt{3}}{2\sqrt{5} - 5\sqrt{3}}$ **53.** $\dfrac{2\sqrt{5} + 3\sqrt{2}}{4\sqrt{5} - \sqrt{2}}$ **54.** $\dfrac{\sqrt{a} + \sqrt{b}}{\sqrt{a} - \sqrt{b}}$ **55.** $\dfrac{3\sqrt{x} - 1}{\sqrt{x} + 1}$

Factor over the real numbers.

Example: $x^2 - 5 = x^2 - (\sqrt{5})^2 = (x + \sqrt{5})(x - \sqrt{5})$

56. $y^2 - 7$ **57.** $a^2 - 10$ **58.** $2b^2 - 12$ **59.** $5x^2 - 25$

60. $27 - r^2$ **61.** $1 - 2x^2$ **62.** $t^2 - 5v^2$ **63.** $a^2 - 2a\sqrt{5} + 5$

Puzzle

See if you can solve the following problems involving radicals.

1. Solve: $\sqrt{\sqrt{\sqrt{x + 37} + 2} + 6} = 3$

2. Three of the statements below are true. Which one is false?

    a. $\sqrt{1\tfrac{1}{3}} = 2\sqrt{\tfrac{1}{3}}$ **b.** $\sqrt{2\tfrac{2}{3}} = 2\sqrt{\tfrac{2}{3}}$ **c.** $\sqrt{3\tfrac{3}{3}} = 3\sqrt{\tfrac{2}{3}}$ **d.** $\sqrt{5\tfrac{1}{3}} = 4\sqrt{\tfrac{1}{3}}$

3. Show that this statement is true: $\sqrt{x + \dfrac{x}{x^2 - 1}} = x\sqrt{\dfrac{x}{x^2 - 1}}$.

    (HINT: Work on the left side only.)

REVIEW CAPSULE FOR SECTION 12–9

Simplify. *(Pages 432–433)*

1. $(\sqrt{5})^2$ **2.** $(\sqrt{15})^2$ **3.** $(\sqrt{11})^2$ **4.** $(\sqrt{565})^2$ **5.** $(\sqrt{x})^2$

6. $(\sqrt{a - 1})^2$ **7.** $(\sqrt{2b - 1})^2$ **8.** $(3\sqrt{x})^2$ **9.** $(4\sqrt{2b})^2$ **10.** $(5\sqrt{a - 1})^2$

Determine whether the given number is a solution of the given equation. Answer *Yes* or *No*. *(Pages 18–20)*

11. $2 + \sqrt{x} = 4$;   4   **12.** $2 - 4\sqrt{y} = 3$; $\tfrac{1}{16}$ **13.** $1 + \sqrt{x} = 0$; -1

14. $\sqrt{y} - 48 = 2$;   2500   **15.** $2\sqrt{a} - 14 = 0$;   7   **16.** $3\sqrt{b} + 1 = 8$; $\tfrac{55}{9}$

12-9 Solving Radical Equations

An equation such as $3 + \sqrt{x} = 6$ is a radical equation. A **radical equation** contains a radical that includes a variable.

EXAMPLE 1 Solve: $3 + \sqrt{x} = 6$

Solution: Add -3 to each side in order to get the radical alone on the left side.

$$3 + \sqrt{x} = 6$$
$$-3 + 3 + \sqrt{x} = -3 + 6$$
$$\sqrt{x} = 3 \quad \longleftarrow \quad \textbf{Now square both sides.}$$
$$(\sqrt{x})^2 = (3)^2 \quad \longleftarrow \quad (\sqrt{\textbf{x}})^2 = \textbf{x}$$
$$x = 9$$

Check: $3 + \sqrt{x} = 6 \quad \longleftarrow \quad \textbf{Replace x with 9.}$
$$3 + \sqrt{9} \overset{?}{=} 6$$
$$3 + 3 \overset{?}{=} 6$$
$$6 \overset{?}{=} 6 \quad \text{Yes} \; \checkmark$$

Solution set: $\{9\}$

In Example 2, the radicand of $3\sqrt{2a - 1}$ is a binomial.

EXAMPLE 2 Solve: $3\sqrt{2a - 1} + 4 = 7$

Solution:
$$3\sqrt{2a - 1} + 4 = 7 \quad \longleftarrow \quad \textbf{Add (−4) to each side.}$$
$$3\sqrt{2a - 1} + 4 + (-4) = 7 + (-4)$$
$$3\sqrt{2a - 1} = 3 \quad \longleftarrow \quad \textbf{Multiply each side by } \tfrac{1}{3}.$$
$$\sqrt{2a - 1} = 1 \quad \longleftarrow \quad \textbf{Square both sides.}$$
$$(\sqrt{2a - 1})^2 = 1^2$$
$$2a - 1 = 1 \quad \longleftarrow \quad \textbf{Solve for a.}$$
$$2a = 2$$
$$a = 1$$

The check is left for you.

Solution set: $\{1\}$

Squaring both sides of an equation sometimes results in an "apparent solution" that does not check in the original equation. An "apparent solution" is not a member of the solution set. This is why it is important to check all your answers in the original equation.

EXAMPLE 3   Solve: $6 + \sqrt{x - 5} = 3$

Solution: $6 + \sqrt{x - 5} = 3$ $\longleftarrow$ **Add (−6) to each side.**

$\sqrt{x - 5} = -3$ $\longleftarrow$ **Square both sides.**

$(\sqrt{x - 5})^2 = (-3)^2$ $\longleftarrow$ $(\sqrt{x - 5})^2 = x - 5$

$x - 5 = 9$

$x = 14$

Check: $6 + \sqrt{x - 5} = 3$ $\longleftarrow$ **Replace x with 14.**

$6 + \sqrt{14 - 5} \overset{?}{=} 3$

$6 + \sqrt{9} \overset{?}{=} 3$ No $\longleftarrow$ **14 is not a solution.**

Solution set: ϕ

CLASSROOM EXERCISES

Solve.

1. $\sqrt{y} = \dfrac{2}{5}$ **2.** $\sqrt{3x - 2} = 7$ **3.** $\sqrt{4x} = 10$ **4.** $\sqrt{\dfrac{a}{4}} = 25$

State the first step you would use to solve each equation. Do *not* solve the equation.

5. $3\sqrt{y} = 1$ **6.** $12 + 3\sqrt{x} = 0$ **7.** $\sqrt{3x} + 4 = 7$ **8.** $\sqrt{x} + 9 = 20$

WRITTEN EXERCISES

A   Solve and check each equation. If an apparent solution does not check in the original equation, give the solution set as ϕ.

1. $\sqrt{x} = 6$ **2.** $\sqrt{x} = \dfrac{3}{4}$ **3.** $\sqrt{\dfrac{n}{5}} = 2$

4. $8 = \sqrt{x - 9}$ **5.** $8 = \sqrt{5r + 1}$ **6.** $\sqrt{x + 5} = 4$

7. $3 + \sqrt{x - 1} = 5$ **8.** $6 + \sqrt{x} = 13$ **9.** $6 - \sqrt{x - 5} = 3$

10. $5 + \sqrt{x} = 3$ **11.** $8 + 2\sqrt{x} = 0$ **12.** $2\sqrt{x} = 5$

13. $5\sqrt{x} = 2$ **14.** $-\sqrt{x} = 6$ **15.** $-7 = \sqrt{y}$

16. $-\sqrt{m} = -5$ **17.** $-9 = -\sqrt{y}$ **18.** $-\sqrt{x} = \dfrac{3}{4}$

19. $\sqrt{x} = -3$ **20.** $\sqrt{x} = \sqrt{5}$ **21.** $-1 = \sqrt{x - 5}$

22. $\sqrt{a - 1} = \sqrt{3}$ **23.** $\sqrt{7 + 3x} = -4$ **24.** $-9 = \sqrt{6 - x}$

25. $\sqrt{3y + 2} = 2\sqrt{y}$ **26.** $5 = \dfrac{15}{\sqrt{2a - 3}}$ **27.** $\sqrt{\dfrac{9}{16}} = x$

28. $-\sqrt{\dfrac{81}{25}} = x$ **29.** $\sqrt{2x + 1} = \sqrt{x + 5}$ **30.** $3\sqrt{5b + 1} + 5 = 8$

APPLICATIONS: Using Radical Equations

31. Five times the square root of a number is 2. Find the number.

32. Eight less than the square root of a number is 0. What is the number?

33. Three more than the square root of a number is 7. What is the number?

34. A number is increased by 3. The square root of this sum is 5. Find the number.

35. Twice a number is decreased by 3. The square root of this difference equals 6. Find the number.

36. The quotient of the square root of a number and 5 equals $\frac{3}{4}$. What is the number?

37. The formula

$$s = \sqrt{30fd}$$

can be used to estimate the speed, s, in miles per hour that a car was traveling when it skidded d feet after the brakes were applied. In the formula, f is the coefficient of friction. Find the distance a car will travel on a wet concrete road ($f = 0.4$) if the car is traveling 50 miles per hour when the brakes are applied.

38. The formula

$$T = 2\pi \sqrt{\frac{L}{9.8}}$$

relates the time, T, in seconds that it takes for a pendulum to swing back and forth once with the length, L, of the pendulum in meters. What is the length of a pendulum that takes 3 seconds to swing back and forth once? Use $\pi = 3.14$. Round the answer to the nearest tenth.

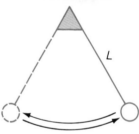

39. The formula

$$t = \sqrt{\frac{d^3}{216}}$$

relates the time, t, in hours that a storm with diameter, d, in miles will last. What is the diameter of a storm that lasts one hour?

40. The time, t, in seconds that it takes a body to fall a distance of s feet from rest is given by the formula

$$t = \sqrt{\frac{2s}{g}}$$

where g is the acceleration due to gravity. Find s when $t = 6.25$ and $g = 32$.

Solve and check each equation.

41. $\sqrt{x^2 + 5} = x + 1$

42. $\sqrt{x^2 - 5} = x - 5$

43. $\sqrt{x^2 + 24} = x + 12$

44. $\sqrt{3b^2 - 5} = 11$

45. $\sqrt{y^2 + 4y} = \sqrt{5}$

46. $\sqrt{a^2 - 7a} = \sqrt{18}$

C

47. $4\sqrt{2a + 2} - 9 = 2\sqrt{2a + 2}$

48. $\sqrt{4b - 3} - \sqrt{3b + 4} = 0$

49. $5\sqrt{3t - 1} - 4 = 3\sqrt{3t - 1}$

50. $\sqrt{2q + 6} - \sqrt{5q} = 0$

Determine whether each pair of equations is equivalent (has the same solution set). Give a reason for each answer.

51. $x^2 + y^2 = 1$; $y = \sqrt{1 - x^2}$

52. $x^2 + y^2 = 1$; $\sqrt{x^2 + y^2} = 1$

Write each product as a base with a single exponent. *(Pages 280–282)*

1. $x^3 \cdot x^4$ **2.** $a \cdot a^6$ **3.** $c^2 \cdot c$ **4.** $5^3 \cdot 5^2$ **5.** $10^2 \cdot 10^5$

Simplify. *(Pages 285–287)*

6. $(x^2)^2$ **7.** $(x^2)^3$ **8.** $(x^3)^2$ **9.** $(x^3)^3$ **10.** $(4b^3)^2$

11. $(z^4)^3$ **12.** $(\frac{1}{2}z)^2$ **13.** $(4t)^3$ **14.** $(-4c^2)^3$ **15.** $(0.5d)^2$

Write each expression with positive exponents. Simplify the result when possible. *(Pages 290–293)*

16. 5^{-3} **17.** $3b^{-2}$ **18.** $(3b)^{-2}$ **19.** $(-4)^{-3}$ **20.** 10^{-2}

21. 6^{-1} **22.** $\dfrac{4}{b^{-2}}$ **23.** $(-2)^{-4}$ **24.** $\left(\dfrac{1}{6}\right)^{-1}$ **25.** $\left(-\dfrac{1}{2}\right)^{-4}$

12–10   Rational Exponents

The properties of positive and negative integral exponents can be extended in order to define rational exponents. Consider the following.

You already know that

$$\sqrt{5} \cdot \sqrt{5} = (\sqrt{5})^2 = 5.$$

If the exponent theorems hold for rational exponents, then

$$5^{\frac{1}{2}} \cdot 5^{\frac{1}{2}} = 5^{\frac{1}{2}+\frac{1}{2}} = 5^1, \text{ or } 5.$$

Thus, it seems reasonable to define

$$\sqrt{5} = 5^{\frac{1}{2}}.$$

The following expresses the definition in general form.

Definition

> **Rational Exponents**
>
> For any positive integer n where n is odd and a is any real number, or for any positive integer n where n is even and $a \geq 0$,
>
> $$a^{\frac{1}{n}} = \sqrt[n]{a}.$$

EXAMPLE 1   Simplify: **a.** $81^{\frac{1}{2}}$ **b.** $-(81)^{\frac{1}{2}}$ **c.** $81^{\frac{1}{4}}$ **d.** $(-8)^{\frac{1}{3}}$

Solutions: **a.** $81^{\frac{1}{2}} = \sqrt{81}$ **b.** $-(81)^{\frac{1}{2}} = -\sqrt{81}$

                       $= 9$ $= -9$

          c. $81^{\frac{1}{4}} = \sqrt[4]{81}$ **d.** $(-8)^{\frac{1}{3}} = \sqrt[3]{-8}$

                  $= 3$ ◄——— **Since** $3^4 = 81$ $= -2$

By the definition of rational exponents, $\sqrt[5]{7} = 7^{\frac{1}{5}}$. Then, by the laws of exponents,

$$\sqrt[5]{7^3} = (7^3)^{\frac{1}{5}} = 7^{3 \cdot \frac{1}{5}} = 7^{\frac{3}{5}} \quad \text{Thus,} \quad \sqrt[5]{7^3} = 7^{\frac{3}{5}}.$$

When the conditions of the definition are satisfied, rational exponents may be viewed in two ways. Thus,

$$7^{\frac{3}{5}} = (\sqrt[5]{7})^3 \quad \text{or} \quad \sqrt[5]{7^3}.$$

Example 2 illustrates the value of taking the root first.

EXAMPLE 2 Simplify: **a.** $4^{\frac{3}{2}}$ **b.** $-(27)^{\frac{2}{3}}$ **c.** $(16)^{\frac{5}{4}}$

Solutions: **a.** $4^{\frac{3}{2}} = (4^{\frac{1}{2}})^3 = (\sqrt{4})^3 = 2^3 = \mathbf{8}$

b. $-(27)^{\frac{2}{3}} = -(27^{\frac{1}{3}})^2 = -(\sqrt[3]{27})^2 = -3^2 = \mathbf{-9}$

c. $16^{\frac{5}{4}} = [(16)^{\frac{1}{4}}]^5 = (\sqrt[4]{16})^5 = (2)^5 = \mathbf{32}$

CLASSROOM EXERCISES

Write using rational exponents.

1. $\sqrt{7}$ **2.** $\sqrt[3]{2}$ **3.** $\sqrt{5^3}$ **4.** $\sqrt[5]{6^2}$ **5.** $\sqrt[4]{9^3}$

Simplify.

6. $16^{\frac{1}{2}}$ **7.** $(-64)^{\frac{1}{3}}$ **8.** $-(4^{\frac{3}{2}})$ **9.** $(8)^{\frac{5}{3}}$ **10.** $243^{\frac{3}{5}}$

WRITTEN EXERCISES

A Simplify.

1. $9^{\frac{1}{2}}$ **2.** $125^{\frac{1}{3}}$ **3.** $16^{\frac{1}{4}}$ **4.** $(-27)^{\frac{1}{3}}$ **5.** $81^{\frac{1}{4}}$

6. $625^{\frac{1}{4}}$ **7.** $121^{\frac{1}{2}}$ **8.** $144^{\frac{1}{2}}$ **9.** $-(36)^{\frac{1}{2}}$ **10.** $-(81)^{\frac{1}{4}}$

11. $-(\frac{1}{4})^{\frac{1}{2}}$ **12.** $(\frac{1}{27})^{\frac{1}{3}}$ **13.** $-(\frac{1}{27})^{\frac{1}{3}}$ **14.** $(-\frac{1}{27})^{\frac{1}{3}}$ **15.** $27^{\frac{1}{3}}$

16. $-(27)^{\frac{1}{3}}$ **17.** $(\frac{4}{9})^{\frac{1}{2}}$ **18.** $(-\frac{8}{125})^{\frac{1}{3}}$ **19.** $-(\frac{8}{125})^{\frac{1}{3}}$ **20.** $-(25)^{\frac{1}{2}}$

21. $-(64)^{\frac{1}{2}}$ **22.** 15^0 **23.** $-(9)^{\frac{1}{2}}$ **24.** $-(16)^{\frac{1}{4}}$ **25.** $25^{\frac{1}{2}}$

26. $81^{\frac{1}{2}}$ **27.** $8^{\frac{1}{3}}$ **28.** $64^{\frac{1}{3}}$ **29.** $32^{\frac{1}{5}}$ **30.** $-(16)^{\frac{1}{2}}$

31. $64^{\frac{1}{2}}$ **32.** $27^{\frac{1}{3}}$ **33.** $-(49^{\frac{1}{2}})$ **34.** $(-8)^{\frac{1}{3}}$ **35.** $-(125)^{\frac{1}{3}}$

36. $(\frac{1}{16})^{\frac{1}{2}}$ **37.** $(\frac{4}{25})^{\frac{1}{2}}$ **38.** $-(\frac{1}{36})^{\frac{1}{2}}$ **39.** $(-\frac{1}{8})^{\frac{1}{3}}$ **40.** $(\frac{1}{64})^{\frac{1}{3}}$

41. $27^{\frac{4}{3}}$ **42.** $(\frac{1}{64})^{\frac{2}{3}}$ **43.** $16^{\frac{3}{4}}$ **44.** $4^{\frac{3}{2}}$ **45.** $49^{\frac{3}{2}}$

Use a radical to name each of the following. Variables represent positive integers.

46. $7^{\frac{1}{2}}$ **47.** $(-8)^{\frac{1}{3}}$ **48.** $16^{\frac{1}{4}}$ **49.** $93^{\frac{1}{n}}$ **50.** $x^{\frac{1}{2}}$

51. $y^{\frac{1}{3}}$ **52.** $a^{\frac{1}{4}}$ **53.** $(x^2)^{\frac{1}{3}}$ **54.** $(xy)^{\frac{1}{2}}$ **55.** $(ab)^{\frac{1}{3}}$

B   Evaluate each expression for $a = 8$, $b = 9$, and $c = 1$.

56. $a^{\frac{1}{3}} - b^{\frac{1}{2}}$ **57.** $(a + c)^{\frac{1}{2}}$ **58.** $-a^{\frac{1}{3}}$ **59.** $-(b)^{\frac{1}{2}}$ **60.** $a^{\frac{5}{3}}$

61. $b^{\frac{3}{2}}$ **62.** $-(bc)^{\frac{3}{2}}$ **63.** $c^{\frac{1}{8}}$ **64.** $(a - b)^{\frac{1}{3}}$ **65.** $(ab + c)^{\frac{1}{2}}$

Review

Multiply and simplify. Variables represent positive numbers. *(Section 12–6)*

1. $\sqrt{3} \cdot \sqrt{12}$ **2.** $-3\sqrt{14} \cdot 2\sqrt{6}$ **3.** $\sqrt{x} \cdot \sqrt{xy}$ **4.** $\sqrt{6a} \cdot \sqrt{3a}$

Simplify. Variables represent positive numbers. *(Section 12–7)*

5. $\sqrt{\dfrac{4}{9}}$ **6.** $\dfrac{1}{\sqrt{6}}$ **7.** $\sqrt{\dfrac{2}{5}}$ **8.** $\sqrt{\dfrac{5}{x^3}}$ **9.** $\dfrac{\sqrt{18a^3}}{\sqrt{3ab^2}}$

Add or subtract as indicated. *(Section 12–8)*

10. $3\sqrt{5} + \sqrt{5} - 4\sqrt{5}$ **11.** $6\sqrt{5} + \sqrt{8} - \sqrt{45}$ **12.** $\sqrt{6r^2} + \sqrt{24r^2}$

Solve and check each equation. If an apparent solution does not check in the original equation, give the solution set as ϕ. *(Section 12–9)*

13. $\sqrt{x + 1} = 10$ **14.** $2 + \sqrt{x} = 7$ **15.** $3\sqrt{x - 2} = 6$

Simplify. *(Section 12–10)*

16. $1000^{\frac{1}{3}}$ **17.** $-(25)^{\frac{1}{2}}$ **18.** $(-32)^{\frac{1}{5}}$ **19.** $4^{\frac{5}{2}}$ **20.** $(-8)^{\frac{2}{3}}$

 CALCULATOR APPLICATIONS

Evaluating Formulas

You can use a calculator with a square root key to evaluate formulas that include radicals.

EXAMPLE   Use the formula $T = 2\pi\sqrt{\dfrac{L}{9.8}}$ to find T when $L = 2.2$. Use $\pi = 3.14$. (See Exercise 38 on page 459.)

SOLUTION   Evaluate the radical first.

$$2 \;.\; 2 \;\boxed{\div}\; 9 \;.\; 8 \;\boxed{=}\; \boxed{\sqrt{}} \;\boxed{\times}\; 2 \;\boxed{\times}\; 3 \;.\; 1\;4 \;\boxed{=}\; \boxed{2.9754853}$$

EXERCISES

Use the formula $T = 2\pi\sqrt{\dfrac{L}{9.8}}$ to find T for each value of L. Round your answers to the nearest tenth.

1. $L = 5$ **2.** $L = 8.5$ **3.** $L = 10.4$ **4.** $L = 13$ **5.** $L = 19.7$ **6.** $L = 0.5$

BASIC: COMPUTING SQUARE ROOTS

BASIC has the SQR function for computing square roots. But how does a function like this work? The **algorithm** (step-by-step procedure) for approximating the square root of a positive real number is shown below.

Procedure

> **1** Make an estimate, e, of the square root. For example, let e be the greatest integer less than or equal to $\frac{1}{2}x$.
>
> **2** Divide x by e. Call this quotient a.
>
> **3** Take the average of a and e. Let this average become e_2.
>
> **4** Repeat steps 2 and 3 until the difference between a and e becomes less than a specified tolerance (for example, 0.1). Then, that value of e is the approximate square root.

EXAMPLE   Use the algorithm to approximate $\sqrt{17}$.

Solution: **1** Let $e_1 = 8$.

2 Then $a_1 = \dfrac{17}{8} \approx 2.13$.   **3** $\dfrac{8 + 2.13}{2} \approx 5.07$ $e_2 = 5.07$

4 Repeat steps 2 and 3.

$$a_2 = \frac{17}{5.07} \approx 3.35 \qquad\qquad e_3 = \frac{5.07 + 3.35}{2} = 4.21$$

$$a_3 = \frac{17}{4.21} \approx 4.04 \qquad\qquad e_4 = \frac{4.21 + 4.04}{2} \approx 4.13$$

Since the difference between e_4 and a_3 is less than 0.1, **4.13** is a reasonable approximation of $\sqrt{17}$.

Problem: *Write a program to calculate the square root of any positive integer. Do not use the SQR function.*

```
100 PRINT "ENTER A POSITIVE REAL NUMBER."
110 INPUT X
120 IF X <= 0 THEN 100
130 LET E = INT(X/2)           ←——————— Step 1
140 LET A = X/E                ←——————— Step 2
150 LET E = (A + E)/2          ←——————— Step 3
160 IF ABS(A - E) > .0001 THEN 140 ←——— Step 4 (Tolerance: 0.0001)
170 PRINT "SQUARE ROOT OF";X;" = ";E
180 PRINT
190 PRINT "ANY MORE SQUARE ROOTS (1=YES, 0=NO)";
200 INPUT Z
210 IF Z = 1 THEN 100
220 END
```

The following is the output from a sample run of the program on page 463.

Output:
```
RUN
ENTER A POSITIVE REAL NUMBER.
? 17
SQUARE ROOT OF 17 = 4.12311

ANY MORE SQUARE ROOTS (1=YES, 0=NO)? 1
ENTER A POSITIVE REAL NUMBER.
? -13
ENTER A POSITIVE REAL NUMBER.
? 89
SQUARE ROOT OF 89 = 9.43398

ANY MORE SQUARE ROOTS (1=YES, 0=NO)? 0
READY
```

EXERCISES

A   Run the program on page 463 for the following values of x.

1. $x = 5$ **2.** $x = 13$ **3.** $x = 26$ **4.** $x = 36$

5. $x = 42$ **6.** $x = 0$ **7.** $x = -7$ **8.** $x = 115$

9. Add statements to the program on page 463 so that the successive values of e and a are printed in two labeled columns.

Write a BASIC program for each problem.

10. Given the area of a square, compute and print the length of a side. (See Example 3 on page 435.)

11. Given the area of a circle, compute and print the length of the radius. (Use $\pi = 3.14$.) (See Exercise 38 on page 436.)

12. Given the lengths of the two legs of a right triangle, compute and print the length of the hypotenuse. (See Example 1 on page 439.)

13. Given the lengths of the hypotenuse and one leg of a right triangle, compute and print the length of the other leg. (See Example 2 on page 440.)

B

14. Given three positive real numbers a, b, and c, decide whether they could be the lengths of the sides of a right triangle. Do not assume that c will be the largest number.

15. Given the coordinates of two points, compute and print the distance between the points.

C

16. Given the coordinates of three points (not in a straight line), calculate and print the perimeter of the triangle formed by joining the points.

Chapter Summary

IMPORTANT IDEAS

1. For any real number a, $\sqrt{a^2} = |a|$.

2. If a and b are real numbers and $a \geq 0$, $b \geq 0$, *then*
$$\sqrt{ab} = \sqrt{a} \cdot \sqrt{b}.$$

3. **Pythagorean Theorem:** If a, b, and c are the lengths of the sides of a right triangle and c is the hypotenuse (longest side), then
$$a^2 + b^2 = c^2.$$

4. If the sum of the squares of the lengths of the two shorter sides (legs) of a triangle is equal to the square of the length of the longest side (hypotenuse), then the triangle is a right triangle.

5. **Distance Formula:** If $P_1(x_1, y_1)$ and $P_2(x_2, y_2)$ are any two points in the coordinate plane, then the distance, d, between the points is given by the formula
$$d = \sqrt{(x_2 - x_1)^2 + (y_2 - y_1)^2}.$$

6. If a and b are real numbers where $a \geq 0$ and $b > 0$, *then* $\sqrt{\dfrac{a}{b}} = \dfrac{\sqrt{a}}{\sqrt{b}}$.

7. A radical is in simplest form when
   $\boxed{1}$ The radicand contains no factor that is a perfect square.
   $\boxed{2}$ The radicand does not contain a fraction.
   $\boxed{3}$ No radical appears in a denominator.

8. For any positive integer n where n is odd and a is any real number, or for any positive integer n where n is even and $a \geq 0$, $a^{\frac{1}{n}} = \sqrt[n]{a}$.

Chapter Objectives and Review

Objective: *To find the square roots of numbers or expressions that are perfect squares (Section 12-1)*

Simplify.

1. $\sqrt{121}$

2. $-\sqrt{y^{12}}$

3. $\sqrt{9x^2y^6}$

4. $\sqrt{(37d^3)^2}$

Objective: *To find rational approximations for square roots (Section 12-2)*

Write each rational number in the form $\dfrac{a}{b}$.

5. $0.\overline{5}$

6. $0.\overline{18}$

7. $0.1\overline{6}$

8. $0.4\overline{07}$

9. The area of a square is 20 square meters. Find the length of a side to the nearest tenth of a meter.

10. The area of the face of an old coin is 6.28 square centimeters. Find the radius of the coin to the nearest tenth. (Use $A = \pi r^2$, where $\pi = 3.14$.)

Objective: *To simplify radicals (Section 12–3)*

Simplify. All variables represent positive numbers.

11. $\sqrt{18}$

12. $6\sqrt{32}$

13. $\sqrt{54x^3}$

14. $-2\sqrt{4a^3b^5}$

Objective: *To find the length of a side of a right triangle using the Pythagorean Theorem (Section 12–4)*

The lengths of the legs of a right triangle are a and b, and c is the length of the hypotenuse. Use the Pythagorean Theorem to find the length of the unknown side to the nearest tenth.

15. $a = 12$, $b = 16$, $c = $ __?__

16. $a = $ __?__, $b = 7$, $c = 10$

17. A sidewalk is built diagonally across a rectangular park 200 meters long and 300 meters wide. Find the length of the sidewalk to the nearest meter.

18. The diagonal of a square rug is 3 meters in length. Find the length of each side of the square to the nearest tenth of a meter.

Objective: *To find the distance between two points in the coordinate plane (Section 12–5)*

Find the distance between each pair of points.

19. $C(3, -4)$ and $D(6, 0)$

20. $R(6, 2)$ and $S(-1, 2)$

21. $W(3, -6)$ and $X(-6, 3)$

Objective: *To multiply radicals (Section 12–6)*

Multiply and simplify. All variables represent positive numbers.

22. $\sqrt{2} \cdot \sqrt{6}$

23. $3\sqrt{8} \cdot (-5\sqrt{12})$

24. $\sqrt{2a^2} \cdot \sqrt{2b^2}$

25. $-\sqrt{3n^3} \cdot \sqrt{6n^2}$

Objective: *To divide radicals (Section 12–7)*

Simplify. All variables represent positive real numbers.

26. $\pm\sqrt{\dfrac{36}{25}}$

27. $\dfrac{1}{\sqrt{10}}$

28. $\sqrt{2 + \dfrac{1}{4}}$

29. $\sqrt{\dfrac{12}{8y^5}}$

30. $\dfrac{\sqrt{30a^3b}}{\sqrt{5a}}$

Objective: *To add and subtract radicals (Section 12–8)*

Add or subtract as indicated.

31. $6\sqrt{7} - 4\sqrt{7} - \sqrt{7}$

32. $4\sqrt{18} + 5\sqrt{2}$

33. $4\sqrt{24x^2} - 2\sqrt{54x^2}$

Rationalize the denominator.

34. $\dfrac{1}{3 + \sqrt{2}}$

35. $\dfrac{3}{4 - \sqrt{3}}$

36. $\dfrac{4}{\sqrt{5} + 1}$

37. $\dfrac{2}{\sqrt{8} - 4}$

Objective: *To solve radical equations (Section 12–9)*

Solve and check each equation.

38. $\sqrt{x-3} = 1$ **39.** $6 + \sqrt{3x-5} = 2$ **40.** $\sqrt{2x-1} = \sqrt{x+4}$

41. Nine more than the square root of a number is 14. Find the number.

42. Twelve, divided by the square root of a number, equals $1\frac{1}{2}$. Find the number.

Objective: *To simplify expressions containing rational exponents (Section 12–10)*

Simplify.

43. $100^{\frac{1}{2}}$ **44.** $(-27)^{\frac{1}{3}}$ **45.** $144^{\frac{1}{2}}$ **46.** $625^{\frac{3}{4}}$ **47.** $-(1000)^{\frac{2}{3}}$

_____ Chapter Test _____

Simplify.

1. $\pm\sqrt{100}$ **2.** $\sqrt{\frac{9}{16}}$ **3.** $\sqrt{63}$ **4.** $-\sqrt{108}$ **5.** $(-8)^{\frac{1}{3}}$ **6.** $27^{\frac{2}{3}}$

The lengths of the sides of a right triangle are *a* and *b*, and *c* is the length of the hypotenuse. Find the length of the unknown side.

7. $a = 15$, $b = 20$, $c = $ ___?___ **8.** $a = 24$, $b = $ ___?___, $c = 25$

Find the distance between each pair of points.

9. $A(3, 6)$ and $B(0, 2)$ **10.** $K(6, -2)$ and $L(-3, -2)$

Perform the indicated operations. Simplify the answers.

11. $\sqrt{5} \cdot \sqrt{8}$ **12.** $-3\sqrt{2} \cdot \sqrt{10}$ **13.** $6\sqrt{2} + 3\sqrt{8}$

14. $\dfrac{3\sqrt{12}}{2\sqrt{18}}$ **15.** $\sqrt{2n} \cdot \sqrt{6n}$ **16.** $6\sqrt{5x^2} - \sqrt{45x^2}$

Solve and check each equation.

17. $\sqrt{x-2} = 3$ **18.** $4\sqrt{x+6} = 8$

14. The length of a parking lot is 24 meters and the width is 10 meters. Find the length of a diagonal of the lot.

20. Four less than the square root of a number is 6. What is the number?

Additional Practice

Skills

Simplify. *(Section 12–1)*

1. $-\sqrt{144}$ **2.** $\sqrt{0.36}$ **3.** $\pm\sqrt{19^2}$ **4.** $\sqrt{9a^2b^4}$ **5.** $\sqrt{\frac{64}{81}}$

Write each rational number in the form $\frac{a}{b}$. *(Section 12-2)*

6. $0.\overline{7}$ **7.** $0.\overline{81}$ **8.** $1.\overline{3}$ **9.** $0.\overline{297}$ **10.** $0.41\overline{6}$

Simplify. All variables represent positive numbers. *(Section 12-3)*

11. $\sqrt{54}$ **12.** $2\sqrt{75}$ **13.** $-3\sqrt{80x^3}$ **14.** $4\sqrt{63}$ **15.** $5\sqrt{180a^4b^5}$

The lengths of the sides of a right triangle are a and b, and c is the length of the hypotenuse. Find the length of the unknown side. *(Section 12-4)*

16. $a = 15, b = 36, c = \underline{\;?\;}$ **17.** $a = \underline{\;?\;}, b = 12, c = 15$

Find the distance between each pair of points. *(Section 12-5)*

18. $A(2, 3)$ and $B(2, -5)$ **19.** $P(0, 3)$ and $Q(-8, -3)$ **20.** $S(2, 12)$ and $T(-3, 0)$

Multiply and simplify. Variables represent positive numbers. *(Section 12-6)*

21. $\sqrt{6} \cdot \sqrt{18}$ **22.** $\sqrt{75} \cdot \sqrt{2}$ **23.** $\sqrt{14a} \cdot \sqrt{2a}$ **24.** $\sqrt{15xy} \cdot \sqrt{3xy}$

Simplify. Variables represent positive numbers. *(Section 12-7)*

25. $\sqrt{\dfrac{3}{16}}$ **26.** $\dfrac{3\sqrt{6}}{2\sqrt{3}}$ **27.** $\dfrac{\sqrt{6}}{\sqrt{8}}$ **28.** $\sqrt{\dfrac{35a^2}{7}}$ **29.** $\dfrac{\sqrt{12x^3}}{\sqrt{3x}}$

Add or subtract as indicated. *(Section 12-8)*

30. $2\sqrt{3} + \sqrt{3} + 4\sqrt{3}$ **31.** $3\sqrt{5} - 2\sqrt{20}$ **32.** $6\sqrt{8} + 3\sqrt{18} - \sqrt{32}$

Solve and check each equation. *(Section 12-9)*

33. $\sqrt{x-2} = 5$ **34.** $5 + \sqrt{x} = 12$ **35.** $3\sqrt{2x+4} = 9$

Simplify. *(Section 12-10)*

36. $216^{\frac{1}{3}}$ **37.** $-(49)^{\frac{1}{2}}$ **38.** $(-64)^{\frac{1}{3}}$ **39.** $\left(\dfrac{1}{16}\right)^{\frac{1}{2}}$ **40.** $16^{\frac{3}{4}}$

Applications

41. The length of a rectangle is twice its width. The area of the rectangle is 60 square meters. Find the length and width to the nearest tenth of a meter. *(Section 12-2)*

42. The foot of a ladder lies 1.5 meters from the base of a wall. The top lies against the wall, 3.5 meters above the ground. Find the length of the ladder (nearest tenth). *(Section 12-4)*

43. The diagonal of a square measures 12 centimeters. Find the length of each side of the square to the nearest tenth of a centimeter. *(Section 12-4)*

44. The diagonal of the floor of a tent measures 4 meters. The tent is twice as long as it is wide. Find the dimensions to the nearest tenth. *(Section 12-4)*

45. Five less than the square root of a number is 4. Find the number. *(Section 12-9)*

46. Twice a number is increased by 6. The square root of this sum is 8. Find the number. *(Section 12-9)*

CHAPTER **13** **Quadratic Functions and Equations**

13-1 Quadratic Equations

Equations such as the following are *quadratic equations*.

$$a^2 = 5 \qquad g^2 - 9 = 0 \qquad y^2 + 5y = 0 \qquad x^2 - 4x + 4 = 0$$

Definition

> A **quadratic equation** is an equation that can be written in the form (**standard form**)
> $$ax^2 + bx + c = 0$$
> where a, b, and c are real numbers and $a \neq 0$.

In Chapter 9, you solved certain quadratic equations by factoring. Quadratic equations of the form $x^2 = k$ where $k \geq 0$ can be solved by factoring or by taking the square root of each side of the equation. This last procedure results in two linear equations which *together* are equivalent to the original quadratic equation.

> If $x^2 = k$, then $x = \sqrt{k}$ <u>or</u> $x = -\sqrt{k}$ for any real number k, $k \geq 0$.

EXAMPLE 1 Solve: $x^2 - 7 = 0$

Solution: **Method 1** By factoring

$$x^2 - 7 = 0$$
$$(x - \sqrt{7})(x + \sqrt{7}) = 0 \longleftarrow \textbf{By the Zero-Product Theorem}$$
$$x = \sqrt{7} \quad \underline{\text{or}} \quad x = -\sqrt{7}$$

Method 2 By taking the square root

$$x^2 - 7 = 0$$
$$x^2 = 7$$
$$x = \pm\sqrt{7}$$

Check:

$$x^2 - 7 = 0 \longleftarrow \begin{array}{l}\textbf{Replace } \underline{x} \\ \textbf{with } \sqrt{7}.\end{array} \qquad\qquad x^2 - 7 = 0 \longleftarrow \begin{array}{l}\textbf{Replace } \underline{x} \\ \textbf{with } -\sqrt{7}.\end{array}$$
$$(\sqrt{7})^2 - 7 \overset{?}{=} 0 \qquad\qquad\qquad (-\sqrt{7})^2 - 7 \overset{?}{=} 0$$
$$7 - 7 \overset{?}{=} 0 \qquad\qquad\qquad\qquad 7 - 7 \overset{?}{=} 0$$
$$0 \overset{?}{=} 0 \quad \text{Yes } \checkmark \qquad\qquad\qquad 0 \overset{?}{=} 0 \quad \text{Yes } \checkmark$$

Thus, the **solution set** is $\{-\sqrt{7}, \sqrt{7}\}$.

Quadratic equations such as $(x - 5)^2 = 36$ can also be solved by taking the square root of each side of the equation.

EXAMPLE 2   Solve: $(x - 5)^2 = 36$

> **Solution:** $(x - 5)^2 = 36$ ◄────── **Take the square root of both sides.**
>
> $$x - 5 = \pm 6$$
>
> $x - 5 = 6$ <u>or</u> $x - 5 = -6$
>
> $x = 11$ <u>or</u> $x = -1$
>
> The check is left for you.   **Solution set: $\{-1, 11\}$**

CLASSROOM EXERCISES

Solve each equation.

1. $x^2 = 25$
2. $x^2 - 8 = 0$
3. $(x - 2)^2 = 9$
4. $(x + 5)^2 = 16$
5. $(x - \frac{1}{2})^2 = \frac{1}{4}$
6. $(x + 1)^2 = 81$
7. $3a^2 = 36$
8. $3y^2 = 4$

WRITTEN EXERCISES

A   Solve each equation.

1. $x^2 = 16$
2. $y^2 - 4 = 0$
3. $x^2 - 11 = 0$
4. $n^2 - 7 = 12$
5. $m^2 + 2 = 3$
6. $7 - 2x^2 = -15$
7. $4x^2 = 36$
8. $3x^2 + 5 = 26$
9. $2r^2 = 200$
10. $2s^2 - 18 = 0$
11. $z^2 = 32$
12. $y^2 - 19 = 0$
13. $x^2 - \frac{1}{4} = 0$
14. $2x^2 = \frac{1}{2}$
15. $99 = b^2 - 22$
16. $3n^2 - n = 15 - n$
17. $4m^2 - 3 = 9$
18. $3y^2 - 9 = 0$
19. $3z^2 = \frac{12}{9}$
20. $r - r^2 = 5r^2 + r$
21. $(x - 2)^2 = 0$
22. $(x + 5)^2 = 16$
23. $(x - 3)^2 = 25$
24. $(x - 1)^2 = 1$
25. $(x + 7)^2 = 49$
26. $(x + 6)^2 = 100$
27. $(x - \frac{1}{2})^2 = 4$
28. $(x + 17)^2 = 49$
29. $3(a + 6)^2 = 27$
30. $5(b - 2)^2 = 125$
31. $3(z - 6)^2 = 48$
32. $3(t + 9)^2 = 27$

B

33. $(b + \frac{3}{4})^2 = 16$
34. $(c + \frac{3}{2})^2 = \frac{1}{4}$
35. $(x - \frac{1}{4})^2 = \frac{1}{16}$
36. $(t - \frac{8}{3})^2 = \frac{1}{9}$
37. $(x + \frac{3}{7})^2 = \frac{1}{49}$
38. $(2m + 4)^2 = 1$
39. $(2k - 6)^2 = 16$
40. $(2q - 9)^2 = 25$
41. $(2n - 5)^2 = 49$
42. $(3p - 7)^2 = 1$
43. $(4r - 8)^2 = 16$
44. $(6s - 1)^2 = 25$
45. $5(2y - 1)^2 = 80$
46. $4(3x - 2)^2 = 36$
47. $3(2v + 7)^2 = 27$
48. $10(3a + 7)^2 = 1000$

C   Solve for x where a, b, and c are nonnegative constants.

49. $x^2 = a + b$
50. $\dfrac{x^2}{a} = 1$
51. $\dfrac{x^2}{a} = b$
52. $x^2 - 2a = 0$
53. $4x^2 = a^2$
54. $\dfrac{ax^2}{b} = 1$
55. $\dfrac{ax^2}{b} = ac$
56. $\dfrac{ab^2}{x^2} = 1$
57. $(x + a)^2 = b$
58. $(x - a)^2 = b$
59. $(2x + a)^2 = b$
60. $(3x - c)^2 = d$
61. $(ax + b)^2 = c$
62. $(ax - b)^2 = d$
63. $(ax - b)^2 = 4$
64. $(ax + c)^2 = 3d$

Express each trinomial as the square of a binomial. When a trinomial is not a perfect square, write *NP*. *(Pages 326–328)*

1. $m^2 - 4m + 4$ **2.** $v^2 + 4v + 8$ **3.** $h^2 + h + 1$

4. $t^2 + 0.2t + 0.01$ **5.** $q^2 - 0.6q + 0.09$ **6.** $p^6 - 12p^3 + 36$

7. $r^2 + \frac{2}{3}r + \frac{1}{9}$ **8.** $y^2 - \frac{7}{6}y + \frac{49}{36}$ **9.** $b^2 - \frac{7}{2}b + \frac{49}{16}$

10. $t^2 - \frac{1}{3}t + \frac{1}{36}$ **11.** $a^2 + \frac{6}{5}a + \frac{9}{25}$ **12.** $c^2 + \frac{3}{4}c + \frac{9}{64}$

13-2 Completing the Square

When a quadratic equation cannot be easily solved by factoring or by taking the square root of each side, a method called **completing the square** can be used. Recall that

$$(x + 7)^2 = x^2 + 2 \cdot 7 \cdot x + 49 = x^2 + 14x + 49.$$

Note that the last term, 49, is the square of one-half the coefficient of the middle term, $14x$. That is,

$$49 = \left(\frac{1}{2} \cdot 14\right)^2.$$

EXAMPLE 1   Complete the square.

     a. $a^2 + 8a$ **b.** $x^2 - 10x$

Solutions: **a.** Think: What is $\left(\frac{1}{2} \cdot 8\right)^2$?   **b.** Think: What is $\left[\frac{1}{2}(-10)\right]^2$?

$$\left(\frac{1}{2} \cdot 8\right)^2 = 4^2 = 16 \qquad\qquad \left[\frac{1}{2}(-10)\right]^2 = (-5)^2 = 25$$

$$a^2 + 8a + 16 = (a + 4)^2 \qquad\qquad x^2 - 10x + 25 = (x - 5)^2$$

The following procedure summarizes the steps for completing the square of $x^2 + bx$.

Procedure

> **To complete the square of $x^2 + bx$:**
>
> ☐1   Find one-half the coefficient of x.   ⟶ $\frac{b}{2}$
>
> ☐2   Square the result of step 1.   ⟶ $\left(\frac{b}{2}\right)^2 = \frac{b^2}{4}$
>
> ☐3   Add the result of step 2 to $x^2 + bx$.   ⟶ $x^2 + bx + \frac{b^2}{4}$

You can find the solutions of a quadratic equation by completing the square. Example 2 shows the steps you use to solve an equation by this method.

EXAMPLE 2   Solve $x^2 + 6x + 8 = 0$ by completing the square.

Solution: $\boxed{1}$ Write the equation in the
form $x^2 + bx = c$.

$$x^2 + 6x + 8 = 0$$
$$x^2 + 6x = -8$$

$\boxed{2}$ Complete the square for
$x^2 + 6x$.

Think: $\left(\frac{1}{2} \cdot 6\right)^2 = 9$

Add this number to each side
of the equation.

$$x^2 + 6x + 9 = -8 + 9$$
$$x^2 + 6x + 9 = 1$$

$\boxed{3}$ Write the left member as a
perfect square. Solve the
equation.

$$(x + 3)^2 = 1$$
$$x + 3 = 1 \quad \underline{\text{or}} \quad x + 3 = -1$$
$$x = -2 \quad \underline{\text{or}} \quad x = -4$$

$\boxed{4}$ The check is left for you.

Solution set: $\{-4, -2\}$

Before attempting to solve a quadratic equation by completing the square,
be sure that the equation is in the form $x^2 + bx + c = 0$, where the coefficient
of the x^2-term is **1.**

EXAMPLE 3   Solve $4x^2 - 4x - 7 = 0$ by completing the square.

Solution: Since the coefficient of $4x^2$ is not 1, divide *each side* of the equation by 4,
the coefficient of $4x^2$.

$$4x^2 - 4x - 7 = 0 \quad \longleftarrow \quad \text{Divide each side by 4.}$$

$$x^2 - x - \frac{7}{4} = 0 \quad \longleftarrow \quad \text{Add } \left(\frac{7}{4}\right) \text{ to each side.}$$

$$x^2 - x = \frac{7}{4} \quad \longleftarrow \quad \left[\frac{1}{2}(-1)\right]^2 = \frac{1}{4}. \text{ Add } \frac{1}{4} \text{ to each side.}$$

$$x^2 - x + \frac{1}{4} = \frac{7}{4} + \frac{1}{4} \longleftarrow \quad \frac{7}{4} + \frac{1}{4} = \frac{8}{4} = 2$$

$$\left(x - \frac{1}{2}\right)^2 = 2$$

$$x - \frac{1}{2} = \sqrt{2} \qquad \underline{\text{or}} \quad x - \frac{1}{2} = -\sqrt{2}$$
$$x = \frac{1}{2} + \sqrt{2} \quad \underline{\text{or}} \qquad x = \frac{1}{2} - \sqrt{2}$$

Check:

$$4x^2 - 4x - 7 = 0$$
$$4(\tfrac{1}{2} + \sqrt{2})^2 - 4(\tfrac{1}{2} + \sqrt{2}) - 7 \overset{?}{=} 0$$
$$4(\tfrac{1}{4} + \sqrt{2} + 2) - 2 - 4\sqrt{2} - 7 \overset{?}{=} 0$$
$$1 + 4\sqrt{2} + 8 - 2 - 4\sqrt{2} - 7 \overset{?}{=} 0$$
$$0 \overset{?}{=} 0 \quad \text{Yes}$$

$$4x^2 - 4x - 7 = 0$$
$$4(\tfrac{1}{2} - \sqrt{2})^2 - 4(\tfrac{1}{2} - \sqrt{2}) - 7 \overset{?}{=} 0$$
$$4(\tfrac{1}{4} - \sqrt{2} + 2) - 2 + 4\sqrt{2} - 7 \overset{?}{=} 0$$
$$1 - 4\sqrt{2} + 8 - 2 + 4\sqrt{2} - 7 \overset{?}{=} 0$$
$$0 \overset{?}{=} 0 \quad \text{Yes}$$

Solution set: $\left\{\frac{1}{2} + \sqrt{2}, \frac{1}{2} - \sqrt{2}\right\}$

CLASSROOM EXERCISES

Write the term needed to complete the square.

1. $x^2 + 4x + \underline{\ ?\ }$
2. $x^2 - 2x + \underline{\ ?\ }$
3. $x^2 + 8x + \underline{\ ?\ }$
4. $c^2 - 14c + \underline{\ ?\ }$
5. $x^2 - x + \underline{\ ?\ }$
6. $d^2 - \frac{4}{5}d + \underline{\ ?\ }$
7. $t^2 + \frac{1}{2}t + \underline{\ ?\ }$
8. $x^2 + bx + \underline{\ ?\ }$
9. $x^2 - \frac{b}{a}x + \underline{\ ?\ }$

WRITTEN EXERCISES

A   Complete the square. Then write the trinomial as the square of a binomial.

1. $x^2 + 10x$
2. $y^2 - 8y$
3. $m^2 + 4m$
4. $a^2 + 2a$
5. $r^2 - r$
6. $x^2 + 12x$
7. $r^2 - 20r$
8. $a^2 + a$
9. $x^2 + 5x$
10. $x^2 - 11x$
11. $x^2 - \frac{2}{5}x$
12. $y^2 + 7y$

Solve by completing the square.

13. $x^2 + 4x = 12$
14. $x^2 + 6x = 27$
15. $n^2 - 8n = -15$
16. $n^2 - 2n - 8 = 0$
17. $a^2 - 6a + 8 = 0$
18. $x^2 + 8x = -12$
19. $a^2 + 4a = 5$
20. $b^2 + 10b = -16$
21. $x^2 - 14x = -40$
22. $x^2 - 12x = -35$
23. $x^2 - 10x = -24$
24. $c^2 + 2c = 15$
25. $x^2 - 16x = -60$
26. $x^2 - 16x = 17$
27. $a^2 - 3a = -2$
28. $x^2 - 7x + 10 = 0$
29. $x^2 - 9x = -18$
30. $a^2 - 3a = 10$
31. $n^2 + 6 = -5n$
32. $n^2 - 12 = n$
33. $x^2 - x = 6$
34. $x^2 + x = 6$
35. $x^2 - x = 30$
36. $y^2 + 3y = 4$
37. $y^2 - y = 2$
38. $p^2 + 5p = 0$
39. $x^2 = 3x$

B   Solve by completing the square. Irrational solutions may be left in simplified radical form.

40. $3n^2 - 2n = 1$
41. $2n^2 = n + 3$
42. $5n^2 + 2 = 11n$
43. $3x^2 - 2x = 8$
44. $2y^2 - 3y = 35$
45. $4n^2 + 4 = 17n$
46. $6p^2 - 9p = 27$
47. $2x^2 - 7x + 3 = 0$
48. $3a^2 + 8a + 5 = 0$
49. $2a^2 - 5a - 12 = 0$
50. $3x^2 - x - 2 = 0$
51. $2p^2 - 2p - 1 = 0$
52. $2a^2 + 3a = 17$
53. $3 = 6x^2 - x$
54. $7x^2 - 14x = 28$

C

55. $\frac{1}{4}x^2 - \frac{3}{2}x - 1 = 0$
56. $1 + \frac{7}{x} + \frac{2}{x^2} = 0$
57. $2x = 5 + \frac{4}{x}$
58. $x^2 + bx + 1 = 0$
59. $x^2 + bx = -c$
60. $ax^2 + bx + c = 0$
61. $\frac{5x + 7}{x - 1} = 3x + 2$
62. $\frac{5x - 1}{x + 1} = \frac{3x}{2}$
63. $\frac{3t - 8}{t - 2} = \frac{5t - 2}{t + 5}$
64. $\frac{a + 3}{2a - 7} - \frac{2a - 1}{a - 3} = 0$
65. $\frac{1}{3 - b} - \frac{4}{5} = \frac{1}{9 - 2b}$
66. $\frac{5}{d - 2} - \frac{4}{d} = \frac{3}{d + 6}$

Simplify. *(Pages 437–438)*

1. $\sqrt{54}$ 2. $-\sqrt{24}$ 3. $9\sqrt{48}$ 4. $5\sqrt{18}$ 5. $-2\sqrt{32}$

6. $7\sqrt{50}$ 7. $-\sqrt{8}$ 8. $-3\sqrt{40}$ 9. $-4\sqrt{50}$ 10. $5\sqrt{44}$

Evaluate $b^2 - 4ac$ for the given values of a, b, and c. *(Pages 5–8)*

11. $a = 3$, $b = 5$, $c = 1$ 12. $a = 2$, $b = -1$, $c = 3$ 13. $a = -8$, $b = 7$, $c = 1$

14. $a = 1$, $b = -6$, $c = 0$ 15. $a = 2$, $b = 0$, $c = -5$ 16. $a = 5$, $b = -8$, $c = -2$

13-3 The Quadratic Formula

By completing the square of the standard form of the quadratic equation,

$$ax^2 + bx + c = 0,$$

you can determine the **solutions** or **roots** of the equation.

Compare the method for the specific case shown on the left with that for the general case shown on the right.

Specific Case		**General Case**

$3x^2 - 2x - 2 = 0$ ←— Divide each side by the coefficient of the x^2-term. —→ Solve $ax^2 + bx + c = 0$.

$$x^2 - \frac{2}{3}x - \frac{2}{3} = 0 \qquad\qquad x^2 + \frac{b}{a}x + \frac{c}{a} = 0$$

$$x^2 - \frac{2}{3}x = \frac{2}{3} \qquad\qquad x^2 + \frac{b}{a}x = -\frac{c}{a}$$

$$\frac{1}{2}\left(-\frac{2}{3}\right) = -\frac{1}{3}; \left(-\frac{1}{3}\right)^2 = \frac{1}{9} \quad \longleftarrow \left[\frac{1}{2}(\text{coefficient of } x)\right]^2 \longrightarrow \quad \frac{1}{2}\left(\frac{b}{a}\right) = \frac{b}{2a}; \left(\frac{b}{2a}\right)^2 = \frac{b^2}{4a^2}$$

$$x^2 - \frac{2}{3}x + \frac{1}{9} = \frac{2}{3} + \frac{1}{9} \quad \longleftarrow \text{Complete the square.} \longrightarrow \quad x^2 + \frac{b}{a}x + \frac{b^2}{4a^2} = \frac{b^2}{4a^2} - \frac{c}{a}$$

$$\left(x - \frac{1}{3}\right)^2 = \frac{7}{9} \qquad\qquad \left(x + \frac{b}{2a}\right)^2 = \frac{b^2 - 4ac}{4a^2}$$

$$x - \frac{1}{3} = \pm\sqrt{\frac{7}{9}} \quad \longleftarrow \text{Solve for } x. \longrightarrow \quad x + \frac{b}{2a} = \pm\sqrt{\frac{b^2 - 4ac}{4a^2}}$$

$$x = \frac{1}{3} \pm \frac{\sqrt{7}}{3} \qquad\qquad x = -\frac{b}{2a} \pm \frac{\sqrt{b^2 - 4ac}}{2a}$$

$$x = \frac{1 \pm \sqrt{7}}{3} \qquad\qquad x = \frac{-b \pm \sqrt{b^2 - 4ac}}{2a}$$

The check is left for you.   The check is left for you.

Solution set: $\left\{\dfrac{1 + \sqrt{7}}{3}, \dfrac{1 - \sqrt{7}}{3}\right\}$ Solution set: $\left\{\dfrac{-b + \sqrt{b^2 - 4ac}}{2a}, \dfrac{-b - \sqrt{b^2 - 4ac}}{2a}\right\}$

The solutions for the general equation are usually referred to as the *quadratic formula*.

Quadratic Formula

For the quadratic equation $ax^2 + bx + c = 0$, where a, b, and c are real numbers and $a \neq 0$,

$$x = \frac{-b \pm \sqrt{b^2 - 4ac}}{2a}.$$

EXAMPLE   Use the quadratic formula to solve $3x^2 + 2x - 3 = 0$.

Solution: Identify a, b, and c. Then use the quadratic formula.

$3x^2 + 2x - 3 = 0$ ⟵ —————— **$a = 3$; $b = 2$; $c = -3$**

$x = \dfrac{-b \pm \sqrt{b^2 - 4ac}}{2a}$ ⟵ —————— **Quadratic formula**

$x = \dfrac{-2 \pm \sqrt{(2)^2 - 4(3)(-3)}}{2(3)}$

$x = \dfrac{-2 \pm \sqrt{4 + 36}}{6}$

$x = \dfrac{-2 \pm \sqrt{40}}{6}$ ⟵ —————— **Simplify $\sqrt{40}$.**

$x = \dfrac{-2 \pm 2\sqrt{10}}{6}$ ⟵ —————— **Factor the numerator.**

$x = \dfrac{2(-1 \pm \sqrt{10})}{6}$ ⟵ —————— **Simplify.**

$x = \dfrac{-1 \pm \sqrt{10}}{3}$ ⟵ —————— **The check is left for you.**

Solution set: $\left\{ \dfrac{-1 + \sqrt{10}}{3}, \dfrac{-1 - \sqrt{10}}{3} \right\}$

Be sure to express a quadratic equation in the form $ax^2 + bx + c = 0$ before using the quadratic formula. For example, to solve $2x^2 - x = 3$, first write the equation in the form

$$2x^2 - x - 3 = 0.$$

Then identify a, b, and c and use the quadratic formula.

CLASSROOM EXERCISES

For each quadratic equation, identify a, b, and c.

1. $x^2 - 4x - 5 = 0$

2. $3x^2 - 5x - 4 = 0$

3. $4x^2 + 12x = 7$

4. $3x^2 = 7 + 3y$

5. $7 - a^2 = 3a$

6. $4t^2 = 9 + 2t$

7. $3x^2 = 45$

8. $5b^2 = 3b + 2$

9. $5y^2 - 1 = 2y$

WRITTEN EXERCISES

A   Use the quadratic formula to solve each equation. Write irrational roots in simplest radical form.

1. $x^2 - 4x = 21$ 2. $x^2 + 6x = 16$ 3. $2x^2 - x - 3 = 0$

4. $x^2 = 3x$ 5. $p^2 - 4p = 0$ 6. $n^2 - 2n - 8 = 0$

7. $a^2 + 4a = 5$ 8. $6a^2 + 13a + 6 = 0$ 9. $n^2 + 6 = -5n$

10. $2y^2 = 5y - 3$ 11. $2x^2 + x = 3$ 12. $y^2 + 3y = 4$

13. $y^2 - y = 2$ 14. $10b^2 + 7b - 12 = 0$ 15. $x^2 + 6x = -9$

16. $x^2 - 2x = 4$ 17. $x^2 + 2x = 1$ 18. $x^2 + 4x = -2$

19. $x^2 + 6x + 3 = 0$ 20. $x^2 - x - 1 = 0$ 21. $x^2 + 3x + 1 = 0$

22. $2x^2 - 4x - 3 = 0$ 23. $2x^2 + x - 5 = 0$ 24. $3x^2 - 2x = 1$

25. $2x^2 + 7x + 2 = 0$ 26. $6x^2 - 3x - 4 = 0$ 27. $3x^2 + 10x + 5 = 0$

B

28. $2x^2 - 7x + 2 = 0$ 29. $2x^2 - x - 1 = 0$ 30. $3x^2 - 2x = 7$

31. $2y^2 - 3y = 4$ 32. $4n^2 - 4 = n$ 33. $7x^2 - 3x - 1 = 0$

34. $9n^2 + 2 + 9n = 0$ 35. $8n^2 + 7n - 2 = 0$ 36. $4a^2 - 5 = 3a$

37. $4 + \dfrac{9}{b^2} - \dfrac{12}{b} = 0$ 38. $\dfrac{6d + 10}{d} = -\dfrac{3}{d^2}$ 39. $\dfrac{3}{t - 1} - 4 = \dfrac{1}{t + 1}$

In Exercises 40–45, use the quadratic formula to solve each equation. Use the Table of Square Roots on page 541 or use a calculator to approximate irrational roots to the nearest tenth.

40. $3n^2 - 2n = 2$ 41. $3x^2 - x - 3 = 0$ 42. $2a^2 - 5a - 1 = 0$

43. $2n^2 = n + 2$ 44. $5n^2 + 3 = 11n$ 45. $3b^2 + 5b + 1 = 0$

C   In Exercises 46–51, use the quadratic formula to solve each equation. Write irrational roots in simplest radical form.

46. $\dfrac{1}{a}x^2 + \dfrac{1}{b}x + \dfrac{1}{c} = 0$ 47. $\dfrac{1}{c}x^2 + dx = 2c$ 48. $3gx^2 - 2hx + k = 0$

49. $\dfrac{1}{4}x^2 = \dfrac{1}{2}x - \dfrac{1}{4}$ 50. $(2r + 1)^2 = (r + 1)^2 + 6$ 51. $(a - 5)^2 = (a - 5) + 4$

In Exercises 52–53, refer to the quadratic equation $ax^2 + bx + c = 0$, where $a \neq 0$ and $b^2 - 4ac > 0$.

52. Show that the sum of the roots of the equation is $-\dfrac{b}{a}$.

53. Show that the product of the roots of the equation is $\dfrac{c}{a}$.

54. Write a quadratic equation whose roots are $1 \pm \sqrt{3}$. (HINT: Use the results of Exercises 52 and 53 to find the sum and product of the roots and thus to find the relationship between a, b, and c.)

55. Write a quadratic equation whose roots are $2 \pm \sqrt{5}$.

56. Write two quadratic equations whose solutions are $2 \pm \sqrt{3}$.

In Exercises 1–6, use one variable to represent the unknowns.
(Pages 107–109, 125–128)

1. Three consecutive integers

2. Two consecutive odd integers

3. The reciprocal of a certain number

4. Five less than a number's reciprocal

5. The number of seats in a row is ten fewer than the number of rows.

6. The denominator of a fraction is one more than twice the numerator.

Problem Solving and Applications

13–4   Using Quadratic Equations

When the conditions of a problem can be represented by a quadratic equation, the equation can then be solved by one of the methods you have learned.

EXAMPLE 1   In a school auditorium, the number of seats in each row is 8 fewer than the number of rows (Condition 1). The auditorium seats 609 persons (Condition 2). How many seats are there in each row?

Solution: $\boxed{1}$ Use Condition 1 to represent the unknowns.

Let s = the number of seats in each row.
Then $s + 8$ = the number of rows.

$\boxed{2}$ Use Condition 2 to write an equation.

$$s(s + 8) = 609 \quad \longleftarrow \quad \binom{\text{Number of}}{\text{Rows}}\binom{\text{Number of Seats}}{\text{per Row}} = \frac{\text{Total}}{\text{Seats}}$$

$\boxed{3}$ $s^2 + 8s = 609 \quad \longleftarrow$ **Solve for s.**

$s^2 + 8s - 609 = 0 \quad \longleftarrow$ **a = 1, b = 8, c = −609.**

$$s = \frac{-b \pm \sqrt{b^2 - 4ac}}{2a}$$

$$s = \frac{-8 \pm \sqrt{64 + 2436}}{2}$$

$$s = \frac{-8 \pm \sqrt{2500}}{2}$$

$$s = \frac{-8 + 50}{2} \quad \longleftarrow \quad \text{\textbf{The number of seats}}$$
cannot be negative.

$$s = \frac{-8 + 50}{2} = \frac{42}{2}, \text{ or } \mathbf{21} \longleftarrow \text{\textbf{Number of seats per row}}$$

$\boxed{4}$ The check is left for you.   There are **21 seats** per row.

When the solutions to a quadratic equation are irrational numbers, use the Table of Square Roots on page 541 or use a calculator to approximate the solutions to the nearest tenth, to the nearest hundredth, and so on, as directed.

EXAMPLE 2   The **Golden Rectangle,** discovered by the Greeks in the fifth century B.C., was considered to have the most "pleasing" shape. In a golden rectangle, the length is about 1.6 times the width (Condition 1). Find, to the nearest tenth, the dimensions of the golden rectangle with an area of 48 square centimeters.

Solution: $\boxed{1}$ Let w = the width.
Then $1.6w$ = the length.

$\boxed{2}$ $w(1.6w) = 48$
$\boxed{3}$ $\quad 1.6w^2 = 48$
$\qquad w^2 = 30$
$\qquad w = \pm\sqrt{30}$ ◄──────── **The width cannot be negative.**
$\qquad w \approx 5.5$ ◄──────── **Don't forget to find the length.**
$\qquad 1.6w \approx 8.8$

Check: $\boxed{4}$ Is $(5.5)(8.8) \approx 48$?   Yes ✔

The width is about **5.5 centimeters**; the length is about **8.8 centimeters**.

CLASSROOM EXERCISES

In Exercises 1–6:
a. Use Condition 1 to represent the variables.
b. Use Condition 2 to write an equation for the problem.

1. The length of a rectangle is 3 meters longer than the width. The area is 40 square meters.

2. The base of a triangle is 3 feet longer than the altitude. The area is 44 square feet.

3. The product of two consecutive odd integers is 35.

4. A certain number exceeds its square by 15.

5. The square of a number is 10 more than three times the number.

6. The sum of a number and six times its reciprocal is 5.

WORD PROBLEMS

A   Use a quadratic equation to represent the conditions of each problem. Then solve the equation. Approximate irrational roots to the nearest hundredth.

1. In a theater, the number of seats in each row is 16 fewer than the number of rows. How many seats are in each row of a 1161-seat theater?

2. The length of a rectangular piece of sheet metal is 3 times its width. What is its length if its area is 192 square centimeters?

Quadratic Functions and Equations   **479**

3. Find the dimensions of a golden rectangle with an area of 40 square centimeters.

4. One number is 3 more than another. The product of the numbers is 54. Find the numbers.

5. The square of a number is 56 more than the number itself. What is the number?

6. The length of a rectangle is 3 meters longer than its width. Its area is 40 square meters. Find its dimensions.

7. The perimeter of a rectangle is 30 meters and its area is 54 square meters. What are its dimensions?

8. What is the length of the diagonal of a square if it is 3 centimeters longer than a side of the square?

9. A number exceeds its square by $\frac{2}{9}$. Find the number.

10. The square of a number exceeds the number by 42. Find the number.

11. The hypotenuse of a right triangle is 2 centimeters longer than one side and 4 centimeters longer than the other side. How long is the hypotenuse?

12. A rectangular strip of asphalt paving is 5 meters longer than it is wide. Its area is 300 square meters. Find the length and width of the strip.

13. The difference in the squares of two consecutive odd integers is 56. What are the integers?

14. If a number is decreased by 18 times its reciprocal, the difference will be 7. What is the number?

15. A rectangular city lot has an area of 1000 square meters. If the length of the lot is 10 meters more than twice its width, find its length and width.

16. There are two numbers such that one is 3 more than half the other. The difference of the squares of the two numbers is 495. What are the numbers?

B

17. The numerator of a fraction is 1 less than its denominator. If the fraction is increased by 2 times its reciprocal, the sum will be $3\frac{5}{12}$. Find the numerator and the denominator.

18. The denominator of a fraction is 2 more than its numerator. If the fraction is increased by 3 times its reciprocal, the sum will be $5\frac{3}{5}$. Find the numerator and the denominator.

19. The figure below shows a rectangular park with a border of chestnut trees. The border has an area of 225 square meters. How wide is this border if the outside length is 25 meters and the outside width is 15 meters?

20. A box is to be made by cutting squares measuring 4 centimeters on a side from the square piece of cardboard shown below. If the volume of the box is to be 100 cubic centimeters, find the length of a side of the original square.

21. Sam and his mother drove 294 miles to the State Fair. Sam drove the farm truck at an average speed of 7 miles per hour slower than his mother drove the family car. It took Sam an hour longer than it took his mother. What was Sam's rate?

22. Mrs. and Mr. Murphy can do a piece of work together in 5 hours. Alone Mrs. Murphy can do the job in 3 hours less than Mr. Murphy can do it alone. How many hours, to the nearest tenth, will it take each to do the job?

_____ **Review** _____

Solve each equation. Irrational solutions may be left in simplified radical form. *(Section 13–1)*

1. $x^2 = 64$

2. $y^2 + 6 = 7$

3. $3x^2 = 36$

4. $4n^2 + 5 = 21$

5. $(x - 4)^2 = 0$

6. $4(a - 5)^2 = 16$

Solve by completing the square. Irrational solutions may be left in simplified form. *(Section 13–2)*

7. $x^2 - 2x - 15 = 0$

8. $x^2 + 5x + 6 = 0$

9. $n^2 - 2n = 8$

10. $a^2 - a = 2$

11. $2t^2 + t - 6 = 0$

12. $3s^2 - 6s = 1$

Use the quadratic formula to solve each equation. Irrational solutions may be left in simplified radical form. *(Section 13–3)*

13. $a^2 - 4a - 21 = 0$

14. $c^2 = 4c$

15. $y^2 - 2y = 8$

16. $3b^2 + 2b = 3$

17. $2x^2 + 4x = 1$

18. $2y^2 = y + 2$

Solve each problem. Approximate irrational roots to the nearest tenth. *(Section 13–4)*

19. On a pegboard, the number of pegs in each row is 4 more than the number of rows. There are 96 pegs in all. How many pegs are in each row?

20. The hypotenuse of a right triangle is one meter longer than one leg and 3 meters longer than the other leg. How long is the hypotenuse?

_____ **REVIEW CAPSULE FOR SECTION 13–5** _____

Complete the table of ordered pairs for each function. *(Pages 181–184)*

1. $y = x^2 - x + 6$

x	−2	−1	0	1	2	3
y	?	?	?	?	?	?

2. $y = 2x^2 - 9x + 11$

x	−4	−2	0	2	4	6
y	?	?	?	?	?	?

Career Applications

Meteorology

Meteorologists study the atmosphere, its physical composition, its motions, and its processes. Specialists in weather forecasting, called **synoptic meteorologists,** are the most well-known of these scientists. They use present and past data to predict future weather patterns.

One item of the weather forecast that is very important is the **wind chill** factor. Wind chill results from the combination of cold air and strong winds that often occurs in cold weather. It is the temperature a person feels rather than the actual temperature.

The National Weather Service publishes a table for estimating wind chill. Part of that table is shown below.

Penny Griego, Weather Forecaster

Winds in MPH	Temperatures in °F																	
	35	30	25	20	15	10	5	0	−5	−10	−15	−20	−25	−30	−35	−40	−45
5	33	27	21	19	12	7	0	−5	−10	−15	−21	−26	−31	−36	−42	−47	−52
10	22	16	10	3	−9	−15	−22	−27	−34	−40	−46	−52	−58	−64	−71	−77
15	16	9	2	−5	−11	−18	−25	−31	−38	−45	−51	−58	−65	−72	−78	−85	−92
20	12	4	3	−10	−17	−24	−31	−39	−46	−53	−60	−67	−74	−81	−88	−95	−103
25	8	1	7	−15	−22	−29	−36	−44	−51	−59	−66	−74	−81	−88	−96	−103	−110
30	6	−2	−10	−18	−25	−33	−41	−49	−56	−64	−71	−79	−86	−93	−101	−109	−116
35	4	−4	−12	−20	−27	−35	−43	−52	−58	−67	−74	−82	−89	−97	−105	−113	−120
40	3	−5	−13	−21	−29	−37	−45	−53	−60	−69	−76	−84	−92	−100	−107	−115	−123
45	2	−6	−14	−22	−30	−38	−46	−54	−62	−70	−78	−85	−93	−102	−109	−117	−125

EXAMPLE 1   Find the wind chill temperature when the actual temperature is 5°F and the wind speed is 30 miles per hour.

Solution: Find 30 in the "Winds" column. Look directly to the right to the number in the "5" column. The wind chill temperature is −41°F.

The following formula has been developed for approximating the wind chill temperature in Celsius degrees.

$$C = 33 - \frac{(10\sqrt{r} + 10.45 - r)(33 - t)}{22.1}$$

←
C = wind chill temperature in °C
t = actual temperature in °C
r = wind speed in meters/second

EXAMPLE 2   Use a scientific calculator to find the wind chill temperature when the actual temperature is 3.2°C and the wind speed is 18.5 meters per second.

Solution: $C = 33 - \dfrac{(10\sqrt{18.5} + 10.45 - 18.5)(29.8)}{22.1}$ $\longleftarrow$ **(33 – 3.2)**

3 3 $\boxed{-}$ $\boxed{(}$ $\boxed{(}$ 1 0 $\boxed{\times}$ 1 8 . 5 $\boxed{\sqrt{}}$ $\boxed{+}$ 1 0 . 4 5 $\boxed{-}$ 1 8 . 5 $\boxed{)}$ $\boxed{\times}$

$\boxed{(}$ 2 9 . 8 $\boxed{)}$ $\boxed{\div}$ 2 2 . 1 $\boxed{)}$ $\boxed{=}$ $\boxed{-14.142826}$

Thus, the wind chill temperature is **−14.1°C.** Subtracting the actual temperature from the wind chill temperature,

$$-14.1 - 3.2 = -17.3$$

it feels **17.3°C** colder than the actual temperature.

EXERCISES

In Exercises 1–8, use the table on page 482 to find the wind chill temperature.

	Winds in MPH	Temperature	Wind Chill
1.	20	25°F	?
2.	15	−10°F	?
3.	35	15°F	?
4.	40	−20°F	?

	Winds in MPH	Temperature	Wind Chill
5.	25	5°F	?
6.	10	−10°F	?
7.	45	−5°F	?
8.	30	0°F	?

In Exercises 9–14,

a. Use the formula in Example 2 to find the wind chill temperature to the nearest tenth of a degree.

b. State how much colder the wind chill temperature makes it feel.

	Winds in Meters per Second	Temperature	Wind Chill
9.	9.2	−5.2°C	?
10.	10.3	2.0°C	?
11.	8.9	−10.8°C	?
12.	4.6	3.9°C	?
13.	16.3	−5.8°C	?
14.	21.2	−19.3°C	?

13–5 Graphing Quadratic Functions

Each of these equations defines a *quadratic function.*

$$y = 2x^2 \qquad\qquad y = -3x^2 + 5 \qquad\qquad y = 2x^2 + 5x - 9$$

Definition | A **quadratic function** is a function defined by the equation $y = ax^2 + bx + c$, where a, b, and c are real numbers and $a \neq 0$.

The graph of a quadratic function is a **parabola.** To sketch the graph of a parabola, make a table of ordered pairs. Then graph the points and draw a smooth curve connecting them.

EXAMPLE 1 Graph the function $y = x^2 - 2x - 3$.

Solution: 1   Make a table of values.   2 Graph the ordered pairs. Draw a smooth curve.

x	$x^2 - 2x - 3$	y
-2	$(-2)^2 - 2(-2) - 3$	5
-1	$(-1)^2 - 2(-1) - 3$	0
0	$0^2 - 2(0) - 3$	-3
1	$1^2 - 2(1) - 3$	-4
2	$2^2 - 2(2) - 3$	-3
3	$3^2 - 2(3) - 3$	0

x	y
-2	5
-1	0
0	-3
1	-4
2	-3
3	0

The x coordinate of a point where the curve intersects the x axis is called an **x intercept.** Thus, in Example 1, the x intercepts are -1 and 3.

To find the *zeros* of a function, you find the values of x that make y equal to 0. This can be done by graphing to find the x intercepts.

Definition | The **zeros** of a function are the values of x for which the function equals zero.

EXAMPLE 2 Graph the function $y = 2x - x^2$.

Determine the zeros of the function.

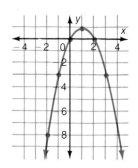

Solution:

x	-2	-1	0	1	2	3
y	-8	-3	0	1	0	-3

The zeros of the function are **0** and **2**.

CLASSROOM EXERCISES

Write *Yes* or *No* to indicate whether each function is quadratic.

1. $y = -5x$
2. $y = 3x^2$
3. $y = -5x^2 + 9$
4. $x + 2y - 3 = 0$
5. $3x^2 + 5x - 7 = y$
6. $x^2 + x = 2 + y$
7. $y = 4$
8. $x^2 + x = y$

WRITTEN EXERCISES

A   Graph each quadratic function.

1. $y = x^2 + 8x + 12$
2. $y = x^2 + 6x + 8$
3. $y = x^2 - 6x + 8$
4. $y = x^2 - 8x + 12$
5. $y = x^2 - 2x - 8$
6. $y = x^2 - 2x - 24$
7. $y = x^2 - 16$
8. $y = x^2 - 25$
9. $y = x^2 - x - 6$
10. $y = x^2 + 2x - 3$
11. $y = x^2 + 6x + 8$
12. $y = x^2 - 49$

In Exercises 13–18:
a. Determine the x intercepts from the graph of the function.
b. Write the zeros of the function.

13.

14.

15.

16.

17.

18.

B   Graph each function. Determine the zeros of each function.

19. $y = x^2 + x - 6$
20. $y = x^2 - 15x + 54$
21. $y = x^2 - 9$
22. $y = x^2 + 3x - 10$
23. $y = x^2 + 2x + 1$
24. $y = x^2 - 5x - 36$
25. $y = 13 + 12x - x^2$
26. $y = 10 + 3x - x^2$
27. $y = 5 - 4x - x^2$

C
28. $y = 2x^2 - x - 15$
29. $y = 3x^2 - x - 2$
30. $y = 2x^2 - 9x - 11$
31. $y = x^2 + \frac{1}{4}x - \frac{3}{8}$
32. $y = x^2 - 0.5x - 8.4$
33. $y = 15 - 4x - 4x^2$

Classify each number as *rational* or *irrational.* *(Pages 25-29)*

1. $-\frac{1}{2}$ **2.** $\sqrt{5}$ **3.** $\sqrt{81}$ **4.** $-\sqrt{100}$ **5.** $2\sqrt{3}$ **6.** $5 - 6\sqrt{2}$

Solve each quadratic equation by factoring. *(Pages 332-334)*

7. $a^2 - 121 = 0$ **8.** $16x^2 = 9$ **9.** $12y^2 + 11y + 2 = 0$

10. $3b^2 - 10b + 3 = 0$ **11.** $29d + 7 = -4d^2$ **12.** $4t^2 + 25 = 20t$

Use the quadratic formula to solve each equation. *(Pages 475-477)*

13. $x^2 - 10x + 25 = 0$ **14.** $9 = b^2 - 6b$ **15.** $r^2 = 5$

16. $3z - 5z^2 + 1 = 0$ **17.** $2q^2 - 3q - 1 = 0$ **18.** $5d^2 + 7d = 10$

13-6   The Discriminant

Note where the zeros occur in each of these functions.

Two x Intercepts	One x Intercept	No x Intercepts
$y = x^2 + 5x - 14$	$y = x^2 - 10x + 25$	$y = x^2 + 1$

Function	x Intercepts	Nature of the Solutions
$y = x^2 + 5x - 14$	Two distinct points	Two real zeros
$y = x^2 - 10x + 25$	One point	One real zero
$y = x^2 + 1$	None	No real zeros

The number and kind of solutions of quadratic equations can be determined from a part of the quadratic formula, that is, from

$$b^2 - 4ac.$$

This portion of the formula that determines the nature of the solutions of a quadratic equation is called the **discriminant.**

Equation	$\sqrt{b^2 - 4ac}$	Nature of $b^2 - 4ac$	Solutions
$x^2 + 5x - 14 = 0$	$\sqrt{25 + 56}$	Positive: two real-number solutions	$\{2, -7\}$
$x^2 - 10x + 25 = 0$	$\sqrt{100 - 100}$	Zero: one real-number solution	$\{5\}$
$x^2 + 1 = 0$	$\sqrt{0 - 4}$	Negative: no real-number solutions	ϕ

For convenience, the solutions of $x^2 - 10x + 25 = 0$ are often said to be equal since factoring $x^2 - 10x + 25 = 0$ as $(x - 5)(x - 5) = 0$ gives $+5$ and $+5$ as solutions. However, there is only one distinct solution, 5.

For $x^2 + 1 = 0$, there is no solution in the set of real numbers. The number $\sqrt{0 - 4}$, or simply $\sqrt{-4}$, is not a real number.

Nature of the solutions of $ax^2 + bx + c = 0$

1. If $b^2 - 4ac > 0$, there are two distinct, real solutions.
2. If $b^2 - 4ac = 0$, there is one distinct, real solution.
3. If $b^2 - 4ac < 0$, there are no real solutions.

EXAMPLE Use the discriminant to determine the nature of the solutions of each equation.

    a. $3x^2 - 11 = 0$ **b.** $-x^2 + x - 5 = 0$ **c.** $-x^2 + 6x - 9 = 0$

Solutions: **a.** $3x^2 - 11 = 0$ ⟵ $a = 3, b = 0, c = -11$

$$b^2 - 4ac = 0 - 4(3)(-11)$$
$$= 132$$

Since $b^2 - 4ac > 0$ there are **two real-number solutions.**

    b. $-x^2 + x - 5 = 0$ ⟵ $a = -1, b = 1, c = -5$

$$b^2 - 4ac = 1 - 4(-1)(-5)$$
$$= -19$$

Since $b^2 - 4ac < 0$, there are **no real-number solutions.**

    c. $-x^2 + 6x - 9 = 0$ ⟵ $a = -1, b = 6, c = -9$

$$b^2 - 4ac = 6^2 - 4(-1)(-9)$$
$$= 0$$

Since $b^2 - 4ac = 0$, there is **one distinct real-number solution.**

CLASSROOM EXERCISES

Evaluate $b^2 - 4ac$ for each equation. Then state the number of solutions.

1. $2x^2 - 3x - 1 = 0$ **2.** $n^2 - 2n + 4 = 0$ **3.** $x^2 - 6x + 9 = 0$

4. $3y^2 - y = -1$ **5.** $b^2 + b + 1 = 0$ **6.** $2a^2 + 1 = 4a$

WRITTEN EXERCISES

A   Evaluate $b^2 - 4ac$ for each equation.

1. $x^2 + 9x + 5 = 0$

2. $x^2 + 8x - 4 = 0$

3. $x^2 + 6x + 9 = 0$

4. $x^2 - 4x + 4 = 0$

5. $2x^2 + x + 6 = 0$

6. $2x^2 + 7x + 9 = 0$

7. $x^2 - 9 = 0$

8. $x^2 - 16 = 0$

9. $x^2 + 12 = 0$

10. $3x^2 + 6x - 7 = 0$

11. $-5x^2 - 2x - 3 = 0$

12. $-4x^2 + 3x + 7 = 0$

Without solving, give the nature of the solutions of each equation.

13. $x^2 + 2x + 8 = 0$

14. $3x^2 - 3x - 4 = 0$

15. $3y^2 - \frac{1}{3}y = \frac{2}{5}$

16. $x^2 = 5x + 5$

17. $3x^2 + 4x - \frac{3}{4} = 0$

18. $2y^2 - 4y = -2$

19. $x^2 - x + \frac{6}{25} = 0$

20. $20x = x^2 + 100$

21. $\frac{1}{2}x^2 - 16x + 132 = 0$

22. $4x^2 + 2x - 9 = 0$

23. $x^2 - 5x + 6 = 0$

24. $-x^2 + 7x - 15 = 0$

B

25. For what values of k will the equation $x^2 + kx + 25 = 0$ have only one solution?

26. For what values of k are the solutions of $x^2 + 4x + k = 0$ real numbers?

27. For what values of k will the equation $x^2 + kx + 3 = 0$ have two real solutions?

28. For what values of k are the solutions of $x^2 + 6x + k = 0$ not real numbers?

C   In Exercises 29–32, describe the solutions of the quadratic equation $ax^2 + bx + c = 0$ according to the given conditions.

29. $b^2 = 4ac$

30. $a \neq 0$, $b \neq 0$, $c = 0$

31. $b = 0$, a and c have opposite signs

32. $b = 0$, a and c have the same sign

CALCULATOR APPLICATIONS

Evaluating Irrational Solutions

To evaluate an irrational solution on a calculator, you use the square root and memory keys.

EXAMPLE Evaluate $\dfrac{-1 - \sqrt{10}}{3}$ to the nearest hundredth (Example, page 476).

SOLUTION First evaluate the numerator. To do this, first find $\sqrt{10}$ and store.

1 0 [√] [M+] 1 [+/−] [−] [MR] [=] [÷] 3 [=] $\boxed{-1.3874258}$

To the nearest hundredth, the answer is **−1.39**.

EXERCISES

Evaluate each of the following to the nearest hundredth.

1. $\dfrac{-1 + \sqrt{10}}{3}$

2. $\dfrac{1 - \sqrt{25}}{12}$

3. $\dfrac{1 + \sqrt{41}}{4}$

4. $\dfrac{3 - \sqrt{29}}{10}$

5. $\dfrac{-4 - \sqrt{33}}{6}$

6. $\dfrac{-7 + \sqrt{249}}{10}$

13-7 Maximum and Minimum

In the graph below, the dashed line through the **turning point**, or **vertex**, of the parabola $P(1, -4)$ is called the **axis of symmetry**. The equation of the axis of symmetry is $x = 1$. If the parabola were folded along this line, the left side of the parabola would fit exactly over the right side. The axis of symmetry is halfway between any two points on the parabola that have the same y coordinate. Thus, the line $x = 1$ is halfway between the points $(-1, 0)$ and $(3, 0)$ and the points are said to be **mirror images** of each other.

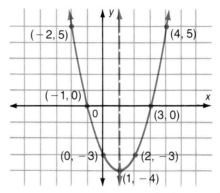

The minimum (least) value of the quadratic function shown above is the value of y on the axis of symmetry. Thus, the minimum value is -4.

The axis of symmetry for the quadratic function $y = ax^2 + bx + c$ is midway between the two roots. To find this point, find the *mean*, or *average*, of the roots.

$$\frac{\dfrac{-b + \sqrt{b^2 - 4ac}}{2a} + \dfrac{-b - \sqrt{b^2 - 4ac}}{2a}}{2} = -\frac{b}{2a}$$

Thus, the axis of symmetry is a line parallel to the y axis; its equation is $x = -\dfrac{b}{2a}$.

For the quadratic function, $y = ax^2 + bx + c$, the equation of the axis of symmetry is $x = -\dfrac{b}{2a}$.

NOTE: The maximum or minimum point of a quadratic function is the *only* point of the function that lies on the axis of symmetry; it occurs at the *vertex*, or *turning point*, of the parabola, where $x = -\dfrac{b}{2a}$.

EXAMPLE 1 For the parabola $y = x^2 + x - 6$, find each of the following.

   a. The equation of the axis of symmetry

   b. The coordinates of the vertex

   c. The minimum value of the function

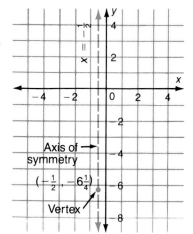

Solutions: **a.** Equation of axis of symmetry: $x = -\dfrac{b}{2a}$

   $x = -\dfrac{1}{2}$ ⟵ $a = 1; b = 1$

   b. Since the vertex of the parabola lies on the axis of symmetry, find y when $x = -\dfrac{1}{2}$.

   $y = x^2 + x - 6$

   $y = (-\tfrac{1}{2})^2 - \tfrac{1}{2} - 6$

   $y = \tfrac{1}{4} - \tfrac{1}{2} - 6 = -6\tfrac{1}{4}$

   Coordinates of vertex: $(-\tfrac{1}{2}, -6\tfrac{1}{4})$

   c. Minimum value: $-6\tfrac{1}{4}$

You can use the results of Example **1a** and **1b** to sketch the graph.

EXAMPLE 2 Sketch the graph of $y = x^2 + x - 6$.

   Solution: Use the information from Example 1 and the zeros of the function.

   Axis of symmetry: $x = -\dfrac{1}{2}$

   Vertex: $\left(-\dfrac{1}{2}, -6\dfrac{1}{4}\right)$

   Zeros of the function: -3 and 2

   Sketch the parabola.

When the coefficient of the square term of a quadratic function is positive, the graph of the function opens upward; when the coefficient is negative, the graph opens downward.

$y = x^2 - 4x + 3$

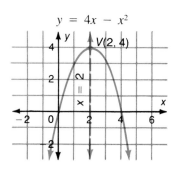

$y = 4x - x^2$

> For the quadratic function $y = ax^2 + bx + c$, the graph opens **upward** when $a > 0$, and the graph opens **downward** when $a < 0$.

CLASSROOM EXERCISES

State whether each function will have a maximum value or a minimum value.

1. $y = 3x^2$

2. $y = 2x + x^2$

3. $y = 6 + x - x^2$

4. $y = 9 + x^2$

5. $y = -(1 - x)^2$

6. $y = (x + 1)^2$

WRITTEN EXERCISES

A For each parabola in Exercises 1–15:
  a. Write the equation of the axis of symmetry.
  b. Write the coordinates of the vertex and tell whether it is a maximum or minimum point.
  c. Sketch the parabola.

1. $y = 2x^2$

2. $y = 4x^2$

3. $y = x^2 + 4$

4. $y = x^2 - 6x + 5$

5. $y = x^2 + 8x + 7$

6. $y = x^2 - 2x - 8$

7. $y = x^2 - 3x$

8. $y = x^2 + 2x - 8$

9. $y = x^2 - 2x$

B

10. $y = -2x^2$

11. $y = -x^2 + 1$

12. $y = -x^2 + 3x$

13. $y = -x^2 - 2x + 8$

14. $y = -x^2 - 2x + 3$

15. $y = -x^2 + 3x - 2$

16. Find the minimum value of y if $y = x^2 - 6x + 8$.

17. Find the maximum value of y if $y = 5 - x^2$.

18. Find the maximum value of y if $y = -x^2 + 3x - 2$.

19. Find the minimum value of y if $y = x^2 - 2x - 24$.

APPLICATIONS: **Maximum and Minimum**

Myra wishes to use 100 feet of fencing to build a rectangular pen for her dog. The sum of the length and width of the yard will be 50 feet. The area, y, of the yard will equal $x(50 - x)$.

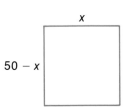

20. Find x so that the area, y, is a maximum.

21. Find the maximum area.

22. A farmer uses 250 feet of fence to enclose a rectangular garden. What should be the length and width of the garden if the farmer is to have the maximum area to plant?

A homeowner wishes to make a rectangular garden surrounded on three sides by a decorative fence. (The house forms the fourth side.) The owner buys 60 feet of fence.

23. If x represents the width of the garden, represent the second width and the length in terms of x.

24. Find the width that will make the area a maximum.

25. What is the maximum area that can be enclosed with the fence?

26. Suppose the homeowner in Exercises 23–25 had 40 feet of fence. What would be the dimensions of the garden that would make the area a maximum?

Ⓒ

27. Determine a formula that will give the maximum or minimum value of the quadratic function $y = ax^2 + bx + c$.

13–8 Quadratic Inequalities

The graph of an equation such as $y = -x^2 + 1$ divides the coordinate plane into three sets of points: the set of points on the curve, the set of points inside the curve, and the set of points outside the curve. The solution of an inequality such as $y > -x^2 + 1$ is made up of one or two of these sets of points.

To determine the solution set of $y > -x^2 + 1$, first graph $y = -x^2 + 1$. Then test points inside and outside the curve to find those that satisfy the inequality.

EXAMPLE   Graph: $y > -x^2 + 1$

Solutions: **1** Graph $y = -x^2 + 1$.

Use a dashed line to show that the solutions of $y > -x^2 + 1$ are *not* on the graph of $y = -x^2 + 1$.

2 Test points inside and outside the parabola.

Inside: Test $(0, 0)$	Outside: Test $(0, 3)$
$y > -x^2 + 1$	$y > -x^2 + 1$
$0 > 0 + 1$?	$3 > 0 + 1$?
$0 > 1$? No	$3 > 1$? Yes ✔

3 Shade the region outside the parabola.
The graph of $y > -x^2 + 1$ is the **set of points outside the parabola.**

NOTE: The inequality is *never* satisfied by the set of points inside the curve <u>and</u> the set of points outside the curve.

You can test points inside and outside the graph of $y = -x^2 + 1$ to show that the shaded region on each graph below represents the given set of points.

$y < -x^2 + 1$ $y \geq -x^2 + 1$ $y \leq -x^2 + 1$

  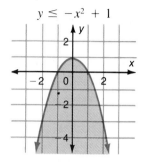

CLASSROOM EXERCISES

For each parabola in Exercises 1–8:
a. State whether the graph will include a solid, *S*, or a dashed, *D*, curve.
b. State whether the graph includes the region inside the curve or outside the curve.

1. $y > x^2$ **2.** $y \geq x^2$ **3.** $y \leq x^2 - 1$ **4.** $y < x^2 - 1$

5. $y \geq 2x - x^2$ **6.** $y \leq 1 - x^2$ **7.** $y < x^2 - 3x$ **8.** $y > x^2 + 5x + 6$

WRITTEN EXERCISES

A   Graph each inequality.

1. $y \leq x^2$ **2.** $y > x^2 - 1$ **3.** $y \geq x^2 + 4$ **4.** $y < -x^2$

5. $y > -2x^2$ **6.** $y > x^2 - 2x$ **7.** $y \leq x^2 - 3x$ **8.** $y \geq 1 - x^2$

9. $y \leq x^2 - 4x + 4$ **10.** $y \geq x^2 - 2x + 1$ **11.** $y < 2 - x^2$ **12.** $y \leq -x^2 + 3$

13. $y > x^2 + 2x - 8$ **14.** $y \leq x^2 - 5x - 6$ **15.** $y \geq 6 - x^2$ **16.** $y \geq 5 - x^2$

B   Graph the solution set of each system.

17. $\begin{cases} y \geq x^2 \\ y < 4 \end{cases}$ **18.** $\begin{cases} y \geq x^2 \\ x \leq 0 \end{cases}$ **19.** $\begin{cases} y < -x^2 + 1 \\ y \geq 0 \end{cases}$ **20.** $\begin{cases} y \geq -x^2 \\ x \geq 0 \end{cases}$

21. $\begin{cases} y > x^2 - 3 \\ y < x \end{cases}$ **22.** $\begin{cases} y > -x^2 + 4 \\ y \geq x \end{cases}$ **23.** $\begin{cases} y \leq x^2 + 2 \\ y \geq x \end{cases}$ **24.** $\begin{cases} y \leq 2x^2 \\ y \geq 2x - 3 \end{cases}$

25. $\begin{cases} y > x^2 - 4 \\ y \leq 4 \end{cases}$ **26.** $\begin{cases} y < x^2 + 5 \\ y < 5 \end{cases}$ **27.** $\begin{cases} y < -x^2 + 5 \\ y \geq 0 \end{cases}$ **28.** $\begin{cases} y > -x^2 + 2 \\ y \geq -5 \end{cases}$

C

29. $\begin{cases} y \geq x^2 \\ y \leq -x^2 \end{cases}$ **30.** $\begin{cases} y \geq x^2 - 2 \\ y \leq -x^2 + 4 \end{cases}$ **31.** $\begin{cases} y \geq x^2 - 4 \\ y \leq \frac{1}{4}x^2 \end{cases}$ **32.** $\begin{cases} y \leq 1 - x^2 \\ y \leq x^2 + 1 \end{cases}$

BASIC: SOLVING QUADRATIC EQUATIONS

Problem: *Write a program which solves quadratic equations of the form $ax^2 + bx + c = 0$ ($a \neq 0$). If the equation has no real roots, print* NO REAL ROOTS.

```
100 PRINT "FOR THE EQUATION A*X↑2 + B*X + C = 0,"
110 PRINT "WHAT ARE A,B,C";
120 INPUT A, B, C
130 LET D = B↑2 - 4*A*C
140 IF D = 0 THEN 200
150 IF D < 0 THEN 230
160 LET X1 = (-B + SQR(D))/(2*A)
170 LET X2 = (-B - SQR(D))/(2*A)
180 PRINT "THE TWO ROOTS ARE ";X1;"AND ";X2
190 GOTO 240
200 LET X = -B/(2*A)
210 PRINT "DOUBLE ROOT IS ";X
220 GOTO 240
230 PRINT "NO REAL ROOTS"
240 PRINT
250 PRINT "ANY MORE EQUATIONS TO SOLVE (1=YES, 0=NO)";
260 INPUT Z
270 IF Z = 1 THEN 120
280 END
```

The following is the output from a sample run of the program above.

Output:
```
RUN
FOR THE EQUATION A*X↑2 + B*X + C = 0,
WHAT ARE A,B,C? 1,0,-16
THE TWO ROOTS ARE  4 AND -4

ANY MORE EQUATIONS TO SOLVE (1=YES, 0=NO)? 1
? 1,1,-6
THE TWO ROOTS ARE  2 AND -3

ANY MORE EQUATIONS TO SOLVE (1=YES, 0=NO)? 1
? 5,4,2
NO REAL ROOTS

ANY MORE EQUATIONS TO SOLVE (1=YES, 0=NO)? 1
? 2,-3,-35
THE TWO ROOTS ARE  5 AND -3.5
```

```
ANY MORE EQUATIONS TO SOLVE (1=YES, 0=NO)? 1
? 1,-4,4
DOUBLE ROOT IS  2

ANY MORE EQUATIONS TO SOLVE (1=YES, 0=NO)? 0
READY
```

Analysis

Statements 130–150:   D is the discriminant of the equation. If D = 0, there is a double root. If D < 0, there are no real roots.

Statements 160–180:   These steps compute and print the two real roots, X1 and X2. The only difference between the roots is that X1 is computed using the positive square root of the discriminant, while X2 uses the negative square root.

Statements 200–210:   These statements, which compute the double root when D = 0, could be combined into the following single statement.

```
200  PRINT "DOUBLE ROOT IS"; -B/(2*A)
```

EXERCISES

A   Run the program on page 494 for the following values of a, b, and c.

1. $a = 1; b = 1; c = -6$

2. $a = 1; b = -8; c = 15$

3. $a = 1; b = 8; c = -42$

4. $a = 3; b = 12; c = 10$

5. $a = -4; b = 2; c = -3$

6. $a = 4; b = -20; c = 25$

Write each equation in the form $ax^2 + bx + c = 0$. Then use the program on page 494 to find the roots.

7. $x^2 + 5x = 7$

8. $3x^2 = 8 + 2x$

9. $12x = 4x^2 + 9$

10. $4x = 3x^2 + 6$

11. $4x^2 = 5x$

12. $24x^2 = 18$

13. $2x^2 = 7x - 6$

14. $6x^2 + 3 = 7x$

15. $13x = 2x^2 + 15$

16. The program on page 494 assumes that $a \neq 0$. Add statements to the program to print NOT A QUADRATIC EQUATION if 0 is entered for a.

Write a BASIC program for each problem.

17. For a function of the form $y = ax^2 + bx + c$, enter a, b, and c $(a \neq 0)$. Print whether the function has 0, 1, or 2 real zeros.

B

18. Solve equations of the form $(ax + b)^2 = c$. If $c < 0$, print NO REAL ROOTS.

19. Given a and b of $ax^2 + bx$, find c, if possible, in order to complete the square $ax^2 + bx + c$. Print the complete trinomial.

Review

Graph each quadratic function. Determine the zeros of each function. *(Section 13-5)*

1. $y = x^2 + 5x + 6$ **2.** $y = x^2 - 1$ **3.** $y = -x^2 + 4x - 4$

Without solving, give the nature of the solutions of each equation. *(Section 13-6)*

4. $3y^2 - 3y - 4 = 0$ **5.** $x^2 + 2x + 8 = 0$ **6.** $2a^2 - 4a = -3$

For each parabola in Exercises 7-9:
a. Write the equation of the axis of symmetry.
b. Write the coordinates of the vertex and tell whether it is a maximum or a minimum point.
c. Sketch the parabola. *(Section 13-7)*

7. $y = -2x^2$ **8.** $y = x^2 + 6$ **9.** $y = x^2 - 8x + 7$

Graph each inequality. *(Section 13-8)*

10. $y > -2x^2$ **11.** $y < x^2 + 2$ **12.** $y \geq -x^2 + 2x$

Chapter Summary

IMPORTANT TERMS

Completing the square (p. 472)
Discriminant (p. 486)
Parabola (p. 484)
Quadratic equation (p. 470)

Quadratic function (p. 484)
Roots of an equation (p. 475)
Zeros of a function (p. 484)

IMPORTANT IDEAS

1. If $x^2 = k$, then $x = \sqrt{k}$ <u>or</u> $x = -\sqrt{k}$ for any real number k, $k \geq 0$.

2. **Steps for Completing the Square of** $x^2 + bx$

    ☐1 Find one-half the coefficient of x.

    ☐2 Square the result of Step 1.

    ☐3 Add the result of Step 2 to $x^2 + bx$.

3. **Quadratic Formula:** For the quadratic equation $ax^2 + bx + c = 0$, where a, b, and c are real numbers and $a \neq 0$,

$$x = \frac{-b \pm \sqrt{b^2 - 4ac}}{2a}.$$

4. **The Nature of the Solutions of** $ax^2 + bx + c = 0$

    ☐1 If $b^2 - 4ac > 0$, there are two distinct, real solutions.

    ☐2 If $b^2 - 4ac = 0$, there is one distinct, real solution.

    ☐3 If $b^2 - 4ac < 0$, there are no real solutions.

Chapter Objectives and Review

Objective: *To solve quadratic equations by factoring or by taking the square root of each side of the equation (Section 13–1)*

Solve each equation. Irrational solutions may be left in simplified radical form.

1. $x^2 = 121$

2. $4n^2 = 32$

3. $2y^2 - 8 = 10$

4. $(y - 5)^2 = 0$

5. $6(t + 3)^2 = 24$

6. $(3b - 1)^2 = 81$

7. $(6y + 3)^2 = 1$

8. $(x - \frac{3}{4})^2 = \frac{9}{16}$

9. $2(x - 3)^2 = \frac{8}{25}$

Objective: *To solve quadratic equations by completing the square (Section 13–2)*

Solve by completing the square. Irrational solutions may be left in simplified radical form.

10. $x^2 + 6x = 7$

11. $a^2 - 6a - 7 = 0$

12. $y^2 + 3y = 4$

13. $x^2 - x = 30$

14. $r^2 + 4r = -2$

15. $b^2 = 3b + 10$

16. $2n^2 - 4n + 3 = 0$

17. $3c^2 + 8c = -5$

18. $2x^2 - x = 3$

Objective: *To solve quadratic equations using the quadratic formula (Section 13–3)*

Use the quadratic formula to solve each equation. Irrational solutions may be left in simplified radical form.

19. $y^2 + 6y - 16 = 0$

20. $x^2 - 3x = 0$

21. $b^2 = 5 - 4b$

22. $c^2 + 6c - 1 = 0$

23. $2x^2 + 11x + 5 = 0$

24. $2y^2 - 7y + 4 = 0$

25. $9c^2 + 2 + 9c = 0$

26. $x^2 + 4x - 2 = 0$

27. $3d^2 + 5 = 16d$

Objective: *To solve problems using quadratic equations (Section 13–4)*

Solve each problem. Approximate irrational roots to the nearest tenth.

28. The sum of a positive number and its square is 72. Find the number.

29. The sum of the squares of two consecutive positive integers is 85. Find the integers.

30. The perimeter of a rectangle is 32 meters, and its area is 48 square meters. What are its dimensions?

31. The length of a rectangular sign is one meter longer than its width. Its area is 11 square meters. Find its dimensions.

Objective: *To graph quadratic functions and read the zeros of each function from its graph (Section 13–5)*

Graph each quadratic function. Write the zeros of the function.

32. $y = x^2 + 2x - 8$

33. $y = x^2 - 3x$

34. $y = x^2 + 4x + 4$

35. $y = x^2 - 5x + 4$

36. $y = x^2 - 4$

37. $y = -x^2 + 6x - 9$

Objective: *To state the nature of the solutions of a quadratic equation by evaluating the discriminant (Section 13–6)*

Without solving, give the nature of the solutions of each equation.

38. $x^2 - 5x - 5 = 0$

39. $2x^2 - 3x = 0$

40. $y^2 - 20y + 100 = 0$

41. $3y^2 = 1 + 2y$

42. $x^2 - 14x + 48 = 0$

43. $a^2 + 2 = 2a$

44. $x^2 = 8x - 16$

45. $3n = 4n^2 + 1$

46. $x^2 + x + \frac{1}{4} = 0$

47. For what values of k will the equation $x^2 + kx + 64 = 0$ have only one real solution?

48. For what values of k will the equation $x^2 + x + k = 0$ have two real solutions?

_____ Chapter Test _____

Solve each equation. Irrational solutions may be left in simplified radical form.

1. $2x^2 + 3 = 11$

2. $(y - 1)^2 = 9$

3. $3(x + 4)^2 = 48$

4. $x^2 + 3x + 2 = 0$

5. $x^2 - 9x = -18$

6. $a^2 + 6 = -5a$

7. $y^2 + 3y - 4 = 0$

8. $n^2 + 32 = 12n$

9. $c^2 - 4c + 2 = 0$

10. $4y^2 - 2y - 1 = 0$

11. $x^2 - 8x + 16 = 0$

12. $3x^2 - 6x + 1 = 0$

Write the zeros of the functions graphed below.

13.

14.

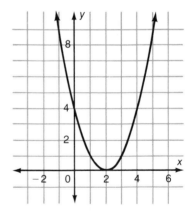

Without solving, give the nature of the solutions of each equation.

15. $x^2 - 8x + 16 = 0$

16. $x^2 + 5x + 8 = 0$

17. $6x^2 + 13x - 5 = 0$

18. $9x^2 + 1 = 6x$

19. The width of a picture window is 2 feet more than its height. If the area of the window is 24 square feet, what are its width and height?

20. In a right triangle, one leg is 2 meters shorter than the hypotenuse. The other leg is 4 meters shorter than the hypotenuse. Find the length of the hypotenuse.

Additional Practice

Skills

Solve each equation. Irrational solutions may be left in simplified radical form. *(Section 13-1)*

1. $y^2 = 81$

2. $x^2 - 100 = 0$

3. $2x^2 + 5 = 155$

4. $(x - 3)^2 = 4$

5. $2(x + 1)^2 = 18$

6. $7(y - 4)^2 = 343$

Solve by completing the square. Irrational solutions may be left in simplified radical form. *(Section 13-2)*

7. $x^2 - 4x = 0$

8. $x^2 - 6x = 0$

9. $x^2 + 2x - 4 = 0$

10. $x^2 - 8x = 9$

11. $x^2 = 5x$

12. $y^2 = 4y + 2$

Use the quadratic formula to solve each equation. Irrational solutions may be left in simplified radical form. *(Section 13-3)*

13. $x^2 - 3x = 40$

14. $y^2 + 64 = 16y$

15. $2a^2 - a = 3$

16. $3r^2 + 2r = 4$

17. $4p^2 - 3p - 1 = 0$

18. $2x^2 - 6x = 0$

Graph each quadratic function. Determine the zeros of each function. *(Section 13-5)*

19. $y = x^2 - 3x - 4$

20. $y = x^2 + 2x + 1$

21. $y = x^2 - 36$

22. $y = x^2 - 3x$

23. $y = x^2 - 4x + 4$

24. $y = -x^2 - 5x + 6$

Without solving, give the nature of the solutions of each equation. *(Section 13-6)*

25. $x^2 + 2x - 48 = 0$

26. $x^2 + 18x + 81 = 0$

27. $x^2 + 3x + 4 = 0$

28. $x^2 = 8x + 20$

29. $x^2 + 5 = x$

30. $x^2 + 15x + 36 = 0$

Applications

Solve each problem. *(Section 13-4)*

31. In a theater, the number of seats in each row is 2 more than the number of rows. The theater seats 624 people. How many seats are there in each row?

32. A driveway is 10 meters longer than it is wide. Its area is 35 square meters. Find its length and width to the nearest tenth of a meter.

33. The combined areas of two square flower gardens is 65 square meters. Each side of the larger garden is 3 feet longer than a side of the smaller garden. Find the length of a side of each garden.

34. A small city lot is in the shape of a right triangle. The hypotenuse is 40 meters longer than one leg and 5 meters longer than the other leg. Find the length of each side of the lot.

Review of Word Problems: Chapters 1–13

1. José is saving money in order to buy a lawn mower. He has already saved $138 which is 60% of the price of the mower. What is the price of the mower? *(Section 3–7)*

2. In triangle ABC, the measure of angle A is three times that of angle B. The measure of angle C is 12° greater than that of angle A. Find the measure of each of the three angles. *(Section 4–4)*

3. Jeff's earnings vary directly with the number of hours that he works. One week he earned $110.50 for 26 hours of work. How much did he earn in a week during which he worked 32 hours? *(Section 5–10)*

4. The length of a rectangle is 18 centimeters more than its width. The perimeter is 128 centimeters. What are its length and width? *(Section 6–4)*

5. The sum of an integer and three times its square is 114. Find the integer. *(Section 9–9)*

6. Table tennis is played on a rectangular table top with an area of 45 square feet and a perimeter of 28 feet. What are the length and width of the table top? *(Section 9–9)*

7. A house painter and his assistant agree to share the money earned on a job in the ratio 4:3. If they are paid $1288 for the job, how much money will each receive? *(Section 10–1)*

8. A boat can travel at a rate of 40 kilometers per hour in still water. It takes $1\frac{1}{2}$ times as long for the boat to travel 80 kilometers upstream as to travel the same distance downstream. Find the rate of the current. *(Section 11–5)*

9. Linda drove 73 kilometers in the same time that Bob drove 68 kilometers. Linda's average rate was 5 kilometers per hour greater than Bob's. Find the average rate for each person. *(Section 11–5)*

10. The area of a square sign is 6 square meters. What is the length of a side of the sign, to the nearest tenth of a meter? *(Section 12–2)*

11. A 17–meter wire stretches from the top of a vertical pole to a hook in the ground 8 meters from the base of the pole. Find the height of the pole. *(Section 12–4)*

12. Twice the square root of a number, plus 8, is 14. Find the number. *(Section 12–9)*

13. A rectangular garden is 6 meters long and 4 meters wide. It is surrounded by a walk of uniform width. If the area of the walk is 39 square meters, how wide is the walk? *(Section 13–4)*

14. The hypotenuse of a right triangle is 4 centimeters longer than one leg and 8 centimeters longer than the other leg. How long is the hypotenuse? *(Section 13–4)*

15. There are two numbers such that one is 6 less than twice the other. The difference of the squares of the two numbers is 1311. What are the two numbers? *(Section 13–4)*

Cumulative Review: Chapters 1–13

Choose the best answer. Choose a, b, c, or d.

1. Find A in $A = P(1 + 0.09t)$ when $P = \$800$ and $t = 3.5$ years.
   a. $1000   b. $1052   c. $600   d. $3052

2. Which statement is true?
   a. $Q \subset N$ b. $Ir \subset Q$ c. $N \subset W$ d. $R \subset Ir$

3. Solve: $-a = 12$
   a. $\{0\}$ b. $\{12\}$ c. $\{-12\}$ d. $\{4\}$

4. Which number is rational?
   a. $\sqrt{2}$ b. $\sqrt{9}$ c. π d. $\sqrt{28}$

5. Simplify: $2[4 + 6(2 - 7)]$
   a. -52 b. 52 c. -63 d. 63

6. Evaluate $3b - 5c + 6$ when $b = 3.2$ and $c = 2$.
   a. -5.6 b. 4 c. -6.4 d. 5.6

7. Simplify: $3.4a + 2b - 6a + 5b$
   a. $4.4ab$ b. $-2.6a + 7b$ c. $-2.6a^2 + 7b^2$ d. $2.6a - 7b$

8. Solve: $4b - 6 = 22$
   a. $\{4\}$ b. $\{6\frac{1}{2}\}$ c. $\{-7\}$ d. $\{7\}$

9. At an average speed of 80 kilometers per hour, how many hours will it take to travel 680 kilometers?
   a. 8 b. $8\frac{1}{2}$ c. $\frac{2}{17}$ d. 7

10. The length of a rectangle is 4 times its width. If the perimeter of the rectangle is 100 centimeters, how many centimeters are in the length?
    a. 10 b. 50 c. 40 d. 30

11. Solve: $-2(3x + 6) = -8x - 6$
    a. $\{0\}$ b. $\{-3\}$ c. $\{6\}$ d. $\{3\}$

12. Solve: $n - 8 < -18$
    a. $n < -10$ b. $n < -26$ c. $n > -10$ d. $n > -26$

13. Solve: $-3x + 7 > 2x + 32$
    a. $x < 5$ b. $x < -5$ c. $x > 5$ d. $x > -5$

14. Solve for w: $P = 2(l + w)$
    a. $w = P - l$ b. $w = 2P - l$ c. $w = l - P$ d. $w = \frac{P}{2} - l$

15. What is the slope of the line containing the points $A(5, 6)$ and $B(-2, -3)$?
    a. $-\frac{9}{7}$ b. $\frac{9}{7}$ c. $\frac{7}{9}$ d. $-\frac{7}{9}$

16. What is the slope of the graph of $3x - y = 8$?
    a. 3 b. -3 c. 8 d. -8

17. What is the y intercept of the graph of $2x + 3y = 7$?

    a. 7   **b.** $\frac{3}{7}$ **c.** $\frac{7}{3}$ **d.** -7

18. If y varies directly as x, and $y = 14$ when $x = 4$, find y when $x = 6$.

    a. 7   **b.** 12   **c.** 8   **d.** 21

19. Solve this system: $\begin{cases} x + y = 8 \\ x - y = 28 \end{cases}$

    a. $(-10, 18)$ **b.** $(18, -10)$ **c.** $(18, 10)$ **d.** $(10, -18)$

20. Solve this system: $\begin{cases} 2x + 3y = 20 \\ 3x - 4y = -21 \end{cases}$

    a. $(1, 6)$ **b.** $(6, 1)$ **c.** $(-6, -1)$ **d.** $(-1, -6)$

21. The sum of two numbers is 28. Three times the smaller is 4 more than the larger. What are the numbers?

    a. 10 and 18   **b.** 13 and 15   **c.** 20 and 8   **d.** 16 and 12

22. Louise has \$0.85 in nickels and dimes. She has 5 more nickels than dimes. How many nickels does she have?

    a. 4   **b.** 9   **c.** 10   **d.** 8

23. Almonds at \$4.00 per pound are mixed with walnuts at \$2.00 per pound to make a mixture worth \$3.50 per pound. If there are 20 pounds of the mixture, how many pounds of almonds are there?

    a. 10   **b.** 15   **c.** 5   **d.** 12

24. Which of the following is equivalent to $3n \geq 17$?

    a. $3n > 17$ and $3n = 17$ **b.** $3n > 17$ or $3n = 17$

    c. $3n < 17$ or $3n = 17$ **d.** $3n < 17$ and $3n = 17$

25. Solve: $|3(x + 2) - 9| = 6$

    a. $\{3\}$ **b.** $\{-1\}$ **c.** $\{-3, 1\}$ **d.** $\{3, -1\}$

26. What is the maximum value of $2x - y$ in the system $\begin{cases} x \geq 0 \\ y \geq 0 \\ x + y \leq 6 \end{cases}$

    a. 3   **b.** -6 **c.** 12   **d.** -12

27. Simplify: $\dfrac{(9a^2b^3)(8a^3b^4)}{(6ab^2)^2}$

    a. $4ab^3$ **b.** a^2b^2 **c.** $2a^3b^3$ **d.** $(2ab)^3$

28. Write in scientific notation: 0.000046

    a. 4.6×10^5 **b.** 4.6×10^{-5} **c.** 4.6×10^3 **d.** 4.6×10^6

29. Subtract: $(3xy + 7xy^2 - 4) - (9xy^2 - 4xy + 8)$

    a. $-7xy + 2xy^2 - 12$ **b.** $xy - 2xy^2 + 12$ **c.** $-xy - 2xy^2 + 12$ **d.** $7xy - 2xy^2 - 12$

30. Subtract: $6 - 8(3b + 6)$

    a. $-24b - 42$ **b.** $24b + 12$ **c.** $24b$ **d.** $-24b - 48$

31. What does $(a + 2b)^2$ equal?

    a. $a^2 - 4ab + 4b^2$ **b.** $a^2 + 4ab + 4b^2$ **c.** $a^2 + 4b^2$ **d.** $a^2 - 4b^2$

32. Multiply: $(2x - 4y)(2x + 4y)$
  a. $4x^2 - 16y^2$ **b.** $4x^2 + 8xy + 16y^2$ **c.** $4x^2 + 16y^2$ **d.** $2x^2 - 4y^2$

33. Multiply: $(3c - 2d)(4c + 3d)$
  a. $12c^2 + cd - 6d^2$ **b.** $12c^2 - cd - 6d^2$ **c.** $12c^2 - 17cd + 6d^2$ **d.** $12c^2 + cd + 6d^2$

34. Write the prime factorization of 75.
  a. $3 \cdot 5$ **b.** $3^2 \cdot 5^2$ **c.** $3 \cdot 5^2$ **d.** $3^2 \cdot 5$

35. Which of the following is a perfect square trinomial?
  a. $x^2 + 6x + 9$ **b.** $2x^2 + 6x + 9$ **c.** $4x^2 - 8x - 25$ **d.** $x^2 - 9x + 16$

36. Solve: $2x^2 = 50x$
  a. $\{0\}$ **b.** $\{0, 25\}$ **c.** $\{25\}$ **d.** $\{0, -25\}$

37. Solve: $3x^2 = 13x + 10$
  a. $\{-\frac{2}{3}, -5\}$ **b.** $\{-\frac{2}{3}, 5\}$ **c.** $\{0, -5\}$ **d.** $\{-\frac{2}{3}, 0\}$

38. Solve: $\dfrac{a + 7}{3} = \dfrac{a + 8}{4}$
  a. $a = 8$ **b.** $a = 4$ **c.** $a = 16$ **d.** $a = -4$

39. Divide and simplify: $\dfrac{x^2 - 1}{x^2 + 3x + 2} \div \dfrac{x^2 + 4x - 5}{x^2 - 4}$
  a. $\dfrac{x - 2}{x + 5}$ **b.** $\dfrac{x + 5}{x - 2}$ **c.** $\dfrac{x - 1}{x + 5}$ **d.** $\dfrac{x + 2}{x + 1}$

40. Simplify: $\sqrt{x^2 y^6}$
  a. xy^3 **b.** $\pm xy^3$ **c.** xy^4 **d.** $\pm xy^4$

41. What is the greatest integer for x that will make $x < \sqrt{125}$ a true statement?
  a. 10   **b.** 11   **c.** 12   **d.** 124

42. Simplify: $\sqrt{80}$
  a. 20   **b.** $4\sqrt{20}$ **c.** $2\sqrt{20}$ **d.** $4\sqrt{5}$

43. Multiply and simplify: $-2\sqrt{10} \cdot 3\sqrt{6}$
  a. $-8\sqrt{15}$ **b.** $-5\sqrt{60}$ **c.** $-12\sqrt{15}$ **d.** $-6\sqrt{60}$

44. Which of the following is *not* equivalent to the other three?
  a. $\dfrac{1}{\sqrt{6}}$ **b.** $\sqrt{\dfrac{2}{12}}$ **c.** $\dfrac{\sqrt{6}}{1}$ **d.** $\dfrac{\sqrt{6}}{6}$

45. Simplify: $2\sqrt{8} - 5\sqrt{2} + 4$
  a. $-\sqrt{2} + 4$ **b.** $3\sqrt{2}$ **c.** $-3\sqrt{6} + 4$ **d.** $6\sqrt{8} - 5\sqrt{2}$

46. The lengths of the sides of a rectangle are 5 centimeters and 12 centimeters. What is the length of the diagonal?
  a. 17 cm   **b.** 13 cm   **c.** 34 cm   **d.** 60 cm

47. Solve: $4\sqrt{3y - 2} - 1 = 19$
  a. $\{9\}$ **b.** $\{\pm 9\}$ **c.** $\{34\}$ **d.** $\{9, 34\}$

48. Simplify: $(-8)^{\frac{1}{3}}$
  a. $-2\frac{2}{3}$ **b.** 2   **c.** -2 **d.** ± 2

49. A square has each of its vertices on the x or the y axis. One vertex is at $(0, 5)$. How long is each side of the square?

    a. 5   **b.** $2\sqrt{5}$ **c.** 10   **d.** $\sqrt{5}$

50. Solve: $9x^2 = x$

    a. $\{0\}$ **b.** $\{\frac{1}{9}\}$ **c.** $\{\pm 3\}$ **d.** $\{0, \frac{1}{9}\}$

51. For which equation is $\{8, -2\}$ *not* the solution set?

    a. $(x - 3)^2 = 25$ **b.** $(x - 8)(x + 1) = 0$

    c. $x^2 - 6x = 16$ **d.** $x^2 - 6x - 16 = 0$

52. What must be added to each side of $x^2 + 8x = 7$ to make the left side a perfect square?

    a. 16   **b.** 4   **c.** $4x$ **d.** 23

53. Which equation has $\left\{\dfrac{-5 \pm \sqrt{17}}{4}\right\}$ as its solution set?

    a. $2x^2 - 5x + 1 = 0$ **b.** $2x^2 + 5x + 1 = 0$

    c. $2x^2 + 5x - 1 = 0$ **d.** $x^2 + 5x + 1 = 0$

54. When is the solution of $ax^2 + bx + c = 0$ two different real numbers?

    a. When $b - 4ac > 0$ **b.** When $b^2 - 4ac = 0$

    c. When $b^2 - 4ac < 0$ **d.** When $b^2 - 4ac > 0$

55. A quadratic function crosses the x axis at $(3, 0)$ and $(-4, 0)$. What are the zeros of the function?

    a. 0, 3   **b.** 0, 4   **c.** 3, -4 **d.** 3, 5

56. When is the graph of $y = ax^2 + bx + c$ tangent to the x axis?

    a. When $b^2 - 4ac = 0$ **b.** When $b^2 - 4ac$ is positive

    c. When $-b \pm \sqrt{b^2 - 4ac} = 0$ **d.** When $b = \sqrt{b^2 - 4ac}$

57. The width of a rectangle is 5 centimeters less than the length. The area is 104 square centimeters. What is the length of the rectangle?

    a. 8 cm   **b.** 28.5 cm   **c.** 23.5 cm   **d.** 13 cm

58. The vertex of the graph of $y = 3x^2 - 5x + 8$ occurs at what value of x?

    a. $x = 5$ **b.** $x = -\frac{5}{6}$ **c.** $x = -5$ **d.** $x = \frac{5}{6}$

59. Find the minimum value of y in $y = x^2 + 6x + 5$.

    a. 5   **b.** -4 **c.** -6 **d.** $\frac{5}{6}$

60. The equation $x^2 = 49$ is equivalent to

    a. $x = 7$ and $x = -7$ **b.** $x = 7$ or $x = -7$

    c. $(x - 7)^2 = 0$ **d.** $x = \sqrt{49}$

61. The graph of which of the following has no points on the x axis?

    a. $y = 3x^2 + x + 1$ **b.** $y = 3x^2 + 3x$

    c. $y = 3x^2 - 4x + 1$ **d.** $y = 16x^2$

62. Find the equation for the axis of symmetry for $y = x^2 - 2x - 8$.

    a. $x = -1$ **b.** $x = 2$ **c.** $x = 1$ **d.** $x = -2$

Preparing for College Entrance Tests

Instead of solving a given equation, it is sometimes easier to try each of the given "solutions" to see which one makes the equation true.

REMEMBER: Watch for clues that will enable you to eliminate one or more of the possibilities without extensive calculations.

EXAMPLE: Which of the following numbers is in the solution set for $3x^2 - 14x + 16 = 0$?

    (a) 4   (b) 2   (c) -4 (d) -8

Think: If $3x^2 - 14x + 16 = 0$, then $3x^2 = 14x - 16$.
But $3x^2$ is positive. Therefore, $14x - 16$ must be positive.
Thus, $14x - 16 > 0$, or $14x > 16$ and $x > 1$.
This eliminates choices (c) and (d). Test choices (a) and (b).

Solution: Test (a): $3(4)^2 - 14(4) + 16 = 8 \neq 0$ ←———— **4 is not a solution.**

             Test (b): $3(2)^2 - 14(2) + 16 = 0$ ←———— **2 is a solution.**   **Answer: b**

Choose the best answer. Choose a, b, c, or d.

1. Which of the following numbers is in the solution set for $x^2 + 13x + 12 = 0$?

    (a) -4 (b) -1 (c) 1   (d) 6

2. Which of the following numbers is in the solution set for $x^2 - 14x + 24 = 0$?

    (a) -12 (b) -2 (c) 2   (d) 8

3. Which of the following numbers is in the solution set for $2x^2 + 11x + 12 = 0$?

    (a) -4 (b) -1 (c) 2   (d) 4

4. Which of the following numbers is in the solution set for $3x^2 + 4x - 4 = 0$?

    (a) -4 (b) -2 (c) $\frac{1}{3}$ (d) 4

5. Which of the following numbers is in the solution set for $x^2 + 16x - 36 = 0$?

    (a) -18 (b) -1 (c) 4   (d) 6

6. Which of the following numbers is in the solution set for $6x^2 - 23x - 4 = 0$?

    (a) -4 (b) -1 (c) $\frac{1}{2}$ (d) 4

7. If $\dfrac{1}{2 + \dfrac{1+x}{2}} = \dfrac{1}{2}$, what is the value of x? (HINT: $\dfrac{1+x}{2}$ must equal 0.)

    (a) -2 (b) -1 (c) 0   (d) 1

8. If $\dfrac{2}{3 + \dfrac{2+x}{3}} = \dfrac{2}{3}$, what is the value of x?

    (a) -2 (b) -1 (c) 0   (d) 1

Preparing for College Entrance Tests

Some items on College Entrance tests are designed so that one or more of several given statements are correct, or no statement is correct. In such cases, you must examine each of the possibilities before deciding on the answer.

EXAMPLE: If n is a rational number, which of the following must be rational numbers?

$$\text{I. } \sqrt{n} \qquad \text{II. } n^2 \qquad \text{III. } \sqrt{n^2}$$

(a) II only   (b) I and II only

(c) II and III only   (d) I, II, and III

Solution: I is not always true. (For example, $\sqrt{2}$ is not rational.)

II is true, since n^2 means $n \cdot n$, and the product of two rational numbers is rational.

III is true, since $\sqrt{n^2} = |n|$, which is rational when n is rational.

Answer: c

Choose the best answer. Choose *a, b, c,* or *d.*

1. If x is an integer greater than 1, which of the following statements are true?

    I. $\sqrt{x} < x$ II. $\sqrt{x} < x^2$ III. $\dfrac{1}{x} < \sqrt{x}$

    (a) I and II only   (b) I and III only   (c) II and III only   (d) I, II, and III

2. If y is an integer less than 0, which of the following statements are true?

    I. $\sqrt[3]{y} < 0$ II. $\sqrt{1-y} < 0$ III. $\sqrt{1+y^2} < 0$

    (a) I only   (b) II only   (c) I and III only   (d) None of these

3. If $\sqrt{p}$ is a rational number, which of the following must be rational numbers?

    I. $\sqrt{p+1}$ II. $\sqrt{p+4}$ III. $\sqrt{p+9}$

    (a) II only   (b) III only   (c) I and II only   (d) None of these

4. If k is an integer, which of the following must be integers?

    I. $\dfrac{k}{2}$ II. $k - 2$ III. $\sqrt{k}$

    (a) I only   (b) II only   (c) I and II only   (d) II and III only

5. If x is a nonzero real number, which of the following statements must be true?

    I. $\left(\dfrac{x}{x}\right)^x = 1$ II. $x^{\frac{x}{x}} = 1$ III. $x^{x-x} = 1$

    (a) I only   (b) II only   (c) I and II only   (d) I and III only

6. Which of the following statements are true?

    I. $\sqrt{9 \cdot 16} > \sqrt{9} \cdot \sqrt{16}$ II. $\sqrt{9} \cdot \sqrt{16} > \sqrt{9} + \sqrt{16}$ III. $\sqrt{9} + \sqrt{16} > \sqrt{9+16}$

    (a) II only   (b) I and III only   (c) II and III only   (d) I, II, and III

CHAPTER **14** # Statistics and Probability

14-1 Statistical Averages

People in many careers collect, organize, and analyze data for use in decision-making. Researchers collect and analyze data from a **sample** or subset of a larger **population** in order to discover characteristics or trends. Two important measures used to analyze data are the *mean* (arithmetic average) and the *median*.

Definitions

> The **mean**, $\bar{x}$, of a set of data is the sum of all the values divided by the number of values.
>
> The **median** of a set of data that contains an odd number of values is the middle measure. When the number of elements in the set of data is an even number, the median is the mean of the two middle measures.

EXAMPLE 1 Roberto Rivera is designing an electric power plant that will use garbage as a primary fuel. A survey of 40 families was conducted to determine the number of pounds of garbage the average family disposes of each week. The analysis of the data will help to determine the capacity of the power plant and how much electricity can be generated.

The data below represents the results of the survey.

130	131	132	133	133	135	136	136
136	137	137	137	137	137	138	138
140	140	140	140	141	141	142	142
142	142	142	143	143	145	146	146
147	148	150	150	151	153	155	158

Will the mean or the median be the better average for the data?

Analysis: [1] Mean $(\bar{x}) = \dfrac{\text{sum of values}}{\text{number of values}} = \dfrac{5650}{40} = \textbf{141}$ (nearest whole number)

[2] To find the median, organize the data in order from least to greatest. Since there are 40 measures, find the mean of the 20th and 21st measures. The median is $(140 + 141) \div 2$, or **140.5**.

Conclusion: Both the mean and the median summarize data with a single number. **Either statistic** is appropriate for Roberto's purposes.

In most cases, the mean is the most useful statistical measure.

The *mode* is a third statistical average.

Definition	The **mode** is the measure that occurs most often.

NOTE: A set of data may have more than one mode. In the table on page 508, the modes for the data are 137 and 142.

EXAMPLE 2   This table shows the traffic count at an intersection from 7 A.M. to 12 noon.

a. During which hour would a traffic policeman be needed most?

b. What hour is the mode for this data?

Time (A.M.)	Count
7–8	650
8–9	1350
9–10	550
10–11	510
11–12	405

Solutions: a. Since the highest traffic count occurs between 8 and 9, a traffic policeman would be needed most during this hour.

b. The mode is 8–9.

CLASSROOM EXERCISES

In Exercises 1–2, calculate the mean and the median to the nearest integer.

1. 42   45   41   38
    40   42   32   40

2. $8439 $7680 $6755
    $7521 $6350 $5949

In Exercises 3–4, calculate the median and the mode(s).

3. 85   86   89   89   70
    74   88   85   100   85

4. 16   15   15   17   16
    17   14   16   18   14

WRITTEN EXERCISES

A A store manager recorded the number of customers entering the store from 9 A.M. to 6 P.M. on an average day. Use this information for Exercises 1–5.

Hours	Customers
9:00–10:00	10
10:00–11:00	21
11:00–12:00	25
12:00–1:00	27
1:00–2:00	30
2:00–3:00	40
3:00–4:00	35
4:00–5:00	45
5:00–6:00	53

1. Over what 5-hour period does the store have the greatest number of customers?

2. During what hour does the mode occur?

3. Suppose that the manager decides to hire part-time help from 4:00 P.M. to 6:00 P.M. Why is this a reasonable decision?

4. What is the mean number of customers per hour coming into the store? Round your answer to the nearest whole number.

5. Is the answer to Exercise 4 helpful to the manager in deciding when to hire part-time help? Explain.

The table at the right shows yearly salaries for six persons who work at the Torvale Car Rental Agency. Use this table for Exercises 6–10.

Yearly Salaries	
Manager	$40,000
Assistant	$25,000
Clerk	$12,500
Clerk	$12,000
Clerk	$11,500
Clerk	$10,000

6. What is the mean yearly salary?

7. Is the mean yearly salary greater or less than most of the salaries?

8. What is the median yearly salary?

9. Are most of the salaries closer to the mean yearly salary or the median yearly salary?

10. Which average – the mean yearly salary or the median yearly salary – best represents most of the yearly salaries?

This table shows the number of centimeters of rain that fell in Barrow, Alaska in a recent year. Refer to the table for Exercises 11–14.

Rainfall in Barrow			
Jan.	0.5 cm	July	2 cm
Feb.	0.5 cm	Aug.	3 cm
March	0.5 cm	Sept.	2 cm
April	0.5 cm	Oct.	2 cm
May	0.5 cm	Nov.	1 cm
June	1 cm	Dec.	0.5 cm

11. What is the mean monthly rainfall (nearest whole number)?

12. What is the median monthly rainfall?

13. What is the mode for this data?

14. Meteorologists and weather reporters use the mean to give average monthly rainfall. Why is the mean considered the best average in this case?

14-2 Frequency and Histograms

The mean, median, and mode are called **measures of central tendency**. For the data of Example 1 on page 508, the mean and median were very close together. When this is not the case, further analysis is necessary to determine the most useful measure of central tendency.

One way to do this is to organize the data in a table, using intervals for the measures and showing the number of occurrences, or **frequency**, of the measures in each interval. Then the table is used to make a *histogram*, or "picture" of the *frequency distribution*. A **histogram** is a kind of bar graph.

EXAMPLE A used-car dealer wanted an estimate of the prices being paid for certain used cars in the community. The following data was collected and listed in order from the least to the greatest dollar amounts.

2700	2800	2800	2800	2800	2800
2800	3400	3700	3700	3700	4100
4400	4400	4400	4400	4400	4400
4700	4700	4700	4800	4800	4900
4900	5700	5800	5800	6400	6700

Which will give the better estimate, the mean or the median?

Analysis: ☐1 Mean $= \dfrac{128,400}{30} = $ **4280**   Median = **4500**

☐2 Make a frequency table and draw a histogram.

Price Interval (hundreds of dollars)	Frequency
25–30	7
30–35	1
35–40	3
40–45	7
45–50	7
50–55	0
55–60	3
60–65	1
65–70	1

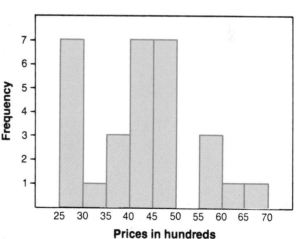

Conclusion: The histogram shows that the prices are not distributed symmetrically with many prices at the extreme lower level. When this happens, the **median** is the better measure of central tendency.

NOTE: When the intervals in the frequency table have a common boundary such as 30, 35, and so on, any boundary measure is counted in the interval to the right.

CLASSROOM EXERCISES

In Exercises 1–2, use the given frequency intervals to make a frequency table of the data. Then draw a histogram to show the data.

1.

Tractor Output Per Day for 24 Factories												Intervals	

31	40	35	67	85	90	32	39	68	87	55	50
33	43	64	78	82	70	54	60	42	85	32	68

Intervals: 31–41; 41–51; 51–61; 61–71; 71–81; 81–91

2.

Cars	A	B	C	D	E	F	G	H	I	J	K	L	M	N
Gas Mileage (mi/gal)	28	32	25	33	30	24	35	27	32	34	27	38	37	37

Intervals: 21–26; 26–31; 31–36; 36–41

WRITTEN EXERCISES

A   In Exercises 1–5:
a. Calculate the mean and median to the nearest whole number.
b. Complete the frequency table.
c. Make a histogram for the data.

1. Diameters of Twenty Trees (cm)

25	32	36	28	20
26	35	40	27	30
36	23	29	30	25
29	32	43	25	30

Interval	Frequency
17–24	?
24–31	?
31–38	?
38–44	?

2. Bowling Scores for One Week

162	125	146	150
170	190	155	175
135	144	170	165
155	185	162	184

Interval	Frequency
121–141	?
141–161	?
161–181	?
181–201	?

3. Miles Bicycled Per Day for Triathlon Training

25	30	22	32	37
34	15	25	38	24
32	18	30	35	32
20	25	31	28	30

Interval	Frequency
14–19	?
19–24	?
24–29	?
29–34	?
34–39	?

4.

Hours Per Week of Evening Television Viewing by Teens					Interval	Frequency
4	6	9	11	8	0–5	?
1	12	9	4	11	5–10	?
16	2	9	6	13	10–15	?
4	9	18	4	9	15–20	?

5.

Ages of Trees in a Park							Interval	Frequency
17	42	21	78	16	21	31	10–20	?
29	29	16	49	19	81	16	20–30	?
69	69	18	31	22	14	21	30–40	?
75	42	78	18	41	22	16	40–50	?
18	81	42	42	42	16	16	50–60	?
21	19	18	44	18	22	14	60–70	?
49	17	16	18	18	18	17	70–80	?
							80–90	?

6. In Exercise 5, which measure of central tendency gives a better description of the data, the mean or the median? Explain your answer.

B   In Exercises 7–9:
   a. Calculate the mean and median to the nearest whole number.
   b. Make a frequency table.
   c. Make a histogram to show the data.
   d. State which measure of central tendency, the mean or the median, gives the better description of the data. Explain your answer.

7. The following numbers were drawn from a table of random numbers.

28	53	58	66
37	36	78	41
87	35	13	38
61	46	1	83
47	15	96	3
57	84	66	47
37	81	46	4
86	78	55	12
93	76	91	83

8. These scores represent time (in hours) between failures in aircraft radios.

108	168	152	74	85
136	52	34	62	137
150	175	121	136	126
120	143	174	164	48
42	127	148	81	137
243	74	122	86	128
139	123	86	85	125
103	115	132	49	72
110	82	111	137	77

9. The coach of a high school football team measured the weight (in pounds) of every 25th boy on the enrollment list.

120	210	194	167	205	183
127	185	176	155	157	138
148	169	145	176	118	136
162	175	161	189	171	201
148	184	176	171	187	152

14–3 Standard Deviation

The mean, median, and mode are measures that approximate the center of a distribution. In certain problems, this may not be adequate. It may be necessary to find the **variation,** or difference, between the measures in a distribution. One measure that is computed is the **standard deviation.** This is a measure of how the data disperses, or spreads out, from the mean. The symbol for standard deviation is the Greek letter σ (sigma).

The graph at the right illustrates the ideal distribution for test results. In this model, the mean, median, and mode have the same value. The graph is bell-shaped and symmetrical. Such a graph is called the **normal curve.** This graph is that of the **standard normal distribution** with a mean of 0, and a standard deviation of 1. In a normal distribution, 68% of the data falls within 1 standard deviation of the mean, about 95% within 2 standard deviations, and about 99% within 3 standard deviations.

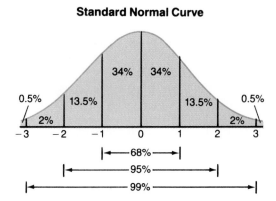

Standard Normal Curve

Thus, the more dispersed the data, the larger σ will be.

EXAMPLE 1 Find the standard deviation, σ, to the nearest tenth for these test scores: 80, 84, 87, 89, 90

Solution:
1 Find the mean, $\bar{x}$.

$$\bar{x} = \frac{80 + 84 + 87 + 89 + 90}{5} = \mathbf{86}$$

2 Complete this table. In the table, the variable x represents each score from the given set of scores.

Score	$x - \bar{x}$	$(x - \bar{x})^2$
80	$80 - 86 = -6$	36
84	$84 - 86 = -2$	4
87	$87 - 86 = 1$	1
89	$89 - 86 = 3$	9
90	$90 - 86 = 4$	16

3 Compute $\dfrac{(x - \bar{x})^2}{n}$. $\qquad \dfrac{36 + 4 + 1 + 9 + 16}{5} = 13.2 \longleftarrow$ This is called the variance.

4 Since $\sigma = \sqrt{\dfrac{(x - \bar{x})^2}{n}}$, find σ. $\quad \sigma = \sqrt{13.2} = \mathbf{3.6} \longleftarrow$ Nearest tenth

EXAMPLE 2 A manufacturer of calculator batteries tested operating life of 20,000 batteries over a one-year period. The results from this survey were distributed normally. The mean lifetime of a battery was 400 hours and the standard deviation was 50 hours. If a customer buys a battery with a lifetime of less than 300 hours, the customer can return the battery for a new one. About how many of the 20,000 batteries will be returned?

Solution:

$\boxed{1}$ Find how many standard deviations 300 is from 400.

$$400 - 300 = 100 \text{ and } 100 \div 50 = 2$$

Thus, 300 is **2 standard deviations** from the mean.

$\boxed{2}$ Using the graph on page 514, you can see that 2.5% of the batteries are below 2 standard deviations from the mean.

$$2.5\% \text{ of } 20,000 = 0.025 \times 20,000 = 500$$

Thus, **500 batteries** will probably be returned.

CLASSROOM EXERCISES

Find the standard deviation to the nearest tenth.

1. Science Test Scores

| 75 | 78 | 84 | 91 |

2. Heights of Players in Inches

| 76 | 74 | 77 | 70 | 73 |

3. Miles Per Gallon For Six Cars

| 22 | 30 | 18 | 17 | 25 | 15 |

4. Number of Hits in Six Baseball Games

| 1 | 1 | 3 | 5 | 6 | 2 |

WRITTEN EXERCISES

A Solve.

1. A typing test was administered to 10 candidates. The number of typing errors for the candidates was 4, 2, 0, 8, 9, 3, 0, 1, 6, and 2. Calculate this standard deviation to the nearest tenth.

2. Over an eight-week period, the Ecology Club collected the following number of pounds of aluminum cans.

   39, 31, 28, 29, 52, 58, 44, 39

   Calculate the standard deviation to the nearest tenth.

For Exercises 3–10, refer to Example 2 and the standard normal curve on page 514.

3. What percent of bulbs can be expected to last fewer than 350 days?

4. What percent of bulbs will probably last between 350 and 450 days?

5. How many light bulbs can be expected to last fewer than 300 days?

6. How many light bulbs can be expected to last longer than 450 days?

7. How many light bulbs can be expected to last more than 300 days and fewer than 450 days?

8. How many light bulbs can be expected to last more than 350 days and fewer than 500 days?

9. How many light bulbs can be expected to last not more than 500 days?

10. How many light bulbs can be expected to last not more than 350 days?

B

11. The eleventh–grade class was given a standardized test in mathematics. The mean score was 63 and the standard deviation was 6.

   a. Based on the normal curve, what percent of the students should score above 69?

   b. What percent should score between 57 and 69?

   c. What percent should score between 51 and 75?

12. A teacher gave a test to 100 students and graded the test according to the distribution shown below.

$$A \geq \bar{x} + 2\sigma$$
$$\bar{x} + 1\sigma \leq B < \bar{x} + 2\sigma$$
$$\bar{x} - 1\sigma \leq C < \bar{x} + 1\sigma$$
$$\bar{x} - 2\sigma \leq D < \bar{x} - 1\sigma$$
$$F < \bar{x} - 2\sigma$$

If the students' knowledge of the subject is distributed normally, how many students should receive an A? a B? a C? a D? an F?

13. Suppose a teacher gave a test to 140 students, and the teacher graded on the normal curve. The teacher used the distribution given in Exercise 12. How many students would receive an A? a B? a C? a D? an F?

C

14. The school nurse measured the heights in inches of 53 juniors. The data is shown in the table at the right. Do you think the normal curve can be used as a model to represent the data? Explain your answer.

Height	Frequency
74	1
72	3
70	5
68	10
66	15
64	10
62	5
60	3
58	1

15. Without actually calculating them, compare the mean and the standard deviation for the following data.

   X: 6, 2, 8, 1, 5   Y: 60, 20, 80, 10, 50

Review

For Exercises 1–2, calculate the mean, the median, and the mode(s) to the nearest whole number. *(Section 14–1)*

1.

32	35	28	26	24
20	22	32	29	23

2.

$1,350	$1,420	$1,240	$1,350
$1,610	$1,580	$1,060	$1,440

For Exercises 3–4, calculate the mean and the median to the nearest whole number. Then complete the frequency table and make a histogram for the data. *(Section 14–2)*

3.

Height in Centimeters of Two-Year Old Seedlings

62	76	89	56	79
67	100	63	52	76
74	61	72	70	57
82	62	67	60	65

Intervals: 51–61; 61–71; 71–81; 81–91; 91–101

4.

Amount of Electricity Used by 30 Houses in 1 Month

753	850	906	903	788
1040	883	764	976	825
815	910	1030	930	777
823	791	821	897	820
932	861	924	771	993
811	854	806	868	948

Intervals: 751–801; 801–851; 851–901; 901–951; 951–1001; 1001–1051

5. The following scores represent the number of sales completed by 10 appliance clerks in one week: 3, 3, 4, 5, 6, 6, 7, 8, 9, 9
Calculate the standard deviation to the nearest tenth. *(Section 14–3)*

6. On a mathematics test, the mean score was 72 and the standard deviation was 5. A grade of C is given for scores in the interval, $\bar{x} - 1\sigma \leq C < \bar{x} + 1\sigma$. *(Section 14–3)*

  a. List all test scores that receive a grade of C.

  b. If the scores are normally distributed, what percent of the students will have a grade of C?

More Challenging Problems

For Exercises 1–4, list a set of numbers that satisfies the conditions.

1. The mean, median, and mode are all the same number.

2. The mean is greater than the median.

3. The mode is 20 and the median is greater than the mean.

4. The mean is 5, the median is 4, and the mode is 8.

5. A teacher scores a spelling test as the number of words spelled correctly. The average score is listed as 32.4. Which average must this be? Why?

Career Applications: Psychology

Educational psychologists gather data about student interests and abilities. They develop and administer tests and interpret test results.

A **stem-leaf plot** is a useful way to group test results.

Test Scores for 20 Students: (verbal, math)

(320,340)	(570,650)	(730,430)	(480,490)
(460,640)	(650,440)	(570,580)	(290,380)
(600,690)	(380,370)	(470,400)	(500,480)
(450,530)	(340,400)	(370,390)	(600,440)
(510,580)	(400,330)	(440,400)	(420,400)

EXAMPLE Make a stem-leaf plot for the test scores above.

1. Write the leading digits, 2, 3, 4, and so on, vertically in order from least to greatest. This is called the **stem.**

2. Since all the scores end in 0, fill in the second digits of the scores on either side of the stem. These are the **leaves.** Order the leaves. Thus, 8 3 5 represents a verbal score of 380 and a math score of 350.

   NOTE: When the stem-leaf plot is turned to either side, an appropriate histogram is formed.

Verbal		Math
9	2	
8742	3	34789
8765420	4	000034489
7710	5	38
500	6	4589
3	7	

EXERCISES

1. Use the stem-leaf plot to find the median of the verbal scores.

2. Use the stem-leaf plot to find the median of the math scores.

Quartiles are the values that divide the data into fourths.

3. Use the median from Exercise 1 to divide the verbal scores into halves. Find the median of each half. These are the quartiles.

4. Use the median from Exercise 2 to divide the math scores into halves. Find the math quartiles.

To construct a whisker and box plot, first draw a number line. Label points from 200 to 800. Draw short vertical lines at each quartile and at the median. Draw horizontal lines to complete the box. From each end of the box, draw lines to the extreme values.

5. Construct a whisker and box plot for the math scores above.

Whisker and Box Plot: Verbal Scores

14-4 Probability

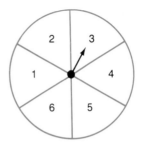

When you spin the arrow on this spinner, there are 6 possible outcomes: 1, 2, 3, 4, 5, or 6. The chances that the arrow stops on 3 are one out of six, or $\frac{1}{6}$. Similarly, the chances that the arrow stops on an odd number are three out of six, or $\frac{1}{2}$.

The ratio of the number of successful outcomes to the number of possible outcomes is the **probability** that an outcome will occur.

The probability that you will get a number greater than 6 when you spin the arrow is 0.

Postulate 14–1

The probability of an outcome that cannot happen is 0.

When you spin the arrow, the probability that you will get a positive integer less than 6 is 1.

Postulate 14–2

The probability of an event that is certain to happen is 1.

A probability is a number p, where $0 \leq p \leq 1$.

EXAMPLE 1 In spinning the arrow, what is the probability of getting a positive integer less than 5?

Solution: Possible outcomes: 1, 2, 3, 4, 5, 6
Successful outcomes: 1, 2, 3, 4

$p \text{ (positive integer} < 5) = \frac{4}{6} = \frac{2}{3}$ ⟵ **Number of successful outcomes**
Number of possible outcomes

The set of possible outcomes in probability is called a **sample space**. Each outcome or element in a sample space is a **sample point**.

EXAMPLE 2 In spinning the arrow, what is the probability of getting a number divisible by 2?

Solution: Possible outcomes (sample space): $\{1, 2, 3, 4, 5, 6\}$
Successful outcomes: $\{2, 4, 6\}$

$p \text{ (number divisible by 2)} = \frac{3}{6} = \frac{1}{2}$ ⟵ **Number of successful outcomes**
Number of possible outcomes

In Example 2, each of the successful outcomes, 2, 4, or 6 is equally likely to happen. Because of this, you can find the probability of each successful outcome and add the three probabilities to find the probability of getting an even number.

Probability of Spinning a 2 4 6	Probability of Spinning a 2, 4, or 6
$\dfrac{1}{6}$ $\dfrac{1}{6}$ $\dfrac{1}{6}$	$\dfrac{1}{6}+\dfrac{1}{6}+\dfrac{1}{6}=\dfrac{3}{6}=\dfrac{1}{2}$

Postulate 14–3

If two or more outcomes cannot happen at the same time, the probability of any one of these outcomes happening is the sum of the probabilities that each will occur.

In Examples 1 and 2, the set of successful outcomes is subset of the sample space (possible outcomes). The subset is called an **event.**

CLASSROOM EXERCISES

A penny is tossed. The possible outcomes are H (heads) and T (tails).

1. How many elements are there in the sample space?

2. What is the probability of getting a head?

3. What is the probability of getting a tail?

4. What is the probability of not getting a tail?

WRITTEN EXERCISES

A   Exercises 1–11 refer to one toss of a die.

1. List the elements in the sample space.

Find the probability of each event.

2. p (getting a 2)

3. p (getting a 6)

4. p (getting an even number)

5. p (getting an odd number)

6. p (getting a prime number)

7. p (getting a composite number)

8. p (getting a number greater than 2)

9. p (getting a negative integer)

10. p (getting a counting number less than 7)

11. p (getting a 2, a 3, or a 5)

A bag contains 3 red, 4 blue, and 5 green marbles. One marble is drawn at random.
Find each probability.

12. p (marble is red)

13. p (marble is green)

14. p (marble is not blue)

15. p (marble is not red, blue, or green)

16. p (marble is red or green)

17. p (marble is blue or green)

18. p (marble is red or blue)

19. p (marble is not red or blue)

B

A penny and a dime are tossed. The possible outcomes are shown in the tree diagram at the right.

20. List the elements in the sample space.

21. How many ways are there to get one head and one tail?

22. How many ways are there to get two heads?

For Exercises 23–28, use the tree diagram and your answers to Exercises 20–22 to find each probability.

23. p (TT)

24. p (HT)

25. p (HT or TH)

26. p (TT or HH)

27. p (exactly one head)

28. p (at least one head)

B   For Exercises 29–38, a pair of dice is tossed once.

29. How many elements are there in the sample space?

30. What is the probability that both dice show the same number?

31. What is the probability that the dice show a sum of 8?

32. What is the probability that the dice show a sum of 12?

33. What is the probability that the dice show a sum greater than 3?

34. What is the probability that the dice show a sum less than or equal to 7?

35. What is the probability that both dice show an even number?

36. What is the probability that both dice show a prime number?

37. What is the probability that the dice show a sum less than 2?

38. What is the probability that the dice show a sum greater than or equal to 2 and less than or equal to 12?

C

39. Clarence types 3 letters and addresses 3 envelopes. Before he places the letters in the envelopes, he accidentally drops them on the floor. Suppose that he picks up the letters and envelopes and inserts each letter at random (without looking) into an envelope. What is the probability that each letter will be inserted in the correct envelope?

14–5   Mutually Exclusive Events

When a sample space has n equally likely outcomes, the probability of any one outcome (simple event) is $\frac{1}{n}$. When an event E in the same sample space has k outcomes, $p(E) = \frac{k}{n}$.

EXAMPLE 1   Eight marbles of the same size are placed in a box. Three are blue, one is green and four are red. What is the probability of drawing a blue marble?

Solution: Sample space: {Blue, Blue, Blue, Green, Red, Red, Red}

Event (drawing a blue):   {Blue, Blue, Blue}

$$p.(E) = \frac{3}{8} \longleftarrow \frac{\textbf{Number of successful outcomes}}{\textbf{Number of possible outcomes}}$$

When events have no elements (sample points) in common, they are said to be **mutually exclusive**. In Example 2, events E_1 and E_2 have no elements in common.

EXAMPLE 2   To play a board game, each player spins the arrow once on each spinner. What is the probability of getting a number less than 3 or getting a number greater than 8?

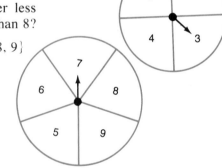

Solution: Sample space: {1, 2, 3, 4, 5, 6, 7, 8, 9}

Event E_1 (number less than 3):   {1, 2}

Event E_2 (number greater than 8):   {9}

E_1 or E_2: {1, 2, 9}

$p(E_1 \text{ or } E_2)$: $\frac{3}{9} = \frac{1}{3}$

In Example 3, events E_1 and E_2 have common elements. They are <u>not</u> mutually exclusive events.

EXAMPLE 3   In the sample space of Example 2, what is the probability of getting a number less than 8 or an even number?

Solution: Event E_1 (number less than 8):   {1, 2, 3, 4, 5, 6, 7}

Event E_2 (even numbers):   {2, 4, 5, 8}

E_1 or E_2:   {1, 2, 3, 4, 5, 6, 7, 8} $\longleftarrow$ **Common elements are listed only once.**

$p(E_1 \text{ or } E_2) = \frac{8}{9}$

CLASSROOM EXERCISES

A single die is tossed. Identify each pair of events as mutually exclusive or not mutually exclusive.

1. E_1: the top face shows a 4; E_2: the top face shows an even number.

2. E_1: the top face shows a 6; E_2: the top face shows an odd number.

3. E_1: the top face shows a number greater than 5; E_2: the top face shows a number less than 5.

4. E_1: the top face shows a 1;   the top face shows a prime number.

WRITTEN EXERCISES

A   The arrow of the spinner is spun once. Find each probability.

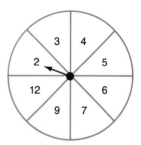

1. p (getting a prime number)

2. p (getting an odd number)

3. p (getting a multiple of 2)

4. p (getting an odd number or a multiple of 2)

In Exercises 5–10, one number is selected at random from 25 cards numbered 1–25. Find each probability.

5. The number ends with 5.

6. The number begins with 2 or 5.

7. The number ends in 0 or 5.

8. The number ends in 7 or 9.

9. The number is divisible by 5 or 10.

10. The number is divisible by 3 or 6.

B   Each spinner is spun once and the sum of the numbers is listed.

11. List the sample space.

12. How many elements are there in the sample space?

13. What is the probability that the sum is 9?

14. What is the probability that the sum is an even number <u>or</u> is a two-digit number?

15. What is the probability that the sum is a multiple of 2 <u>or</u> a multiple of 3?

16. What is the probability that the sum is a two-digit number that ends in 0 <u>or</u> that the two-digits are alike?

14-6 Experimental Probability

When an experiment is repeated many times, the results can be used to approximate the probability of an event. Such probabilities are called *experimental probabilities*.

> An experiment is carried out n times, and a particular event E occurs e of these times. Then the experimental probability p that the event E will occur in the next trial is $\frac{e}{n}$. That is,
>
> $$p\,(E) = \frac{\text{number of occurrences of } E}{\text{number of trials}} = \frac{e}{n}$$

The results of a greater number of experiments will give a closer experimental probability than the results of fewer experiments.

EXAMPLE 1　A baseball player hit the ball 42 times out of the last 150 times at bat. What is the player's probability of getting a hit the next time at bat?

Solution:　$p\,(\text{hit}) = \dfrac{\text{number of hits}}{\text{number of times at bat}}$　◄────　**This ratio is called "batting average."**

$p\,(\text{hit}) = \dfrac{42}{150}$, or **0.28**

As Example 1 shows, you can also express a probability as a decimal.

Since the experimental probability that the batter will get a hit the next time at bat is 0.28, or $\frac{28}{100} = \frac{7}{25}$, you can say that you would expect the batter to get a hit 7 out of every 25 times at bat.

EXAMPLE 2　Use the experimental probability of Example 1 to determine how many hits the batter can expect to get in the next 50 times at bat.

Solution:　Experimental probability:　0.28

Number of hits in next 50 times at bat:　$50 \times 0.28 = 14.00$

The batter can expect to get about **14 hits.**

CLASSROOM EXERCISES

A thumbtack lands "point up" 40 times out of 100 times.

1. What is the experimental probability that it will land "point up" on the next throw?

2. What is the experimental probability that it will <u>not</u> land "point up" on the next throw?

3. How many times can you expect it to land "point up" on the next 60 throws?

4. How many times can you expect it to land "point down" on the next 70 throws?

WRITTEN EXERCISES

A   A football quarterback completes passes at the rate of 80%. In Exercises 1–2, find each experimental probability.

1. p (completing next pass)

2. p (not completing the next pass)

3. How many completed passes can the player expect on the next 15 tries?

4. How many uncompleted passes can the player expect on the next 15 tries?

A poll of the recreational preferences of 400 high school students give the results shown in this table.

	Jogging	Aerobics	Bicycling
Seniors	42	35	23
Juniors	38	35	27
Sophomores	35	30	35
Freshmen	35	25	40
Total	150	125	125

For Exercises 5–10, find each experimental probability. Express the probability as a two-place decimal.

5. p (sophomore prefers aerobics)

6. p (junior does not prefer jogging)

7. p (senior prefers bicycling)

8. p (freshman prefers aerobics)

9. p (high school student prefers jogging)

10. p (high school student prefers aerobics)

A high school has 4,000 students. Refer to the table above to determine how many students you could expect to prefer each of the following.

11. jogging

12. aerobics

13. bicycling

According to the laws of genetics, if two red–colored flowers each carry a gene for white–colored flowers, then the probability that a flower resulting from cross–pollination will be white is $\frac{1}{4}$.

14. How many white-colored flowers could you expect in 100 flowers that resulted from this cross–pollination?

15. How many non–white flowers could you expect in 150 flowers that resulted from this cross–pollination?

Review

A bag of marbles contains 4 white, 2 blue, and 6 yellow marbles. One marble is drawn at random. Find each probability. *(Section 14-4)*

1. p (marble is white)

2. p (marble is blue)

3. p (marble is not yellow)

4. p (marble is blue <u>or</u> yellow)

In Exercises 5–9, the arrow of the spinner is spun once. *(Section 14-5)*

5. List the elements in the sample space.

Find each probability.

6. p (getting a composite number)

7. p (getting a number less than 6)

8. p (getting a multiple of 3 <u>or</u> a factor of 8)

9. p (getting a number divisible by 2 or 5)

A tennis player won 25 out of the last 40 games played. In Exercises 10–11, find each experimental probability. *(Section 14-6)*

10. p (winning next game)

11. p (not winning next game)

12. How many games can the player expect to win out of the next 16 games played?

13. How many games can the player expect to lose out of the next 24 games played?

Chapter Summary

IMPORTANT TERMS

Event (p. 520)
Experimental probability (p. 524)
Frequency distribution (p. 511)
Histogram (p. 511)
Leaves (p. 518)
Mean (p. 508)
Measures of central tendency (p. 511)
Median (p. 508)
Mode (p. 508)
Mutually exclusive events (p. 522)
Normal curve (p. 514)

Probability (p. 519)
Quartile (p. 518)
Sample point (p. 519)
Sample space (p. 519)
Standard deviation (p. 514)
Standard normal distribution (p. 514)
Stem-leaf plot (p. 518)
Stem (p. 518)
Variance (p. 514)
Whisker and box plot (p. 518)

IMPORTANT IDEAS

1. The **mean** of a set of data is the sum of all the values divided by the number of values. The **median** of a set of data that contains an odd number of values is the middle value. When the set of data contains an even number of values, the median is the mean of the two middle values. The **mode** of a set of data is the measure that occurs most often.

2. It is helpful to organize data by constructing a frequency table. Such an organization is called a **frequency distribution** and can be represented by a graph called a **histogram.**

3. The **variance** of a set of measures is the average of the squares of the differences of the measures from the mean. The **standard deviation** of the set of measures is the positive square root of the variance.

4. A **probability** is a number p, such that $0 \le p \le 1$.

5. The probability of an event that cannot occur is 0.

6. The probability of an outcome that must occur is 1.

7. When events have no sample points in common, they are said to be **mutually exclusive.**

8. An experiment is carried out n times and a particular event E occurs e of these times. Then, the experimental probability, $p\ (E)$, that the event E will occur in the next trial is as follows.

$$p(E) = \frac{\textbf{number of occurrence of } E}{\textbf{number of trials}} = \frac{e}{n}$$

_____ Chapter Objectives and Review _____

Objective: *To find the mean, median, and mode of a list of data (Section 14-1)*

The data at the right shows the scores of the Walker High basketball team for 8 basketball games.

81	87	76	91
75	96	83	75

1. What is the mean score?

2. What is the median score?

3. Will the mean or the median be the better average for the data?

4. What is the mode of the data?

Objective: *To organize data by using a frequency table and a histogram (Section 14-2)*

In Exercises 5 and 6:

a. Calculate the mean and the median to the nearest whole number.

b. Make a frequency table.

c. Make a histogram for the data.

5.

**Heights in Meters of
Fifteen Trees**

23	14	17	22	16
23	19	12	15	11
18	23	16	11	19

Intervals: 11–14; 14–17; 17–20; 20–23;
23–26

6.

**Number of Words Typed
per Minute**

35	32	27	46	54	39	42
32	35	40	48	52	45	59
29	30	57	60	38	50	

Intervals: 26–35; 35–44; 44–53; 53–62

Objective: *To find the standard deviation for a set of data (Section 14-3)*

Find the standard deviation to the nearest tenth.

7. Runs Scored in Five Games

| 12 | 14 | 8 | 6 | 5 |

8. Number of Wrong Answers

| 1 | 1 | 2 | 4 | 3 | 1 |

9. A spelling test was given to 10 students. The number of misspelled words for the students was 2, 4, 5, 0, 3, 4, 0, 7, 3, and 2. Calculate the standard deviation to the nearest tenth.

10. During a five-week fund-raising drive, the art club sold the following number of boxes of cards.

35, 45, 27, 33, 50

Calculate the standard deviation to the nearest tenth.

Objective: *To compute the probability that an event will occur (Section 14-4)*

In Exercises 11–15, the spinner is spun once.

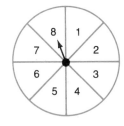

11. List the elements in the sample space.

Find the probability of each event.

12. p (getting a 3)

13. p (getting a composite number)

14. p (getting a number greater than 4)   15. p (getting a 0)

A bag contains four red cubes, five black cubes, and one white cube. One cube is drawn at random. Find each probability.

16. p (cube is red)

17. p (cube is white)

18. p (cube is red or black)

19. p (cube is not green)

Objective: *To compute the probability that at least one of two or more events in a given sample space will occur (Section 14-5)*

In Exercises 20–23, a single die is tossed. Write E if the pair of events is mutually exclusive and write NE if the pair of events is not mutually exclusive. Then find each probability.

20. p (getting a 5 <u>or</u> an even number)

21. p (getting an odd number <u>or</u> a multiple of 3)

22. p (getting a prime number <u>or</u> an even number)

23. p (getting a number less than 2 <u>or</u> a composite number)

In Exercises 24–27, one card is selected at random from 50 cards numbered 1–50. Find each probability.

24. The number begins with a 2 or a 3.

25. The number is divisible by 3 or 6.

26. The number ends in a 2 or a 3.

27. The number ends in a 0 or a 5.

Objective: *To find the experimental probability of an event (Section 14-6)*

The table at the right shows the shooting record for a high school basketball player.

For Exercises 28–31, find each experimental probability. Express the probability as a two–place decimal.

Shot	Number Attempted	Baskets
Lay-up	40	36
Hook	25	15
Jump	32	16
Set	20	8

28. *p* (player makes a lay–up shot)

29. *p* (player makes a set shot)

30. *p* (player does not make a hook shot)

31. *p* (player does not make a jump shot)

32. How many baskets can the player expect to make out of the next 30 lay–up shots?

33. How many baskets can the player expect to miss out of the next 15 set shots?

Chapter Test

A small business employs 14 people. The yearly salaries are listed below. Refer to this data for Exercises 1–4.

| $29,000 | $29,000 | $18,500 | $15,000 | $10,500 | $10,500 | $9100 |
| $9100 | $9100 | $9100 | $9100 | $8000 | $8000 | $8000 |

1. Find the mean.

2. Find the median and mode.

3. Is the mean salary greater or less than most of the salaries?

4. Which average, the mean or the median, best represents most of the salaries? Explain.

In Exercises 5–6, refer to the data below.

Pulse Rates of Twenty People

| 68 | 71 | 83 | 72 | 74 | 77 | 74 | 78 | 73 | 78 |
| 73 | 76 | 73 | 74 | 76 | 78 | 78 | 73 | 68 | 83 |

Intervals: 65–70; 70–75; 75–80; 80–85

5. Calculate the mean and median to the nearest whole number.

6. Make a frequency table of the data. Then draw a histogram for the data.

Find the standard deviation to the nearest tenth.

7. **English Test Scores**

| 85 | 91 | 93 | 87 |

8. **Number of Goals in 5 Soccer Games**

| 3 | 4 | 1 | 2 | 5 |

The numbers 1–15 are printed on 15 tokens, one number per token. In Exercises 9–12, one token is drawn at random.

9. How many elements are there in the sample space?

10. What is the probability of getting a 5?

11. What is the probability of getting an even number?

12. What is the probability of getting a number greater than 6?

In Exercises 13–16, the arrow is spun once. Find each probability.

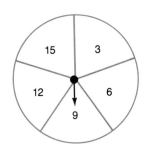

13. p (getting an odd number)

14. p (getting a number divisible by 5 or by 2)

15. p (getting an even number or a composite number)

16. p (getting a number divisible by 3 or by 6)

A darts player hits the center circle of the dart board 24 times out of 60 throws.

17. What is the experimental probability that the player will hit the center circle on the next throw?

18. What is the experimental probability that the player will not hit the center circle on the next throw?

19. How many times can you expect the player to hit the center circle on the next 25 throws?

20. How many times can you expect the player to miss the center circle on the next 40 throws?

Additional Practice

Skills

In Exercises 1–4, calculate the mean and median to the nearest integer. (Section 14–1)

1. Number of Long Distance Calls

9	11	6	10
8	3	10	7

2. Inches of Snowfall

11	22	15	18	17
11	15	16	13	19

3. Number of Passengers in Six Taxis

6	5	3	5	5	4

4. Ages of Twelve Club Members

14	12	13	15	14	14
13	14	12	13	14	13

5. Find the mode in Exercise 1.

6. Find the mode in Exercise 4.

In Exercises 7–8, use the given frequency intervals to make a frequency table of the data. Then draw a histogram to show the data. (Section 14–2)

7. Miles Per Day on a Bicycle Trip

16	30	33	34	37
34	39	26	21	38
32	36	35	24	33

Intervals: 15–20; 20–25; 25–30; 30–35; 35–40

8. Times in Seconds for a 100-meter Dash

10.2	9.6	11.5	10.7	12.3
12.5	11.4	10.5	12.6	11.4
12.2	12.9	11.8	12.2	11.9

Intervals: 9–10; 10–11; 11–12; 12–13

Find the standard deviation to the nearest tenth.
(Section 14–3)

9. Hours of Overtime for Five Weeks

6	5	4	7	3

10. Number of Points in Six Football Games

21	20	14	17	35	7

11. Ages of Ten Club Members

13	15	16	14	15
16	15	14	14	13

12. Miles Driven Per Day

25	32	16	40
18	26	31	16

A bag contains 4 white, 2 blue, and 3 green marbles. One marble is drawn at random. Find each probability.
(Section 14–4)

13. p (marble is white)

14. p (marble is blue)

15. p (marble is not green)

16. p (marble is blue <u>or</u> green)

In Exercises 17–20, the arrow of the spinner is spun once. Find each probability.
(Section 14–5)

17. p (getting a 5)

18. p (getting an even number)

19. p (getting an odd number <u>or</u> a multiple of 3)

20. p (getting a multiple of 10 <u>or</u> a multiple of 4)

Applications

A poll of the reading preferences of 500 high school students shows that 125 students prefer to read science fiction, 45 students prefer to read non-fiction, and 100 students prefer to read popular fiction. Use this information in Exercises 21–24.
(Section 14–6)

21. What is the experimental probability that a high school student prefers reading science fiction? Express the answer as a two–place decimal.

22. What is the experimental probability that a high school student prefers reading non-fiction? Express the answer as a two–place decimal.

23. In a group of 1500 high school students, how many would you expect to prefer reading popular fiction?

24. In a group of 2400 high school students, how many would you expect not to prefer reading science fiction?

CHAPTER # 15 Other Applications of Algebra

15–1 Angles and Algebra

The following table shows some basic geometric figures that you will study when you take a course in geometry.

Geometric Figure	Name	Description
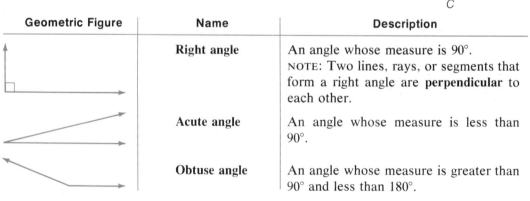 $G \bullet \!\!\!-\!\!\!-\!\!\!-\!\!\!-\!\!\!-\!\!\! \bullet K$	**Segment GK:** $\overline{GK}$ or **Segment KG:** $\overline{KG}$	Consists of two **endpoints**, G and K, and all the points between them.
	Ray AB: $\overrightarrow{AB}$	Extends without end in one direction from its one endpoint, A.
	Line RS: $\overleftrightarrow{RS}$	Extends without end in two opposite directions.
	Angle WXY: $\angle WXY$ or **Angle YXW:** $\angle YXW$	Two different rays that have the same endpoint. $\overrightarrow{XW}$ and $\overrightarrow{XY}$ are the **sides** of the angle. The common endpoint, X, is the **vertex.**

Angles can be classified according to their measures. The unit of measure is the **degree**, °. The degree measure of $\angle ABC$ is 1° or m $\angle ABC = 1°$.

Geometric Figure	Name	Description
	Right angle	An angle whose measure is 90°. NOTE: Two lines, rays, or segments that form a right angle are **perpendicular** to each other.
	Acute angle	An angle whose measure is less than 90°.
	Obtuse angle	An angle whose measure is greater than 90° and less than 180°.

Angle pairs that occur often in geometry have special names.

Model	Name	Description
	Complementary angles	Two angles whose measures have a sum of 90°. Each angle is a **complement** of the other.
	Supplementary angles	Two angles whose measures have a sum of 180°. Each angle is a **supplement** of the other.

Algebra plays an important part in geometry, as the Example shows.

EXAMPLE The measure of an angle is 20° less than its supplement.

    a. Find the measures of the angle and its supplement.

    b. Find the measure of its complement.

Solutions: **a.** Let x = the measure of the angle.
          Let y = the measure of its supplement.
          Then $x = y - 20$.

$$x + y = 180 \quad \longleftarrow \quad \textbf{Definition of supplementary angles}$$
$$y - 20 + y = 180 \quad \longleftarrow \quad \textbf{Replace x with y} - \textbf{20.}$$
$$2y = 200$$
$$y = 100 \quad \longleftarrow \quad \textbf{The measure of the supplement is 100°.}$$
$$y - 20 = 100 - 20$$
$$y - 20 = 80 \quad \longleftarrow \quad \textbf{The measure of the angle is 80°.}$$

    b. The measure of the complement is $(90° - 80°) = \mathbf{10°}$.

WORD PROBLEMS

A   Solve.

1. The measure of an angle is 30° more than its complement. Find the measures of the angle and its complement.

2. The measure of an angle is 50° less than its supplement. Find the measures of the angle and its supplement.

3. Find the measure of the supplement of the angle in Exercise 1.

4. Find the measure of the complement of the angle in Exercise 2.

5. The measure of an angle is the same as its complement. Find the measure of the angle.

6. The measure of an angle is $\frac{2}{3}$ the measure of its supplement. Find the measure of the angle.

7. Find the measure of the supplement of the angle in Exercise 5.

8. Find the measure of the complement of the angle in Exercise 6.

9. The measure of an angle is twice that of its supplement. Find the measures of the angle and its supplement.

10. The measure of an angle is $\frac{3}{4}$ the measure of its complement. Find the measures of the angle and its complement.

B   Choose one of the given measures to complete each statement.

11. Angles A and B are supplementary. If m $\angle A = x$, then m $\angle B = $ __?__ .
$(90 - x,\ 90 + x,\ 180 - x,\ 180 + x)$

12. Angles C and D are complementary. If m $\angle C = y - 10$, then m $\angle D = $ __?__ .
$(80 - y,\ 100 - y,\ y + 80,\ y + 100)$

13. Angle A is supplementary to angle B, and angle B is supplementary to angle C. If m $\angle A = x$, then m $\angle C = $ __?__ .
$(90,\ x,\ 180 + x,\ 180 - x)$

14. Angle F is supplementary to angle G, and angle G is complementary to angle H. If m $\angle F = x$, then m $\angle H = $ __?__ .
$(x - 90,\ x,\ 2x,\ 180 - x)$

Problem Solving and Applications

15-2 Triangles and Algebra

The study of triangles is an important part of geometry. You use the following theorem and your knowledge of algebra (solving equations) to find the measures of angles in triangles.

<table>
<tr><td>Theorem
15-1</td><td>Triangle – Sum Theorem
The sum of the measures of the angles of a triangle is 180°.</td></tr>
</table>

The symbol "m $\angle A$" represents the "measure of angle A." In the following Example, you use Theorem 14–1 to write an equation for the problem.

EXAMPLE 1 In Triangle RST, the measure of $\angle S$ is three times the measure of $\angle R$, and $\angle T$ is 40° more than the measure of $\angle R$. Find the measure of each angle.

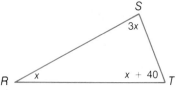

Solution: ☐1 Let $x =$ the measure of $\angle R$.
Then $3x =$ the measure of $\angle S$, and ⎫ ← **Condition 1**
$x + 40 =$ the measure of $\angle T$. ⎭

☐2 $x + 3x + x + 40 = 180$ ← **Use Theorem 15–1 (Condition 2)**
to write an equation.

$$5x = 140$$
$$x = 28$$
$$3x = 84$$
$$x + 40 = 68$$

Thus, **m $\angle R = 28°$, m $\angle S = 84°$, and m $\angle T = 68°$.**

You have used the Pythagorean Theorem (page 439) to find the length of an unknown side of a right triangle. By applying the following definition, you can use the Pythagorean Theorem to find the length of an unknown side in an **isosceles triangle** (a triangle with two sides of equal measure). The third side is called the **base**.

<table>
<tr><td>Definition</td><td>An **altitude of a triangle** is a segment drawn from any vertex perpendicular to the opposite side.</td></tr>
</table>

In an isosceles triangle the angle opposite the base is the **vertex angle**.

EXAMPLE 2 In an isosceles triangle, the altitude (height) drawn from the vertex angle to the base bisects the base. Find the height, BD, of $\triangle ABC$. Write the answer in simplest radical form.

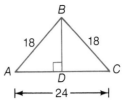

Solution: Use the Pythagorean Theorem.

$$AD^2 + BD^2 = AB^2 \longleftarrow \text{Pythagorean Theorem}$$

$$\left(\tfrac{1}{2}AC\right)^2 + BD^2 = 18^2$$

$$12^2 + BD^2 = 18^2$$

$$BD^2 = 180$$

$$BD = \sqrt{180}$$

$$BD = \sqrt{36 \cdot 5} = 6\sqrt{5}$$

CLASSROOM EXERCISES

In Exercises 1–4, measures of angles in $\triangle ABC$ are given. Find the measure of $\angle C$.

1. $m \angle A = 60°$, $m \angle B = 70°$

2. $m \angle A = 120°$, $m \angle B = 34°$

3. $m\angle B = 60°$, $m\angle A = 60°$

4. $m \angle B = 90°$, $m \angle A = 25°$

Use the Pythagorean Theorem to replace each __?__ with the correct length. Refer to the figure. Write answers in simplest form.

5. $a = 1$, $b = 1$, $c = $ __?__

6. $a = 1$, $c = 2$, $b = $ __?__

7. $b = 3$, $c = 5$, $a = $ __?__

8. $b = 2$, $a = 2$, $c = $ __?__

9. $b = 2$, $c = 4$, $a = $ __?__

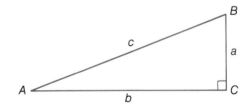

WORD PROBLEMS

A

1. In triangle KGH, the measure of $\angle K$ is the same as the measure of $\angle H$. The measure of $\angle G$ is $2\tfrac{1}{2}$ times the measure of $\angle K$. Find the measure of each angle.

2. In triangle XYZ, the measure of $\angle Y$ is $25°$ less than the measure of $\angle Z$. The measure of $\angle X$ is $\tfrac{1}{2}$ the measure of $\angle Z$. Find the measure of each angle.

3. In triangle ABC, the measure of $\angle A$ is $\tfrac{2}{3}$ the measure of $\angle C$. The measure of $\angle B$ is $5°$ more than the measure of $\angle A$. Find the measure of each angle.

4. In triangle PQR, the measure of $\angle P$ is $\tfrac{1}{3}$ the measure of $\angle Q$. The measure of $\angle R$ is $9°$ less than the measure of $\angle Q$. Find the measure of each angle.

Other Applications of Algebra **537**

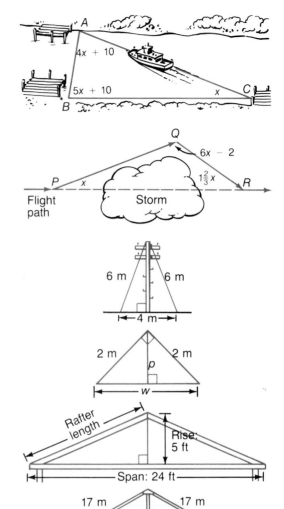

5. The figure at the right shows a ferry traveling between points A, B, and C. The measure of $\angle A$ is 10° more than 4 times the measure of $\angle C$. The measure of $\angle B$ is 10° more than 5 times the measure of $\angle C$. Find the measure of each angle.

6. The flight path of an airplane around a storm is shown at the right. The measure of $\angle Q$ is 2° less than 6 times the measure of $\angle P$. The measure of $\angle R$ is $1\frac{2}{3}$ times the measure of $\angle P$. Find the measure of each angle.

7. A telephone pole is supported by two guy wires that form an isosceles triangle with the ground. Each guy wire is 6 meters long, and the two wires are anchored 4 meters apart. Find the height of the pole.

8. The two sides of a tent are each 2 meters long. If the tent is pitched so that the sides meet in a right angle at the top, find w, the width of the tent, and p, the height of the center pole.

9. The **span** of a roof (see the figure at the right) is 24 feet long and the **rise** is 5 feet long. Find the length of each rafter.

10. A truss for a footbridge has equal sides 17 meters long, and a vertical tie rod 8 meters long, as shown at the right. Find the length of the footbridge.

B

11. The length of a side of an equilateral A-frame house is 30 feet. Find the height of the house.

12. Compute the length of the altitude to the shortest side of a triangle whose sides are 17, 25, and 26 centimeters long.

13. Compute the length of the altitude to the longest side of a triangle whose sides are 10, 6, and 12 decimeters long.

14. Write a formula that can be used to find the altitude of an equilateral triangle with side s. Use the figure at the right to solve for h in terms of s.

15–3 Similar Triangles and Algebra

Your knowledge of ratio and proportion will be useful in geometry in solving problems that deal with *similar triangles.* **Similar triangles** have the same shape; that is, corresponding angles have equal measures. In similar triangles, corresponding sides are opposite *congruent angles.* **Congruent angles** are angles that have the same measure.

Similar Triangles	Corresponding Angles	Corresponding Sides
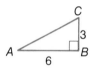	$\angle A$ and $\angle D$	$\overline{AB}$ and $\overline{DE}$
	$\angle B$ and $\angle E$	$\overline{BC}$ and $\overline{EF}$
	$\angle C$ and $\angle F$	$\overline{AC}$ and $\overline{DF}$
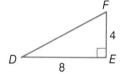	$\angle K$ and $\angle X$	$\overline{KL}$ and $\overline{XZ}$
	$\angle L$ and $\angle Z$	$\overline{LM}$ and $\overline{YZ}$
	$\angle M$ and $\angle Y$	$\overline{KM}$ and $\overline{XY}$

EXAMPLE 1   **a.** Find the ratio of each pair of corresponding sides in these similar right triangles.

b. Compare the ratios.

Solutions: **a.** $\dfrac{AB}{DE} = \dfrac{6}{8} = \dfrac{3}{4}; \quad \dfrac{BC}{EF} = \dfrac{3}{4}$

$AC^2 = 6^2 + 3^2 \qquad\qquad DF^2 = 8^2 + 4^2$

$AC^2 = 36 + 9 \qquad\qquad DF^2 = 64 + 16$

$AC = \sqrt{45} \qquad\qquad\quad DF = \sqrt{80}$

$AC = \sqrt{9 \cdot 5} = 3\sqrt{5} \qquad DF = \sqrt{16 \cdot 5} = 4\sqrt{5}$

$\dfrac{AC}{DF} = \dfrac{3\sqrt{5}}{4\sqrt{5}} = \dfrac{3}{4}$

b. Each of the three ratios equals $\dfrac{3}{4}$.

This example suggests the following theorem.

Theorem 15–2   If two triangles are similar, then their corresponding sides are proportional.

Thus, when you know that two triangles are similar, you can write a proportion to find the length of an unknown side.

EXAMPLE 2 Find the unknown length in these similar triangles.

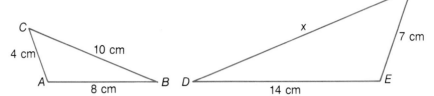

Solutions: **1** Write a ratio of an unknown side to the corresponding known side.

$$\frac{DF}{BC} = \frac{x}{10} \longleftarrow \frac{\triangle DEF}{\triangle ABC} \text{ is the } \underline{\text{order.}}$$

2 Write a ratio of known corresponding sides in the <u>same order</u> as in step 1.

$$\frac{DE}{BA} = \frac{14}{8} = \frac{7}{4} \longleftarrow \frac{\triangle DEF}{\triangle ABC} \text{ is the same order, not } \frac{\triangle ABC}{\triangle DEF}.$$

3 Use the two ratios to write a proportion and solve.

$$\frac{x}{10} = \frac{7}{4}$$
$$4x = 70$$
$$x = 17.5 \text{ cm}$$

CLASSROOM EXERCISES

In Exercises 1–4, each pair of triangles is similar. In Exercises 1–2, find the ratio comparing corresponding known sides of each pair.

1.

2.

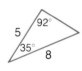

Write a proportion comparing corresponding sides of each pair.

3.

4.

WRITTEN EXERCISES

A   In Exercises 1–2, each pair of triangles is similar. Find the unknown length.

1.

2.

APPLICATIONS: **Using Similar Triangles**

3. Norman is 1.8 meters tall. On a sunny day, Patty measured Norman's shadow and the shadow of the school. Use the similar triangles shown below to find the height of the school to the nearest tenth.

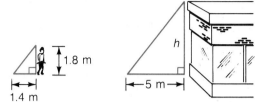

4. On the same sunny day, the shadow of a tree was 12 meters long. Use the similar triangles below to find the height of the tree to the nearest tenth.

5. Jorge found the height of a street lamp by placing a mirror on the sidewalk. Then he walked backwards until he saw the top of the streetlight in the mirror. The figure below shows how he formed similar triangles. Find the height of the street lamp to the nearest tenth.

6. Find the distance across this lake to the nearest tenth of a meter.

Review

Solve each problem.

1. The measure of an angle is 55° less than its complement. Find the measures of the angle, its supplement, and its complement. *(Section 15–1)*

2. The measure of an angle is $\frac{2}{5}$ the measure of its supplement. Find the measures of the angle, its supplement, and its complement. *(Section 15–1)*

3. In $\triangle ABC$, the measure of $\angle A$ is $\frac{1}{3}$ the measure of $\angle B$. The measure of $\angle C$ is 5° more than the measure of $\angle B$. Find the measures of the angles. *(Section 15–2)*

4. A road sign in the shape of an equilateral triangle is 60 centimeters long on each side. Find the height of the sign. Write your answer in simplest form. *(Section 15–2)*

Find the unknown length in each pair of similar triangles. *(Section 15–3)*

5.

6.

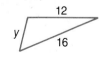

15-4 The Tangent Ratio

These three right triangles are similar.

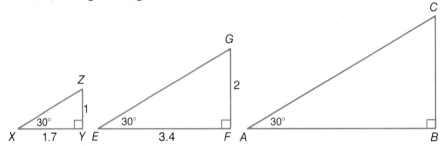

Since $\dfrac{YZ}{FG} = \dfrac{XY}{EF}$, the following proportion is true.

$$\frac{YZ}{XY} = \frac{FG}{EF}$$

Thus, for the above triangles,

$$\frac{1}{1.7} = \frac{2}{3.4} = \frac{BC}{AB}.$$

The ratio $\dfrac{BC}{AB}$ in *any* right triangle ABC, where $\angle B$ is a right angle, is the **tangent of angle** C.

Definition	In a right triangle, the **tangent of an acute angle** is the ratio $$\frac{\text{length of the leg opposite the angle}}{\text{length of the leg adjacent to the angle}}.$$

Tangent of angle A is abbreviated tan A.

EXAMPLE 1   Find each ratio. Write a decimal for the ratio.

    a. tan A **b.** tan B

Solutions: **a.** $\tan A = \dfrac{BC}{AC}$ ⟵ **BC is opposite $\angle$ A.** / **AC is adjacent to $\angle$ A.**

        $\tan A = \dfrac{5}{12}$

        $\tan A = .4167$ ⟵ **Rounded to 4 decimal places.**

    b. $\tan B = \dfrac{AC}{BC}$ ⟵ **AC is opposite $\angle$ B.** / **BC is adjacent to $\angle$ B.**

        $\tan B = \dfrac{12}{5}$

        $\tan B = \mathbf{2.4}$

A ratio of the lengths of two sides of a right triangle is a **trigonometric ratio.** The study of trigonometry originated in connection with real-world measurement problems that involve right triangles.

A trigonometric ratio depends only on the measure of an acute angle, *not* on the size of the right triangle. The **Table of Sines, Cosines, and Tangents** on page 568 gives these values for acute angles.

Although most values are approximations for the ratios, the "=" symbol is used because it is more convenient. Thus, in Example 1, write tan $A = .4167$ instead of tan $A \approx .4167$.

EXAMPLE 2 Find the tangent of 41°.

Solution: Find 41 in the **Angle–column. Move directly right to the Tangent–column.**

tan 41° = **.8693**

Angle	Sine	Cosine	Tangent
40°	.6428	.7660	.8391
41	.6561	.7547	.8693
42	.6691	.7431	.9004

You use the tangent to find the measure of an angle.

EXAMPLE 3 What is the measure of the angle whose tangent is 1.1106?

Solution: Find 1.1106 in the **Tangent–column.** Move directly left to the **Angle–column.**

The measure of the angle whose tangent is 1.1106 is **48°.**

Angle	Sine	Cosine	Tangent
47°	.7314	.6820	1.0724
48	.7431	.6691	1.1106
49	.7547	.6561	1.1504

You also use the tangent to find the measure of a side.

EXAMPLE 4 A flagpole is side BC in triangle ABC pictured at the right. Point A is 14 meters from point C and $\angle A$ is 47°. How high is the flagpole to the nearest meter?

Solution:

$$\tan 47° = \frac{BC}{14}$$

$$1.0724 = \frac{BC}{14} \longleftarrow \text{From the table, tan } 47° = 1.0724.$$

$$14(1.0724) = BC \longleftarrow \text{Solve for } BC.$$

$$15.0136 = BC$$

The height of the flagpole is about **15 meters.**

CLASSROOM EXERCISES

In Exercises 1–3, find tan *A* and tan *B*.

1.

2.

3.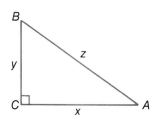

Use the table of values on page 568 to find *x*.

4. $\tan 76° = x$ **5.** $\tan 10° = x$ **6.** $\tan x = 1.3270$

WRITTEN EXERCISES

A Use the table on page 568 to find the tangent of each angle measure.

1. 20° **2.** 40° **3.** 22° **4.** 45° **5.** 55° **6.** 70°

7. 5° **8.** 25° **9.** 37° **10.** 80° **11.** 85° **12.** 89°

Find *x*.

13. $\tan x = .5774$ **14.** $\tan x = 1.7321$ **15.** $\tan x = .1228$

16. $\tan x = .6009$ **17.** $\tan x = 1.6003$ **18.** $\tan x = 2.2460$

19. Refer to the table to complete the following sentence.

As the measure of an angle increases from 0° to 89°, the tangent of the angle measure __?__ (increases or decreases) from .0000 to __?__ .

APPLICATIONS: Using the Tangent Ratio

20. The triangle at the right is a right triangle. Use the tangent ratio to find the distance between Tom's home and John's home, directly through the park.

Find *x*.

21.

22.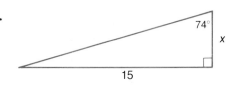

23. In right triangle XYZ, m $\angle X$ is 45°. Since the sum of $\angle X$, $\angle Y$, and $\angle Z$ is 180°, m $\angle Y$ is also 45°. If two angles of a triangle have the same measure, the sides opposite these angles have the same length and the triangle is isosceles.

Triangle XYZ is isosceles and $XZ = YZ$.

$$\tan X = \frac{YZ}{XZ} = \underline{\ ?\ } \qquad \tan Y = \frac{XZ}{YZ} = \underline{\ ?\ } \qquad \tan 45° = \underline{\ ?\ }$$

24. To the nearest foot, how long is $\overline{DF}$ in $\triangle DEF$ below?

25. In $\triangle PQR$ above, what is m $\angle P$, to the nearest degree?

26. Use Figure 1 below to find the length of $\overline{BC}$ to the nearest foot.

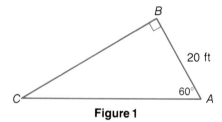

Figure 1   **Figure 2**

27. In Figure 2 at the right above, find the length of $\overline{HF}$ to the nearest centimeter.

28. In the figure at the right, angle C is the right angle of $\triangle ABC$. What measurements could you make to find BC, the distance across the pond?

29. Using the figure for Exercise 28, find BC if $\angle A$ is 42° and AC is 80 meters.

30. The figure below shows a television tower and support cables. Find m $\angle A$ to the nearest degree.

31. A surveyor is measuring the width of a valley, as shown below. Find w to the nearest meter.

15-5 The Sine and Cosine Ratios

Suppose you wanted to determine the height of a plane or the distance across a pond as shown below.

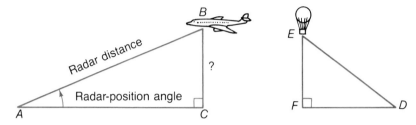

If both situations are represented by right triangles, where you know the length of the hypotenuse and the measure of one acute angle, you still would not be able to find either *BC* or *FD* using the tangent ratio. There are two other ratios, the *sine ratio* and the *cosine ratio,* that you can use.

Definitions

> In a right triangle, the **sine of an acute angle** is the ratio
>
> $$\frac{\text{length of opposite side}}{\text{length of hypotenuse}}.$$
>
> In a right triangle, the **cosine of an acute angle** is the ratio
>
> $$\frac{\text{length of adjacent side}}{\text{length of hypotenuse}}.$$

The abbreviation for sine is sin (pronounced "sign"). The abbreviation for cosine is cos (pronounced "co-sign").

EXAMPLE 1   Use the figure at the right to determine sin *A* and cos *A* for each of the triangles *ABC, ADE* and *AFG,* where *AB* = 5, *AD* = 10, and *AF* = 15.

Solutions:

Triangle	sin A	cos A
ABC	$\sin A = \dfrac{BC}{AB} = \dfrac{4}{5}$	$\cos A = \dfrac{AC}{AB} = \dfrac{3}{5}$
ADE	$\sin A = \dfrac{DE}{AD} = \dfrac{8}{10} = \dfrac{4}{5}$	$\cos A = \dfrac{AE}{AD} = \dfrac{6}{10} = \dfrac{3}{5}$
AFG	$\sin A = \dfrac{FG}{AF} = \dfrac{12}{15} = \dfrac{4}{5}$	$\cos A = \dfrac{AG}{AF} = \dfrac{9}{15} = \dfrac{3}{5}$

Since the triangles in Example 1 are similar, the ratios of corresponding sides are equal. Thus, for each of the triangles,

$$\sin A = \frac{4}{5} \quad \text{and} \quad \cos A = \frac{3}{5}.$$

Now you can solve the problems mentioned at the beginning of this section.

EXAMPLE 2   The distance from the tower to the plane is 40 kilometers and the measure of angle A is 12°. Find the height of the plane to the nearest tenth.

Solution: Since you know the measure of $\angle A$ and of the hypotenuse, and you want to find the side opposite $\angle A$, use sin A.

$$\sin A = \frac{BC}{AB}$$

$$\sin 12° = \frac{BC}{40} \longleftarrow \textbf{Find sin 12° in the table.}$$

$$.2079 = \frac{BC}{40} \longleftarrow \textbf{Solve for } \textbf{\textit{BC}}.$$

$$BC = 40(.2079)$$

$$BC = 8.3160$$

The height of the plane is about **8.3 kilometers.**

EXAMPLE 3   Find the distance across the pond shown at the right to the nearest meter.

Solution: Since you know the measure of $\angle D$ and of the hypotenuse, and you want to find the side adjacent to $\angle D$, use cos D.

$$\cos D = \frac{FD}{ED}$$

$$\cos 35° = \frac{FD}{650} \longleftarrow \textbf{Find cos 35° in the table.}$$

$$.8192 = \frac{FD}{650} \longleftarrow \textbf{Solve for } \textbf{\textit{FD}}.$$

$$FD = 650(.8192)$$

$$FD = 532.48$$

The distance is about **532 meters.**

CLASSROOM EXERCISES

Use the table on page 568 to find the following.

1. sin 12° **2.** cos 63° **3.** cos 45°

In Exercises 4–6, find the sine and cosine of angle *A*.

4.

B, 13, 5, *A*, 12, *C*

5.

C, 2, 2, *A*, *D*, *B*, |←1→|

6.

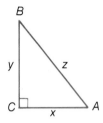

WRITTEN EXERCISES

A Use the table of values on page 568 to find approximations for the sine and the cosine of the following angles.

1. 35° **2.** 42° **3.** 54° **4.** 83° **5.** 72° **6.** 61°

Find *x*.

7. sin *x* = .1392 **8.** sin *x* = .3907 **9.** sin *x* = .6561

10. sin *x* = .7547 **11.** sin *x* = .9135 **12.** sin *x* = .9962

13. Look at your results for Exercises 7–12. As the size of an acute angle increases, does the sine ratio increase or decrease?

Find *x*.

14. cos *x* = .9336 **15.** cos *x* = .7660 **16.** cos *x* = .5299

17. cos *x* = .1736 **18.** cos *x* = .0175 **19.** cos *x* = .9877

20. Look at the cosine values in the table. As the size of an acute angle increases, does the value of the cosine increase or decrease?

APPLICATIONS: Using the Sine and Cosine Ratios

21. Bea's kite string is 60 meters long and makes an angle of 42° with the horizontal in the figure below. How high above the ground is the kite?

22. In the figure above, $\overline{AB}$ represents a wire supporting a pole, $\overline{BC}$. Find AB.

B

23. The railroad that runs to the summit of Pike's Peak makes, at the steepest place, an angle of 27° with the horizontal. How many meters would you rise in walking 30 meters up the railroad track?

24. In △ABC below, c is 25 meters and ∠A is 65°. How long is b?

25. In the figure at the right above, the balloon at B is anchored to the ground at a point E by a wire. The wind blows the balloon so the wire makes an angle of 48° with the ground. If point D, directly under the balloon, is 85 meters from E, how long is the wire?

26. How far above the ground is the balloon in Exercise 25?

27. The scouts of the Lynx Patrol want to know the distance across a pond. They laid off $\overline{CA}$ at right angles to $\overline{BC}$. They extended $\overline{CA}$ until they came to a point A from which they could measure $\overline{AB}$. They measured $\overline{AB}$ and angle A. If AB is 195 meters and ∠A is 57°, find BC.

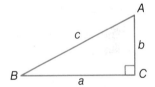

Exercises 28–31 refer to right triangles. Make a drawing for each. In triangle ABC, a is the side opposite ∠A, b is the side opposite ∠B, and c is the side opposite ∠C, a right angle.

28. Find c when a is 26 centimeters and ∠A is 54°.

29. Find c when a is 8.4 centimeters and ∠A is 62°.

30. Find a when c is 65 meters and ∠A is 45°.

31. Find b when c is 100 meters and ∠A is 35°.

32. If XY is 110 feet and m ∠YXZ is 27°, how long is d in Figure 1 below?

Figure 1

Figure 2

C

33. The diagonals of a square are perpendicular to each other, as shown in Figure 2 above. If a circle is circumscribed about the square, the diagonals are also diameters of the circle. Use the cosine ratio to find the radius of a circle circumscribed about a square whose side is 3.5 centimeters.

34. Use the Pythagorean Theorem to check your answer to Exercise 33.

Problem Solving and Applications

15-6 Using the Sine, Cosine, and Tangent Ratios

An important step in using trigonometric ratios to solve problems is deciding which ratio to use. When no figure is given, you should first draw one, carefully labeling what is known and what is to be found. The ratio that involves both the known parts and the part to be found is the one to use in solving the problem.

Known and Unknown Sides of the Right Triangle	Ratios to Use
opposite and adjacent	tangent
opposite and hypotenuse	sine
adjacent and hypotenuse	cosine

To describe the angles found by lines of sight to objects, two angles are used. They are the **angle of elevation** and the **angle of depression.**

EXAMPLE 1 To find the height of a tree, a girl measures 9 meters along a straight line from its base. From the end of this line, she finds the angle of elevation to the top of tree to be 41°. How high is the tree (to the nearest meter)?

Solution: Let $y =$ the height of the tree.

$\tan 41° = \dfrac{y}{9}$ ⟵ The opposite side is unknown; the adjacent side is known. Use the tangent ratio.

$.8693 = \dfrac{y}{9}$ ⟵ **tan 41° = .8693**

$y = 9(.8693)$

$y = 7.8237$

The tree is about **8 meters** tall.

EXAMPLE 2 The diagonal of a rectangle is 8 centimeters long and makes an angle of 25° with the longer side of the rectangle. Find the length of the base to the nearest centimeter.

Solution:

Draw a figure and label the parts.

$$\cos A = \frac{AC}{AB}$$

The hypotenuse is known; the adjacent side is unknown. Use the cosine ratio.

$$\cos 25° = \frac{AC}{8}$$

Find cos 25° from the table.

$$.9063 = \frac{AC}{8}$$

Solve for **AC**.

$$AC = 8(.9063)$$

$$AC = 7.2504$$ The base is about **7 centimeters** long.

CLASSROOM EXERCISES

Use each figure to tell which trigonometric ratio could be used to find x.

1.   **2.**   **3.**   **4.**   **5.**

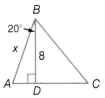

WORD PROBLEMS

A   Solve each problem.

1. To find the distance across a pond between two points, M and N, Fred measured off 250 meters on a line MR perpendicular to segment MN. He found $\angle MRN$ to be 35°. Find MN.

2. Some girl scouts measured the height of a mound. They stretched a string from a point, A, at the bottom of the mound to the top, T, finding AT to be 24 meters. The measure of the angle of elevation of the top from point A was 35°. How high was the mound?

3. If AB and BC in the figure at the right are each 30 meters, and BD is 18 meters, what is the measure of angle A?

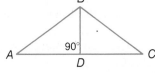

4. You are given rectangle $ABCD$ with diagonal AC drawn. The measure of the angle between $\overline{AD}$ and $\overline{AC}$ is 31° and AD is 16.3 centimeters. How long is $\overline{AC}$?

5. Find the angle of elevation of the sun to the nearest degree when a church steeple 200 feet high casts a shadow 80 feet long.

6. From the top of a cliff 1200 meters above a lake, the angle of depression of the nearest shore is 18°. Find the distance from the top of the cliff to the edge of the lake.

7. In the figure at the right, AB is 215 centimeters, $\angle A$ is 35°, $\angle C$ is 65°, and the angles at D are right angles. How long are $\overline{BD}$ and $\overline{BC}$?

8. Use your own height in meters to find how long a shadow you will cast if the angle of elevation of the sun is 37°.

9. A tower that is 50 meters high has a support wire that makes an angle of 35° with the ground. How long is the wire? How far from the foot of the tower is the support wire attached to the ground?

_____ Review _____

In Exercises 1–16, use the table on page 568.
Complete. *(Section 15–4)*

1. tan 32° = __?__   2. tan 47° = __?__   3. tan 15° = __?__   4. tan 86° = __?__
5. tan x = .4040; x = __?__   6. tan x = 2.1445; x = __?__   7. tan x = 8.1443; x = __?__

8. In the figure at the right, point B is 60 meters from the base of the water tower and $\angle B$ is 41°. Find side AC, the height of the tower, to the nearest meter. *(Section 15–4)*

Complete. *(Section 15–5)*

9. sin 25° = __?__   10. cos 63° = __?__   11. sin 84° = __?__   12. cos 13° = __?__
13. sin x = .3090; x = __?__   14. cos x = .8387; x = __?__   15. sin x = .9613; x = __?__

16. An airplane approaching an airport is 800 meters above the control tower. The angle of elevation from the tower to the plane is 8°. Find the distance between the plane and the tower to the nearest meter. *(Section 15–6)*

15-7 The Field Postulates

As you will discover in geometry, a **postulate** is a mathematical statement that is accepted without proof—just as in algebra. (See page 30.) Postulates are an important part of the structure of geometry. As the following illustrates, postulates are also important in the structure of algebra.

If it is nine o'clock, then five hours from now it will be two o'clock. Although $9 + 5 = 14$, in *clock arithmetic*

$$9 + 5 = 2.$$

In clock arithmetic you only use the whole numbers 1 through 12.

$$C = \{1, 2, 3, 4, 5, 6, 7, 8, 9, 10, 11, 12\}$$

Set C is a **finite set** because you can count the number of elements and the counting comes to an end.

Here is the procedure for adding numbers in clock arithmetic.

Procedure

> If the sum of any two numbers named in C is greater than 12, you subtract 12 to find the clock sum.

Here is the addition table for C.

+	1	2	3	4	5	6	7	8	9	10	11	12
1	2	3	4	5	6	7	8	9	10	11	12	1
2	3	4	5	6	7	8	9	10	11	12	1	2
3	4	5	6	7	8	9	10	11	12	1	2	3
4	5	6	7	8	9	10	11	12	1	2	3	4
5	6	7	8	9	10	11	12	1	2	3	4	5
6	7	8	9	10	11	12	1	2	3	4	5	6
7	8	9	10	11	12	1	2	3	4	5	6	7
8	9	10	11	12	1	2	3	4	5	6	7	8
9	10	11	12	1	2	3	4	5	6	7	8	9
10	11	12	1	2	3	4	5	6	7	8	9	10
11	12	1	2	3	4	5	6	7	8	9	10	11
12	1	2	3	4	5	6	7	8	9	10	11	12

EXAMPLE 1 Find the clock sums: **a.** $8 + 5$ **b.** $7 + 9$

Solutions: **Method 1: Using the Procedure**

a. $8 + 5 = 13$ and $13 - 12 = 1$ **b.** $7 + 9 = 16$ and $16 - 12 = 4$

Method 2: Using the Table

a. Find 8 in the $+$ column. Look directly right to the **5**–column.
$$8 + 5 = 1$$

b. Find 7 in the $+$ column. Look directly right to the **9**–column.
$$7 + 9 = 4$$

The following is the procedure for multiplying numbers in clock arithmetic.

Procedure

> If the product of any two numbers named in C is greater than 12, you subtract 12 or a multiple of 12 to find the clock product.

Here is the multiplication table for C.

×	1	2	3	4	5	6	7	8	9	10	11	12
1	1	2	3	4	5	6	7	8	9	10	11	12
2	2	4	6	8	10	12	2	4	6	8	10	12
3	3	6	9	12	3	6	9	12	3	6	9	12
4	4	8	12	4	8	12	4	8	12	4	8	12
5	5	10	3	8	1	6	11	4	9	2	7	12
6	6	12	6	12	6	12	6	12	6	12	6	12
7	7	2	9	4	11	6	1	8	3	10	5	12
8	8	4	12	8	4	12	8	4	12	8	4	12
9	9	6	3	12	9	6	3	12	9	6	3	12
10	10	8	6	4	2	12	10	8	6	4	2	12
11	11	10	9	8	7	6	5	4	3	2	1	12
12	12	12	12	12	12	12	12	12	12	12	12	12

EXAMPLE 2 Find the clock products: **a.** 9×2 **b.** 8×4

Solutions: **Method 1: Using the Procedure**

a. $9 \times 2 = 18$ and $18 - 12 = 6$ **b.** $8 \times 4 = 32$ and $32 - 24 = 8$

Method 2: Using the Table

a. Find 9 in the ×–column. Look directly right to the 2–column.
$$9 \times 2 = 6$$

b. Find 8 in the ×–column. Look directly right to the 4–column.
$$8 \times 4 = 8$$

Note that in the finite set C under the operations of clock arithmetic, 12 acts the same as 0 does in the set of real numbers. That is, 12 is the additive identity element and 12 times any number is 12. Therefore, if the clock had been labeled as shown below, the pattern for addition and multiplication would be the same with 12 being replaced by 0.

A set of numbers together with two operations for which the eleven postulates given below hold is called a **field**, *F*.

To determine if C is a field, check each postulate with the addition and multiplication tables for C.

Field Postulates	**Does C satisfy the postulate?**
Closure	
1. $a + b$ is an element of the set.	**1–2.** Yes. The sum or product of any two numbers is in C.
2. $a \times b$ is an element of the set.	
Commutativity	
3. $a + b = b + a$	**3–4.** Yes. All cases can be checked. Draw a diagonal from upper left to lower right of the table. The pattern on either side of the diagonal is the same. This shows commutativity.
4. $a \times b = b \times a$	
Associativity	
5. $a + (b + c) = (a + b) + c$	**5–6.** Yes. Check a few cases. All cases should be checked to show that these postulates hold.
6. $a \times (b \times c) = (a \times b) \times c$	
Identity Element	
7. There is an identity element, 0, such that $a + 0 = a$.	**7.** Yes. The identity element is 12. 12 added to any number in C gives that number.
8. There is an identity element, 1, such that $a \times 1 = a$.	**8.** Yes. The identity element is 1. 1 times any number in C gives that number.
Inverse Element	
9. For each element a in F, there is an inverse element, $-a$, such that $a + -a = 0$.	**9.** Yes. The additive identity element, 12, appears in each column. So each number in C has an additive inverse.
10. For each element a in F, there is an inverse element, $\frac{1}{a}$, $a \neq 0$, such that $a \times \frac{1}{a} = 1$.	**10.** No. There is no number in C by which to multiply 2, 3, 4, 6, 8, 9, 10, or 12 to get the identity element 1.
Distributive	
11. $a \times (b + c) = a \times b + a \times c$	**11.** Yes. Try a few cases. All combinations could be checked.

If one postulate is not satisfied, then the set of numbers is not a field. Thus, you could have stopped after finding that Postulate 10 did not hold. The set of clock numbers is *not* a field.

WRITTEN EXERCISES

Complete the following tables for a "four-hour clock."

1.

+	0	1	2	3
0	0	1	2	3
1	1	?	?	?
2	2	3	?	?
3	3	?	?	2

2.

×	0	1	2	3
0	0	0	0	0
1	0	?	?	?
2	0	2	?	?
3	0	?	?	1

3. Does the set of numbers on a "four-hour clock" meet all the requirements for a field? If not, which postulate(s) is (are) not satisfied? Give examples.

Complete the following tables for a "six-hour clock."

4.

+	0	1	2	3	4	5
0	0	1	2	3	4	5
1	1	?	?	?	?	0
2	2	?	4	?	?	?
3	3	?	?	?	?	2
4	4	?	?	?	2	?
5	5	?	1	?	?	?

5.

×	0	1	2	3	4	5
0	0	0	0	0	0	0
1	0	?	2	?	?	?
2	0	?	?	?	?	?
3	0	?	?	?	0	?
4	0	4	?	?	?	2
5	0	?	4	?	?	1

6. Does the set of numbers on a "six-hour clock" meet all the requirements for a field? Explain.

7. Is any set of numbers on an "even-number clock" a field? Explain.

Complete the following tables for a "three-hour clock."

8.

+	0	1	2
0	0	?	?
1	?	2	?
2	?	?	1

9.

×	0	1	2
0	0	0	0
1	0	?	?
2	0	?	?

10. Is the set of numbers on a "three-hour clock" a field?

11. Is the set of numbers on a "five-hour clock" a field?

12. Addition and multiplication tables for the finite set S = {E, O} are shown below. Is set S a field?

+	E	O
E	E	O
O	O	E

×	E	O
E	E	E
O	E	O

15-8 Logic and Algebra

The study of geometry is an application of logical reasoning. An understanding of some of the elementary aspects of logic can prove to be helpful to you in geometry and in your next algebra course, particularly when dealing with theorems that are often stated in the *if–then* form.

In mathematics, a statement in the *if–then* form is a **conditional statement.** You can think of a conditional statement as a *promise.*

<u>If it is cold, then I wear my coat.</u>

If you keep your promise, then the conditional is true; if you do not, it is false.

In the following table, T stands for *True* and F stands for *False.*

It is cold.	You wore your coat.	You kept your promise.	
T	T	T	
F	T	T ←	You did not say that you wouldn't wear your coat if it wasn't cold. Thus, you kept your promise.
F	F	T ←	This case is *True* because you didn't break your promise.
T	F	F ←	This case is *False* because you broke your promise.

Notice that the only case where the conditional is false is when the if–part is true and the then–part is false. This analysis of a conditional statement suggests the truth table below. The symbol for the conditional is $p \rightarrow q$, where the $\rightarrow$ connects the then–part, q, with the if–part, p.

p	q	$p \rightarrow q$
T	T	T
F	T	T
F	F	T
T	F	F

The symbol "~" is read **"not."** Thus, in Example 1, $\sim q$ is the negation of the then–part of the statement, q.

EXAMPLE 1 Tell when the conditional is false if p is true and q is true.

If <u>it is raining</u>, then <u>I will use my umbrella.</u>

Solution: Keep p true and make q false.

p	$\sim q$
It is raining	I will *not* use my umbrella

A conditional statement is a **compound statement** since it is formed by combining two *simple* statements.

EXAMPLE 2   Combine these two simple statements or the negatives of these statements to form a true conditional.

3 is an even number.   3 is a real number.

Solution: There are three ways to do this.

	p	q	p → q
If 3 is an even number, then 3 is a real number.	F	T	T
If 3 is an even number, then 3 is *not* a real number.	F	F	T
If 3 is *not* an even number, then 3 is a real number.	T	T	T

The **converse** of a conditional statement is formed by interchanging the *p* and *q* statements.

EXAMPLE 3   Write the converse for each of the true conditionals in Example 2.

	q	p	q → p
If 3 is a real number, then 3 is an even number.	T	F	F
If 3 is *not* a real number, then 3 is an even number.	F	F	T
If 3 is a real number, then 3 is *not* an even number.	T	T	T

As Example 3 shows, the converse of a true conditional is not always true. However, for a definition, *both* the conditional and its converse must be true.

EXAMPLE 4   Write the definition as a conditional and its converse.

An even number is a number divisible by 2.

Solution:

If a number is an even number, then it is divisible by 2. ◄——— **Conditional**
If a number is divisible by 2, then it is an even number. ◄——— **Converse**

CLASSROOM EXERCISES

Write each definition as a conditional and its converse.

1. A right triangle is a triangle with one right angle.
2. An isosceles triangle is a triangle with two equal sides.
3. An odd number is a number that is not divisible by two.
4. An inequality is a mathematical sentence that contains >, < or ≠.

WRITTEN EXERCISES

A Tell when each conditional is *false*.

1. If you have no more than 2 errors, then you get an A.
2. If our team wins this game, then our team goes to the Rose Bowl.
3. If I drive over the speed limit, then I break the law.
4. If the sun is shining, then I cast a shadow.

Write *True* or *False* for each conditional.

5. If 7 is a whole number, then 7 is an even number.
6. If $\sqrt{2}$ is an irrational number, then $\sqrt{2}$ is an even number.
7. If $2 \times 3 = 8$, then $2 + 3 = 5$.
8. If $4 + 7 > 6$, then $7 > 6 - 4$.
9. If $25 + 60 = 85$, then $85 - 60 = 25$.

Combine each pair of statements to form a true conditional.

10. $\sqrt{2}$ is irrational; 7 is an even number.
11. 15 is a real number; 15 is a rational number.
12. 9 is a factor of 12; 3 is a factor of 12.

Write the converse of each conditional.

13. If I work hard, then I get tired.
14. If x is a rose, then x is a flower.
15. If Q is a triangle, then Q has exactly three sides and three angles.

Write each definition as a conditional and its converse.

16. An equilateral triangle is a triangle with three equal sides.
17. An irrational number is a number that cannot be expressed as the ratio of an integer and a natural number.
18. An acute angle is an angle whose measure is less than 90°.
19. An obtuse angle is an angle whose measure is greater than 90° and less than 180°.
20. Perpendicular lines are lines that meet at right angles.
21. Equivalent equations are equations that have the same solution set.
22. A set is a subset of a second set if all its members are also members of the second set.

B

23. A binomial is a polynomial of two terms.
24. A compound statement is formed by combining two simple statements.

Other Applications of Algebra   **559**

15-9 Direct Proof and Algebra

As was indicated in the previous section, theorems are often stated as conditionals. One way to prove a theorem is by a *direct proof*. **A direct proof** shows that the then-statement follows from the if-statement. In a proof, the if-statement is called the **hypothesis** and is always taken to be true. The then-statement is called the **conclusion.** It is the statement that is to be proved true.

Each statement in a proof must be justified by a reason. The reason may be the hypothesis, a definition, postulate, or a theorem.

Not only will you write proofs when you study geometry, you may also be asked to prove theorems like the following in your next algebra course.

EXAMPLE 1   Prove the following theorem.

   If x, y, and z are any real numbers, then $(x + y)z = xz + yz$.

   Proof: **Hypothesis:** x, y, and z are any real numbers.

   Conclusion: $(x + y)z = xz + yz$

Statements	Reasons
1. x, y, and z are any real numbers.	1. Given (hypothesis)
2. $(x + y)z = z(x + y)$	2. Commutative postulate for multiplication
3. $z(x + y) = zx + zy$	3. Distributive postulate
4. $zx + zy = xz + yz$	4. Commutative postulate for multiplication
5. $(x + y)z = xz + yz$	5. Substitution principle

NOTE: Statements that have been proved may be used in later proofs.

To prove the next theorem, you will need these definitions.

Definitions

An **even number** is a number of the form $2n$, where n is an integer.

An **odd number** is a number of the form $2n + 1$, where n is an integer.

For example,

   20 is an even number, because $20 = 2 \cdot 10$.

   $2k + 2$ is an even number, because $2k + 2 = 2(k + 1)$.

   21 is an odd number, because $21 = (2 \cdot 10) + 1$.

   $2k + 3$ is an odd number, because $2k + 3 = 2(k + 1) + 1$.

EXAMPLE 2   Prove the following theorem.

If two numbers are odd numbers, then their sum is an even number.

Proof: **Hypothesis:** a and b are any two odd numbers.

Conclusion: $a + b$ is an even number.

Statements	Reasons
1. a and b are odd numbers.	1. Given
2. Let $a = 2k + 1$; let $b = 2p + 1$; $a + b = 2k + 1 + 2p + 1$	2. Definition of odd number; addition property for equations
3. $2k + 1 + 2p + 1 = 2k + 2p + 2$	3. Addition
4. $2k + 2p + 2 = 2(k + p + 1)$	4. Distributive postulate
5. $k + p + 1$ is an integer.	5. Closure postulate for addition
6. $2(k + p + 1)$ is an even number.	6. Definition of even number
7. $a + b$ is an even number.	7. Substitution

WRITTEN EXERCISES

A   Prove each of the following.

1. $2x + 3x = 5x$

2. $n + n = 2n$

3. $3x + (5y + 7x) = 10x + 5y$

4. $3(4x) = 12x$

5. $(-2a)(-3a) = 6a^2$

6. $a(b + c + d) = ab + ac + ad$

7. $(x + 3)(x + 4) = x^2 + 7x + 12$

8. $(x + y)^2 = x^2 + 2xy + y^2$

Write a proof for each statement. Statements that have been proved may be used in later proofs.

9. The square of an even number is even.

10. The square of an odd number is odd.

11. The sum of two even numbers is an even number. (HINT: Let $2n$ be one even number and let $2k$ be the other. Then find $2n + 2k$.)

12. The sum of an even number and an odd number is an odd number.

13. The product of two odd numbers is an odd number.

14. The product of two even numbers is an even number.

15. The product of an even number and an odd number is an even number.

16. The sum of two multiples of 3 is a multiple of 3. (HINT: A multiple of 3 is a number of the form $3n$, where n is an integer.)

17. The product of two multiples of 3 is a multiple of 3.

18. The sum of two multiples of 6 is a multiple of 6.

19. If a number is divisible by 6, then it is divisible by 2. (HINT: Show that a number divisible by 6 is a multiple of 2.)

20. If a number is divisible by 6, then it is divisible by 3.

21. The product of two multiples of 5 is a multiple of 5.

22. If a number is even, then the cube of the number is even.

B

23. For all real numbers a and b, $a - b$ and $b - a$ are opposites. (HINT: Prove that $(a - b) + (b - a) = 0$ is true. Then refer to the meaning of opposites.)

24. If a number is odd, then the cube of the number is odd. (HINT: $(2n + 1)^3 = (2n + 1)^2 (2n + 1)$)

25. If one of two given numbers is even and the other is odd, then the square of their sum is an odd number.

26. If one of two given numbers is even and the other is odd, then the sum of the square of their sum and the odd number is an even number. (HINT: Let x be the even number and y the odd number. Prove that $(x + y)^2 + y$ is an even number.)

27. If a number is not a multiple of 4, then its square is not a multiple of 8. (HINT: Numbers that are not multiples of 4 have the form $4n + 1$, $4n + 2$, or $4n + 3$, where n is an integer.)

—— **Review** ——

Using clock addition and multiplication, determine whether each finite set under these operations determines a field. If it does not, give an example to show that at least one postulate is not satisfied. *(Section 15–7)*

1. $\{0, 2, 4\}$ 2. $\{0, 1, 2, 3, 4, 5\}$ 3. $\{0, 1\}$ 4. $\{0, 2, 4, 6\}$

In Exercises 5–7, combine each pair of statements to form a true conditional. *(Section 15–8)*

5. A number is an odd number; a number is a rational number.

6. The sky is not cloudy; it is sunny outside.

7. The electricity is working; the lights are shining.

8. Write the converse of each conditional in Exercises 5–7. Then write *True* or *False* for each converse. *(Section 15–8)*

Write a direct proof for each of the following. *(Section 15–9)*

9. If a number is odd, then the cube of the number is odd.

10. The sum of three odd numbers is an odd number.

Chapter Summary

IMPORTANT IDEAS

1. **Triangle – Sum Theorem**
   The sum of the measures of the angles of a triangle is 180°.

2. If two triangles are similar, then the corresponding sides are proportional.

3. A trigonometric ratio depends only on the measure of an acute angle, *not* on the size of the right triangle.

4. In using trigonometric ratios to solve problems, use the ratio that involves both the known parts and the part to be solved.

5. For a given set to be a field, it must satisfy the field postulates.

6. Each statement in a proof must be justified by a reason. The reason may be the hypothesis, a definition, a postulate, or a previously proved theorem.

Chapter Objectives and Review

Objective: *To use algebra to find the complement and supplement of an angle (Section 15–1)*

1. The measure of an angle is 10° more than its complement. Find the measures of the angle, its complement, and its supplement.

2. The measure of an angle is 30° less than its supplement. Find the measures of the angle, its supplement and its complement.

Objective: *To find the measures of the angles of a triangle, given a relationship between the measures of the angles (Section 15–2)*

3. In triangle FGH, the measure of $\angle F$ is $\frac{1}{2}$ the measure of $\angle G$. The measure of $\angle H$ is 20° less than the measure of $\angle F$. Find the measure of each angle.

4. In triangle CDE, the measure of $\angle E$ is 5° less than the measure of $\angle C$. The measure of $\angle D$ is 3 times the measure of $\angle C$. Find the measure of each angle.

Objective: *To find the length of an unknown side in an isosceles (or equilateral) triangle, using the altitude of the triangle (Section 15–2)*

5. In the baseball diamond shown at the right, the distance between each base is 90 feet. Find the distance between home plate and second base. Write your answer in simplest form.

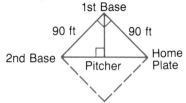

Objective: *To find the unknown lengths in similar triangles (Section 15–3)*

6. Triangles MRT and QSH are similar, with $MR = 7$, $RT = 6$, $MT = 4$ and $QH = 12$. Find HS and QS.

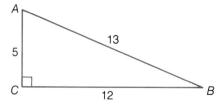

Objective: *To define and use the sine, cosine, and tangent ratios (Sections 15–4, 15–5, 15–6)*

Use triangle ABC to determine each ratio.

7. $\tan A$

8. $\tan B$

9. $\sin A$

10. $\cos A$

11. $\sin B$

12. $\cos B$

In each triangle, find x and y. Round answers to the nearest tenth.

13.

14.

In each triangle, find the measure of $\angle A$. Round answers to the nearest degree.

15.

16.

17. If you want the top of the 10-meter ladder shown below to be 8 meters from the ground, what must be the measure of angle B?

10 meters

B

18. If you want the bottom of the ladder above to be 7 meters from the building, what must be the measure of angle B?

Objective: *To test whether a given finite set of numbers under two given operations satisfies the postulates for a field (Section 15–7)*

Using clock addition and multiplication, determine whether each finite set under these operations determines a field. If it does not, show by an example that at least one postulate is not satisfied.

19. $\{0, 1, 2\}$ **20.** $\{0, 1, 2, 3\}$ **21.** $\{0, 1, 2, 3, 4\}$

Objective: *To determine when a conditional is false (Section 15–8)*

22. Under what conditions is the following statement false?
If I use an umbrella, then it is raining.

Objective: *To combine two statements to make a true conditional (Section 15–8)*

23. Combine these two statements to make a true conditional.
6 is a factor of 12; 6 is a factor of 24.

Objective: *To state the converse of a conditional (Section 15–8)*

24. State the converse of the conditional in Exercise 23. When is the converse false?

Objective: *To relate definitions to conditionals and their converses (Section 15–8)*

25. Write this definition as a conditional and its converse.
An odd number is a natural number that is not divisible by two.

Objective: *To write a direct proof (Section 15–9)*

Write a direct proof for each of the following.

26. $(3x^2)(-7x^3) = -21x^5$

27. The sum of two multiples of 4 is a multiple of 4.

Chapter Test

1. The measure of an angle is $\frac{1}{2}$ the measure of its supplement. Find the measures of the angle, its complement, and its supplement.

2. In $\triangle XYZ$, m $\angle X$ is 10° more than m $\angle Y$ and m $\angle Z$ is 6° less than twice m $\angle Y$. Find the measures of the angles.

3. Two identical bookends are back-to-back, as shown at the right. Each base is 8 centimeters long, and each angled side is 15 centimeters long. Find the height of each bookend.

15 cm

h

8 cm   8 cm

Find the unknown lengths in each pair of similar triangles.

4.

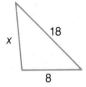

x 18

8

6   9

4

5.

y 4.5

3

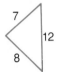

7   12

8

Use triangle *ABC* to write each ratio.

6. sin A

7. tan A

8. cos A

9. tan B

10. sin B

11. cos B

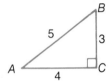

B

5   3

A 4 C

12. One angle of a right triangle measures 70° and the side adjacent to it measures 19 meters. To the nearest tenth of a meter, what is the measure of the side opposite the 70° angle?

Combine each pair of statements to form a true conditional.

13. 5 is a whole number; 5 is a rational number.

14. Today is Saturday; Saturday is the last day of the week.

15. A figure is a square; a figure is a rectangle.

16. His name is Joe Junior; his father's name is Joe.

17. Write the converse of each conditional in Exercises 13–16. Then write *True* or *False* for each converse.

18. Prove: **If n is an odd integer, then n^2 is an odd integer.**

19. Determine whether the set of integers is a field under the usual definitions of addition and multiplication. Explain your answer.

20. Prove: $5(x + 2) = 10 + 5x$

Table of Squares and Square Roots

No.	Square	Square Root	No.	Square	Square Root	No.	Square	Square Root
1	1	1.000	51	2601	7.141	101	10,201	10.050
2	4	1.414	52	2704	7.211	102	10,404	10.100
3	9	1.732	53	2809	7.280	103	10,609	10.149
4	16	2.000	54	2916	7.348	104	10,816	10.198
5	25	2.236	55	3025	7.416	105	11,025	10.247
6	36	2.449	56	3136	7.483	106	11,236	10.296
7	49	2.646	57	3249	7.550	107	11,449	10.344
8	64	2.828	58	3364	7.616	108	11,664	10.392
9	81	3.000	59	3481	7.681	109	11,881	10.440
10	100	3.162	60	3600	7.746	110	12,100	10.488
11	121	3.317	61	3721	7.810	111	12,321	10.536
12	144	3.464	62	3844	7.874	112	12,544	10.583
13	169	3.606	63	3969	7.937	113	12,769	10.630
14	196	3.742	64	4096	8.000	114	12,996	10.677
15	225	3.873	65	4225	8.062	115	13,225	10.724
16	256	4.000	66	4356	8.124	116	13,456	10.770
17	289	4.123	67	4489	8.185	117	13,689	10.817
18	324	4.243	68	4624	8.246	118	13,924	10.863
19	361	4.359	69	4761	8.307	119	14,161	10.909
20	400	4.472	70	4900	8.367	120	14,400	10.954
21	441	4.583	71	5041	8.426	121	14,641	11.000
22	484	4.690	72	5184	8.485	122	14,884	11.045
23	529	4.796	73	5329	8.544	123	15,129	11.091
24	576	4.899	74	5476	8.602	124	15,376	11.136
25	625	5.000	75	5625	8.660	125	15,625	11.180
26	676	5.099	76	5776	8.718	126	15,876	11.225
27	729	5.196	77	5929	8.775	127	16,129	11.269
28	784	5.292	78	6084	8.832	128	16,384	11.314
29	841	5.385	79	6241	8.888	129	16,641	11.358
30	900	5.477	80	6400	8.944	130	16,900	11.402
31	961	5.568	81	6561	9.000	131	17,161	11.446
32	1024	5.657	82	6724	9.055	132	17,424	11.489
33	1089	5.745	83	6889	9.110	133	17,689	11.533
34	1156	5.831	84	7056	9.165	134	17,956	11.576
35	1225	5.916	85	7225	9.220	135	18,225	11.619
36	1296	6.000	86	7396	9.274	136	18,496	11.662
37	1369	6.083	87	7569	9.327	137	18,769	11.705
38	1444	6.164	88	7744	9.381	138	19,044	11.747
39	1521	6.245	89	7921	9.434	139	19,321	11.790
40	1600	6.325	90	8100	9.487	140	19,600	11.832
41	1681	6.403	91	8281	9.539	141	19,881	11.874
42	1764	6.481	92	8464	9.592	142	20,164	11.916
43	1849	6.557	93	8649	9.644	143	20,449	11.958
44	1936	6.633	94	8836	9.695	144	20,736	12.000
45	2025	6.708	95	9025	9.747	145	21,025	12.042
46	2116	6.782	96	9216	9.798	146	21,316	12.083
47	2209	6.856	97	9409	9.849	147	21,609	12.124
48	2304	6.928	98	9604	9.899	148	21,904	12.166
49	2401	7.000	99	9801	9.950	149	22,201	12.207
50	2500	7.071	100	10,000	10.000	150	22,500	12.247

Table of Sines, Cosines, and Tangents

Angle	Sin	Cos	Tan	Angle	Sin	Cos	Tan
0°	.0000	1.0000	.0000	45°	.7071	.7071	1.0000
1	.0175	.9998	.0175	46	.7193	.6947	1.0355
2	.0349	.9994	.0349	47	.7314	.6820	1.0724
3	.0523	.9986	.0524	48	.7431	.6691	1.1106
4	.0698	.9976	.0699	49	.7547	.6561	1.1504
5	.0872	.9962	.0875	50	.7660	.6428	1.1918
6	.1045	.9945	.1051	51	.7771	.6293	1.2349
7	.1219	.9925	.1228	52	.7880	.6157	1.2799
8	.1392	.9903	.1405	53	.7986	.6018	1.3270
9	.1564	.9877	.1584	54	.8090	.5878	1.3764
10	.1736	.9848	.1763	55	.8192	.5736	1.4281
11	.1908	.9816	.1944	56	.8290	.5592	1.4826
12	.2079	.9781	.2126	57	.8387	.5446	1.5399
13	.2250	.9744	.2309	58	.8480	.5299	1.6003
14	.2419	.9703	.2493	59	.8572	.5150	1.6643
15	.2588	.9659	.2679	60	.8660	.5000	1.7321
16	.2756	.9613	.2867	61	.8746	.4848	1.8040
17	.2924	.9563	.3057	62	.8829	.4695	1.8807
18	.3090	.9511	.3249	63	.8910	.4540	1.9626
19	.3256	.9455	.3443	64	.8988	.4384	2.0503
20	.3420	.9397	.3640	65	.9063	.4226	2.1445
21	.3584	.9336	.3839	66	.9135	.4067	2.2460
22	.3746	.9272	.4040	67	.9205	.3907	2.3559
23	.3907	.9205	.4245	68	.9272	.3746	2.4751
24	.4067	.9135	.4452	69	.9336	.3584	2.6051
25	.4226	.9063	.4663	70	.9397	.3420	2.7475
26	.4384	.8988	.4877	71	.9455	.3256	2.9042
27	.4540	.8910	.5095	72	.9511	.3090	3.0777
28	.4695	.8829	.5317	73	.9563	.2924	3.2709
29	.4848	.8746	.5543	74	.9613	.2756	3.4874
30	.5000	.8660	.5774	75	.9659	.2588	3.7321
31	.5150	.8572	.6009	76	.9703	.2419	4.0108
32	.5299	.8480	.6249	77	.9744	.2250	4.3315
33	.5446	.8387	.6494	78	.9781	.2079	4.7046
34	.5592	.8290	.6745	79	.9816	.1908	5.1446
35	.5736	.8192	.7002	80	.9848	.1736	5.6713
36	.5878	.8090	.7265	81	.9877	.1564	6.3138
37	.6018	.7986	.7536	82	.9903	.1392	7.1154
38	.6157	.7880	.7813	83	.9925	.1219	8.1443
39	.6293	.7771	.8098	84	.9945	.1045	9.5144
40	.6428	.7660	.8391	85	.9962	.0872	11.4301
41	.6561	.7547	.8693	86	.9976	.0698	14.3007
42	.6691	.7431	.9004	87	.9986	.0523	19.0811
43	.6820	.7314	.9325	88	.9994	.0349	28.6363
44	.6947	.7193	.9657	89	.9998	.0175	57.2900
45	.7071	.7071	1.0000	90	1.0000	.0000	

GLOSSARY

Abscissa In an ordered pair, the first number, or x coordinate, is the *abscissa*. (Page 169)

Absolute value The *absolute value* of a real number x is the distance of x from 0. It is written $|x|$. (Page 47)

Acute angle An *acute angle* is an angle whose measure is less than 90°. (Page 534)

Additive inverses *Additive inverses* are the same distance from zero on the number line. Their sum is zero. (Page 47)

Algebraic expression An *algebraic expression* contains at least one variable. (Page 2)

Altitude of a triangle An *altitude of a triangle* is a segment drawn from any vertex perpendicular to the opposite side. (Page 536)

Angle Two different rays that have the same endpoint form the sides of an *angle*. (Page 534)

Arithmetic mean The *arithmetic mean* of a set of numbers, scores, and so on, is the sum of the elements in the set divided by the number of elements. (Page 69)

Axis of symmetry A parabola can be folded so that its right side fits exactly over its left side. The line on which this fold can be made is called the *axis of symmetry*. (Page 489)

Binomial A *binomial* is the sum or difference of two monomials. (Page 296)

Combining like terms To *combine like terms* means to add or subtract the like terms. (Page 60)

Complementary angles Two angles whose measures have a sum of 90° are *complementary angles*. (Page 534)

Composite number A *composite number* is any integer greater than 1 that is not prime. (Page 316)

Compound sentence A *compound sentence* can be written as two simple sentences joined by a connective, such as *and* or *or*. (Page 250)

Conditional statement In mathematics, a statement in the if-then form is a *conditional statement*. (Page 557)

Congruent angles *Congruent angles* are angles that have the same measure. (Page 539)

Conjunction A compound sentence with *and* is a *conjunction*. (Page 250)

Consistent system A system of equations that has a solution set is a *consistent system*. (Page 213)

Constant of variation In the direct variation $y = kx$, k is called the *constant of variation*. (Page 197)

Converse The *converse* of a conditional statement is formed by interchanging the if- and then-statements. (Page 558)

Coordinate plane A plane that associates number pairs or coordinates with points is called a *coordinate plane*. The x and y axes separate the coordinate plane into four regions or quadrants. (Page 169)

Cosine ratio In a right triangle, the *cosine* of an acute angle is the ratio $\dfrac{\text{length of adjacent side}}{\text{length of hypotenuse}}$. (Page 546)

Counting numbers The set of *counting numbers* or natural numbers is the set of numbers whose members are 1 and every number found by adding 1 to a member of the set. (Page 22)

Direct proof A *direct proof* of a theorem shows that the then-statement follows from the if-statement. (Page 560)

Direct variation The equation $y = kx$, where k is a constant, expresses *direct variation* between x and y. (Page 197)

Discriminant The *discriminant* of the quadratic equation $ax^2 + bx + c = 0$ is the number $b^2 - 4ac$. (Page 486)

Disjunction A compound sentence with *or* is a *disjunction*. (Page 250)

Distance Formula If $P_1(x_1, y_1)$ and $P_2(x_2, y_2)$ are any two points in the coordinate plane, then the *distance*, d, between the points is given by the formula $d = \sqrt{(x_2 - x_1)^2 + (y_2 - y_1)^2}$. (Page 443)

Domain For ordered pairs of a relation, the set of all first coordinates is the *domain* of the relation. (Page 177)

Equation A mathematical sentence that contains the symbol "=" is an *equation*. (Page 18)

Equivalent equations *Equivalent equations* have the same solutions for the same replacement set. (Page 84)

Equivalent inequalities Inequalities that have the same solution set are called *equivalent inequalities*. (Page 140)

Equivalent systems Systems of equations that have the same solution set are *equivalent systems*. (Page 217)

Evaluate To *evaluate* means to find the value. (Page 5)

Even number An *even number* is a number of the form $2n$, where n is an integer. (Page 560)

Event The set of successful outcomes is a subset of the sample space. The subset is called an *event*. (Page 520)

Experimental probability An experiment is carried out n times and a particular event E occurs e of these times. Then the *experimental probability* p that the event E will occur in the next trial is $\frac{e}{n}$. That is,

$$p(E) = \frac{\text{number of occurrences of } E}{\text{number of trials}} = \frac{e}{n}$$

(Page 524)

Exponent The second power of 3 is written as 3^2. The raised two is called an *exponent*. The *exponent* indicates how many times a number is multiplied by itself. (Page 9)

Factor Since $35 = 7 \cdot 5$, 7 and 5 are *factors* of 35. (Page 9)

Field A set of numbers for which the field postulates hold for addition and multiplication

is called a *field*. (Page 555)

Formula In a *formula*, variables and symbols are used to represent words. (Page 9)

Frequency distribution A *frequency distribution* is an arrangement of data that uses intervals for the measures and shows the number of occurrences, or frequency, of the measures in each interval. (Page 511)

Function A *function* is a relation for which no two ordered pairs have the same first element. (Page 177)

Half-plane If a line is drawn on the coordinate plane, a *half-plane* is the set of points that is on one side of the line. (Page 254)

Histogram A *histogram* is a bar graph that lists data by intervals. (Page 511)

Hypotenuse In a right triangle, the longest side is the *hypotenuse*. (Page 439)

Hypothesis In a proof, the if-statement is called the *hypothesis*. It is always taken to be true. (Page 560)

Inconsistent system A system of equations having no solution is called an *inconsistent system*. (Page 213)

Inequality A mathematical sentence that uses $>, <$, or $\neq$ is an *inequality*. (Page 18)

Integers The set of *integers* consists of the set of whole numbers and their opposites. (Page 22)

Intersection of two lines The *intersection of two lines* is the set of points common to both lines. (Page 212)

Inverse variation If the product of two variables is a nonzero constant, the variables are in *inverse variation*. The equation for the inverse variation may be written as $xy = k$ or $y = \frac{k}{x}$, where k is the constant of variation. (Page 412)

Irrational number *Irrational numbers* cannot be represented in the form $\frac{a}{b}$, where a is an integer and b is a natural number. (Page 26)

Joint variation When one variable varies directly as the product of two or more variables, the variation is called *joint variation*. Joint variation can be expressed by the equation $x = kyz$. (Page 416)

Least common denominator The *least common denominator* (LCD) of two or more rational expressions is the least common multiple of the denominators of the rational expressions. (Page 368)

Like radicals Radicals with the same radicands are *like radicals*. (Page 454)

Like terms *Like terms* have the same variables. In like terms, corresponding variables have the same exponents. (Page 60)

Linear equation An equation that can be written in the form $Ax + By = C$, where A, B and C are real numbers and A and B are not both zero, is a *linear equation* in two variables. (Page 182)

Linear function A function whose ordered pairs satisfy a linear equation is a *linear function*. (Page 182)

Mean The *mean* of a set of data is the sum of all the values divided by the number of values. (Page 508)

Median The *median* of a set of data that contains an odd number of values is the middle measure. When the number of elements in the set of data is an even number, the median is the mean of the two middle measures. (Page 508)

Mode In a listing of data, the *mode* is the measure that occurs most often. (Page 509)

Monomial A *monomial* is a term that is the product of numbers and variables with nonnegative integral exponents. (Page 283)

Mutually exclusive events Events are *mutually exclusive* if they have no elements in common. (Page 522)

Numerical expression A *numerical expression* contains at least one of the operations of addition, subtraction, multiplication, and division. (Page 3)

Obtuse angle An *obtuse angle* is an angle whose

measure is greater than 90° and less than 180°. (Page 534)

Odd number An *odd number* is a number of the form $2n + 1$, where n is an integer. (Page 560)

Open sentence An equation that contains a variable is an *open sentence*. (Page 18)

Ordered pair An *ordered pair* is a pair of numbers, one of which is designated as first and the other as second. (Page 169)

Ordinate In an ordered pair, the second number, or the y coordinate, is the *ordinate*. (Page 169)

Origin In the coordinate plane, the axes cross at the point (0, 0), called the *origin*. (Page 169)

Per cent *Per cent* means per hundred or hundredths. (Page 103)

Perfect square A rational number is a *perfect square* if it is the square of a rational number. (Page 435)

Perimeter The *perimeter* of a geometric figure is the distance around it. To find this *perimeter*, add the lengths of the sides. (Page 129)

Perpendicular Two lines that are *perpendicular* to each other meet at right angles. (Page 169)

Polynomial A *polynomial* is a monomial or the sum of monomials. (Page 296)

Postulate A *postulate* is a statement that is accepted as true. (Page 30)

Prime factorization When a composite number is written as a product of prime-number factors or of powers of prime-number factors, the number is in *prime-factorization* form. (Page 316)

Prime number A *prime number* is an integer greater than 1 that has exactly two positive integral factors, itself and 1. (Page 316)

Prime polynomial When a polynomial has no polynomial factors with integral coefficients except itself and 1, it is a *prime polynomial* with respect to the integers. (Page 319)

Probability The ratio of the number of successful outcomes to the number of possible outcomes is the *probability* that an outcome will occur. (Page 519)

Proportion A *proportion* is a statement that shows that two ratios are equal. (Page 350)

Quadrant A *quadrant* is one of four regions formed by the axes of a coordinate plane. (Page 169)

Quadratic equation An equation that can be written in the form $ax^2 + bx + c = 0$, where a, b, and c are real numbers and $a \neq 0$, is a *quadratic equation*. (Page 470)

Quadratic formula For any quadratic equation $ax^2 + bx + c = 0$, the solutions are
$$x = \frac{-b \pm \sqrt{b^2 - 4ac}}{2a}.$$ This is called the *quadratic formula*. (Page 476)

Quadratic function A *quadratic function* is a function defined by the equation $y = ax^2 + bx + c$, where a, b and c are real numbers and $a \neq 0$. (Page 484)

Radical symbol In the expression $\sqrt{25}$, $\sqrt{}$ is the *radical symbol*. (Page 432)

Radicand In the expression $\sqrt{25}$, 25 is the *radicand*. (Page 432)

Range For ordered pairs, the set of all second coordinates is the *range*. (Page 177)

Ratio A *ratio* is a comparison of two numbers by division. (Page 350)

Rational expression A *rational expression* is an expression of the form $\frac{P}{Q}$, where P and Q are polynomials and $Q \neq 0$. (Page 357)

Rational number A *rational number* is a number that can be expressed in the form $\frac{a}{b}$, where a is an integer and b is a natural number. (Page 22)

Rationalizing the denominator Eliminating the radical in the denominator of a fraction is called *rationalizing the denominator*. (Page 450)

Real numbers The union of the set of rational numbers and the set of irrational numbers is the set of *real numbers*. (Page 26)

Reciprocals Any two numbers whose product is 1 are called *reciprocals*, or multiplicative inverses, of each other. (Page 68)

Relation A *relation* is a set of ordered pairs. (Page 176)

Replacement set The *replacement set* is the set of numbers from which replacements for the variable are chosen. (Page 9)

Right angle An angle whose measure is $90°$ is a *right angle*. (Page 534)

Sample space In probability, the set of possible outcomes is the *sample space*. (Page 519)

Scientific notation When a number is represented as the product of some power of 10 and a number from 1 to 10, it is expressed in *scientific notation*. (Page 290)

Simplest form When the numerator and denominator of a rational expression have no common factors except 1 and −1, the expression is in *simplest form*. (Page 357)

Simplified radical A radical is in simplest form when the radicand does not contain a perfect square factor. (Page 437)

Sine ratio In a right triangle, the *sine* of an acute angle is the ratio $\dfrac{\text{length of opposite side}}{\text{length of hypotenuse}}$. (Page 546)

Slope The *slope* of a line is the ratio of the vertical change to the horizontal change between any two points on the line. That is, slope $= \dfrac{\text{vertical change}}{\text{horizontal change}}$, (horizontal change $\neq 0$). (Page 189)

Slope-intercept form of a linear equation The equation $y = mx + b$ is called the *slope-intercept form of the linear equation*. (Page 195)

Solution set A *solution set* of an open sentence is the set of numbers that makes the sentence true. (Page 18)

Solve an equation To *solve an equation* means to find the number or numbers that will make the equation true. (Page 87)

Standard deviation The *standard deviation* is a measure of how data disperses, or spreads out, from the mean. (Page 514)

Standard Normal Distribution The *standard normal distribution* is a distribution with a mean of 0 and a standard deviation of 1. The graph of a standard normal distribution is shown below. (Page 514)

Standard Normal Curve

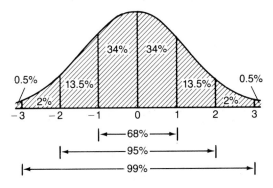

Supplementary angles Two angles whose measures have a sum of 180° are *supplementary angles.* (Page 534)

System of linear equations Two or more linear equations in the same two variables form a *system of linear equations.* (Page 212)

Tangent ratio In a right triangle, the *tangent* of an acute angle is the ratio $\dfrac{\text{length of opposite side}}{\text{length of adjacent side}}$. (Page 542)

Term A *term* is a real number, a variable, or the product of real numbers and variables. (Page 60)

Theorem A *theorem* is a statement that can be proved from postulates and definitions. (Page 51)

Trinomial A polynomial with three terms is called a *trinomial.* (Page 296)

Unit price The *unit price* is the cost per gram, per ounce, and so on. (Page 12)

Variable A *variable* is a letter representing one or more numbers. (Page 2)

Whole numbers The set of *whole numbers* is the set of counting numbers and zero. (Page 22)

x intercept The *x* coordinate of a point where the line intersects the *x* axis is called an *x intercept.* (Page 484)

y intercept The *y* coordinate at which a line crosses the *y* axis is called the *y intercept.* (Page 194)

Zeros of a function The *zeros of a function* are the values for which the function equals zero. (Page 484)

INDEX

Boldfaced numerals indicate the pages that contain formal or informal definitions.

ANSWERS TO SELECTED EXERCISES

The answers are provided for all of the problems in the *Reviews* and *Review Capsules*. The answers for the *Computer Applications* and the *Puzzles* appear in the *Solution Key*. For all other types of exercises, the answers to the odd-numbered problems are provided.

Answers to Selected Exercises

CHAPTER 1: USES OF ALGEBRA

Page 3 Classroom Exercises 1. d   3. b   5. c   7. 34   9. 7

Page 3 Written Exercises 1. 5 subtracted from q   3. q subtracted from 5   5. q multiplied by 5   7. q divided by 5   9. s multiplied by r   11. 4 subtracted from s   13. s multiplied by 16   15. n divided by t   17. $d + \ell$ 19. $d + i$ 21. $180 - a$ 23. $150 - s$ 25. 4.50h   27. 3c   29. $\frac{t}{24}$ 31. $\frac{s}{40}$ 33. 26   35. 9   37. 20   39. 0   41. 0   43. 48   45. 1   47. 16   49. The sum of a and b, divided by 5   51. The difference of a and b, multiplied by 9

Page 4 Review Capsule for Section 1-2 1. $\frac{2}{3}$ 2. $\frac{1}{4}$ 3. $\frac{1}{3}$ 4. $\frac{3}{4}$ 5. $\frac{2}{3}$ 6. $\frac{7}{8}$ 7. $\frac{1}{6}$ 8. $\frac{1}{5}$ 9. $\frac{4}{15}$ 10. $2\frac{5}{8}$ 11. $2\frac{2}{3}$ 12. 8.97   13. 25.17   14. 60.637   15. 5.4   16. 5.36   17. 3.0672   18. 190.6   19. 84.1   20. 0.064   21. 65.333   22. 1880   23. 0.138   24. 6.2   25. 35   26. 45

Page 6 Classroom Exercises 1. 10   3. 30   5. 22   7. 14   9. 340   11. 32   13. $2\frac{3}{5}$ 15. 1

Page 7 Written Exercises 1. 69   3. 84   5. 18   7. 57   9. 23   11. 12   13. 0   15. 184   17. 100   19. 360   21. 7   23. $\frac{6}{7}$ 25. $\frac{4}{9}$ 27. $\frac{1}{11}$ 29. $\frac{3}{8}$ 31. 34   33. 160   35. 24   37. 44   39. $\frac{4}{23}$ 41. 130   43. 18   45. 19   47. 1   49. 8   51. 9.99   53. 42.2   55. $2\frac{4}{5}$ 57. 2.25   59. $(1 + 9)$ $\cdot (2 + 7)$ 61. $2(5 + 7 + 9)$ 63. $(2 \cdot 12) \div (2 + 6)$ 65. $25 + 11t$ 67. $475 - 15w$

Page 8 Puzzle See Solution Key.

Page 8 Review Capsule for Section 1-3 1. 0.08   2. 0.02   3. 0.12   4. 1.28   5. 0.045   6. 0.005   7. 9.982   8. 29.230   9. 2.1504   10. 0.01   11. 6.25   12. $\frac{1}{9}$ 13. $\frac{125}{512}$ 14. $\frac{8}{9}$ 15. $1\frac{1}{2}$ 16. $1\frac{5}{8}$ 17. $1\frac{13}{28}$ 18. $6\frac{1}{2}$ 19. $10\frac{3}{10}$ 20. $12\frac{3}{4}$ 21. $16\frac{21}{40}$ 22. $\frac{7}{30}$ 23. $\frac{11}{20}$ 24. $\frac{7}{24}$ 25. $\frac{29}{63}$ 26. $4\frac{3}{4}$ 27. $4\frac{11}{24}$ 28. $2\frac{17}{48}$ 29. $\frac{17}{40}$ 30. $4\frac{5}{12}$ 31. $1\frac{5}{24}$ 32. $4\frac{1}{3}$ 33. $2\frac{11}{12}$

Page 10 Classroom Exercises 1. $0.54; $0.72; $1.20   3. 64   5. $\frac{1}{25}$ 7. $\frac{1}{16}$ 9. $0; \frac{1}{2}; 6$ 11. 0; 2; 24

Page 10 Written Exercises 1. $0.80; $2; $4   3. $1; $2.50; $5   5. 4; 8; 12   7. 0; 1; 2   9. 6; 9; 14   11. $\frac{1}{3}; \frac{2}{3}; 1$ 13. 16; 20; 24   15. 18; 22; 26   17. $8\frac{1}{2}; 10\frac{1}{2}; 12\frac{1}{2}$ 19. 11; 12; 13   21. $5\frac{1}{2}; 6\frac{1}{2}; 7\frac{1}{2}$ 23. 512; 1000; 1728   25. 32   27. 0.01   29. 1.44   31. 0.0016   33. 0.000064   35. $\frac{16}{81}$ 37. 1.0404   39. 100,000   41. $\frac{1}{4}; \frac{1}{100}; \frac{9}{100}$ 43. 0.0225; 0.0625; 2.0449   45. $\frac{1}{2000}; \frac{1}{1000}; \frac{1}{10}; 1; 10$ 47. 180; 360; 540; 720   49. Represents even numbers only   51. Does not represent even numbers only   53. 0.25   55. 1   57. 0.0625   59. 0.015625   61. 0

Page 11 Puzzle See Solution Key.

Page 11 Review Capsule for Section 1-4 1. 0.9   2. 1.1   3. 37.5   4. 0.5   5. 101.0   6. 0.007   7. 1.913   8. 333.333   9. 0.001   10. 4340   11. 8160   12. 78,480   13. 184,000   14. $\frac{5}{12}$ 15. $51\frac{3}{5}$ 16. $58\frac{9}{40}$

Page 13 Classroom Exercises 1. $2800   3. 4.5¢

Page 13 Written Exercises 1. $1950   3. $1060   5. $1190.91   7. $0.007   9. $1.913   11. $0.124   13. 946-ml bottle   15. 24-ounce container   17. 60 cubic in   19. 2160 cubic cm   21. 504 cubic ft   23. 3.6 cubic m   25. 115 square units   27. 15 sq units   29. 1 square unit   31. 10%   33. $33\frac{1}{3}\%$ 35. 30%   37. $3112.50   39. $12,812.50   41. $C = 40\pi, A = 400\pi$ 43. $C = 80\pi, A = 1600\pi$ 45. $C \approx 62.8$ units, $A \approx 314$ square units   47. $C \approx 628$ units, $A \approx 31,400$ square units   49. a. $12, $15

b. 3   51. a. 280, 560, 1120, 2240   b. 7A   53. a. $352.75, $365.50, $378.25, $391, $403.75

b. $340; 340 + 12.75h   55. a. 11 m, 16.5 m, 22 m, 24.75 m, 27.5 m   b. 5.5, 5.5 · $\frac{r}{16}$

Page 16   Review Capsule for Section 1-5   1. 16   2. 10   3. 5   4. 52   5. 30.5   6. 2.5   7. 1, 9, 17, 25,
33   8. 3, 17, 31, 45, 59   9. 1, 201, 401, 601, 801   10. 2, $\frac{14}{11}$, $\frac{22}{19}$, $\frac{10}{9}$, $\frac{38}{35}$ 11. 6, 14, 22, 30, 38
12. 1, 1, 1, 1, 1

Page 17   Consumer Applications   1. $5691; 28.5¢   3. $6168.25; 29.4¢

Page 19   Classroom Exercises   1. F; $1\frac{7}{8} \neq 13\frac{1}{3}$ 3. F; 0 = 0   5. F; $\frac{57}{60} < \frac{67}{60}$ 7. {5}   9. {3, 7, 9, 11}

Page 19   Written Exercises   1. T   3. F; 16 ≠ 18   5. T   7. T   9. T   11. F; 56 > 55   13. {8}
15. {10}   17. {2, 4, 6, 8, 10}   19. {4}   21. {2, 4, 6, 8, 10}   23. {2}   25. {0, 1, 2, 3, 4, 5}   27. {5}
29. φ   31. {4, 5}   33. φ   35. {20}   37. {5, 10, 15, 20}   39. {0, 10, 15, 20}   41. {15}   43. {2}
45. {1}   47. {1, 2}   49. {4, 5, 6}   51. T   53. F; $1^2 \not> 1 + 1$ 55. T   57. T   59. T   61. F;
$2 \cdot \frac{1}{2} = 1$ and $\frac{1}{2}$ is not a whole number.   63. F; $(0.2)^3 \not> (0.2)^2$

Page 20   Review   1. 3 · d, or 3d   2. m ÷ 15, or $\frac{m}{15}$ 3. 22   4. 7   5. $\frac{9}{40}$ 6. 4   7. 0   8. 11   9. 10;

38; 54   10. $2\frac{1}{2}$; 6; 8   11. $\frac{1}{8}$; 64; 216   12. 30; 72; 96   13. 135 square units   14. 0.042 square units;
15. $\frac{1}{3}$ square unit   16. {1, 2}   17. {1, 2, 3, 5}   18. {3, 4, 5}   19. {1, 2}

Page 21   Calculator Exercises   1. 20   3. 100   5. 37   7. 7.39216   9. 9.866

Page 21   Review Capsule for Section 1-6   1. 2   2. 6   3. 15   4. 70   5. 15   6. 43   7. 76   8. 47

Page 23   Classroom Exercises   1. whole number, integer, rational number   3. rational number   5. rational
number   7. $\frac{0}{1}$ 9. $\frac{50}{3}$ 11. $\frac{-52}{10}$

Page 23   Written Exercises   1. F; it is not a positive integer   3. T   5. T   7. T   9. T   11. F; it includes
positive and negative rational numbers and zero.   13. $\frac{4}{10}$ 15. $\frac{37}{100}$ 17. $\frac{-19}{3}$ 19. $\frac{15}{4}$ 21. $\frac{6725}{100}$ 23. $\frac{0}{1}$

25. 6   27. −462   29. 525   31. −155   33. 12   35. −15   37. $4\frac{1}{2}$ 39. −6   41. −1   43. $2\frac{3}{4}$
45. −31   47. 73.20   49. −250   51. −3.5   53. −315   55. −500   57. F; negative integers are not
whole numbers.   59. F; zero is not a natural number.   61. F; fractions are not integers.   63. F; fractions
and negative natural numbers are not whole numbers.   65. F; zero is not a natural number.

Page 25   Review Capsule for Section 1-7   1. 0.66666   2. 0.27272   3. 0.22222   4. 0.58333   5. 0.16666
6. 60   7. 70, 0.7   8. 95   9. 100, 0.46   10. 100, 0.72   11. 525, 5.25   12. 7.5   13. 0.75   14. 0.2,
8.2

Page 27   Classroom Exercises   1. Ir; there is no positive integer n such that n · n = 5.   3. Ir; there is no
positive integer n such that n · n = 21.   5. Q; $\sqrt{144}$ = 12 and 12 is a rational number.   7. N, W, I, Q, R
9. Q, R   11. Q, R   13. 4.359   15. 10.050   17. 12.207

Page 27   Written Exercises   1. $0.\overline{6}$ 3. $5.\overline{3}$ 5. 7.1875   7. 1.375   9. 0.15   11. $-0.\overline{27}$ 13. Ir; there
is no positive integer n such that n · n = 7.   15. Ir; there is no positive integer n such that n · n = 11.
17. Q; $\sqrt{625}$ = 25 and 25 is a rational number.   19. Ir; there is no positive integer n such that n · n = 83.

21. Q; $\sqrt{\frac{36}{16}} = \frac{6}{4}$ and $\frac{6}{4}$ is a rational number.   23. Q; $\sqrt{100}$ = 10 and 10 is a rational number.   25. Q, R
27. Ir, R   29. Ir, R   31. I, Q, R   33. Q, R   35. A: 2; B: −3; C: −5; D: −2; E: −4   37. K: $\sqrt{3}$;
L: $\frac{1}{3}$; M: $\frac{-1}{3}$; O: $\frac{5}{6}$; P: $\frac{-5}{6}$ 39. 4.243   41. 10.488   43. 4.123   45. 8.944   47. 8.718   49. The
point would be close to 4.1.   51. The point would be close to 8.7.   53. 8   55. 16   57. 9   59. 21
61. 25   63. 39   65. 3.141666   67. 3.141600   69. ⊄   71. ⊂   73. ⊄   75. ⊂   77. ⊂   79. natural,
whole, rational, irrational   81. real

Page 29   Puzzle   See Solution Key.

Page 32 Classroom Exercises 1. Dist. post. 3. Comm. post. for mult. 5. Identity post. for add. 7. Identity post. for mult. 9. Comm. post. for add. 11. Closure post. for mult.

Page 32 Written Exercises 1. Comm. post. for add. 3. Comm. post. for mult. 5. Assoc. post. for mult. 7. Comm. post. for add. 9. Comm. post. for add. 11. Dist. post. 13. Closure post. for add. 15. 12, Comm. post. for mult. 17. 10, Comm. post. for add. 19. 0, Ident. post. for add. 21. 32 23. 8365 25. 24 27. 190 29. 12,000 31. 2600 33. 48 35. 19 37. 940 39. 100 41. 56 43. 670 45. 63 47. 2255 49. 430 51. 260 53. Assoc. post. for mult., Comm. post. for mult. 55. Dist. post., Comm. post. for mult. 57. 5x; 50; 110; 1340 59. 2; 0 61. 16; 12 63. No 65. No; $6 \div 2 \neq 2 \div 6, 3 \neq \frac{1}{3}$ 67. F; $6 \div (3 \cdot 1) \neq (6 \div 3) \cdot (6 \div 1), 2 \neq 12$ 69. F; $6 - (3 + 1) \neq (6 - 3) + (6 - 1)$, $2 \neq 8$ 71. F; $6 - (3 - 1) \neq (6 - 3) - (6 - 1), 4 \neq {}^-2$

Page 36 Computer Exercises See Solution Key.

Page 37 Review 1. $-12\frac{1}{2}$ 2. 1.25 3. True 4. False; fractions and negative numbers are not natural numbers. 5. True 6. True 7. True 8. Q; $\sqrt{16} = 4$ 9. Ir; there is no positive integer n such that n • n = 33 10. Q; $\sqrt{\frac{9}{36}} = \frac{1}{2}$ 11. Q; $\sqrt{\frac{100}{49}} = \frac{10}{7}$ 12. Ir; there is no positive integer n such that n • n = 18 13. Ir; there is no positive integer n such that n • n = 50 14. 14 15. 6 16. 13 17. Comm. post. for mult. 18. Comm. post. for add. 19. Dist. post. 20. 19 21. 19.2 22. 56

Page 38 Chapter Objectives and Review 1. 5x 3. $\frac{a}{4}$ 5. 5 7. 5 9. 55 11. 16 13. $\frac{1}{3}$ 15. 176 17. 75 19. 2 21. 0.21; 0.35; 0.49 23. 4; 5; 6 25. $\frac{9}{64}$ 27. 1 29. $\{3\}$ 31. ϕ 33. T 35. T 37. T 39. $^-3$ 41. 10 43. I, Q, R 45. Ir, R 47. Q, R 49. Ir, R 51. $-1\frac{3}{4}$ 53. $\sqrt{2}$ 55. 2.646 57. 10.630 59. Comm. post. for add. 61. Assoc. post. for mult. 63. $\frac{1}{8}$; Assoc. post. for mult. 65. 6

Page 41 Chapter Test 1. b − v 3. 7.55y 5. 12 7. 4 9. 11.6 11. 35 m² 13. $\{0, 1, 2\}$ 15. T 17. F; the opposite of 2 is $^-2$. 19. $^-105.1$ 21. I, Q, R 23. Ir, R 25. 7300

Page 42 Additional Practice 1. 10 3. 6 5. $\frac{2}{21}$ 7. $\frac{1}{3}$ 9. 11; 14; 17 11. 19; 28; 39 13. $\{9\}$ 15. $\{5, 7, 9\}$ 17. $\frac{3}{10}$ 19. $\frac{7}{3}$ 21. $\frac{-38}{1}$ 23. Ir; there is no positive integer n such that n • n = 5 25. Q; $\sqrt{100} = 10$ 27. Ir; there is no positive integer n such that n • n = 52. 29. 6.403 31. 10.536 33. 8.660 35. Ident. post. for add. 37. Comm. post. for add. 39. C = 12p + 7 41. 270 square in

CHAPTER 2: OPERATIONS WITH REAL NUMBERS

Page 45 Classroom Exercises 1. −2 3. 7.8 5. $-7\frac{1}{3}$ 7. $\frac{1}{7}$ 9. 0 11. q = −6 13. q = 6 15. > 17. >

Page 45 Written Exercises 1. −6 3. −9 5. $6\frac{1}{2}$ 7. −9.02 9. $\frac{2}{3}$ 11. 9.001 13. −5 15. −3.14 17. $\frac{5}{6}$ 19. −9 21. −0.9 23. −1.2 25. 0 27. −3 29. t 31. m 33. x = −9 35. x = 0 37. y = −3.25 39. $a = \frac{3}{4}$ 41. < 43. < 45. > 47. > 49. > 51. > 53. > 55. > 57. < 59. < 61. 27 = −(−27) 63. −20 = −(20) 65. −(−200) = 200 67. $-1\frac{1}{4} = -\left(1\frac{1}{4}\right)$ 69. −(−500) = 500 71. $-\left(2\frac{3}{4}\right) = -2\frac{3}{4}$ 73. negative 75. positive 77. x = 4 79. x = 0 81. x < 0 83. t > −4

Page 48 Classroom Exercises 1. −6.5 3. m 5. 0 7. 7 9. −7 11. 3 13. < 15. >

Page 49 Written Exercises 1. −6 3. $3\frac{1}{5}$ 5. 6.8 7. π 9. $\sqrt{2}$ 11. −5 13. −4 15. −0.9 17. 12 19. $-15\frac{1}{2}$ 21. 0 23. r 25. −a 27. −x 29. 6 31. π 33. 15 35. 0 37. 100 39. 462 41. 22,000 43. 7.25 45. $\sqrt{5}$ 47. 7.6 49. $\sqrt{7}$ 51. −19 53. 12 55. 15 57. 12 59. 21 61. $\frac{7}{6}$ 63. 251 65. 0 67. 0 69. = 71. > 73. > 75. = 77. < 79. = 81. T 83. T 85. F; | −35 | = 35, and 35 ≯ 35 87. F; | −17.9 | = 17.9, and 17.9 ≮ 17.9 89. F; $\left|-\frac{1}{3}\right| = \frac{1}{3}$, and $\frac{1}{3} > \frac{1}{4}$ 91. T 93. 7 = a 95. $-2\frac{2}{3} = y$ 97. y = ±4 99. x = ±2 101. > 103. T 105. T

Page 50 Calculator Exercises 1. 6 3. 6 5. 6 7. 4

Page 50 Review Capsule for Section 2-3 1. 115 2. 1230 3. 5565 4. 0.76 5. 20.67 6. 55.996 7. $\frac{2}{3}$ 8. $8\frac{3}{5}$ 9. $1\frac{5}{8}$ 10. $\frac{7}{24}$ 11. $13\frac{1}{2}$ 12. $4\frac{1}{2}$ 13. $17\frac{3}{10}$ 14. $15\frac{23}{24}$

Page 53 Classroom Exercises 1. Negative 3. Negative 5. Positive 7. Positive 9. −15 11. −1 13. 1 15. 4 17. −7.3 19. $\frac{5}{6}$ 21. −25 23. 13

Page 53 Written Exercises 1. 3 3. −9 5. 3 7. −3 9. −13 11. 4 13. 4 15. 5 17. −14 19. 9 21. −1 23. 1 25. 15 27. −1 29. −9 31. $1\frac{1}{4}$ 33. $11\frac{1}{2}$ 35. $1\frac{3}{4}$ 37. −2.1 39. −13.2 41. 0.6 43. 4.9 45. −7.6 47. −4 + 5 + 7; 8 yards 49. 52 + (−4) + 2; $50 51. 250 + (−75) + (−40) +110; $245 53. −15,890 + 5750 + 30,765; net profit: $20,625 55. −10 57. 10 59. 17 61. 12 63. −1 65. −9 67. −2 69. $1\frac{2}{5}$ 71. 38 73. −25 75. 16 77. −17 79. −40 81. 1. Renaming 17 as 11 + 6 2. Assoc. post. for add. 3. Additive inv. post. 4. Ident. post. for add. 83. For any real number, a, there is one and only one real number, −a. 85. 1. −9 + 7 = [−2 + (−7)] + 7 (Rename −9 as −2 + (−7).) 2. [−2 + (−7)] + 7 = −2 + [(−7) + 7] (Assoc. post. for add.) 3. −2 + [(−7) + 7] = −2 + 0 (Add. inv. post.) 4. −2 + 0 = −2 (Ident. post. for add.)

Page 55 Review Capsule for Section 2-4 1. 21 2. 17 3. 358 4. 128 5. 5.4 6. 3.8 7. 6.83 8. 3.3 9. $\frac{7}{10}$ 10. $14\frac{3}{8}$ 11. $\frac{0}{12}$ or 0 12. $\frac{1}{10}$ 13. $2\frac{1}{2}$ 14. $2\frac{5}{8}$ 15. $\frac{7}{24}$ 16. $6\frac{17}{24}$

Page 57 Classroom Exercises 1. 6 + (−3) 3. −10 + (−5) 5. −5 + 2 7. 8 + 4 9. 23 11. −5 13. −8.4 15. $\frac{1}{4}$

Page 57 Written Exercises 1. 3 + (−6) 3. 5 + 9 5. 0 + (2) 7. −5 + 5 9. −2 + (−8) 11. −3 + 9 13. $-2\frac{1}{2} + \frac{1}{2}$ 15. 2.9 + (−3.8) 17. −6 19. −9 21. −8 23. 10 25. −10 27. −12 29. 31 31. 0 33. −19 35. −11.8 37. −7.8 39. 1 41. −40 43. 5.6 45. 19.0 47. 6.7 49. 5.6 51. 0 53. 12° 55. 3 m 57. 26° 59. −11 61. 3 63. 11 65. $-\frac{1}{2}$ 67. −17 69. 18 71. 2 73. 2 75. 0 77. −16 79. 14 81. F; $-\frac{2}{3} - (-\frac{2}{3}) = 0, 0 \neq \frac{1}{3}$ 83. F; $0.24 - (-0.24) = 0.48, 0 \neq 0.48$ 85. T 87. T 89. T 91. T

Page 58 Review 1. 1.5 2. −600 3. −37 4. −3.6 5. −(−3) = 3 6. 15 = −(−15) 7. 18 8. $\sqrt{13}$ 9. 7 10. 0 11. x = 6 12. m = −8 13. y = 9 or y = −9 14. a = 3 or a = −3 15. −3 16. −5 17. 5 18. −11 19. −2.51 20. −8

Page 59 Consumer Applications 1. $93 profit 3. $1709.30 loss

Page 61 Classroom Exercises 1. Like; same variable, x, with same exponent, 1. 3. Unlike; different exponents for y. 5. Like; same variables, x and y, with same exponent, 1. 7. 2 9. −0.05 11. 1 13. 5x 15. 4m

Page 61 Written Exercises 1. Like; same variable, x, with same exponent, 1. 3. Unlike; number, 9, has no variable. 5. Unlike; different exponents for x. 7. Unlike; different variables. 9. Like; same variable, t, with same exponent, 1. 11. Like; same variable, x, with same exponent, 4. 13. 10x 15. 21.2m 17. 14mn 19. 10x 21. 5m² 23. 20m 25. −8y 27. −6.4y 29. −17t 31. m 33. 3x 35. 3x 37. −7a 39. 3m 41. −5r 43. 5a + 4 45. 21y + 3 47. 6x + 6 49. 12x − 6y 51. 4x − 15 53. m 55. 6x + 3y + 57 57. 6xy + x 59. $14\frac{1}{12}xy$ 61. 7.37r 63. 7.52q + 4.87 65. 8h 67. $w^2 + 5w + 25$ 69. F; if m = 1, then 3 + 1 = 1 and this is false. 71. F; if m = 0, then 0 − 0 + 0 = 11 and this is false. 73. F; if a = 1 and b = 2, then 4(1)(2) + 1 = 5(1)(2) or 9 = 10 and this is false. 75. T 77. F; if x = 1, then 5 + 2 + 9 = 21 and this is false. 79. $A = 8h - \frac{1}{2}(3h)$, $A = 6\frac{1}{2}h$ 81. $A = \frac{1}{2}(13h) - \frac{1}{2}(8h)$, $A = \frac{5}{2}h$ 83. $\frac{11}{56}c + \frac{7}{20}d$ 85. $\frac{1}{2}c - 1\frac{1}{2}d$ 87. 4x − 4y 89. −2x − 8y 91. $6x^2 - 6y^2$ 93. 2a − 2b 95. (x − y) 97. (7 + 6) 99. (c − d)

Page 63 Review Capsule for Section 2-6 1. 486 2. 2268 3. 300,884 4. 455,005 5. 0.56

6. 45.92   7. 4059   8. 1.9544   9. $\frac{1}{5}$ 10. $\frac{4}{15}$ 11. $\frac{21}{8}$ 12. $35\frac{119}{160}$

Page 65   Classroom Exercises   1. Negative   3. Positive   5. Negative   7. Positive   9. −56   11. 72
13. 20   15. 0

Page 65   Written Exercises   1. −18   3. −10   5. −10   7. 0   9. −12   11. $-\frac{1}{2}$ 13. 10   15. −15
17. 12   19. 0.25   21. 25   23. −18   25. −2   27. −72   29. −5   31. −8   33. −6200   35. $-\frac{33}{25}$
37. 0   39. −1.8   41. 20   43. −20   45. 0   47. −7   49. 1   51. 6.0   53. −1   55. −60   57. −20
59. −0.001   61. −1   63. $-\frac{7}{2}$ 65. $\frac{8}{27}$ 67. −1   69. −40   71. −120   73. 120   75. 0   77. −8
79. 16   81. 1   83. −1   85. =   87. >   89. =   91. =   93. =   95. −6   97. 6   99. 0   101. 18
103. −11   105. −4   107. 9   109. 0   111. Negative   113. Positive   **115.** 1. 4 + (−4) = 0   (Add. inv.
post.)   2. 3[4 + (−4)] = 3 · 0   (Mult. prop. for equations)   3. 3[4 + (−4)] = 0   (Zero mult. theorem)
4. 3 · 4 + 3(−4) = 0   (Dist. post. of mult.   5. Hence, 3 · 4 and 3(−4) are additive inverses. (Add. inv. post.)
6. 3(−4) = −(3 · 4) or −12   (Add. inv. post.)

Page 67   Review Capsule for Section 2-7   1. 5   2. 81   3. 5   4. 7   5. 0.9   6. 9.7   7. 0.0594   8. 70
9. $\frac{1}{3}$ 10. $\frac{3}{16}$ 11. 92   12. $\frac{86}{95}$ 13. $\frac{50}{3}$ 14. $\frac{303}{260}$ 15. 1   16. $\frac{25}{18}$ 17. 1.6   18. 0.4   19. 0.0
20. 21.4   21. 158.0   22. 7.0   23. 14.5   24. 76.1   25. 1.0   26. 0.0

Page 69   Classroom Exercises   1. Neg.   3. Pos.   5. $\frac{1}{7}$ 7. $-\frac{3}{2}$ 9. Undef.   11. 1   13. −1   15. 81

Page 70   Written Exercises   1. Neg.   3. Neg.   5. −4   7. 4   9. 0   11. −50   13. −1   15. −1
17. −6   19. −36   21. 0   23. $\frac{9}{8}$ 25. 3.2   27. −18   29. −7.85   31. $-\frac{16}{9}$ 33. + \$7,600
35. −0.8   37. 0.4   39. 5   41. $\frac{1}{3}$ 43. $\frac{2}{11}$ 45. −3   47. −1   49. −5   51. −17   53. −22.5

Page 71   Review Capsule for Section 2-8   1. $\frac{13}{2}$ 2. $\frac{31}{4}$ 3. $-\frac{25}{4}$ 4. $-\frac{39}{4}$ 5. $\frac{11}{10}$ 6. $-\frac{29}{8}$ 7. $\frac{3}{2}$
8. −26   9. $\frac{363}{8}$ 10. $-\frac{119}{4}$ 11. 0   12. 0   13. −1.5   14. $\frac{2}{3}$ 15. 1   16. 1   17. −12   18. $-\frac{4}{3}$

Page 73   Classroom Exercises   1. −10   3. −2   5. 36   7. 12   9. 12   11. $-\frac{1}{4}$ 13. $-\frac{3}{2}$ 15. 1
17. 9   19. 1

Page 73   Written Exercises   1. −25   3. −30   5. 150   7. 225   9. 325   11. 0   13. 0   15. 5
17. −5   19. 15   21. $\frac{3}{2}$ 23. 0   25. 1   27. y   29. −y   31. −y   33. −5a   35. a   37. −15b
39. $-\frac{3}{8}q$ 41. −4x   43. −15p   45. 15p   47. $\frac{7}{9}$; $\frac{7}{9}(\frac{9}{7}y) = (\frac{7}{9} \cdot \frac{9}{7})y = y$ 49. $-\frac{1}{8}$; $-\frac{1}{8}(-8y) = [-\frac{1}{8}(-8)]y$
$= y$ 51. -5; $-5(-\frac{1}{5}y) = [-5(-\frac{1}{5})]y = y$ 53. $-\frac{5}{2}$; $-\frac{5}{2}(-\frac{2}{5}y) = [-\frac{5}{2}(-\frac{2}{5})]y = y$ 55. $-\frac{8}{3}$; $-\frac{8}{3}(-\frac{3}{8}y)$
$= [-\frac{8}{3}(-\frac{3}{8})]y = y$ 57. −1; −1(−y) = [−1(−1)]y = y   59. 1; 1(1y) = (1 · 1)y = y   61. $\frac{4}{13}$; $\frac{4}{13}(3\frac{1}{4}y)$
$= (\frac{4}{13} \cdot \frac{13}{4})y = y$ 63. $-\frac{2}{17}$; $-\frac{2}{17}(-8\frac{1}{2}y) = [-\frac{2}{17}(-\frac{17}{2})]y = y$ 65. −10; $-10(-\frac{y}{10}) = [-10(-\frac{1}{10})]y = y$
67. −1; x + 1 + (−1) = x + [1 + (−1)] = x + 0 = x   69. 9; x + (−9) + 9 = x + [(−9) + 9] = x + 0 = x
71. 4; x + (−4) + 4 = x + [(−4) + 4] = x + 0 = x   73. 12; (−12) + 12 + x = [(−12) + 12] + x = 0 + x = x
75. −21; 21 + (−21) + x = [21 + (−21)] + x = 0 + x = x   77. 6; x + (−9 + 3) = x + (−6), so add 6;
x + (−6) + 6 = x + (−6 + 6) = x + 0 = x   79. 4; (−3 − 1) + x = [−3 + (−1)] + x = −4 + x, so add 4;
−4 + 4 + x = (−4 + 4) + x = 0 + x = x   81. 5; x + (8 − 13) = x + [8 + (−13)] = x + (−5), so add 5;
x + (−5) + 5 = x + (−5 + 5) = x + 0 = x   83. x − 15 = x + (−15) Opposite of (−15): 15 Therefore, add 15.
85. x − 23 = x + (−23) Opposite of (−23): 23 Therefore, add 23.   87. $x - \frac{1}{5} = x + (-\frac{1}{5})$ Opposite of
$(-\frac{1}{5})$: $\frac{1}{5}$ Therefore, add $\frac{1}{5}$.   89. x − (−2) = x + 2 Opposite of 2: (−2) Therefore, add −2.   91. −30
93. −43   95. 59   97. 20,000   99. $-\frac{1}{2}$ 101. 1

Page 74 Review 1. $5 + 8a$ 2. $-2.5x$ 3. $\frac{1}{4}x + \frac{1}{15}y$ 4. 18 5. $-\frac{9}{16}$ 6. -0.008 7. 25 8. 0
9. -64 10. 1.4 11. $-8\frac{16}{23}$ 12. Add -21. 13. Multiply by -3. 14. Multiply by $\frac{1}{13}$. 15. Add -4.

Page 76 Computer Exercises See Solution Key.

Page 78 Chapter Objectives and Review 1. -2 3. $\sqrt{5}$ 5. $6\frac{1}{2}$ 7. 3.72 9. -16.7 11. -7 13. π
15. $<$ 17. $<$ 19. 18 21. $\sqrt{7}$ 23. $-\frac{1}{3}$ 25. -7 27. a 29. 42,000 31. 256 33. $<$ 35. $<$
37. 15 39. $-1\frac{1}{2}$ 41. $-2°C$ 43. -6 45. $\frac{2}{5}$ 47. $37°$ 49. $14g$ 51. $-24rt$ 53. $15x + 11$
55. $29n + 6mn$ 57. -24 59. -0.62 61. -1 63. $1\frac{1}{3}$ 65. $-\frac{23}{40}$ 67. $84\frac{1}{2}$ 69. -112 71. $-m$
73. $-36x$ 75. $-7x^2$ 77. -9 79. $-\frac{4}{31}$ 81. -11 83. 4 85. -5

Page 80 Chapter Test 1. -19 3. 617.25 5. 102 7. $<$ 9. $=$ 11. 7 13. 9 15. -18 17. $221
19. $27gt + 7$ 21. $-0.7°$ 23. $32\frac{2}{3}r$ 25. 26

Page 81 Additional Practice 1. -4 3. -3 5. x 7. 0 9. π 11. $<$ 13. $>$ 15. $<$ 17. $<$
19. 14 21. 7.5 23. 0 25. -1.3 27. -3 29. 8.2 31. 0 33. 5 35. $-\frac{2}{5}$ 37. 126 39. -7
41. -2 43. $-3r$ 45. $12bc - 7b$ 47. $25x$ 49. $11x + 10$ 51. $-1.9p - 7$ 53. $25a + 3b$ 55. 0
57. 90 59. 0 61. $3x$ 63. $3g$ 65. $\frac{3}{2}$ 67. $-\frac{1}{3}$ 69. $-\frac{3}{10}$ 71. 3 73. 11 75. $-(500) = -500$
77. 2 yd 79. $35°$ 81. 12 w square units 83. $800 loss

CHAPTER 3: SOLVING EQUATIONS

Page 85 Classroom Exercises 1. -2 3. 9 5. 6 7. -9 9. $x = 2$ 11. $t = 24$ 13. $a = 13$
15. $x = 51$

Page 85 Written Exercises 1. $x = 6$ 3. $n = -3$ 5. $y = 20$ 7. $y = 17$ 9. $n = -6$ 11. $y = -9$
13. $x = 19$ 15. $t = 1.1$ 17. $z = 38$ 19. $m = -2$ 21. $t = -5$ 23. $a = 15$ 25. $r = 3.5$ 27. $z = 3.6$
29. $a = 2.78$ 31. $x = 2.18$ 33. $z = 2$ 35. $c = -\frac{1}{2}$ 37. $r = 6\frac{1}{2}$ 39. $y = 3\frac{1}{4}$ 41. 14 43. 6 45. 9
47. 0.1 49. $x = 4$ or $x = -4$ 51. $n = 0$

Page 86 Review Capsule for Section 3-2 1. y 2. $-t$ 3. $-q$ 4. t 5. n 6. $\frac{3}{2}$ 7. $\frac{8}{5}$ 8. -2 9. $-\frac{4}{3}$
10. $-\frac{1}{9}$ 11. $\frac{1}{7}$ 12. $\frac{1}{2}$ 13. $\frac{1}{8}$ 14. $-\frac{4}{3}$ 15. -4 16. $\frac{6}{5}$ 17. -1

Page 88 Classroom Exercises 1. $\frac{1}{3}$ 3. $-\frac{5}{4}$ 5. 5 7. -1 9. $x = 7$ 11. $y = 16$ 13. $z = 60$
15. $t = -20$

Page 88 Written Exercises 1. $x = 4$ 3. $b = -2$ 5. $x = 28$ 7. $s = -2$ 9. $n = 6$ 11. $n = 18$
13. $v = -7\frac{1}{5}$ 15. $x = 0$ 17. $t = -24\frac{1}{2}$ 19. $y = -6$ 21. $r = -\frac{1}{4}$ 23. $n = -\frac{1}{32}$ 25. $t = -32$
27. $t = \frac{2}{15}$ 29. $y = 4$ 31. $c = 0.0075$ 33. $n = -1\frac{2}{3}$ 35. $x = 6$ 37. $y = -2\frac{1}{2}$ 39. $y = 1\frac{2}{3}$ 41. 20
43. 100 45. -21 47. 37 49. 11 51. F; true only for $x = 1$.   53. F; true only for $x = \frac{1}{2}$.

Page 90 Classroom Exercises 1. -7 3. 5 5. 12 7. -10 9. $x = 2$ 11. $t = 2$

Page 90 Written Exercises 1. $n = 6$ 3. $n = 4$ 5. $t = -4$ 7. $n = 6$ 9. $n = 7$ 11. $a = -6$ 13. $a = 6$
15. $b = 9$ 17. $a = -9$ 19. $x = -2$ 21. $t = 4\frac{1}{3}$ 23. $x = -4$ 25. $a = 9$ 27. $y = -12$ 29. $t = -3\frac{2}{3}$
31. $w = 2$ 33. $n = 6$ 35. $n = -30$ 37. $x = 40$ 39. $x = 28$ 41. $t = 105$ 43. $n = 96$ 45. $n = 100$
47. $x = -45$ 49. $x = 172$ 51. $z = -0.09$ 53. 1. Additive inverse post. 2. Comm. post. for add.
3. Additive inverse post. 4. Additive inverse post. 55. 1. Reflexive post. of equality 3. Substitution
principle 4. Comm. post. for add. 5. Substitution principle

Page 91 Calculator Exercises 1. $n = -5$ 3. $y = \frac{16}{7}$

Page 93 Consumer Applications 1. $81 3. $120 5. $45 7. $226.80 9. −1806 Btu's/hr 11. −1960 Btu's/hr

Page 95 Classroom Exercises 1. $1250 3. $5600 5. $90.90

Page 95 Word Problems 1. 9 3. $\frac{1}{3}$ inch 5. 63 7. $1849 9. $8000 11. $5500 13. $80,000 15. $200,000

Page 96 Review 1. x = −2 2. n = 19 3. v = 0.9 4. a = 6 5. x = 2 6. b = −4 7. n = −4 8. y = −$\frac{25}{2}$, or −12$\frac{1}{2}$ 9. a = 3 10. n = −2 11. x = 2 12. m = 2 13. x = −2 14. a = 6 15. y = −24 16. r = −2 17. 240 kilometers 18. $\frac{1}{20}$ hour, or 3 minutes

Page 97 Review Capsule for Section 3-5 1. 16x + 2 2. 9y − 9 3. 5a 4. 5a − 9 5. t + 1 6. 2y 7. −32 − 5r 8. −7 + 5b

Page 98 Classroom Exercises 1. 9x − 9 3. −14x −7 5. −2x − 2 7. −5x + 5 9. a = 2 11. b = 1$\frac{7}{9}$ 13. x = 12

Page 98 Written Exercises 1. 2x − 6 3. 6x + 3 5. 20x − 28 7. 4b − 24 9. −4x + 36 11. −20 + 4n 13. −12 + 4x 15. −9 + 4m 17. x = 2 19. y = 6 21. x = 3 23. n = −4 25. x = −1 27. x = −2 29. x = 7 31 x = 2 33. n = 4 35. b = 28 37. x = 11 39. a = 9 41. x = 10 43. m = −$\frac{1}{3}$ 45. x = 7$\frac{1}{2}$ 47. b = 1 49. m = −4 51. m = −9 53. x = 2 55. a = 4.75 **57.** 2. Add. prop. for equations 3. Assoc. post. for add. 4. Additive inverse post. 5. Identity post. for add. 59. No 61. No 63. Yes

Page 100 Classroom Exercises 1. 30°; 60°; 90° 3. 30°; 30°; 120° 5. 45°; 60°; 75°

Page 101 Written Exercises 1. 42.5°; 52.5°; 85° 3. 75°; 15° 5. 60°; 60°; 60° 7. 90°; 90°; 90°; 90° 9. 66°; 66°; 114°; 114° 11. 60°; 120°; 115°; 65° 13. 20°; 40°; 120° 15. 50°; 65°; 65° 17. 31°; 59° 19. 72°; 108° 21. 45°; 45°; 135°; 135° 23. 22.5°; 67.5°

Page 102 Puzzle See Solution Key.

Page 103 Review Capsule for Section 3-7 1. 0.70 2. 0.60 3. 0.75 4. 5.50 5. 7.25 6. 8.30 7. $\frac{9}{20}$ 8. $\frac{16}{25}$ 9. $\frac{1}{4}$ 10. $\frac{1}{2}$ 11. $\frac{7}{10}$ 12. $\frac{1}{8}$

Page 104 Classroom Exercises 1. 90 3. 75% 5. 86.1 7. 60% 9. 27 11. 40% 13. $70 15. 5$\frac{5}{9}$%

Page 105 Written Exercises 1. 9.8 3. 75% 5. 75 7. 36 9. 900 11. 80% 13. $975 15. 6% 17. 66$\frac{2}{3}$g 19. $175 21. 8% 23. $460 25. 33$\frac{1}{3}$% 27. 70% 29. $1680 31. $24,000 33. $15,625 35. $432

Page 106 Calculator Exercises 1. 15

Page 108 Classroom Exercises 1. 19; 20; 21; 22 3. 1; 2; 3; 4 5. 0; 1; 2; 3 7. 14; 16; 18; 20 9. −10; −8; −6; −4 11. q + 2; q + 4; q + 6; q + 8 13. 11; 13; 15; 17 15. −19; −17; −15; −13 17. k + 2; k + 4; k + 6; k + 8 19. n; n + 1; n + (n + 1) = 43 21. n; n + 2; n + (n + 2) = 0

Page 109 Word Problems 1. −9; −8 3. −34; −33; −32; −31 5. 15; 16; 17 7. −37; −35; −33 9. −3; −1; 1; 3 11. No 13. 3; 4 15. 64; 65; 66; 67 17. 55; 57 19. even 21. 2h 23. 4(3) + 1, 4(4) + 1, 4(7) + 1 25. 37, 41

Page 111 Computer Exercises See Solution Key.

Page 112 Review 1. x = 3 2. y = 2 3. a = 2 4. m = 2 5. x = 5$\frac{3}{25}$ 6. a = −2 7. 95° 8. 30°; 30° 9. 12 10. 56$\frac{1}{4}$% 11. $200 12. 10% 13. 9; 10; 11 14. 22; 24 15. 41; 42; 43; 44 16. −15, −13

Page 113 Chapter Objectives and Review 1. x = 6 3. t = 21 5. r = 5 7. x = 3 9. x = 0.2

11. $m = -\frac{4}{9}$ 13. $x = 4$ 15. $t = 4$ 17. \$754.80 19. $-m - 6$ 21. $-25 + 5a$ 23. $b = 7$ 25. $k = 0$
27. $r = 3$ 29. $40°; 60°; 80°$ 31. 17 33. 150% 35. \$360 37. 20% 39. 40, 42, 44

Page 115 Chapter Test 1. $z = 18$ 3. $t = -4.3$ 5. $x = 14\frac{1}{4}$ 7. $p = 6$ 9. $y = -105$ 11. $b = 4$
13. $d = 1\frac{1}{3}$ 15. $g = 0$ 17. $35°; 55°; 90°$ 19. 34, 36

Page 115 Additional Practice 1. $x = 8$ 3. $s = -3.1$ 5. $y = 2\frac{3}{4}$ 7. $n = 4$ 9. $v = -\frac{7}{8}$ 11. $d = -12.9$
13. $g = 5$ 15. $j = 15$ 17. $w = 3.2$ 19. 24 21. $6x - 54$ 23. $72 - 6y$ 25. $12 - 16y$ 27. -12
$+ 15a$ 29. $y = -5$ 31. $b = -6$ 33. $c = 17$ 35. 14 37. 54 39. $\frac{3}{5}$ in 41. 220 43. $40°; 60°; 80°$
45. $45°; 45°; 90°$ 47. \$4.50 49. $-17; -15$

CHAPTER 4: EQUATIONS AND INEQUALITIES

Page 119 Classroom Exercises 1. $-6y$ 3. $6 + y$ 5. $y - 6$ 7. $6y$ 9. $6 - y$ 11 $y - 6$
13. $\frac{-6}{y}$ 15. $\frac{y}{-6}$ 17. $\frac{6}{2y}$

Page 120 Word Problems 1. $25 - n$ 3. $x + (-6\frac{1}{4})$ 5. $-9 - b$ 7. $\frac{1}{2} + (-a)$ 9. $t - (-100)$

11. $n + \frac{4}{5}$ 13. $r - 4$ 15. $5 - s$ 17. $m - (-30)$ 19. $12 - |y|$ 21. $q + 9\frac{1}{2}$ 23. $r - (-0.5)$

25. $-0.5 - r$ 27. $\frac{9}{x}$ 29. $7q$ 31. $2p$ 33. $\frac{212}{-t}$ 35. $\frac{1}{5}z$ or $\frac{z}{5}$ 37. $\frac{z}{5}$ or $z \div 5$ 39. $-1p$ or $-p$

41. $r(\frac{1}{12})$ or $\frac{r}{12}$ 43. w = width of rectangle, w + 5 45. p = perimeter of base, $\frac{1}{3}$(p) 47. c = cost of
dinner, c + 5.45 49. c = cost of new car, c − 1200 51. a = air distance, 2a 53. c = cost of tennis racquet,
c − 6.90 55. q = number of qts. of oil, 1.10q 57. a = amount of Jeff's checking account, a + 20 59. 6k
61. $\frac{1200}{m}$ or $1200 \div m$ 63. $\frac{3500}{m}$ or $3500 \div m$

Page 121 Calculator Exercises 1. 6 in 3. 1573 in

Page 123 Classroom Exercises 1. $\frac{2p}{7}$ 3. $150 + 3p$ 5. $2d + 25$ 7. $z + 1\frac{3}{4} = 20$ 9. $200 - t = 71\frac{3}{4}$
11. $9 + \frac{n}{2} = 29$

Page 123 Word Problems 1. $3a - 2$ 3. $2r - 20$ 5. $\frac{4\ell}{5}$ or $4\ell \div 5$ 7. $\frac{25n}{100}$ or $25n \div 100$ 9. $b + 0.15b$
11. $t + 19 = 42.6$ 13. $\frac{n}{14} = 9$ 15. $4z - 3 = 35$ 17. $\frac{t}{3} + 7 = 23$ 19. $\frac{5b}{3} = 100$ 21. $12c - 6 = 60$
23. $\frac{q}{6} - 14 = 4$ 25. $4s - 8 = -4$ 27. \$359.70 29. \$31.30 31. \$142.50 33. \$82.50 35. 40
37. 60 39. 6

Page 125 Review Capsule for Section 4-3 1. $59y + 36$ 2. $5p - 8$ 3. $-18z + 12$ 4. $d = \frac{23}{5}$ or $4\frac{3}{5}$
5. $x = 11$ 6. $x = -6$ 7. $t = \frac{7}{2}$ or $3\frac{1}{2}$ 8. $t = 15$ 9. $x = 1$

Page 126 Classroom Exercises 1. e 3. h 5. a 7. d

Page 127 Word Problems 1. 12; 60 3. 12; 8 5. 9; 27 7. 30; 20 9. 33; 43 11. 42; 14; 16
13. 8; 32; 33 15. \$13 = Dan's earnings; \$39 = Bob's earnings 17. \$62.90 = cost of dress; \$98.40 = cost of
coat 19. 560 on first day; 325 on second day 21. \$56.22 = gas bill; \$41.41 = electric bill
23. \$50 = list price; \$10 = discount 25. \$113 = list price; \$22.60 = discount 27. \$70 = list price; \$24.50
= discount 29. 25 of each coin 31. 18 cm; 20 cm; 22 cm

Page 130 Classroom Exercises 1. s = 9 m 3. a = 119 m; 2a = 238 m; a + 147 = 266 m 5. 2t = 6 yd;
t − 1 = 2 yd 7. ℓ = 3 cm; w = 1.6 cm 9. b = 14 m; b − 5 = 9 m; b − 7.5 = 6.5 m; b + 12.5 = 26.5 m

Page 130 Word Problems 1. ℓ = 28 cm; w = 4 cm 3. 8 in; 24 in; 20 in 5. ℓ = 40 in; w = 16 in
7. 8 cm; 8 cm; 11 cm 9. 798 km 11. 8.4 m; 7.2 m 13. AC = BC = 536 m; AB = 857.6 m
15. m∠A = 30°; m∠B = 60°; m∠C = 90° 17. m∠A = 46°; m∠B = 100°; m∠C = 34° 19. m∠D = 20°;

$m\angle E = 100°$; $m\angle F = 60°$ 21. 4 m   23. 8 cm

Page 132 Puzzle See Solution Key.

Page 132 Review Capsule for Section 4-5 1. $-8t - 20$ 2. $-12y + 15$ 3. $-6 + 18r$ 4. $-4 + 6n$
5. $-6 + m$ 6. $-x - 9$ 7. $1 - b$ 8. $2x + 3$

Page 133 Classroom Exercises 1. $-x$ 3. $9y$ 5. $-3a$ 7. $2t$ 9. $9d$ 11. $5m$ 13. $x = -11$ 15. $n = 3$

Page 134 Written Exercises 1. $x = 4$ 3. $y = 4$ 5. $a = 3$ 7. $x = -3$ 9. ϕ 11. $a = 6$ 13. $m = \dfrac{3}{4}$
15. $x = -26$ 17. $a = \dfrac{2}{3}$ 19. $r = 10$ 21. $r = 4$ 23. $y = 20$ 25. $a = 4$ 27. $k = 10\dfrac{1}{2}$ 29. $y = -2$
31. $x = 5$ 33. $p = 6$ 35. $y = -5$ 37. $x = 9$ 39. all real numbers   41. $x = \dfrac{7}{2}$ 43. $x = 4$ 45. $n = 6$
47. $\{1\}$ 49. $\{-4\}$ 51. $\left\{1\dfrac{1}{5}\right\}$ 53. $\{5\}$ 55. $\{-2\}$ 57. $\left\{2\dfrac{1}{2}\right\}$

Page 136 Classroom Exercises 1. $x + 12$ 3. $2z + 2$ 5. $2r + 6$ 7. $t + 6$ 9. $t - 5$

Page 136 Word Problems 1. Anna: 8; Ramon: 2   3. Skip: 20; Paul: 10   5. Andy: 35; Bob: 10
7. 13; 14   9. electrician: 20 yr; apprentice: 4 yr   11. Mr. Connors: 25; Mr. Saito: 40   13. 41
15. 12 yr   17. 8 yr

Page 137 Review 1. $-6m$ 2. $\dfrac{x}{12}$ 3. $2\dfrac{1}{4} + k$ 4. $4.6 - n$ 5. \$16   6. 36; 24   7. Bob: 97 shares;
Jane: 31 shares   8. $\ell = 60$ m; $w = 20$ m   9. $g = -1$ 10. $n = 2$ 11. $b = -6$ 12. $n = -3$ 13. ϕ
14. $c = 1$ 15. Maria: 7; Ann: 10

Page 139 Career Applications 1. 60.5 ft   3. 44 ft   5. 59.4 ft   7. 162 ft   9. 98 ft   11. 42.9 ft;
78 ft; 120.9 ft   13. 49.5 ft; 112.5 ft; 162 ft

Page 140 Review Capsule for Section 4-7 1. $\{-4, -3, -2, -1, 0, 1, 2\}$ 2. $\{3, 4\}$ 3. $\{2, 3, 4\}$
4. $\{-4, -3, -2, -1, 0, 1, 2, 3, 4\}$ 5. $\{-4, -3, -2, -1, 0\}$ 6. $\{-4, -3, -2, -1, 0\}$ 7. $\{-4, -3, -2,$
$2, 3, 4\}$ 8. $\{-3, -2, -1, 0, 1, 2, 3\}$

Page 141 Classroom Exercises 1. $>$ 3. $>$ 5. $>$; $>$ 7. $>$; $>$ 9. $<$; $<$

Page 141 Written Exercises 1. $t > -3$; all points to the right of and not including, -3 3. $y > 12$; all
points to the right of, and not including, 12   5. $r < 7$; all points to the left of, and not including, 7
7. $r < 5$; all points to the left of, and not including, 5   9. $c < -7$; all points to the left of, and not including,
-7 11. $z > 16$; all points to the right of, and not including, 16   13. $x < 6$; all points to the left of, and
not including, 6   15. $x \geq 8$; all points to the right of, and including, 8   17. $r \geq 19$; all points to the right
of, and including, 19   19. $n \geq -2$; all points to the right of, and including, -2 21. $z < -5$; all points
to the left of, and not including, -5 23. $-1 \geq y$; all points to the left of, and including, -1
25. $q \leq -18$; all points to the left of, and including, -18 27. $x > -31$; all points to the right of, and not
including, -31 29. $x \leq 0$; all points to the left of, and including, 0   31. $>$ 33. z   35. 0   37. -5
39. a   41. 3   43. Let $a = 6$, $b = 5$, $c = 4$, and $d = 1$. Then $a - c = 6 - 4 = 2$ and $b - d = 5 - 1 = 4$. Thus,
$a - c > b - d$ is not true because 2 is not greater than 4.

Page 142 Review Capsule for Section 4-8 1. $\{0, 2\}$ 2. ϕ 3. ϕ 4. $\{-2, -1, 0, 1\}$ 5. $\{-3, -1, 1,$
$3\}$ 6. $\{-6, -3\}$

Page 144 Classroom Exercises 1. $>$ 3. $<$ 5. $>$ 7. $>$; $>$ 9. $>$; $>$

Page 144 Written Exercises 1. $x < 4$; all points to the left of, and not including, 4   3. $q > 2$; all points to
the right of, and not including, 2   5. $d > -2$; all points to the right of, and not including, -2 7. $x > 0$;
all points to the right of, and including, 0   9. $t \geq 4$; all points to the right of, and including, 4   11. $z > 6$;
all points to the right of, and not including, 6   13. $a > 4$; all points to the right of, and not including, 4
15. $h \leq 3$; all points to the left of, and including, 3   17. $y < 2$; all points to the left of, and not including, 2
19. $t < 5$ 21. $x < -\dfrac{5}{2}$ 23. $r \leq 5\dfrac{3}{5}$ 25. $a \leq -\dfrac{3}{4}$ 27. $m > 11$ 29. $y \leq -\dfrac{15}{2}$ 31. $x > -15$

33. $x > -\frac{7}{5}$ 35. $x < \frac{4}{3}$ 37. $y < -3$ 39. $x > -\frac{5}{13}$ 41. $k \geq 16$ 43. $r \geq -4$ 45. $z \geq -\frac{3}{5}$ 47. $d < \frac{4}{3}$
49. $>$ 51. $<$ 53. T   55. T   57. F; If $x = 2$ and $y = -2$, then $2(-2) \not> 0$.   59. F; If $x = 10$ and $y = 3$, then $3^2 \not> 10$.   61. F; if $x = -3$ and $y = -5$, then $(-3)(-5) \not< (-3)^2$.

Page 145   Calculator Exercises   1. Correct   3. Correct   5. Incorrect

Page 145   Review Capsule for Section 4-9   1. x = the first integer; $x + (x + 1)$ 2. p = number of pens; $p + 7$
3. n = second number; $3n + 36$ 4. r = Room 201's students; $2r + 5$ 5. a = advertising part; $4a - 10$
6. ℓ = length of each side of the square; $2\ell - 4$

Page 147   Classroom Exercises   1. x = number of pipe sections; $8x > 110$ 3. x = score on third test;
$\frac{82 + 91 + x}{3} \geq 90$

Page 147   Word Problems   1. \$50   3. 89   5. 101   7. \$620.01   9. 1 and 2, or 2 and 3, or 3 and
4, or 4 and 5   11. 27 and 29   13. 12   15. $\{x : x > 4\}$ 17. 24 and 26

Page 148   Review   1. $n < 3$; all points to the left of, and not including, 3   2. $x < -2.5$; all points to the
left of, and not including, -2.5 3. $g \leq -5$; all points to the left of, and including, -5 4. $a > -3$
5. $a \geq -4$ 6. $p < 0$ 7. $h > 3$; all points to the right of, and not including, 3   8. $y \geq -1$; all points to the
right of, and including, -1 9. $s > 1$; all points to the right of, and not including, 1   10. $b > -1$
11. $t \geq -3$ 12. 89   13. 12 and 60

Page 150   Computer Exercises   See Solution Key.

Page 151   Chapter Objectives and Review   1. $4.5 - w$ 3. $5 + x$ 5. \$41.50   7. 413   9. 44; 31
11. last month: \$1600; this month: \$2700   13. length: 50 m; width: 30 m   15. 27 ft; 29 ft; 31 ft
17. $x = 3$ 19. $n = -2$ 21. Tony: 6; Jim: 18   23. 10; 12   25. $y > 6$; all points to the right of, and
not including, 6   27. $b < 5$; all points to the left of, and not including, 5   29. $f \geq 2$ 31. $n < 0$
33. $r < -2$; all points to the left of, and not including, -2 35. $y \geq 5$ 37. 249 mi

Page 153   Chapter Test   1. $t + 9$ 3. $\frac{-6}{w}$ 5. $d = 2$ 7. $y = 1$ 9. $x < -1$; all points to the left of, and
not including, -1 11. $r \leq 1$; all points to the left of, and including, 1   13. $x > -2$ 15. $y > 3$ 17. 500
19. length: 166 cm; width: 140 cm

Page 154   More Challenging Problems   1. $\frac{5}{16}$ 3. $x = \frac{22b + 35d}{5}$ 5. $3y + f + \frac{i}{12}$ 7. $7\frac{1}{2}x + 2\frac{1}{2}y + 13\frac{5}{6}z$
9. 6   11. $6\frac{2}{3}$ 13. loss of \$1000

Page 155   Additional Practice   1. $6.5 - x$ 3. $\frac{28}{c}$ 5. $a = 1$ 7. $x = 3$ 9. $y = 2$ 11. $x > 10$
13. $a \leq -7$ 15. $x \geq 4$ 17. $n > \frac{1}{2}$ 19. \$14   21. Emily: 45; Jean: 65   23. $A = 20°$; $B = 60°$; $C = 100°$
25. 179 ft

Page 156   Review of Word Problems   1. $946 - $ mL bottle   3. $7°C$ 5. \$5400   7. 5%   9. 29, 31, 33
11. \$76   13. length: 32 m; width: 21 m   15. \$57

Page 157   Cumulative Review   1. b   3. a   5. c   7. d   9. a   11. d   13. c   15. c   17. c   19. b
21. b   23. c   25. a   27. c   29. c

Page 159   Preparing for College Entrance Tests   1. a   3. a   5. c   7. a

Page 160   Preparing for College Entrance Tests   1. b   3. c   5. c   7. a   9. c

CHAPTER 5: GRAPHING RELATIONS AND FUNCTIONS

Page 163   Classroom Exercises   1. $x = 7 - b$ 3. $x = t + 2$ 5. $x = \frac{a}{3}$

Page 163   Written Exercises   1. $x = 144$; $x = ab$ 3. $x = \frac{10}{3}$ or $3\frac{1}{3}$; $x = \frac{bc}{a}$ 5. $x = \frac{6}{5}$; $x = \frac{b - a}{5}$ 7. $x = -\frac{4}{3}$
or $-1\frac{1}{3}$; $x = \frac{b}{3} - a$ 9. $x = 3$; $x = \frac{b - a}{-2}$ 11. $d = \frac{C}{\pi}$ 13. $h = \frac{2A}{b}$ 15. $r = \frac{d}{t}$ 17. $r = \frac{i}{pt}$ 19. $F = \frac{9}{5}C + 32$

21. $d = \dfrac{C}{\pi}$; $d = 22.6$ 23. $\ell = \dfrac{P - 2w}{2}$; $\ell = 22$ 25. $w = \dfrac{A}{\ell}$; $w = 2.8$ 27. $n = \dfrac{b - a}{2}$ 29. $n = 3a + b$

31. $n = 5b - 3a$ 33. $n = b + c - a$ 35. $n = 4b$ 37. $n = \dfrac{b + c}{a}$ 39. $b = \dfrac{c}{a} - n$ 41. $a = \dfrac{c}{n} - b$
43. $b = \dfrac{2A}{h} - b'$

Page 164 Puzzle See Solution Key.

Page 166 Classroom Exercises 1. Hiker A: r, 6, 6r; Hiker B: 2r, 6, 12r   3. Passenger: 2r, 3, 6r; Freight: r, 3, 3r

Page 167 Word Problems 1. 3 hr   3. 12 hr   5. 3 hours   7. 240 km/hr; 480 km/hr   9. 10 hours
11. 3 hours   13. 240 km   15. 8 km   17. 4.5 km

Page 170 Classroom Exercises 1. 6   3. 3   5. −4   7. 0   9. 8   11. 0   13. y axis   15. I   17. II
19. y axis   21. II

Page 170 Written Exercises 1. Start at the origin and make the moves given for each point. a. Left 3, up 4
b. Right 5, up 2   c. Right 4, down 3   d. Left 5, down 4   e. Right 6   f. Down 4   g. Up 5   h. Down 3
i. Left 4, down 4   j. The origin   3. abscissa: −3; ordinate: 4   5. abscissa: 0; ordinate: 5   7. abscissa:
0; ordinate: 0   9. 0   11. III   13. II   15. IV   17. y axis   19. II   21. I   23. IV   25. The picture
is an elephant.   27. The graph is a horizontal line 4 units below the x axis.   29. The graph is a vertical line
coinciding with the y axis.   31. The graph is a diagonal line passing through the origin at a 45° angle. The line
is in Quadrants II and IV.   33. A horizontal line parallel to the x axis.   35. A half-plane with the y axis as its
right-hand boundary.   37. (−4, 5)   39. (0, −4)   41. (−3, −3)   43. (−10, 5), (−4, 5), (−4, 1)
45. (2, 10), (2, 4), (4, 4)   47. (−13, 7), (1, 9), (−3, 3)

Page 173 Review 1. x = 36   2. x = 17   3. x = −3   4. $x = 5\frac{1}{2}$ 5. $2\frac{1}{2}$ hours 6. 150 km   7. Start at
the origin and make the moves given for each point. a. Right 10   b. Right 12, down 5   c. Right 4, down 9
d. Left 4, down 9   e. Left 9   f. Left 9, up 4   g. Right 4, up 9   h. Up 9   i. Up 10   j. Right 12, up 5
9. Abscissa: A: 10; B: 12; C: 4; D: −4; E: −9; F: −9; G: 4; H: 0; I: 0; J: 12   Ordinate: A: 0; B: −5;
C: −9; D: −9; E: 0; F: 4; G: 9; H: 9; I: 10; J: 5

Page 173 Puzzle See Solution Key.

Page 175 Career Applications 1. London   3. London   5. Calcutta and Chicago   7. Paris   9. 0
11. −6   13. −10   15. +3   17. 6 hours   19. 14 hours   21. 1:30 P.M.

Page 178 Classroom Exercises 1. D = {0, 2, 4, 6}; R = {1, 3, 5, 7}   3. D = {0, 1, 2, 3}; R = {−2}
5. Not a function; (1, 2) and (1, 3) have the same first element.   7. Is a function

Page 178 Written Exercises 1. D = {1, 2, 3, 4, 5}; R = {50, 100, 150, 200, 250}   3. D = {1, 2, 3, 4, 5};
R = {π, 4π, 9π, 16π, 25π}   5. {(−4, −2), (−2, −3), (−1, 1), (1, −2), (1, 3), (2, 1), (4, 2)}   7. D = {−4,
−2, −1, 1, 2, 4}; R = {−2, −3, 1, 3, 2}   9. {(−3, −3), (−2, −3), (−1, −3), (1, −3), (2, −3), (3, −3)};
D = {−3, −2, −1, 1, 2, 3}; R = {−3}   11. {(1, 4), (2, 4), (3, 4)}   13. {(−5, 0), (−5, 5), (0, 0), (0, 5)}
15. Yes   17. No   19. No   21. Yes   23. Yes   25. No; All ordered pairs have the same first element.
27. Yes   29. {(1976, 11,000), (1978, 12,000), (1980, 13,000), (1982, 15,000), (1984, 16,000)};
D = {1976, 1978, 1980, 1982, 1984}; R = {11,000, 12,000, 13,000, 15,000, 16,000}   31. {(4, 256),
(6, 576), (8, 1024), (10, 1600)}; D = {4, 6, 8, 10}; R = {256, 576, 1024, 1600}   33. {(1, 4), (2, 33),
(3, 113), (5, 523)}; D = {1, 2, 3, 5}; R = {4, 33, 113, 523}   35. All are functions.   37. a. 40, 40, 40,
60, 60, 80, 80, 100   b. 0, 20, 40, 60, 80, 100

c.

Page 182 Classroom Exercises 1. 8, 12 3. −6, −9 5. 4, 6, 10 7. 14, 11, 8, 5, 2 9. No 11. Yes 13. No 15. Yes 17. Yes 19. No 21. Yes 23. Yes 25. Yes 27. No 29. Yes

Page 183 Written Exercises For Exercises 1-28, each graph is a straight line containing the given points. 1. (0, −3), (1, 1) 3. (−2, 0), (0, −4) 5. (0, −5), (5, 0) 7. (0, 10), (10, 0) 9. (0, 0), (2, 1) 11. (0, 0), (4, −1) 13. (0, 4), (2, 0) 15. (0, 2), (3, 0) 17. (0, −4), (2, 0) 19. (0, −4), (4, −4) 21. (0, −9), (9, −9) 23. $(6\frac{1}{2}, 0), (6\frac{1}{2}, 6)$ 25. (−2, 3), (0, 3), (2, 3) 27. (−4, 0), (0, 0), (4, 0) 29. x axis; x axis 31. one real number In Exercises 32-35, the graph is a line parallel to the y axis. It contains the given points. 33. (8, −3), (8, 0), (8, 4) 35. (−9, −2), (−9, 0), (−9, 2) 37. the set of real numbers 39. each ordered pair has the same first element 41. $(0, 2\frac{8}{9}), (−13, 0)$ 43. $(0, 4), (1\frac{1}{3}, 0)$ 45. $(0, −1), (\frac{1}{3}, 0)$ 47. Not a linear function.

$$D = \{x : x \in R, x \neq 0\}$$
$$R = \{y : y \leq 0, y \in R\}$$

49. Not a linear function.

$$D = \{real\ numbers\}$$
$$R = \{y : y \geq 0, y \in R\}$$

Page 185 Classroom Exercises 1. (0, 6), (2, 8), (3, 9) 3. $8\frac{1}{2}$

Page 186 Word Problems 1. (0, 0), (4, 6), (6, 9) 3. 0.75 km 5. $2\frac{2}{3}$ seconds 7. To draw the graph, use multiples of 3 for the d axis and multiples of 16 for the r axis. 9. 12.8 m 11. $5, $10, $15 13. $2.50 15. $20 17. $11.25 19. S = 20t 21. (0, 5) is the endpoint. To draw the graph, use multiples of 5 for the C axis and multiples of 1 for the h axis. 23. $17.50 25. $18 27. 100, 200, 300 29. 150 feet 31. 125 feet 33. A = 50t 35. 20, 37, 54, 71, 88, 105, 122, 139, 156, 173, 190, 207

Page 188 Review 1. D = {1, 2, 3, 4, 5, 6}; R = {12, 14, 8, 4, 6, −2} 2. D = {1, 2, 3, 4, 5, 6}; R = {10, 15, 25, 40, 60, 85} 3. D = {1, 2, 3, 4}; R = $\{\pi, \frac{3\pi}{2}, 2\pi, \frac{5\pi}{2}, 3\pi\}$ 4. 1: Yes; 2: Yes; 3: No For Exercises 5-8, each graph is a straight line containing the given points. 5. (0, 0), (2, 4) 6. (0, −7), (2, −13) 7. (0, −3), (3, −3) 8. (2, 0), (2, 2) 9. (9, 4), (18, 8), (36, 16) 10. (0, 0) is the endpoint. The graph contains (9, 4), (18, 8), and (36, 16). 11. 7 units

Page 188 Review Capsule for Section 5-7 1. −5 2. −3 3. 5 4. −9 5. −10 6. 2 7. 10 8. 3 9. $-\frac{1}{3}$ 10. −8 11. −3 12. 0 13. 0 14. 0 15. −4 16. $\frac{5}{4} = 1\frac{1}{4}$

Page 191 Classroom Exercises 1. Positive 3. ND 5. $-\frac{3}{4}$ 7. $\frac{4}{5}$ 9. $-\frac{8}{7}$ 11. $-\frac{1}{2}$ 13. −1

Page 191 Written Exercises 1. 1 3. $\frac{1}{2}$ 5. $-\frac{1}{3}$ 7. 0 9. 2 11. $-\frac{3}{4}$ 13. $\frac{1}{2}$ 15. $\frac{9}{4}$ 17. $-\frac{1}{3}$ 19. 0 21. $\overline{AB}$: 1; $\overline{AC}$: $-\frac{2}{3}$; $\overline{BC}$: −4 23. $\overline{PQ}$ and $\overline{SR}$: $\frac{3}{7}$; $\overline{PS}$ and $\overline{QR}$: 4 25. $\overline{HD}$ and $\overline{FE}$: $\frac{2}{3}$; $\overline{DE}$ and $\overline{HF}$: $-\frac{2}{3}$ 27. Yes 29. No 31. 14 33. −1 35. $m = \frac{y_2 - y_1}{x_2 - x_1}, x_2 \neq x_1$ 37. $x_1 = x_2$ 39. undefined

Page 193 Calculator Exercises 1. $-18\frac{1}{2}, -17, -16\frac{1}{2}, -15$ 3. $-19\frac{1}{2}, -15, 5\frac{1}{4}, 12$

Page 193 Review Capsule for Section 5-8 1. y = 3x − 4 2. $y = \frac{5}{2}x + 2\frac{1}{2}$ 3. $y = \frac{4}{3}x$ 4. $y = -\frac{2}{3}x + 2\frac{1}{3}$ 5. $y = 4\frac{1}{2}$ 6. y = 3 7. y = 2 8. y = −2

Page 196 Classroom Exercises 1. 2; 5 3. 3; 2 5. $\frac{2}{3}; \frac{1}{2}$ 7. 0; 3

Page 196 Written Exercises 1. y = −2x + 4; −2; 4 3. y = −5x − 3; −5; −3 5. y = 2x − 4; 2; −4

5. $y = 2x - 4; 2; -4$ 7. $y = -2x - \frac{5}{2}; -2; -\frac{5}{2}$ 9. $y = -x + 3; -1; 3$ 11. $y = -4; 0; -4$ For Exercises 13-30, each graph is a straight line containing the given points.   13. $(-1, -3), (0, 6)$ 15. $(0, 1), (1, 4)$ 17. $(0, 0), (3, -2)$ 19. $(0, -2), (1, -2)$ 21. $(-5, 1), (0, -1)$ 23. $(-1, 6), (0, 0)$ 25. $(0, 4), (1, 6)$ 27. $(0, -6), (1, -3)$ 29. $(0, 3), (4, 8)$ 31. Yes   33. Yes   35. No   37. $-\frac{3}{4}$ 39. $y = -\frac{1}{3}x + 5$ 41. $y = -\frac{A}{B}x + \frac{C}{B}$

Page 198 Classroom Exercises 1. Yes   3. Yes   5. No   7. No   9. No   11. No   13. -4 15. 2

Page 198 Written Exercises 1. Yes; P is always 4 times s.   3. Yes; Yes; y is always $\frac{5}{2}$ times x.   5. 20; Yes; doubled   7. Yes   9. Yes   11. No   13. Yes   15. $y = kx$ 17. $r = ks$ 19. $\frac{3}{2}$ 21. -2 23. $\frac{4}{3}$ 25. 3, 3   27. 15   29. -6 31. The slope of the line increases.   33. The y intercept of an equation expressing direct variation is 0, and if $y = 0$, then $x = 0$.   35. 20π; twice   37. increases   39. multiplied by n

Page 200 Calculator Exercises 1. Yes; $y = \frac{1}{2}x$ 3. Yes; $y = 6\frac{3}{4}x$ or $y = \frac{27}{4}x$

Page 201 Classroom Exercises 1. $108.80   3. 2000   5. $8832.96

Page 202 Word Problems 1. $522   3. 125   5. 70   7. 420 mi   9. $4.50   11. 9 min   13. 240 lb

Page 203 Review 1. 1   2. -1 3. $-\frac{15}{11}$ 4. 0   5. $y = -3x + 5; -3; 5$ 6. $y = \frac{3}{2}x - 4; \frac{3}{2}; -4$ 7. $y = -8; 0; -8$ 8. $y = -\frac{3}{5}x; -\frac{3}{5}; 0$ 9. slope: -2; y intercept: 8; the graph contains $(0, 8)$ and $(4, 0)$ 10. Yes   11. Yes   12. Yes   13. No   14. 160   15. 4¢

Page 203 Puzzle See Solution Key.

Page 205 Computer Exercises See Solution Key.

Page 207 Chapter Objectives and Review 1. $n = st$ 3. $n = a - 2b$ 5. $n = \frac{3h - g}{2}$ 7. $h = \frac{A}{b}$ 9. slower runner: 8 km/hr; faster runner: 10 km/hr   11. Start at the origin and make the moves given for each point.   a. Right 3, down 7   b. Left 3, up 7   c. Down 2   d. Right 6, down 5   e. Left 6, down 6   f. Right 7, up 5   g. Right $6\frac{1}{2}$ h. Left 2, down 5   i. Left 1, up 4   j. Right $3\frac{1}{2}$, down 5   13. $(-5, 3)$ 15. D: $\{-2, -1, 0, 1, 2\}$; R: $\{-1, -\frac{1}{2}, 0, \frac{1}{2}, 1\}$ 17. 14. No; 15. Yes; 16. Yes   For Exercises 18-21, the graph is a straight line containing the given points.   19. $(0, 0), (1, -4)$ 21. $(-3, 0), (-3, 3)$ 23. To draw the graph, use multiples of $400 for the t axis and multiples of $10,000 for the p axis.   25. -2 27. 0   29. $y = -x; -1; 0$ For Exercises 31-36, the graph is a straight line through the given points.   31. $(0, 2), (-2, 0)$ 33. $(0, -2), (-4, 0)$ 35. $(0, 6), (-1, 2)$ 37. Yes   39. Yes   41. $y = -18$ 43. $98   45. 4.3 m

Page 209 Chapter Test 1. $x = kp$ 3. $x = y - z$ 5. D: $\{0, 1, 2, 3, 4, 5\}$; R: $\{0, 1, 2, 3\}$; function   7. 0   9. $-\frac{9}{7}$ 11. $y = -\frac{3}{4}x + 1; -\frac{3}{4}; 1$ 13. The graph is a straight line containing $(0, 4)$ and $(-4, 0)$.   15. Yes   17. No   19. $2\frac{1}{2}$ hours

Page 210 Additional Practice 1. $n = \frac{a}{b}$ 3. $n = \frac{d - c}{3}$ For Exercises 4-8, start at the origin and make the moves given for each point.   5. Up 6   7. Right 6, up 7   9. D: $\{-13, -12, 0, 5, 12\}$; R: $\{-13, 0, 5, 12, 13\}$; not a function   For Exercises 11-14, the graph is a straight line containing the given points.   11. $(0, 0), (1, -3)$ 13. $(6, 0), (6, 6)$ 15. 2   17. $-\frac{1}{2}$ 19. $y = -2x + 5; -2; 5$ 21. $y = -12$ 23. $10   25. 35 km

CHAPTER 6: SYSTEMS OF SENTENCES

Page 213 Classroom Exercises 1. $x + y = 5$: 5, 4, 3, 2, 1; $x - y = 3$: $-3, -2, -1, 0, 1$; $(4, 1)$ 3. No   5. No   7. an infinite number   9. one solution   11. an infinite number of solutions

Page 214   Written Exercises   1. (7, 3)   **3.** (4, 0)   **5.** (5, 1)   **7.** (5, 1)   **9.** (1, 3)   **11.** (−2, 4)
13. (3, −4)   **15.** (1, 3)   **17.** (3, 2)   **19.** (0, 1)   **21.** (4, −2)   **23.** one   **25.** none   **27.** none
29. none   **31.** none   **33.** infinitely many   **35.** none   **37.** none   **39.** infinitely many   **41.** All equal
43. Each graph is a straight line. Solar heat contains (1, 10,000) and (11, 12,000). Oil heat contains
(1, 4000) and (11, 12,000).   **45.** 10 years   **47.** $600   **49.** 2 hours   **51.** more than 2 hours   **53.** none
55. one

Page 216   Review Capsule for Section 6-2   1. $x + 2y$ **2.** $4y$ **3.** $x + 2y$ **4.** $-3a$ **5.** $18r - 11t$
6. $-2.5v + 2.2s$

Page 218   Classroom Exercises   1. $x + y = 1$ **3.** $2q = -1$

Page 218   Written Exercises   1. (3, −1)   **3.** (−1, 4)   **5.** (−1, 3)   **7.** $(1\frac{2}{3}, 2)$ **9.** $(1\frac{3}{4}, -\frac{1}{2})$ **11.** (15, 7)
13. $(2\frac{3}{4}, \frac{1}{8})$ **15.** $(3, -\frac{2}{3})$ **17.** $(-3\frac{5}{6}, -6)$ **19.** $(7\frac{1}{5}, 5\frac{2}{5})$ **21.** $(6\frac{1}{2}, 1\frac{3}{4})$ **23.** $(1, -2\frac{1}{2})$

Page 219   Puzzle   See Solution Key.

Page 219   Review Capsule for Section 6-3   1. -21 **2.** 9   **3.** 0   **4.** 11   **5.** -18.3 **6.** $\frac{1}{3}$ **7.** $6x - 4y$
8. $-18a - 3b$ **9.** $-2w + 3s$ **10.** $-r - 3t$ **11.** $v - 7q$ **12.** $-7q + 9$ **13.** $-2r + 3p$ **14.** $-s + 9t$

Page 221   Classroom Exercises   1. Equation 2: 2   **3.** Equation 2: −9   **5.** Equation 1: 5; Equation 2: −2
7. Equation 1: 5; Equation 2: 3

Page 221   Written Exercises   1. (8, −15)   **3.** (−4, 3)   **5.** (−1, −2)   **7.** (6, −2)   **9.** (2, −1)
11. (−1, −1)   **13.** (4, 2)   **15.** (1, −2)   **17.** (0, 2)   **19.** $(1\frac{2}{5}, \frac{1}{5})$ **21.** $(1\frac{2}{7}, -\frac{1}{14})$ **23.** $(\frac{2}{3}, \frac{1}{2})$

25. $(\frac{1}{3}, -\frac{1}{2})$ **27.** (0.8, 5.5)   **29.** (8, 4)   In Exercises 31-34, answers may vary.   **31.** $r = -3, s = 1$; or
$r = 3, s = -1$ **33.** $r = 1; s = 4$ **35.** (−2, 2)   **37.** (2, −4)   **39.** (5.216, 12.24)   **41.** $(2\frac{1}{3}, 3\frac{1}{2})$ **43.** To

prove the statement, first write each equation in slope-intercept form. $Ax + By = C$, $By = -Ax + C$,

$y = -\frac{A}{B}x + \frac{C}{B}$; $Ax + By = D$, $By = -Ax + D$, $y = -\frac{A}{B}x + \frac{D}{B}$ The two lines have the same slope, $-\frac{A}{B}$ But,

since $C \neq D$ (given), their y intercepts are different. Thus, the two lines are parallel, and do not intersect.
The system has no solution set.

Page 222   Review Capsule for Section 6-4   1. x = amount Hal invested; $x + 2100$ **2.** x = Roger's age; $\frac{1}{2}x$
3. x = no. of Jim's pants; $3x$ x = Joe's money; $x + 4$ **5.** x = width of bookcase; $2x$ **6.** x = no. of
Cindy's mother's shoes; $x - 3$ **7.** x = Bakers' children; $2x + 1$ **8.** ℓ = length of pool; $\frac{2}{3}\ell$

Page 224   Classroom Exercises   1. $x + y = 16$ **3.** $x - y = 4$ **5.** $x = y + 105$ **7.** $\ell = 2w$ **9.** $a + p = 5000$

Page 224   Word Problems   1. 16, 36   **3.** 9, 27   **5.** 5, 9   **7.** length: 21 in; width: 15 in   **9.** 404 miles
11. $13\frac{1}{3}$ in; $13\frac{1}{3}$ in; $8\frac{1}{3}$ in   **13.** 50°, 130°   **15.** 8, −4   **17.** father: 40 yr; Enrico: 20 yr

Page 227   Classroom Exercises   1. $\begin{cases} t + u = 12 \\ 10t + u = 12t \end{cases}$ **3.** $\begin{cases} t + u = 10 \\ t = u + 4 \end{cases}$ **5.** $\begin{cases} u = 2t \\ 10t + u = 5u + 6 \end{cases}$

Page 227   Word Problems   1. $\begin{cases} t + u = 12 \\ 10t + u = 12t \end{cases}$; 48   **3.** $\begin{cases} u = 2t \\ u - t = 4 \end{cases}$; 48   **5.** $\begin{cases} u = 2t - 11 \\ 10t + u = 7(t + u) - 6 \end{cases}$; 85
7. $\begin{cases} t + u = 9 \\ 10t + u = 10u + t + 27 \end{cases}$; 63   **9.** $\begin{cases} t + u = 11 \\ 10t + u + 45 = 10u + t \end{cases}$; 38   **11.** $\begin{cases} 10t + u = 5(t + u) \\ u = t + 1 \end{cases}$; 45

13. $\begin{cases} h + t + u = 8 \\ t = h - 2 \\ u = 3h \end{cases}$; 206   **15.** $9t - 9u$ **17.** $9t - 9u = 9(t - u)$; therefore, 9 is always a factor.
19. $100h + 10t + u - (100u + 10t + h) = 100h + 10t + u - 100u - 10t - h$
$= 99h - 99u = 99(h - u)$ Therefore, 99 is always a factor.

Page 228   Review   1. (4, 0)   **2.** (7, 2)   **3.** (3, −4)   **4.** one   **5.** infinitely many   **6.** one   **7.** (−2, −1)
8. (3, −5)   **9.** (0.5, −0.6)   **10.** (1, 5)   **11.** (1, −2)   **12.** (7, −10)   **13.** length: 65 cm; width: 38 cm

596   *Answers to Selected Exercises*

14. Karl: 16 yr; brother: 7 yr   15. 84   16. 78

Page 229 **Calculator Exercises** 1. Checks   3. Does not check; (2, 5)

Page 229 **Review Capsule for Section 6-6** 1. $x = -2y + 3$ 2. $x = 3y - 7$ 3. $x = -\frac{5}{3}y + 3$ 4. $x = 2y - 1$
5. $x = -y + 3$ 6. $x = 3y$ 7. $x = y + 3$ 8. $x = -\frac{7}{12}y$

Page 231 **Consumer Applications** 1. $329   3. $467.50   5. $450   7. $167.40   9. 6000 Btu's
11. 5500 Btu's   13. 5500 Btu's   15. 6500 Btu's   17. 7000 Btu's

Page 232 **Classroom Exercises** 1. (1, 2)   3. (−1, −4)   5. (5, −3)

Page 233 **Written Exercises** 1. (6, 2)   3. (24, 3)   5. $(-\frac{5}{49}, -\frac{25}{49})$ 7. (2, −2)   9. (0, 4)   11. (2, 1)
13. (5, −5)   15. (−2, −3)   17. (5, −5)   19. (3, 5)   21. $(3, \frac{1}{2})$ 23. $(2\frac{1}{2}, 3\frac{1}{2})$ 25. (3, −4)   27. infinite number of solutions   29. (−h, −4h)

Page 233 **Review Capsule for Section 6-7** 1. 5k   2. 25t   3. $\frac{1}{2}b$ 4. 5k   5. 20m   6. 1000p
7. 25q + 10d   8. 10d + 5n   9. 2.5r + 5t   10. 100b + 1000q

Page 236 **Classroom Exercises** 1. Total value of dimes: $0.10x; value of each quarter: $0.25; total value
of quarters: $0.25y; total number of coins: 12; total value: $1.95; $\begin{cases} x + y = 12 \\ 0.10x + 0.25y = 1.95 \end{cases}$
3. Total wages for first job: $4.50x; hourly wage for second job: $4.75; total wages for second job: $4.75y;
total number of hours: 57; total wages: $260.75; $\begin{cases} x + y = 57 \\ 4.50x + 4.75y = 260.75 \end{cases}$

Page 237 **Word Problems** 1. 21 quarters; 24 dimes   3. $900 invested at 9%; $4100 invested at 7%
5. 5000 tickets at $5.50; 2500 tickets at $7.00   7. 23 ten-dollar bills; 73 five-dollar bills   9. 19 calculators
at $15.95; 12 calculators at $22.75   11. $0.15 for first day; $0.10 each day thereafter

Page 239 **Classroom Exercises** 1. Total value of cashews: $6.50x; total value of almonds: $8.00y; weight
of mixture: 100 kg; total value of mixture: $7.40(100); $\begin{cases} x + y = 100 \\ 6.50x + 8.00y = 740 \end{cases}$

Page 240 **Word Problems** 1. 18 lb of $1.70 cookies; 27 lb of $0.95 cookies   3. $\frac{1}{2}$ oz of each type of seed
5. 100 g of the 8% solution; 300 g of the 4% solution   7. 4 kg of alloy that is 65% copper; 16 kg of alloy that
is 35% copper   9. 16 g of 40% acid; 24 g of 15% acid   11. 20 g

Page 241 **Review** 1. (5, 5)   2. (−1, 2)   3. (5, 2)   4. (1, −1)   5. (2, −3)   6. $(\frac{1}{2}, -\frac{1}{2})$ 7. nickels:
32; dimes: 34   8. ten−dollar bills: 9; twenty-dollar bills: 8   9. 10%: $500; 9.5%: $1000   10. $9.50
per pound: 10 lb; $2.25 per pound: 40 lb   11. 12% alloy: 10 kg; 18% alloy: 5 kg   12. 8% solution: $7\frac{1}{2}$
liters; 12% solution: $2\frac{1}{2}$ liters

Page 241 **Puzzle** See Solution Key.

Page 243 **Computer Exercises** See Solution Key.

Page 245 **Chapter Objectives and Review** 1. $x - y = 2$ contains (0, −2) and (2, 0); 2x + y = 4 contains
(0, 4) and (2, 0); intersection: (2, 0)   3. $2x + y = -3$ contains (0, −3) and (−2, 1); 3x + 4y = 3 contains
(1, 0) and (−3, 3); intersection: (−3, 3)   5. none   7. $(-\frac{1}{2}, 4\frac{1}{2})$ 9. $(6, -\frac{1}{2})$ 11. $(-3\frac{1}{2}, -3)$ 13. 14, 8
15. 58   17. (1, 5)   19. $(1, \frac{1}{3})$ 21. 12%: $3000; 15%: $1000   23. Solution A: 4 liters; Solution B:
6 liters

Page 246 **Chapter Test** 1. $2x - y = 8$ contains (0, −8) and (4, 0); x + y = 1 contains (1, 0) and (0, 1);
intersection: (3, −2)   3. (1, 0)   5. (3, −2)   7. Carl: 26 hours; Tony: 32 hours   9. small: 16; large: 8

Page 247 **More Challenging Problems** 1. $(7, -4)$ 3. ϕ 5. $(\dfrac{a^3 - ab^2}{b^2 - a^2}, \dfrac{a^2b - b^3}{b^2 - a^2})$ 7. $7:54\dfrac{6}{11}$ P.M.; $7:21\dfrac{9}{11}$ P.M.

Page 247 **Additional Practice** 1. $x + y = 5$ contains $(5, 0)$ and $(0, 5)$; $2x - y = 4$ contains $(2, 0)$ and $(0, -4)$; intersection: $(3, 2)$ 3. $x - 2y = 8$ contains $(0, -4)$ and $(8, 0)$; $2x + y = 6$ contains $(0, 6)$ and $(3, 0)$; intersection: $(4, -2)$ 5. none 7. $(5, -9)$ 9. $(\dfrac{1}{2}, \dfrac{5}{8})$ 11. $(-2\dfrac{4}{5}, 2)$ 13. $(1, 1)$ 15. $(-5, 5)$ 17. $(3, 2)$ 19. $(3, -2)$ 21. $(1\dfrac{5}{8}, -\dfrac{1}{4})$ 23. $(3, 7)$ 25. line contains $(0, 550)$ and $(4, 890)$; line contains $(0, 650)$ and $(4, 890)$ 27. District A: 3289; District B: 3143 29. 49 31. 12%: \$6500; 14%: \$3500 33. 10%: 15 liters; 5%: 10 liters

CHAPTER 7: INEQUALITIES

Page 251 **Classroom Exercises** 1. $x = 3$ or $x < 3$ 3. $x = -1$ or $x > -1$ 5. $3y = 12$ or $3y < 12$ 7. $x + 2 = 8$ or $x + 2 < 8$ 9. $x \le 5$ 11. $x \le -3$ 13. $4 > x > 1$ 15. $-1 < t < 3$ 17. c 19. d 21. b

Page 252 **Written Exercises** 1. $3x - 1 = 11$ or $3x - 1 < 11$ 3. $3 < y$ and $y < 8$ 5. $t - \dfrac{1}{2} = 3\dfrac{1}{2}$ or $t - \dfrac{1}{2} > 3\dfrac{1}{2}$ 7. $-3 < x + 2$ and $x + 2 < 1$ 9. $-9 < 3k$ and $3k < 15$ 11. All points between, and not including, -2 and 2 13. All points between, and not including, 3 and 5 15. All points to the right of, and not including, 0 17. All points to the left of, and including, -1 19. $x \ge 7$ 21. $-2\dfrac{1}{2} < x < 5$ 23. $2 \le x < 4$ 25. $-3 < t \le 6$ 27. $y \le 3$ 29. $c \ge 2\dfrac{1}{2}$ 31. $x \le -1$ 33. $-3 \le m < 0$ 35. $1 \le m \le 6$ 37. $130, 205$ 39. $76 < y \le 81$ 41. $58 < y \le 60$ 43. $\{51\dfrac{1}{4}, 51\dfrac{3}{8}, 51\dfrac{1}{2}, 51\dfrac{5}{8}, 51\dfrac{3}{4}, 51\dfrac{7}{8}, 52, 52\dfrac{1}{8}, 52\dfrac{1}{4}, 52\dfrac{3}{8}, 52\dfrac{1}{2}, 52\dfrac{5}{8}\}$ 45. $y < -3$ or $y \ge 3$ 47. $2 < n < 3$ 49. $-5 > x \ge -8$ 51. $n < 7$

Page 253 **Puzzle** See Solution Key.

Page 253 **Review Capsule for Section 7-2** 1. No 2. Yes 3. Yes 4. Yes 5. Yes 6. Yes 7. $y = 5x$ 8. $y = -\dfrac{1}{2}x + 3$ 9. $y = 2x - 1$ 10. $y = 5x + 3$ 11. $0; 5$ 12. $\dfrac{3}{4}; -3$ 13. $-\dfrac{1}{2}; \dfrac{1}{2}$ 14. $\dfrac{2}{3}; 2$

Page 255 **Classroom Exercises** 1. Yes 3. No 5. Yes

Page 255 **Written Exercises** 1. none 3. none 5. $(1, 0), (0, 1)$ 7. $(1, -1), (0, 0)$ 9. $(9, 2), (-1, -7)$ Each graph in Exercises 11-30 is an open half-plane. The location of each half-plane with respect to the related dashed line is given along with two points for the line. 11. Above the line that contains $(0, -3)$ and $(1, -2)$ 13. To the left of the line that contains $(0, -4)$ and $(1, -1)$ 15. To the right of the line that contains $(0, 0)$ and $(1, -3)$ 17. To the left of the line that contains $(0, -4)$ and $(1, -6)$ 19. Above the line that contains $(0, 4)$ and $(1, 3)$ 21. Above the line that contains $(0, 2)$ and $(3, 0)$ 23. Above the line that contains $(0, 4)$ and $(2, 4)$ 25. Below the line that contains $(0, -4)$ and $(2, -4)$ 27. To the left of the line that contains $(8, 0)$ and $(8, 2)$ 29. To the left of the line that contains $(-4, 0)$ and $(-4, 2)$ 31. The closed half-plane above the line that contains $(0, -4)$ and $(2, -4)$ 33. The closed half-plane to the right of the line that contains $(1, -6)$ and $(0, -9)$ 35. The closed half-plane below the line that contains $(0, -5)$ and $(2, -5)$ 37. The closed half-plane to the left of the line that contains $(0, 6)$ and $(1, 8)$ 39. $x > 2$ 41. $y < x$ 43. A closed half-plane 45. A closed half-plane 47. A straight line 49. A closed half-plane

Page 256 **Review Capsule for Section 7-3** 1. $(4, -1)$ 2. $(3, 6)$ 3. $(1, -5)$ 4. $(-1\dfrac{1}{2}, -3)$ 5. Yes 6. Yes 7. No

Page 257 **Classroom Exercises** 1. c 3. a

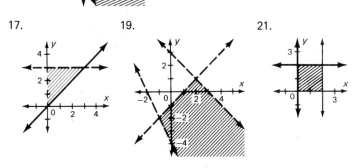

17.   **19.**   **21.**   **23.** The graph consists of only those points on the graph of $y = x$ that are between $(0, 0)$ and $(4, 4)$, including $(0, 0)$ and $(4, 4)$

Page 258   **Calculator Exercises**   See the answers to the Classroom Exercises on page 255.

Page 260   **Classroom Exercises**   1. $24; 0$ 3. $\frac{2}{3}; -2$

Page 260   **Written Exercises**   1. $40; 0$ 3. $60; 0$ 5. a. $(0, 0), (0, 4), (4, 0)$ b. 0 7. a. $(0, 0), (0, 5)$, $(4, 1), (4, 0)$ b. 0 9. $15x + 18y$ 11. Vertices of the polygonal region: $(50, 80), (50, 150), (120, 80)$
13. $3450   15. $\begin{cases} x + y \le 4 \\ x \ge 0 \\ y \ge 0 \end{cases}$ 17. $(0, 4), (0, 0), (4, 0)$

Page 261   **Review**   1. $n \ge 3$; all points to the right of, and including, 3   2. $-3 < x < 2$; all points between, and not including, -3 and 2   3. $y \ge -2$; all points to the right of, and including, -2 4. The closed half-plane to the right of the line that contains $(2, 1)$ and $(2, -2)$ 5. The open half-plane below the line that contains $(2, -2)$ and $(3, -1)$ 6. The open half-plane to the left of the line that contains $(-2, 1)$ and $(-1, 3)$ 7. The open half-plane to the left of the line that contains $(1, -1)$ and $(2, 1)$

8. 9. 10. 11.

12. $25x + 36y$ 13. $\begin{cases} x + y \leq 10 \\ 2x + 3y \leq 24 \\ x \geq 0 \\ y \geq 0 \end{cases}$ 14.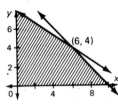

15. 6 plain, 4 fancy

Page 263   Consumer Applications   1. 5   3. 10   11.4   7. 7.8   9. 10.5   11. 12.6   13. 275°F
15. Solution C: $-12°$F; Solution D: $-2°$F   17. Solution A: $-20°$C; Solution B: $-8°$C

Page 264   Review Capsule for Section 7-5   1. 6   2. 3   3. 0   4. -7 5. -10 6. -11 7. 1   8. -2
9. 9   10. -1 11. $x = 5$ or $x = -5$ 12. $y = 4$ 13. $n = -5.7$ 14. $n = 2$ or $n = -2$ 15. $r = 1$

Page 265   Classroom Exercises   1. $x = -15$ or $x = 5$ 3. $t = -2$ or $t = 2$ 5. $n = -2$ or $n = 2$ 7. $y = 2$
9. $q = -2\frac{3}{4}$ or $q = 3\frac{1}{4}$ 11. $k = 4$ or $k = 5$

Page 265   Written Exercises   1. $a = -5$ or $a = -1$ 3. $y = -2$ or $y = 2$ 5. $k = 1\frac{1}{3}$ or $k = 2\frac{2}{3}$ 7. $x = -9$ or

$x = 15$ 9. $k = -13$ or $k = 17$ 11. $t = -10$ or $t = 8$ 13. $t = -4\frac{2}{5}$ or $t = 5\frac{1}{5}$ 15. $k = -1\frac{5}{6}$ or $k = -\frac{1}{6}$

17. $y = -\frac{1}{8}$ or $y = \frac{1}{8}$ 19. $m = -3\frac{1}{3}$ or $m = -\frac{2}{3}$ 21. $x = -1$ or $x = 1$ 23. $w = -3\frac{1}{3}$ or $w = 3\frac{1}{3}$ 25. $y = -\frac{2}{3}$

or $y = 2$ 27. $k = -20$ or $k = 22$ 29. $t = \frac{2}{3}$ or $t = 4$ 31. $x \leq -5$ or $x \geq 5$; all points to the left of, and
including, -5, or all points to the right of, and including, 5   33. $-1 < n < 5$; all points between, and not
including, -1 and 5   35. $-4 \leq x \leq 5$; all points between, and including, -4 and 5   37. $1 \leq n \leq 5$; all
points between, and including, 1 and 5

Page 265   Review Capsule for Section 7-6   1. $x = -5$ 2. $x = 0$ 3. $y = -3x$ 4. $y = 5$ 5. $y = \frac{1}{2}x + 2$
6. 15, 5, 0, -5, -15 7. 7, 5, 4, 3, 1

Page 267   Classroom Exercises   1. 4, 2, 0, 2, 4   3. 1, 0, -1, -2, -1, 0

Page 267   Written Exercises   1. Two vertical lines, one through $(-2, 0)$ and the other through $(2, 0)$
3. Two horizontal lines, one through $(-3, 0)$, and the other through $(3, 0)$ Each graph in Exercises 5-20
consists of two rays. Their initial point and the coordinates of another point on each ray is given.
5. Initial point: $(0, 0)$; one ray: $(-1, 2)$; other ray: $(1, 2)$ 7. Initial point: $(0, 0)$; one ray: $(-2, -2)$;
other ray: $(2, -2)$ 9. Initial point: $(0, -4)$; one ray: $(-2, -2)$; other ray: $(2, -2)$ 11. Initial point:
$(0, 7)$; one ray: $(-1, 10)$; other ray: $(1, 10)$ 13. Initial point: $(0, 0)$; one ray: $(1, 1)$; other ray: $(1, -1)$
15. Initial point: $(-6, 0)$; one ray: $(-8, 1)$; other ray: $(-8, -1)$ 17. Initial point: $(0, 0)$; one ray:
$(-3, 1)$; other ray: $(-3, -1)$ 19. Initial point: $(6, 0)$; one ray: $(7, 1)$; other ray: $(7, -1)$ 21. The graph
consists of four rays. The initial point of two of the rays is $(-5, 0)$. One ray also contains $(-6, 1)$ and the
other ray also contains $(-6, -1)$. The initial point of the other two rays is $(5, 0)$. One ray also contains
$(6, 1)$ and the other ray also contains $(6, -1)$.   23. The graph consists of two lines that intersect at $(0, 0)$.
One line also contains $(1, 1)$ and the other line contains $(1, -1)$.   25. The graph consists of two parallel lines.
One line contains $(0, 3)$ and the other line contains $(0, 5)$.   27. The graph consists of one point: $(0, 0)$

600   *Answers to Selected Exercises*

29.   31.   33.   35.

Page 267 Review 1. $x = -7$ or $x = 3$ 2. $y = -12$ or $y = 12$ 3. $m = -\frac{1}{3}$ or $m = \frac{1}{3}$ 4. $q = -2$ or $q = 2$
5. $s = 1$ 6. $n = 2$ or $n = 2\frac{1}{2}$ 7. $z = -1$ or $z = 1$ 8. $w = -1\frac{1}{2}$ or $w = 1$ 9. $t = -\frac{1}{4}$ or $t = 1\frac{3}{4}$
10. The graph consists of two parallel lines, one four units to the right of the y axis, and the other four units
to the left of the y axis.   11. The graph consists of two rays with their initial point at the origin. The ray in
Quadrant I also passes through (1, 3), and the ray in Quadrant II also passes through (−1, 3).   12. The graph
consists of two rays with their initial point at the origin. The ray in Quadrant III also passes through (−1, −3)
and the ray in Quadrant IV also passes through (1, −3).   13. The graph consists of two rays with their initial
point at (0, 5). The ray in Quadrant I also passes through (3, 8), and the ray in Quadrant II also passes through
(−3, 8).   14. The graph consists of four rays with their initial point at the origin. The ray in Quadrant I
also passes through (1, 2), and the ray in Quadrant IV also passes through (1, −2). The ray in Quadrant II
also passes through (−1, 2), and the ray in Quadrant III also passes through (−1, −2).   15. The graph
consists of two parallel lines, one four units above the x axis, and the other two units above the x axis.

Page 269 Computer Exercises See Solution Key.

Page 270 Chapter Objectives and Review 1. $5x = -10$ or $5x > -10$ 3. $-5 < y$ and $y < 0$ 5. $6s - 8$
$= 4$ or $6s - 8 > 4$ 7. All points between, and not including, −2 and 5   9. All points between −1 and 5,
including 5 but not including −1   11. All points between, and including, −5 and −4   13. The open half-
plane to the right of the line that contains (0, 0) and (2, −8).   15. The open half-plane to the left of the
line that contains (−2, 0) and (1, −3).   17. The closed half-plane below the x axis.   19. The closed
half-plane to the right of the line that contains (0, −3) and (2, −7).   21. d   23. b

25.   27.

29. maximum: 12; minimum: 0
31. maximum: 36; minimum: 0
33. maximum: 24; minimum: −8
35. $4x + 6y$
37. Vertices of the polygonal region: (0, 0),
    (0, 4), (1, 4), (3, 2), (3, 0)
39. 28
41. $x = -1$ or $x = 1$
43. $p = -8$ or $p = 8$
45. $a = -11$ or $a = -1$

47. The graph consists of two parallel lines, one 1 unit to the right of the y axis, and the other one unit to
the left of the y axis.   49. The graph consists of two rays, one in Quadrant I and one in Quadrant II, with
their initial point at the origin. The ray in Quadrant I also passes through (2, 2), and the ray in Quadrant II
also passes through (−2, 2).   51. The graph consists of two rays, one in Quadrant I and one in Quadrant IV,
with their initial point at the origin. The ray in Quadrant I also passes through (6, 2), and the ray in
Quadrant IV also passes through (6, −2).   53. The graph consists of two parallel lines, one two units above
the x axis, and one four units below the x axis.

Page 272 Chapter Test 1. $x - 3 = 9$ or $x - 3 > 9$ 3. $-8 < 2n + 6$ and $2n + 6 < -2$ 5. The graph shows
all real numbers between, but not including, −4 and 4.   7. Exercise 7 is located at the top of page 574.
9. $\begin{cases} x \geq 110 \\ y \geq 60 \\ x + y \leq 300 \end{cases}$ 11. (240, 60), (110, 60), (110, 190)   13. $x = -5$ or $x = 5$ 15. The graph consists of two
rays, one in Quadrant 1 and one in Quadrant II, with their initial point at (0, 0). The ray in
Quadrant I also passes through (2, 6), and the ray in Quadrant II also passes through
(−2, 6).

7.

Page 273   Additional Practice   1. $2y = 5$ or $2y > 5$ **3.** $-6 < 4a + 6$ and $4a + 6 < -2$ **5.** $0 > p > -4$; all points between 0 and -4, including 0 and not including -4 **7.** The open half-plane above the line that contains $(0, -1)$ and $(2, 1)$ **9.** The open half-plane below the line that contains $(0, -4)$ and $(-4, 0)$
11.

13.

15. $x = -2$ or $x = 4$ **17.** $x = -1\frac{1}{3}$ or $x = 4$
19. The graph consists of two parallel lines, one 1 unit above the x axis, and the other two units below the x axis.
21. $15 \le s \le 100$
23. $200x + 140y$
25. $(2, 6), (4, 3), (4, 6)$; $1220

Page 274   Review of Word Problems   1. $60.90   **3.**

s	100	200	300
t	6	12	18

5. $15   **7.** 936 mi   **9.** 52
11. $0.08x + 0.10y$ **13.** Vertices of the polygonal region: $(150, 75), (150, 150), (225, 75)$

Page 275   Cumulative Review Chapters 5-7   1. b   **3.** b   **5.** a   **7.** b   **9.** c   **11.** c   **13.** c   **15.** d
17. a   **19.** c   **21.** c   **23.** d   **25.** d

Page 277   Preparing for College Entrance Tests   1. c   **3.** b   **5.** a   **7.** a   **9.** b   **11.** d   **13.** c   **15.** c
17. c   **19.** c

CHAPTER 8: EXPONENTS AND POLYNOMIALS

Page 281   Classroom Exercises   1. $10; 6; 10 \cdot 10 \cdot 10 \cdot 10 \cdot 10 \cdot 10$ **3.** $3^4; 3 \cdot 3 \cdot 3 \cdot 3$ **5.** $x^6; x; 6$

Page 282   Written Exercises   1. $5; 6; 5 \cdot 5 \cdot 5 \cdot 5 \cdot 5 \cdot 5$ **3.** $2; 6; 2 \cdot 2 \cdot 2 \cdot 2 \cdot 2 \cdot 2$ **5.** 10^5;
$10 \cdot 10 \cdot 10 \cdot 10 \cdot 10$ **7.** $10^4; 10; 4$ **9.** $x^1; x; 1$ **11.** $10,000$ **13.** $100,000$ **15.** $10,000,000,000$
17. a   **19.** -1 **21.** -1 **23.** -1 **25.** 1   **27.** 1   **29.** 1   **31.** 10^5 **33.** 10^6 **35.** 10^3 **37.** 10^9
39. 10^{12} **41.** 2^7 **43.** 10^5 **45.** 2^6 **47.** 2^{17} **49.** a^6 **51.** m^8 **53.** 4   **55.** 2   **57.** 9   **59.** -6
61. 18   **63.** -24

Page 283   Review Capsule for Section 8-2   1. 200   **2.** -378 **3.** -54 **4.** 1   **5.** 0   **6.** 3600
7. -280 **8.** -1

Page 284   Classroom Exercises   1. x^{10} **3.** $-x^5$ **5.** a^9 **7.** $-2a^2b^3$

Page 284   Written Exercises   1. x^7 **3.** $-y^3$ **5.** x^9 **7.** m^7 **9.** n^7 **11.** a^2 **13.** b^5 **15.** $-b^2$
17. $-x^3$ **19.** y^4 **21.** p^5 **23.** $3^{10} = 59,049$ **25.** $2^8 = 256$ **27.** $(-5)^7 = -78,125$ **29.** $20x^3y^2$
31. $-24m^3n^2y^4$ **33.** $-36x^8$ **35.** x^4 **37.** 10^9 **39.** 10^{15} **41.** 6×10^6 **43.** 3×10^9
45. $2.8a \times 10^{11}$ **47.** N   **49.** N   **51.** N   **53.** x^{a+2} **55.** x^{a+b} **57.** x^{5a} **59.** 3^{x+2} **61.** 2^{9a+1}
63. $(x + 2)^{a+6}$

Page 286   Classroom Exercises   1. x^6 **3.** $9x^8$ **5.** $-a^9b^6$ **7.** $\frac{9}{16}$

Page 286   Written Exercises   1. x^6 **3.** x^8 **5.** a^{12} **7.** x^{21} **9.** x^{36} **11.** y^9 **13.** b^{24} **15.** y^{32}

17. x^2y^2 19. $25x^2$ 21. $x^4y^4z^4$ 23. 36   25. x^4 27. y^2 29. $27b^3$ 31. $9a^4b^2$ 33. $-27b^3$
35. $8x^9y^6$ 37. $64x^9y^6$ 39. x^8y^4 41. $64a^{12}c^6d^9$ 43. $64x^{18}y^{12}$ 45. x^8y^6 47. 4×10^6
49. 1.331×10^{18} 51. $\dfrac{x^2}{y^2}$ 53. $\dfrac{8}{27}$ 55. $\dfrac{c^7}{d^7}$ 57. $\dfrac{x^4}{y^6}$ 59. $\dfrac{b^4}{a^2}$ 61. $\dfrac{a^6}{b^9}$ 63. $\dfrac{x^6}{y^4}$ 65. i   67. a
69. f   71. d   73. $\dfrac{a^8}{b^4c^{12}}$ 75. $\dfrac{a^9b^6}{c^{12}}$ 77. $-6a^7b^8$ 79. $\dfrac{-27x^6}{64y^6}$ 81. x^{n^2} 83. $\dfrac{m^k}{n^k}$ 85. $\dfrac{3^cx^{cn}}{5^cy^{cm}}$
87. $\dfrac{3^ka^{km}b^{kn}}{2^kx^ky^k}$

Page 287   Calculator Exercises   1. 225   3. 2025   5. 3645   7. 1,000,000   9. 36,400,000
11. 160,000   13. 107,374.18   15. 11,805,916.2

Page 287   Review Capsule for Section 8-4   1. 1   2. 0   3. -1 4. 4   5. $-\dfrac{1}{4}$ 6. $-z$ 7. $-8x$ 8. 1

Page 288   Classroom Exercises   1. x^6 3. $-xy^2$ 5. $8^2 = 64$

Page 289   Written Exercises   1. 2^2 or 4   3. 5^3 or 125   5. a^5 7. x   9. ay^2 11. a^2b^3 13. k^2m
15. $5x^5y$ 17. $9r^2s^2$ 19. 4   21. P   23. P   25. N   27. P   29. $-2b$ 31. $\dfrac{3ab^3}{2}$ 33. $-125a^3$
35. 25×10^4 37. b   39. $a^{t-v}b^{w-25}$ 41. $x^{u-4v}y$ 43. $a^{2x-1}b^{3y-1}c^{k-1}$ 45. x^{3a+3} 47. x^{9a-39}

Page 289   Review Capsule for Section 8-5   1. 1000   2. 100,000   3. 1,000,000   4. 10   5. 10,000
6. 10,000,000   7. $\dfrac{1}{100}$ 8. $\dfrac{1}{1000}$ 9. 1   10. $\dfrac{1}{1000}$ 11. $\dfrac{1}{100,000}$ 12. $\dfrac{1}{10,000}$

Page 291   Classroom Exercises   1. $\dfrac{1}{16}$ 3. $-\dfrac{1}{4}$ 5. $\dfrac{1}{9b^2}$ 7. 7×10^9 9. 6.3×10^{-5} 11. 7.89×10^2
13. 2.107×10^1

Page 292   Written Exercises   1. 16   3. 1   5. 1000   7. 1   9. $-\dfrac{1}{8}$ 11. $\dfrac{64}{27}$ 13. 16   15. $-\dfrac{64}{27}$
17. $\dfrac{1}{1000}$ 19. $\dfrac{9}{4}$ 21. $\dfrac{1}{a^3}$ 23. $\dfrac{3}{x^5}$ 25. $\dfrac{1}{m}$ 27. $\dfrac{1}{4y}$ 29. $\dfrac{b^2}{a^3}$ 31. $\dfrac{1}{27y^3}$ 33. 4.6×10^3
35. 6.7×10^7 37. 2.4×10^{13} 39. 5.7×10^{-4} 41. 2×10^{-5} 43. 8×10^{-4} 45. 2×10^{-4}
47. 6×10^6 49. 3×10^3 51. 4×10^7 53. 5×10^{-3} 55. 2.976×10^5 km per second
57. 1×10^5 light years   59. 1×10^{11} stars   61. 1.5×10^8 km   63. 1×10^{-8} g   65. 1×10^{15}
67. 6000   69. 0.000000022   71. $\dfrac{1}{a^8}$ 73. $\dfrac{b^2}{a^2}$ 74. x^4 77. x

Page 293   Review   1. -9 2. 3   3. -48 4. 64   5. 36   6. n^4 7. $-x^5$ 8. $-12a^7$ 9. $6c^3d^4$
10. y^8 11. a^8b^4 12. 4×10^8 13. $\dfrac{r^6}{s^3t^3}$ 14. a^2 15. y   16. $-3bc^2$ 17. $-4b^2$ 18. $\dfrac{1}{3^4} = \dfrac{1}{81}$
19. -64 20. $\dfrac{1}{(-\frac{2}{3})^3} = -\dfrac{1}{\frac{8}{27}} = -\dfrac{27}{8} = -3\dfrac{3}{8}$ 21. $\dfrac{3}{y^2}$ 22. $\dfrac{1}{(-3)^3} = \dfrac{1}{-27} = -\dfrac{1}{27}$ 23. 6×10^6
24. 4×10^{-2} 25. 7×10^{-4} 26. 1.5555×10^4

Page 293   Review Capsule for Section 8-6   1. $-2n$ 2. $2n$ 3. $-2x + 5$ 4. $3x^2 + 4x$ 5. $7a^2 + 3a - 4$
6. $2x + (-3x + 5)$ 7. $3a + (-2a + 3b)$ 8. $-3y + (6y + 3y - 4)$ 9. $3a + (-4a - 3b)$ 10. $t + (-4)$
$+ (-2t + 1)$ 11. $9 + (-r) + (-7r + 6)$
Page 295   Career Applications   1. 156   3. 75   5. 3.36×10^{18} 7. 3.31×10^{18} 9. 3.37×10^{18}
11. 8.20×10^{-14} 13. 8.14×10^{-8} cm^3

Page 297   Classroom Exercises   1. $12a + 2b$ 3. $2r + 6s$ 5. $-3x^3 + 6x^2 + 5x + 2$

Page 297   Written Exercises   1. $12a + 2b - 4c$ 3. $-p + 4t + 7x$ 5. $14x + y - 4z$ 7. $-5a^2 - 2ab - 4b^2$
9. $7ab - 3ac$ 11. $4x^2 + 15x - 7$ 13. $6a + 8b - 11c + 2d$ 15. $2x + 4y + 2$ 17. $12a + 20b - 12$
19. $6x + 11y - 8$ 21. $-3b + 3$ 23. $9x + 6$ 25. $-3m^2 + n$ 27. $-2b + 2c$ 29. $a + b$ 31. $-x^2 + 2x$
$+ 8$ 33. $x^2 - 6x - 7$ 35. $3x + 2y$ 37. $x^2 - 9y^2$ 39. $2x^2 - 2xy - 4y^2$ 41. $-9a + 3b - 6c + 3d$
43. $2x^2 + 8xy - 2y^2$ 45. $4xy$ 47. $-3x + 3y$ 49. $a + 2b + c + 1$ 51. The perimeter of the square is 2
meters larger.

Page 299 Review Capsule for Section 8-7 1. $6a + 15b - 12$ 2. $-14x + 7y - 35$ 3. $-2a + 6b - 1$ 4. $20k - 15s + 10$ 5. $-21 + 5t + 3r$ 6. $6u - 10w + 11z$ 7. a^9 8. q^3 9. $-t^7$ 10. a^{10} 11. $-27x^3y^6$ 12. $a - b + 3$ 13. $8b + 3c + 2$ 14. $9n - 2$

Page 300 Classroom Exercises 1. $3x^2 + 27x$ 3. $7x^2 + 25x + 12$ 5. $-12n^4 - 30n^2$ 7. $a^2 + 11a + 18$ 9. $-r^2s + 2rs - 7s$ 11. $x^2 - y^2$

Page 300 Written Exercises 1. $2a^2 + 3a$ 3. $3y^2 - 24y$ 5. $-2y^2 - 12y$ 7. $5m^2 - 2m$ 9. $7s^2 - 8s$ 11. $-12a^2 + 20ab$ 13. $2a^3 - 8a^2 + 6a$ 15. $y^4 - 6y^3 + 3y^2$ 17. $-3x^5y - 12x^3y^2 + 15x^2y^3$ 19. $a^2 + 10a + 21$ 21. $2a^2 + 14a + 20$ 23. $a^2 - a - 12$ 25. $6a^2 - 11a - 10$ 27. $6a^2 + 5a - 6$ 29. $ac + ad + bc + bd$ 31. $ac - ad - bc + bd$ 33. $9b^2 - 16c^2$ 35. $16x^2 - 25$ 37. $9x^2 - 24x + 16$ 39. $15x^2 + 11xy - 12y^2$ 41. $x^2 - \frac{3}{2}xy - y^2$ 43. $0.32n^2 - 9.8n + 45$ 45. $x^4 - y^4$ 47. $8s^3 - 6s^2 + 12s - 9$ 49. $6x^4 + 13x^2y^2 + 6y^4$ 51. $4x^2 + 12xy + 9y^2$ 53. $6x + 35$ 55. $2y^2 - 4y - 48$ 57. $16x^2 - 4y^2$ 59. $-5x + 2$ 61. $x^2 + 4x + 4$ 63. $\frac{h^2 + 3h}{2}$ 65. $\frac{1}{8}\pi(9x^2 - 6x + 1)$ 67. square; 1 square unit 69. square; 1 square unit 71. $x^3 + 3x^2 + 3x + 1$ 73. $n^5 - 7n^4 + 10n^3 + 2n^2 - 4n$ 75. $x^3 - 9x^2y + 9xy + 18xy^2 - 27y^2$ 77. $-2c^3 - 3c^2 + 5c + 6$ 79. $x^4 - 4x^3 + 6x^2 - 4x + 1$

Page 302 Review Capsule for Section 8-8 1. $9c^2$ 2. $15x^5$ 3. $12a^2b^2$ 4. $6x^4$ 5. $8a^5$ 6. $36b^3c^4d^3$ 7. $3x^4y^3z^7$ 8. $-x^6y^{12}z$

Page 302 Classroom Exercises 1. h 3. b 5. a 7. j 9. g

Page 303 Written Exercises 1. $x^2 + 8x + 15$ 3. $x^2 - 4$ 5. $a^2 + a - 6$ 7. $b^2 - 4b - 21$ 9. $p^2 + 20p + 99$ 11. $d^2 + d - 20$ 13. $12y^2 + 17y + 6$ 15. $2x^2 + 13x + 21$ 17. $9x^2 - 16$ 19. $b^2 + 8b + 16$ 21. $m^2 - 4m - 77$ 23. $a^2 - 4c^2$ 25. $3x^2 - x - 2$ 27. $y^4 + 6y^2 + 9$ 29. $16y^2 - 24y + 9$ 31. $4a^2 + 16a + 15$ 33. $5x^2 + 8x + 3$ 35. $35b^2 + 3b - 2$ 37. $24x^2 - 23x - 12$ 39. $6c^2 - 43c + 72$ 41. $x^4 - 16$ 43. $7a^2 + 54a - 16$ 45. $6x^2 - xy - 15y^2$ 47. $\frac{7}{2}x^2 - 17x - 24$ 49. $\frac{1}{12}t^2 + 4t + 48$ 51. $\frac{1}{35}x^2 - 2x + 35$ 53. $0.36w^2 + 0.42w - 1.2$ 55. $s^2 + 8s + 16$ 57. rectangle with length $(a + 2)$ units and width $(a + 1)$ units; 6 square units larger

Page 303 Review Capsule for Section 8-9 1. 4 2. x^2 3. $-x^2$ 4. $x^2y^2z^2$ 5. a^4 6. a^4 7. $-a^4$ 8. $4a^2$ 9. $-4a^2$ 10. $-4a^8$

Page 305 Classroom Exercises 1. $x^2 - 20x + 100$ 3. $x^2 - 4xy + 4y^2$ 5. $4p^2 - 4pq + q^2$ 7. $m^4 - 12m^2 + 36$

Page 305 Written Exercises 1. $a^2 + 6a + 9$ 3. $a^2 + 10a + 25$ 5. $a^2 - 10a + 25$ 7. $x^2 - 2xy + y^2$ 9. $4a^2 + 4a + 1$ 11. $25m^2 - 10m + 1$ 13. $n^2 + 6n + 9$ 15. $9x^2 - 6xy + y^2$ 17. $4x^2 - 12x + 9$ 19. $4x^2 + 4xy + y^2$ 21. $4x^2 - 12xy + 9y^2$ 23. $100a^2 + 40a + 4$ 25. $4x^4 + 12x^2y^2 + 9y^4$ 27. $a^4 - 6a^2b^2 + 9b^4$ 29. $a^4 - 6a^2 + 9$ 31. $121a^4 + 22a^2c^2 + c^4$ 33. 361 35. 2704 37. 441 39. 998,001 41. 10,201 43. $x^2 + x + \frac{1}{4}$ 45. $x^2 - \frac{1}{3}x + \frac{1}{36}$ 47. $36b^2 + 6b + \frac{1}{4}$ 49. $x^2 - ax + \frac{a^2}{4}$ 51. $x^2 + xy + \frac{y^2}{4}$

Page 307 Classroom Exercises 1. $x^2 - 1$ 3. $4r^2 - 25$ 5. $9h^2 - 16s^2$

Page 307 Written Exercises 1. $p^2 - 49$ 3. $p^2 - 64$ 5. $b^2 - c^2$ 7. $4p^2 - 9$ 9. $R^2 - r^2$ 11. $25x^2 - 16y^2$ 13. $36x^4 - 49y^2$ 15. $a^2b^2 - c^2$ 17. $\frac{1}{4} - 4x^2$ 19. $4c^2 - d^2$ 21. $25y^2 - 16$ 23. $x^6 - y^6$ 25. 399 27. 9996 29. 75 31. 396 33. 2499 35. $\frac{1}{2}x^2 + \frac{1}{2}x - 3$ 37. square is 16 square units greater 39. $1 - y^{4a}$ 41. $a^4b^{16} - 25$ 43. $b^{2n} - c^{4n}$

Page 309 Computer Exercises See Solution Key.

Page 310 Review 1. $5a - 2b$ 2. $4x^2y + 7xy^2$ 3. $3d^2 - 3d - 4$ 4. $x^3 - 4x$ 5. $12x - 3$ 6. $4y^3 + 8y^2$ 7. $2c^2 - 7c - 4$ 8. $4c^2 + 12c + 9$ 9. $4a^4 - 6a^2c + 2c^2$ 10. $b + 3$ 11. $y^2 - y - 6$ 12. $6b^2 + 11b + 3$ 13. $3m^4 - 8m^2n - 3n^2$ 14. $x^4 + 3x^2 - 10$ 15. $a^4 - b^2$ 16. $3a^2b^2 - 7ab + 4$ 17. $a^2 - 4a + 4$ 18. $9y^2 + 30y + 25$ 19. $4b^2 - 24bd + 36d^2$ 20. $r^4s^2 + 2r^2st + t^2$ 21. $b^2 - 4$

22. $r^2 - s^2$ 23. $1 - p^2$ 24. $9y^2 - 4$ 25. $9c^2 - 4d^2$ 26. $x^4 - 36$

Page 311 Chapter Objectives and Review 1. -8 3. 1 5. -1 7. 128 9. -128 11. a^8 13. p^5
15. 10^6, or 1,000,000 17. $3m^3n$ 19. x^{15} 21. $27y^3$ 23. $27c^3d^{12}$ 25. $\dfrac{m^6}{p^3n^9}$ 27. 3 29. $3ab^3$
31. $3x^3y$ 33. $s^{2x-1}t^{3y-2}$ 35. $\dfrac{1}{3^4} = \dfrac{1}{81}$ 37. $\dfrac{1}{y^6}$ 39. $\dfrac{3}{n^2}$ 41. 2.9×10^{10} 43. $4x - 2y$ 45. $3m^2$
$+ 5m$ 47. $30y + 15$ 49. $2x^2 + 7xy - 4y^2$ 51. $-x^2 + 2xy - y^2$ 53. $p^2 - 3p - 4$ 55. $6a^2 + ab$
$- 12b^2$ 57. $2d^2 + 5dh - 3h^2$ 59. $c^2 + 12c + 36$ 61. $x^4 + 6x^2 + 9$ 63. $d^2 - 25$ 65. $f^2 - g^2$
67. $25m^2 - 4n^2$

Page 313 Chapter Test 1. 2 3. -32 5. $-5ac^2$ 7. 6.5×10^8 9. 7.0×10^6 11. $4x - 5$
13. $m - n - p + 1$ 15. $x^2 - 8x + 16$ 17. $-w^7$ 19. $6b^2 - 3b$ 21. $3y^2 - 7xy - 6x^2$ 23. $3c^2 - 5cd$
$+ 2d^2$ 25. $4a^2 - b^2$

Page 313 Additional Practice 1. -2 3. -10 5. 400 7. $-12x^2$ 9. $18mn^4$ 11. a^3b^{12} 13. $\dfrac{a^5b^{15}}{c^{20}}$
15. ab^2 17. p^{2k+3} 19. 3.2×10^8 21. 6.52×10^{-5} 23. $7m^2n^3 - 3mn$ 25. $a^2 - 4a - 5$
27. $y^2 + 11y + 24$ 29. $3n^4 - 14n^2 + 15$ 31. $4n^2 - 12n + 9$ 33. $36y^2 - 8y + \dfrac{4}{9}$ 35. $x^2y^2 - 1$
37. $(8b + 12)$ units 39. square; 4 square units greater 41. rectangle with length $(2a + 1)$ units and width
$(2a - 1)$ units; 3 square units greater

CHAPTER 9: FACTORING POLYNOMIALS

Page 317 Classroom Exercises 1. Yes 3. No 5. C 7. P 9. C 11. $2^2 \cdot 5$ 13. $2^3 \cdot 5^2$
15. 41 is prime

Page 317 Written Exercises 1. Yes 3. Yes 5. No 7. No 9. Yes 11. Yes 13. P 15. C 17. C
19. P 21. P 23. C 25. $2 \cdot 3^2$ 27. $3 \cdot 7$ 29. $2 \cdot 3 \cdot 7$ 31. $3^2 \cdot 5$ 33. 5^2 35. $3 \cdot 11$
37. $2^2 \cdot 5^3$ 39. $2^2 \cdot 3 \cdot 5^2$ 41. $2^6 \cdot 3 \cdot 5$ In Exercises 43-54, answers may vary. 43. $2 \cdot 2$
45. $1 \cdot 3$ 47. $1 \cdot 7$ 49. $2 \cdot 4$ 51. $\dfrac{1}{2} \cdot \dfrac{1}{4}$ 53. $\dfrac{1}{2} \cdot \dfrac{1}{5}$ 55. 6 by 12; 8 by 9 57. 5 rows of 20 plants
each; 10 rows of 10 plants each

Page 318 Calculator Exercises 1. 3 3. 31 5. 131,071

Page 318 Review Capsule for Section 9-2 1. $x^2 + 3x$ 2. $-2a + 8$ 3. $a^2b - 2ab$ 4. $x^3y^2 + 7x^2y$
5. $ab + ac - ad$ 6. $-2xy^2 + 12xy - 6x$ 7. $4x + 4y$ 8. $pqr - psq$ 9. $a^2 - 2a + ab - 2b$
10. $xz + 2z + 3x + 6$ 11. $ty - t + 5y - 5$

Page 320 Classroom Exercises 1. 8 3. $3x$ 5. $a + b^2$ 7. $ab - 4bc + 2ac$ 9. $x - y$ 11. $14(p + q)$
13. $t(x + y)$ 15. $13t(s - 2)$ 17. $(a + b)(t + w)$ 19. $(4 + e)(d + 1)$

Page 320 Written Exercises 1. x 3. b 5. x, $2y$ 7. 3 9. 1, $3y$ 11. 5 13. $4m$ 15. $8x$, 1
17. $4a$, 1 19. $2m$, 1 21. 4 23. x 25. $4a$, 1 27. 5 29. 1, $7y$ 31. a, b 33. 2, s 35. $7(x + y)$
37. $4(2x - y)$ 39. $x(3 - aw)$ 41. $c(4 + a + b)$ 43. $d(d + 2 + a)$ 45. $5(x - 2y + 3z^2)$ 47. $2\pi r(r + h)$
49. $cdh(h^2 + c + c^2dh)$ 51. $(a + d)(b - c)$ 53. $(a - s)(q - r)$ 55. $(k + r)(p - n)$ 57. $(x + y)(x - y)$
$(2a + b)$ 59. $7ab(a - 1)$ 61. prime 63. prime 65. prime 67. $7(2x^2 + xy + 3y^2)$ 69. prime
71. $3x(9x^3 + x^2 + 3a)$ 73. $25x(y - 2z + 4)$ 75. $x(3x + 6y - 2x^2)$ 77. $21(1 - 2p)$ 79. $4x(2x - 3y - 4z)$
81. $3x(x^2 - 5x - 2)$ 83. $a^2(3 + 4a - 5a^2b)$ 85. $x^3 + 1$ 87. $2w$

Page 322 Review Capsule for Section 9-3 1. $b^2 - 25$ 2. $4a^2 - 1$ 3. $9x^2 - 4$ 4. $x^4 - y^4$ 5. $\dfrac{1}{4}x^2$
$- y^2$ 6. $81 - p^2q^2$

Page 322 Classroom Exercises 1. $(m + 1)(m - 1)$ 3. $(2r + 1)(2r - 1)$ 5. $(a + 12)(a - 12)$
7. $(y + 2)(y - 2)$ 9. $(b + \dfrac{1}{5})(b - \dfrac{1}{5})$ 11. $(4t + \dfrac{1}{7})(4t - \dfrac{1}{7})$

Page 323 Written Exercises 1. $(y + 3)(y - 3)$ 3. $(x + 5)(x - 5)$ 5. $(2x + 3)(2x - 3)$
7. $4(2y - 3)(2y + 3)$ 9. $(xy + a)(xy - a)$ 11. $(3x^2y + b)(3x^2y - b)$ 13. $(xy + z)(xy - z)$
15. prime 17. $4(x^2 + 4y^2)$ 19. $(5x + 7)(5x - 7)$ 21. $(\dfrac{1}{3}x + 4)(\dfrac{1}{3}x - 4)$ 23. $(\dfrac{2}{3}x + \dfrac{5}{6}y)(\dfrac{2}{3}x - \dfrac{5}{6}y)$

25. $(x + \frac{1}{7})(x - \frac{1}{7})$ 27. $(\frac{1}{8}b + 5)(\frac{1}{8}b - 5)$ 29. a^2; b^2; $a^2 - b^2$; $(a + b)(a - b)$ 31. $\pi R^2 - 4\pi r^2$; $\pi(R + 2r)(R - 2r)$ 33. $(c + a + b)(c - a - b)$ 35. $(r + s + t + u)(r + s - t - u)$ 37. $(2x - 2a + 3y + 3b)$ $(2x - 2a - 3y - 3b)$

Page 324 Review 1. Yes 2. Yes 3. No 4. $3^2 \cdot 5$ 5. $2^4 \cdot 3$ 6. $2^3 \cdot 7$ 7. $2 \cdot 3 \cdot 13$ 8. $2 \cdot 5^3$
9. $2^4 \cdot 3^2 \cdot 5$ 10. $5(a + 2b)$ 11. $x(3 + a + d)$ 12. $pr(r - p)$ 13. $y(y + 3)$ 14. Prime
15. $s^2 t(st + t^2 - 1)$ 16. $(a - 2)(b + c)$ 17. $(k + w)(x + y)$ 18. $(x + 2)(y + 2)$ 19. $(1 + m)(1 - m)$
20. $(a + 3)(a - 3)$ 21. $(3b + 4)(3b - 4)$ 22. $(9x + 1)(9x - 1)$ 23. Prime 24. $(2a + b^2)(2a - b^2)$
25. $(xy + 3)(xy - 3)$ 26. $(p^3 + q^4)(p^3 - q^4)$ 27. $(x + \frac{1}{2})(x - \frac{1}{2})$ 28. $(2t + \frac{1}{3})(2t - \frac{1}{3})$
29. $(\frac{2}{5}p + 1)(\frac{2}{5}p - 1)$ 30. $(\frac{n}{4} + \frac{m}{2})(\frac{n}{4} - \frac{m}{2})$, or $(\frac{1}{4}n + \frac{1}{2}m)(\frac{1}{4}n - \frac{1}{2}m)$

Page 324 Puzzle See Solution Key.

Page 324 Review Capsule for Section 9-4 1. $a^2 - 6a + 9$ 2. $x^2 + 8x + 16$ 3. $4x^2 - 20x + 25$
4. $81 + 18b + b^2$ 5. $4a^2 + 20at + 25t^2$ 6. $9p^4 - 12p^2 + 4$ 7. $0.01 + 0.2z + z^2$ 8. $\frac{1}{4} - bc + b^2c^2$

Page 325 Consumer Applications 1. about 131 pounds 3. about 178 pounds

Page 327 Classroom Exercises 1. Yes 3. Yes 5. Yes 7. $2b$ 9. 1 11. $3t$

Page 327 Written Exercises 1. Yes 3. No 5. Yes 7. 5 9. 5 11. 1 13. $-$ 15. $-$ 17. $(x + 3)^2$
19. $(n + 7)^2$ 21. $(2x + 3y)^2$ 23. $(1 + 4x)^2$ 25. $(a + 4)^2$ 27. $(2x + 1)^2$ 29. $(3y + 2)^2$ 31. $(b - 3)^2$
33. $(3a - 2)^2$ 35. $(7a - 6)^2$ 37. $(x - 9)^2$ 39. $(1 - 3b)^2$ 41. $(a + b + c)(a + b - c)$
43. $(x - y + 3)(x - y - 3)$ 45. $(a + b + 3)(a + b - 3)$

Page 328 Calculator Exercises 1. 28 3. 231 5. 1711 7. 125,751

Page 328 Review Capsule for Section 9-5 1. $a^2 + 3a + 2$ 2. $x^2 - 5x + 6$ 3. $y^2 + y - 12$ 4. $10 - 3t$ $- t^2$ 5. $y^2 - 3yz - 10z^2$ 6. $d^2 + 3dg - 88g^2$ 7. $r^2 + 4rs - 21s^2$ 8. $x^2 - 7xy - 18y^2$
9. $w^2 + wz - 2z^2$

Page 330 Classroom Exercises 1. 4, 3 3. 8, -3 5. $-3, -3$ 7. $-6, -3$ 9. $-8, 4$ 11. 9, -8

Page 330 Written Exercises 1. $(x + 4)(x + 3)$ 3. $(y + 5)(y + 3)$ 5. $(a + 4)(a - 1)$ 7. $(y + 8)(y - 1)$
9. $(x - 3)(x - 2)$ 11. $(x - 9)(x - 4)$ 13. $(x - 5)(x + 3)$ 15. $(x - 9)(x + 8)$ 17. $(x + 8)(x - 3)$
19. $(x + 8)(x - 4)$ 21. $(x - 7)(x - 3)$ 23. $(x + 8)(x + 6)$ 25. $(x + 8)(x + 1)$ 27. $(x + 4)(x - 2)$
29. $(y - 11)(y - 6)$ 31. $(y - 13)(y + 12)$ 33. $(y + 12)(y - 6)$ 35. $(10 + v)(2 + v)$ 37. $(17 - k)(3 - k)$
39. $(r - 4t)(r - 2t)$ 41. $(a - 12b)(a - 2b)$ 43. $(x - 6y)(x + y)$ 45. $(x + 9y)(x - 2y)$ 47. $(a + 6b)$ $(a + 2b)$ 49. $(r + 5t)(r + 3t)$ 51. $(x - 15y)(x + 4y)$ 53. r^2 55. $(x + 12)(x + 1)$

Page 331 Puzzle See Solution Key.

Page 331 Review Capsule for Section 9-6 1. $6x^2 + 17x + 12$ 2. $3b^2 - 8b - 35$ 3. $5y^2 - 2y - 16$
4. $25a^2 + 50ab + 21b^2$ 5. $6a^2 - 7ab - 3b^2$ 6. $7c^2 + 33cd - 10d^2$ 7. $15y^2 - 17y + 4$
8. $44p^2 + 25p - 6$ 9. $12x^2 - 13xy + 3y^2$

Page 333 Classroom Exercises 1. d 3. e 5. c 7. 5 9. 4 11. 3

Page 334 Written Exercises 1. 3 3. 1 5. $8n$, $5n$ 7. 7, 1 9. 1, 2 11. $2(x + 2)(x + 1)$
13. $(3y + 2)(3y - 1)$ 15. $(3y - 4)(2y - 3)$ 17. $(3x + 4)(2x - 1)$ 19. $(5x - 1)(x - 3)$ 21. $(3y + 7)$ $(y - 1)$ 23. $(2y + 5)(y + 1)$ 25. $(3x - 2)(x - 3)$ 27. $(3a + 5)(a - 5)$ 29. $(2t - 1)(t + 3)$
31. $(2x + 5)(x - 8)$ 33. $(5q + 3)(q - 9)$ 35. $(4x - 3y)(2x - y)$ 37. $(6 + 7y)(3 - 5y)$ 39. $(2x + 3)$ $(x + 2)$ 41. $(4x - 7y)(3x - 2y)$ 43. $(4a + 7b)^2$ 45. $(8a + 7b)^2$

Page 334 Review Capsule for Section 9-7 1. s 2. 3 3. r 4. $5x$ 5. 9 6. $7a^2b$ 7. 2 8. t 9. N
10. D 11. P 12. N 13. D 14. N 15. P 16. P

Page 336 Classroom Exercises 1. $2(x + 1)^2$ 3. $6(t + 6)(t - 1)$ 5. $x(a + b + c)$

Page 336 Written Exercises 1. $5(b + 6)(b - 2)$ **3.** $3(2x + 1)(x - 4)$ **5.** $2(3x + 2)(2x - 3)$ **7.** $3(x + y)$ $(x - y)$ **9.** $3b(b - 1)$ **11.** $2m(m - 9)(m - 1)$ **13.** $2a(a + 1)(a - 1)$ **15.** $3(4m - 1)(m + 3)$ **17.** $3(x + 4)(x - 2)$ **19.** $2(x + 10)(x - 4)$ **21.** $2(t - 7)^2$ **23.** $x^2(x + 3)(x - 3)$ **25.** $2(a + 4)(a + 3)$ **27.** $s(t - 5)(t + 4)$ **29.** $3(x^2 + 4x + 15)$ **31.** $3t^2(2 - 5t)$ **33.** $a(b - 9)(b + 8)$ **35.** $(3a - 2)(a + 1)$ **37.** prime **39.** $2(x - 4)(x - 3)$ **41.** $(7c + 5)^2$ **43.** $x(x + 1)(x - 1)$ **45.** $(1 + 2y)(1 - 2y)$ **47.** $2y(x + z) + (z + y)(z - y)$ **49.** $(x + 4)(x - 4)(a + b)$ **51.** $[5r(r + 1) + 8](r - 6)$ **53.** $(x - y - 3)$ $(x - y)$ **55.** $(z + 2)(z - 2)(z + 9q)(z - 9q)$ **57.** $(x - 5)^2(x + 4)(x + 6)$ **59.** $4xy$ **61.** $(k + 1)(k + 1)(k - 1)$ **63.** $(t^2 + 2)(t + 1)(t - 1)$ **65.** $(h + a - 3)(h - a + 3)$ **67.** $(3a + 2)(a + 4)$ **69.** $(x + y + 3)(x + y - 3)[(x + y)^2 - 7]$

Page 338 Classroom Exercises 1. $b = 0$ or $b = 1$ **3.** $q = 3$ or $q = 7$ **5.** $t = -3$ or $t = 1$ **7.** $x = -3$ or $x = 3$ **9.** $y = 1\frac{1}{2}$ or $y = 3$

Page 338 Written Exercises 1. $x = -1$ or $x = 6$ **3.** $x = -2$ or $x = 5$ **5.** $n = -1$ or $n = 0$ **7.** $y = -1$ or $y = 9$ **9.** $c = -7$ or $c = 7$ **11.** $y = -2$ or $y = 6$ **13.** $a = -1$ or $a = \frac{2}{5}$ **15.** $a = -\frac{2}{3}$ or $a = \frac{1}{2}$ **17.** $n = 0$ or $n = 7$ **19.** $n = -2\frac{1}{3}$ or $n = 0$ **21.** $a = 0$ or $a = 2\frac{1}{4}$ **23.** $a = -2\frac{1}{4}$ or $a = 1\frac{1}{6}$ **25.** $w = -\frac{1}{3}$ or $w = 0$ or $w = \frac{2}{3}$ **27.** $y = -\frac{1}{2}$ **29.** $y = 0$ or $y = 16$ **31.** $r = -1$ or $r = 1$ **33.** $w = -3$ or $w = 0$ or $w = 5$ **35.** $b = -3$ or $b = 4$ **37.** $z = -5$ or $z = -4$ **39.** $x = -3$ or $x = 0$ or $x = 3$ **41.** $a = -14$ or $a = -4$ **43.** $a = 3$ or $a = 4$ **45.** $z = 1$ or $z = 2$ **47.** $a = -2\frac{2}{3}$ or $a = 2$

Page 338 Puzzle See Solution Key.

Page 340 Classroom Exercises 1. a. Let w = width of hallway, then $4w$ = length **b.** $(4w)(w) = 144$ **3. a.** Let first integer = n, then second integer = $n + 1$ **b.** $n(n + 1) = 182$

Page 340 Word Problems 1. 7, 5 **3.** 15, 14 or -14, -15 **5.** -8, -7 **7.** 9 or -8 **9.** width = 24 m; length = 44 m **11.** -5, -3 **13.** 15 rows **15.** 8 players **17.** width = 4 cm; length = 12 cm **19.** width = 6 cm; length = 8 cm **21.** 18 cm; 22 cm **23.** 2 meters **25.** 20 ft; 50 ft

Page 342 Review 1. $(x + 4)(x + 4)$, or $(x + 4)^2$ **2.** $(8 - a)(8 - a)$, or $(8 - a)^2$ **3.** $(3x + 1)(3x + 1)$, or $(3x + 1)^2$ **4.** $(x + 3)(x + 1)$ **5.** $(b - 2)(b - 4)$ **6.** $(r - 6)(r + 2)$ **7.** $(5x + 1)(x - 2)$ **8.** $(7y - 1)$ $(y - 1)$ **9.** $(3y + 2)(2y + 3)$ **10.** $(3b - 2)(b - 1)$ **11.** $(a - 4)(2a + 3)$ **12.** $(15t - 2)(2t + 3)$ **13.** $4(a - 1)(a + 1)$ **14.** $3(d + 4)(d + 4)$, or $3(d + 4)^2$ **15.** $4(n - 1)(n - 1)$, or $4(n - 1)^2$ **16.** $x(x - 8)$ $(x + 1)$ **17.** $2y(2y - 1)(y + 3)$ **18.** $2b^2(3b + 1)(b - 2)$ **19.** $x = -4$ or $x = 0$ **20.** $y = 0$ or $y = 7$ **21.** $n = -2$ or $n = 3$ **22.** $a = -4$ or $a = 4$ **23.** $p = -3$ **24.** $r = -1\frac{1}{2}$ or $r = 1\frac{1}{3}$ **25.** -2 **26.** width: 15 m; length: 24 m

Page 344 Computer Exercises See Solution Key.

Page 345 Chapter Objectives and Review 1. 3^3 **3.** $2 \cdot 47$ **5.** $2^3 \cdot 3^2 \cdot 5$ **7.** 3, 5, 9, 15, 45 **9.** 2, 7, 14, 49, 98 **11.** $3(a - 2b)$ **13.** Prime **15.** $n(4 + m - n)$ **17.** $(3 + x)(3 - x)$ **19.** $(n - 1)(n + 1)$ **21.** $4(5 - 2x)(5 + 2x)$ **23.** $(mn - c)(mn + c)$ **25.** $(\frac{3}{4} - y)(\frac{3}{4} + y)$ **27.** $(5 - \frac{1}{5}r)(5 + \frac{1}{5}r)$ **29.** $(y - 5)$ $(y - 5)$, or $(y - 5)^2$ **31.** $(4x - 3)(4x - 3)$, or $(4x - 3)^2$ **33.** $(2m - n)(2m - n)$, or $(2m - n)^2$ **35.** $(a + 2)(a + 4)$ **37.** $(s - 5)(s + 2)$ **39.** $(y - 2)(y + 8)$ **41.** $(n + 9)(n - 4)$ **43.** $(t + 5s)(t - 3s)$ **45.** $(y - 2)(5y - 3)$ **47.** $(8x - 1)(x - 3)$ **49.** $(8n + 3)(2n - 1)$ **51.** $(8t - 5)(3t + 2)$ **53.** $2(h + 1)$ $(h + 1)$, or $2(h + 1)^2$ **55.** $4(p - 2)(p - 2)$, or $4(p - 2)^2$ **57.** $5(c - 5)(c + 5)$ **59.** $y(y + 4)(y - 2)$ **61.** $n^2(4n - 3)(2n + 3)$ **63.** $y = -4$ or $y = 0$ **65.** $b = -3$ or $b = 3$ **67.** $t = -12$ or $t = 2$ **69.** $y = -6$ or $y = 0$ or $y = 6$ **71.** 3, 4, 5 **73.** 22 **75.** 14

Page 347 Chapter Test 1. $2^5 \cdot 3$ **3.** 13 **5.** $2^2 \cdot 5 \cdot 11$ **7.** $(3b - 1)(3b + 1)$ **9.** $(y + 3)(y + 8)$ **11.** $a^2b(b^2 - a)$ **13.** $(n + 8)(n - 7)$ **15.** $2(3b - 1)(b + 1)$ **17.** $(ab - 4c)(ab + 4c)$ **19.** $a(a - 3)(a + 2)$ **21.** $x = -5$ or $x = 3$ **23.** $p = -3$ or $p = 1$ **25.** width: 4 cm; length: 12 cm

Page 348   Additional Practice   1. $3^2 \cdot 7$ 3. $2^2 \cdot 3 \cdot 5$ 5. $3 \cdot 5^3$ 7. $3a(5 - 4a)$ 9. $9a^2(1 - 2a)$
11. $(4m - 7n)(4m + 7n)$ 13. $(x^5 - y)(x^5 + y)$ 15. $(2x + 3)(2x + 3)$, or $(2x + 3)^2$ 17. $(x - 7)(x + 2)$
19. $(a + 4b)(a - 3b)$ 21. $2(2x + 5)(x - 1)$ 23. $5(x - 3)(x + 3)$ 25. $2n(3n - 2)(3n + 1)$ 27. $n = -4$
or $n = 6$ 29. 10 rows, 24 chairs; 12 rows, 20 chairs; 15 rows, 16 chairs; 16 rows, 15 chairs; 20 rows,
12 chairs; 24 rows, 10 chairs   31. $(x - 9)$ units; $(x + 4)$ units   33. 6

CHAPTER 10: RATIONAL EXPRESSIONS

Page 351   Classroom Exercises   1. $33\frac{1}{3}\%$ 3. $\frac{3}{8}$ 5. $\frac{3}{1}$, or 3   7. 25%   9. $\frac{1}{8}$

Page 352   Written Exercises   1. $x = 35$ 3. $x = 2$ 5. $x = 63$ 7. $x = 10.5$ 9. $x = 1$ 11. $b = \frac{1}{2}$

13. $r = 10$ 15. $s = -\frac{1}{2}$ 17. $a = -31$ 19. $x =$ miles in 6 hr; $\frac{90}{1\frac{1}{2}} = \frac{x}{6}$ 21. $d =$ distance on map; $\frac{1}{500}$

$= \frac{d}{1500}$ 23. $3\frac{3}{4}$ cups   25. 240 km   27. 2.1 cm   29. 6 runs   31. about 5.5 hr   33. 3200 min
35. $96   37. Sally: $72; Tom: $48   39. length: 132 m; width: 48 m   41. $x = \frac{1}{3}$ 43. $x = 4$
45. $x = -4$ or $x = 4$ 47. $a : b = 4 : 7$ 49. $(p + q) : q = 6 : 5$

Page 353   Review Capsule for Section 10-2   1. 132   2. 147.6   3. 64   4. 38   5. 13   6. 60

Page 355   Classroom Exercises   1. $0.12(\$8000)$ 3. $0.115(y + 8000)$ 5. $0.04(20)$ 7. $0.6(30 - d)$

Page 356   Word Problems   1. $2000 at 6%; $6000 at 9%   3. 40 grams   5. $2500 at 10%; $10,000 at 12%
7. 55.125 liters   9. about 8.57 quarts   11. 20 milliliters   13. 10%: $950; 12%: $1900; 8%: $1400
15. 9%: $38,000; 12%: $19,000

Page 358   Classroom Exercises   1. $\frac{6}{11}$ 3. $\frac{y}{3x}$ 5. 1   7. -2

Page 358   Written Exercises   1. $\frac{5}{4}$ 3. xy 5. $\frac{2}{3}$ 7. $\frac{a}{b}$ 9. $\frac{4}{5y}$ 11. $\frac{3x}{4}$ 13. $\frac{4}{7}$ 15. $\frac{1}{2}$ 17. $\frac{8}{5(x + y)}$

19. $3(x - y)$ 21. $\frac{(x - 6y)^2}{x}$ 23. $\frac{5(a + b)}{2(2a + b)}$ 25. $\frac{x - 2y}{3x + 4y}$ 27. $\frac{b(2a + b)}{(a + b)(a - b)}$ 29. 1   31. $\frac{1}{a + b}$

33. $\frac{1}{x + 1}$ 35. $a + 1$ 37. -1 39. $\frac{1}{9 - b}$ 41. $-\frac{t - 1}{t + 1}$ 43. $-\frac{1}{(n - k)^2}$ 45. $2x$ 47. $\frac{x + 2}{2(x - 4)}$

49. $\frac{6}{x - 3}$ 51. $-3(a + 1)$ 53. $\frac{R - r}{3}$ 55. simplest form   57. $\frac{3(x + 3)}{x - 8}$ 59. $x + y - 1$ 61. $\frac{a + 2}{a - 5}$

Page 359   Review   1. $x = 8$ 2. $x = 12$ 3. $y = 3.25$ 4. $t = 6$ 5. 38.4 columns   6. 12%: $2000;
10%: $4000   7. 7.5 ounces   8. $\frac{4}{7d}$ 9. $\frac{1}{2a - b}$ 10. $\frac{3}{x + y}$ 11. $\frac{3x - 2y}{x - 2y}$

Page 361   Career Applications   1. 128.8 g   3. 2.8 g   5. 1.2 g   7. 0.6 g   9. 8 mL   11. 33.3 mL
Page 362   Review Capsule for Section 10-4   1. $12n^2$ 2. $2a^4 b^4$ 3. $-2c^{10}$ 4. $12x^3 y^3 z^8$ 5. x^{10}
6. $\frac{1}{4b^2}$ 7. $\frac{2rt^2}{5s}$ 8. $\frac{x^3}{36}$ 9. $\frac{9b^2}{2a^3}$ 10. $\frac{36a}{7b^6}$ 11. $6y$ 12. $\frac{9x^2 y^3}{4a^6 b^6}$ 13. $x^2 y^2(3x - 2y)$ 14. $(10z + 1)$
$(10z - 1)$ 15. $4x(2x + 1)(2x - 1)$ 16. $9(t + 1)^2$ 17. $(z - 9)(z + 2)$ 18. $(4q - 1)(q + 3)$

Page 363   Classroom Exercises   1. $\frac{a^2}{c}$ 3. $\frac{a^2 + ab}{b}$ 5. 1

Page 363   Written Exercises   1. $\frac{m}{n}$ 3. $\frac{c}{d}$ 5. $\frac{1}{a^2 by}$ 7. $\frac{2z}{7y}$ 9. 3   11. $\frac{4x^2 + 16x + 15}{2x - 5}$ 13. 1

15. $\frac{n^2 + 6n + 9}{n + 5}$ 17. $\frac{4xy}{1 + y}$ 19. $\frac{n}{m}$ 21. $\frac{a^2}{a^2 - a - 20}$ 23. $\frac{x + 4}{x + 3}$ 25. x 27. $x - 1$ 29. $\frac{1}{x - 4}$

31. 1   33. $\frac{20a^2 + 20ab}{6a^2 b + 21ab^2 + 18b^3}$ 35. $\frac{5m}{(m + n)^2}$ 37. $\frac{5(a + 1)}{a - 1}$ 39. 1   41. $\frac{a^2 + a - 2}{a^2 - 8a + 15}$

43. $\frac{(x + 1)(x^2 - x - 1)^2}{x(x - 1)}$ 45. $\frac{x^2(x + 2)}{y(x^2 - 7)}$ 47. $\frac{2b - 1}{2b - 5}$

608   *Answers to Selected Exercises*

Page 364 Review Capsule for Section 10-5 1. $(3y + 2)(3y - 2)$ 2. $m(m - 9)(m + 2)$ 3. $(3z + 8)(2z - 5)$ 4. $(h + 3)^2(h - 3)^2$ 5. $2(z^2 + 9)(z + 3)(z - 3)$ 6. $2(a + 2b - 2)(a - 2b + 2)$ 7. $x^2(2 + y - z)$ 8. $(5x + 3y)(x - y)$ 9. $3y(x + 1)(x + 1)$ 10. $(2x + 7)(2x + 7)$ 11. $2ax(x + 2y + 1)$ 12. $2a(x^2 + 2)(x - 1)(x + 1)$

Page 366 Classroom Exercises 1. y^3 3. $\dfrac{2}{(x + y)^2}$ 5. $\dfrac{n^2}{3}$ 7. $\dfrac{c + 4}{3(c - 2)}$ 9. x 11. $\dfrac{x}{a + x}$

Page 366 Written Exercises 1. 2 3. $\dfrac{1}{2}$ 5. $\dfrac{x}{3}$ 7. $\dfrac{ad}{bc}$ 9. $\dfrac{b}{a^2}$ 11. $\dfrac{g}{f}$ 13. $\dfrac{1}{6a}$ 15. 1 17. $\dfrac{4}{9a}$ 19. $\dfrac{x + 1}{ax}$ 21. $\dfrac{a - b}{x + y}$ 23. $\dfrac{x + y}{2(x - y)}$ 25. $\dfrac{x + 1}{3x}$ 27. $\dfrac{a}{(a + b)^2}$ 29. $\dfrac{2}{3}$ 31. $\dfrac{b^2}{a}$ 33. $\dfrac{a^2 b^3}{x^3}$ 35. $\dfrac{a^3 b^3}{r^3}$ 37. $\dfrac{x + 5}{x}$ 39. $\dfrac{y(x + y)}{x(x - y)}$ 41. $\dfrac{b^2(a + c)}{c(a + b)}$ 43. $\dfrac{3x^3(4a + b)}{5a^3}$

Page 367 Calculator Exercises 1. 0.4642857 3. 2.7824074

Page 369 Classroom Exercises 1. 24 3. 30 5. $30abc$ 7. $24a^2 b^3 c$ 9. $6(x + y)$ 11. $10r(r + 3)(r - 3)$

Page 369 Written Exercises 1. 12 3. 30 5. 30 7. ab 9. ab^2 11. $6a$ 13. $12p$ 15. $a^2 b^2$ 17. 24 19. 20 21. 48 23. xyz 25. $(x + y)(x - y)$ 27. $12(a - 2b)$ 29. $2(x + y)$ 31. $(x - 1)$ $(x - 2)(x - 3)$ 33. $(x + 2)(x - 2)(x - 4)$ 35. $2(2x + 3y)(2x - 3y)$ 37. $(2b - 3)(b + 1)(3b + 2)$

Page 372 Classroom Exercises 1. $\dfrac{7}{9}$ 3. $\dfrac{2x}{z}$ 5. $\dfrac{abd - 6c}{2b^2 d}$

Page 372 Written Exercises 1. $\dfrac{16}{b}$ 3. $\dfrac{49}{q}$ 5. $\dfrac{2a + 17b - 6}{3}$ 7. $\dfrac{10m + 2}{3}$ 9. $\dfrac{15}{4}$ 11. $\dfrac{-4a - 13b}{12}$ 13. $\dfrac{m + n}{x - y}$ 15. $\dfrac{m}{2y + 5}$ 17. $\dfrac{-2q}{r + 6}$ 19. $\dfrac{13x^2}{42}$ 21. $\dfrac{5x^2 y + 6xy^2}{30}$ 23. $\dfrac{-4a + 23}{18}$ 25. $\dfrac{11n - 14}{20}$ 27. $\dfrac{8b + 17c}{24}$ 29. $\dfrac{3a + 2b}{ab}$ 31. $\dfrac{4y - 5x}{xy}$ 33. $\dfrac{13}{6c}$ 35. $\dfrac{7a - 4b}{10p}$ 37. $\dfrac{3x + 5}{x^2}$ 39. $\dfrac{3x^2 + 2x - 5}{x^3}$ 41. $\dfrac{5a - 7b}{a^2 b^2}$ 43. $\dfrac{9n + 3}{mn^2}$ 45. $\dfrac{1}{4p}$ 47. $\dfrac{a^2 + b^2}{ab}$ 49. $\dfrac{5x - 6}{3x}$ 51. $\dfrac{5bx - 2}{2b^2}$ 53. $\dfrac{3a + ab + 5b}{ab}$ 55. $\dfrac{4x^2 - 3x + xy + 4y}{x^2}$ 57. $\dfrac{3b - 19a}{3a^2}$ 59. $\dfrac{2x - 40}{(x + 5)(x - 5)}$ 61. $\dfrac{2x^2 - xy + 3y^2}{(x + y)(x - y)}$ 63. $\dfrac{2a + b}{3a - b}$ 65. $\dfrac{5xy}{(2y - 3)(3y - 2)}$ 67. $\dfrac{3a - 1}{(a + 3)(a + 5)}$ 69. $\dfrac{3a - 1}{3(a + 2)}$ 71. $\dfrac{a^2 - 2ab + b^2 - a}{(a + b)(a - b)}$ 73. $\dfrac{a + 1}{a + 3}$ 75. $\dfrac{2a - 31}{(a - 1)(a + 2)(a - 3)}$ 77. $\dfrac{5y}{(y + 3)(y - 2)^2}$ 79. $\dfrac{-15x^2 + 7x + 10}{6(x + 1)(x - 1)}$ 81. $\dfrac{-3rs + s^2}{(r + s)^2(r - s)}$

Page 373 Review Capsule for Section 10-8 1. $4x + 5y$ 2. $-2r^2 + 3r + 25$ 3. $11c - 28$ 4. $17a - 17b$ 5. $-18x + 14$ 6. $a^2 + 2a + 2$

Page 375 Classroom Exercises 1. $\dfrac{b + 1}{b}$ 3. $\dfrac{x^2 + 3}{x}$ 5. $\dfrac{t^2 + t + 5}{t}$ 7. $\dfrac{1 - a^2 - a}{a}$

Page 375 Written Exercises 1. $\dfrac{3a + 1}{a}$ 3. $\dfrac{3b + a}{b}$ 5. $\dfrac{7a - 7b - 4}{a - b}$ 7. $\dfrac{a^2 + a + 1}{a + 1}$ 9. $\dfrac{7r + 9s}{r + s}$ 11. $\dfrac{11c - 28}{c - 3}$ 13. $\dfrac{ax^2 + b}{x}$ 15. $\dfrac{ac - b}{c}$ 17. $\dfrac{a^3 - 1}{a}$ 19. $\dfrac{3r - 2r^2 + 18}{r^2 - 9}$ 21. $\dfrac{a^2 + 2a + 2}{a + 1}$ 23. $\dfrac{14 - 18x}{3x - 1}$ 25. $\dfrac{x^2 - 3x - 15}{x + 3}$ 27. $\dfrac{2t^2 + 7t - 6}{t + 6}$ 29. $\dfrac{t^2 + 5t - 15}{t - 4}$ 31. $\dfrac{a^2 + 1}{a - 2}$ 33. $\dfrac{x^2 + 4}{(x + 2)(x - 2)}$ 35. $\dfrac{x^3 - 3x^2 - 13x + 22}{x - 5}$ 37. $\dfrac{x^4 + 11x - 10}{(x + 2)(x - 2)}$ 39. $\dfrac{23}{7}$ 41. $\dfrac{x - 3}{x^2}$ 43. $\dfrac{6a}{3a - 2}$ 45. $\dfrac{r^2 + 2r + 1}{r^2 - 2r - 1}$

Page 376 Review Capsule for Section 10-9 1. $4a$ 2. 9 3. a^2 4. t 5. $3xy$ 6. $3z^2$ 7. 1 8. $2z$

Page 377 Classroom Exercises 1. $0t$ 3. $0a$ 5. $0x^3 + 0x^2 + 0x$ 7. $2r^3 - 9r^2 + 10r + 5$ 9. $6z^2 - 13z + 2$

Page 378 Written Exercises 1. $x + 7$ 3. $c + 4$ 5. $3n + 2$ 7. $4y + 15 + \dfrac{6}{y + 1}$ 9. $3x + 1$

11. $3a - 2 + \dfrac{1}{2a - 3}$ 13. $5n + 2 + \dfrac{6}{3n + 2}$ 15. $a^2 - 3a - 4$ 17. $3x^2 + 5x - 2$ 19. $a^2 + 2ab + \dfrac{3ab^2}{3a + 2b}$

21. $x - 5 + \dfrac{50}{x + 5}$ 23. $a^2 + 2ab + 4b^2$ 25. $2x^2 + x + 1$ 27. $x^2 - 5x + 29 + \dfrac{-148}{x + 5}$

29. $x^2 + 3x + 7$ 31. $x^2 - 3x + 9$ 33. $(3y + 2)(y + 2)$ 35. $(2t + 3)(t - 1)^2$ 37. No; when $6n^3 - 22n + 1$ is divided by $(2n - 4)$, there is a remainder. 39. $k = 6$ 41. $c = 1$

Page 378 Puzzle See Solution Key.

Page 380 Computer Exercises See Solution Key.

Page 381 Review 1. $\dfrac{a}{4}$ 2. $\dfrac{x^2 - 2x - 3}{x - 1}$ 3. $\dfrac{x^2 + x - 2}{x^2 + 5x}$ 4. $\dfrac{a}{3}$ 5. $\dfrac{bx}{2a}$ 6. $2a + 2$ 7. 33 8. $4a^2 b^2$

9. $(x - 4)(x + 1)(x + 2)$ 10. $\dfrac{5a - 1}{a + b}$ 11. $\dfrac{3x + 2y}{x^2 y^2}$ 12. $\dfrac{x - 1}{x(x - 2)}$ 13. $\dfrac{2x + 1}{x}$ 14. $\dfrac{2y^2 - 1}{2y}$

15. $\dfrac{a^2 + b^2}{a + b}$ 16. $\dfrac{-x^2 + 2x}{x - 1}$ 17. $x - 3$ 18. $3b + 4$ 19. $x + 4$ 20. $8y + 1$

Page 382 Chapter Objectives and Review 1. $50\frac{2}{5}$ 3. 12 5. $2\frac{2}{3}$ 7. \$4800 9. 25 11. $\dfrac{3}{5}$

13. $\dfrac{x + y}{3(x - y)}$ 15. $\dfrac{x}{x + 2}$ 17. -2 19. $\dfrac{x}{2}$ 21. $\dfrac{3}{4}$ 23. $\dfrac{x^2 + 3x}{x + 1}$ 25. $\dfrac{b}{2a}$ 27. $\dfrac{2ab^2}{c^2}$

29. $\dfrac{x(a - b)}{a + b}$ 31. 63 33. $9x^2 y^2$ 35. $a^2 - b^2$ 37. 1 39. $\dfrac{2a - b}{2ab}$ 41. $\dfrac{a - 5}{a^2 + 2a - 3}$ 43. $\dfrac{-x + y}{6x + 6y}$

45. $\dfrac{a^2 + b^2}{a^2 - b^2}$ 47. $\dfrac{2b^2 + 3}{2b}$ 49. $\dfrac{3 + 2x^2}{x}$ 51. $\dfrac{x^2 + 2x - 3}{x + 2}$ 53. $\dfrac{a^2}{a - 1}$ 55. $a - 3$ 57. $x - 2$

59. $n^2 + n + 1$ 61. $2a^2 + a - 6 + \dfrac{-17}{2a - 3}$

Page 384 Chapter Test 1. 51 3. 3 5. $\dfrac{3a - 2}{a}$ 7. $\dfrac{3b^3}{13}$ 9. 3 11. $\dfrac{c^2 + d^2}{c^2 d}$ 13. $\dfrac{x - 3}{x^2 + 3x}$ 15. $\dfrac{y - 2}{2}$

17. $x + 2$ 19. 5760

Page 385 More Challenging Problems 1. $a^{2n} + 5a^{n+1} + 5a^{n-1} + 25$ 3. $a^n + b^n + c^n + 2a^{\frac{n}{2}}b^{\frac{n}{2}} + 2a^{\frac{n}{2}}c^{\frac{n}{2}}$

$+ 2b^{\frac{n}{2}}c^{\frac{n}{2}}$ 5. $x^n - y^n$ 7. $(x + 3 - y + 1)(x + 3 + y - 1)$ 9. $(2a + b - 3c + 2d)(2a + b + 3c - 2d)$

11. $x + y$ 13. $\dfrac{4x^2 - 2xy + 2x - y}{2v - 1}$

Page 385 Additional Practice 1. $409\frac{1}{2}$ 3. $3\frac{2}{3}$ 5. $\dfrac{3y}{5w}$ 7. $\dfrac{x + 2}{x + 4}$ 9. $\dfrac{x}{2}$ 11. $\dfrac{c}{2}$ 13. $\dfrac{n + 1}{n - 1}$

15. $16x^2 y^2$ 17. 2 19. $\dfrac{x^2 - x - 2}{x^3 - x^2 - 6x}$ 21. $\dfrac{x^2 + x - 1}{x + 1}$ 23. $x - 5$ 25. $2a + 5$ 27. $4y^2 + 2y - 5$

29. $x^2 - 3x + 1$ 31. 6.5 m 33. 200 km 35. 0.5 liter 37. $85\frac{5}{7}$ grams 39. 8%: \$8000; 12%: \$4000

CHAPTER 11: APPLICATIONS OF RATIONAL EXPRESSIONS

Page 390 Classroom Exercises 1. $x = 12$ 3. $x = 1$ 5. $y = 6$ 7. $x = -5$ 9. $a = -\frac{1}{2}$ or $a = 1$

Page 390 Written Exercises 1. $a = 24$ 3. $a = 15$ 5. $t = 4$ 7. $x = \frac{2}{3}$ 9. $x = 6$ 11. $x = -\frac{1}{9}$ 13. $n = 2$

15. $n = 2$ 17. $x = -\frac{1}{5}$ 19. $x = -6$ 21. $x = 10$ 23. $a = 4$ 25. $x = -5$ 27. $b = 3$ 29. $x = -1$

31. $x = 23$ 33. $x = -2\frac{1}{2}$ 35. $x = 1$ 37. $x = -10$ 39. $x = 24$ 41. $x = 13$ 43. $x = -6\frac{2}{3}$ 45. $a = -3$

47. $k = 6$

Page 391 Puzzle See Solution Key.

Page 391 Review Capsule for Section 11-2 1. 2 2. $-\frac{3}{4}$ 3. 0 4. $\frac{5}{7}$ 5. $1\frac{1}{8}$ 6. 1 7. a. $y = -3x$
+ 6 b. $-3; 6$ 8. a. $y = 5x + 9$ b. 5; 9 9. a. $y = 2x - 6$ b. 2; -6 10. a. $y = -\frac{7}{2}x + 1\frac{2}{3}$ b. $-\frac{7}{2}; 1\frac{2}{3}$

Page 393 Classroom Exercises 1. $y = 4x + 2$ 3. $y = \frac{1}{2}x + 4$ 5. $y = -\frac{1}{4}x - 3$

Page 393 Written Exercises 1. $y = 3x + 4$ 3. $y = \frac{1}{2}x - 3$ 5. $y = -4x + \frac{2}{3}$ 7. $y = 2x - 1$ 9. $y = -3x$
+ 17 11. $y = x + 3$ 13. $y = \frac{1}{2}x + 1\frac{1}{2}$ 15. $y = -\frac{1}{3}x + 3$ 17. $y = \frac{2}{3}x$ 19. $x = 3$ 21. $y = -x$
23. $y = x - 5$ 25. $y = 3x + 3$ 27. $y = 2x - 3$ 29. $y = -4x + 5$ 31. $x = 3$ 33. $y = \frac{1}{4}x + 2\frac{1}{2}$
35. $y = \frac{4}{3}x - 6$ 37. Substitute (x_1, y_1) into $y = mx + b$: $y_1 = mx_1 + b; y_1 - mx_1 = mx_1 - mx_1 + b;$
$b = y_1 - mx_1$

Page 395 Review Capsule for Section 11-3 1. $\frac{1}{9}$ 2. $\frac{1}{11}$ 3. $\frac{1}{6}$ 4. -2 5. $\frac{9}{5}$ 6. -1 7. $y = \frac{3}{4}x + 6\frac{1}{2}$
8. $y = -\frac{1}{2}x + 2\frac{1}{2}$ 9. $y = -\frac{2}{5}x - 2\frac{3}{5}$ 10. $y = \frac{7}{8}x + 11\frac{5}{8}$ 11. $y = -3x - 2$ 12. $y = -\frac{5}{6}x + \frac{1}{3}$

Page 396 Classroom Exercises 1. $y = -x + 2$ 3. $y = 0$ 5. $y = \frac{2}{7}x - 1\frac{5}{7}$

Page 397 Written Exercises 1. $y = 2x - 1$ 3. $y = 1$ 5. $y = -\frac{1}{5}x + 4\frac{3}{5}$ 7. $y = x - 1$ 9. $y = \frac{3}{2}x - 9$
11. $y = -x - 3$ 13. $5x - 2y = -3$ 15. $2x - 3y = -3$ 17. $6x - 5y = 36$ 19. $2x + 3y = 27$
21. $11x - 4y = -12$ 23. $y = \frac{1}{2}x;$ Yes 25. $y = -4x + 14;$ No 27. $y = -3x - 4;$ No 29. $x + y = 12;$
$4x - 5y = -6; 2x - 7y = -12$ 31. $5x + y = -11; 3x + 4y = 7; 2x - 3y = -1$ 33. $x + y = 9; x - 2y = -9;$
$y = 4$

Page 397 Review 1. $a = 12$ 2. $x = -1$ 3. $b = -3$ or $b = 4$ 4. $x = 0$ or $x = 3$ 5. $x = -2$ or $x = 6$
6. $x = -1$ 7. $y = x + 4$ 8. $y = -2x - 1$ 9. $y = -\frac{2}{3}x + \frac{1}{2}$ 10. $y = x$ 11. $y = 3x - 1$ 12. $y = \frac{1}{5}x + \frac{3}{5}$
13. $\frac{1}{2}x + y = 4$, or $x + 2y = 8$ 14. $3x + y = 4$ 15. $\frac{1}{4}x + y = -\frac{3}{4}$, or $x + 4y = -3$

Page 398 Calculator Exercises 1. Yes 3. Yes 5. Yes

Page 398 Review Capsule for Section 11-4 1. $\frac{8}{5}$ 2. $-\frac{3}{7}$ 3. -9 4. $\frac{1}{12}$ 5. a 6. $-\frac{1}{z}, z \neq 0$ 7. $y = 3$
8. $t = \frac{1}{5}$ 9. $s = 2$ 10. $n = \frac{12}{13}$ 11. $x = \frac{2}{9}$ 12. $y = -\frac{4}{13}$ 13. $y = \frac{1}{12}$ 14. $r = 9\frac{1}{2}$

Page 399 Consumer Applications 1. $100.36; $3612.96; $612.96 3. $243.80; $23,404.80; $8404.80
5. $99.85; $2396.40; $396.40

Page 401 Classroom Exercises 1. a. Let x = number added. b. $\frac{3 + x}{7 + x} = \frac{3}{5}$ 3. a. Let x = smaller number,
then $4x$ = larger number. b. $\frac{1}{x} - \frac{1}{4x} = \frac{3}{8}$

Page 401 Word Problems 1. 4 3. 2, 10 5. 4 7. $\frac{1}{4}$ 9. $2\frac{2}{3}, 6\frac{2}{3}$ 11. $\frac{3}{8}, \frac{5}{16}$ 13. 3, 4 15. 5, 6
17. $\frac{5}{4}$ or $\frac{4}{5}$ 19. $\frac{3}{4}$ or $-\frac{4}{3}$

Page 402 Review Capsule for Section 11-5 1. $y = 70$ 2. $x = 6$ 3. $t = 2$ 4. $r = 50$ 5. $x = 30$
6. $r = 4$

Page 404 Classroom Exercises 1. 1250 km/hr 3. $(1250 - w)$ km/h 5. 3750 km 7. 6 hr
9. Distance before headwinds: $2x$; rate after headwinds: $x - 64$; time after headwinds: 3; distance after
headwinds: $3(x - 64)$ 11. 435.2 km/hr

Page 405 Word Problems 1. $8\frac{4}{7}$ mi 3. Jim: 50 km/hr; Ed: 45 km/hr 5. Millan: 45 mph; Sharon:
30 mph 7. 4 mph 9. 27 km/hr 11. $2\frac{2}{9}$ hr 13. 540 km/hr 15. 2 km/hr

Answers to Selected Exercises **611**

Page 406 **Review Capsule for Section 11-6** 1. $\frac{1}{15}$ 2. $\frac{1}{15}$ 3. $\frac{1}{6}$ 4. $\frac{8}{25}$ 5. $\frac{1}{5}$ 6. $\frac{1}{3}$ 7. $n = 12$
8. $w = 3$ 9. $x = 30$ 10. $a = 4\frac{2}{5}$ 11. $x = 10\frac{2}{3}$ 12. $x = 2\frac{3}{4}$ 13. $y = 2$ 14. $x = 0$ 15. $y = -1$ or $y = 2$

Page 409 **Classroom Exercises** 1. $\frac{1}{80}$ 3. $\frac{3}{8}$ 5. $\frac{m}{80}$ 7. $\frac{1}{5}$ 9. $\frac{1}{3}$ 11. $\frac{1}{5} + \frac{1}{3}$, or $\frac{8}{15}$ 13. $\frac{x}{5} + \frac{x}{3} = 1$

Page 409 **Word Problems** 1. $2\frac{2}{17}$ days 3. $3\frac{1}{13}$ minutes 5. $3\frac{3}{5}$ days 7. $\frac{2}{3}$ hour 9. $1\frac{11}{24}$ hours
11. 12 hours 13. 30 min 15. 12 min, 24 min 17. 12 hours 19. 12 hours

Page 411 **Puzzle** See Solution Key.

Page 411 **Review Capsule for Section 11-7** 1. $P = 3r$ 2. $r = kh$ 3. $T = kh$ 4. $d = kt$ 5. $s = 210$
6. $p = 25$

Page 414 **Classroom Exercises** 1. Yes 3. No 5. No 7. Yes 9. y decreases 11. y is divided in half

Page 414 **Written Exercises** 1. Yes; corresponds to $xy = k$ 3. No; does not correspond to $xy = k$ or
$x = \frac{k}{y}$ 5. No; does not correspond to $xy = k$ or $x = \frac{k}{y}$ 7. Yes; corresponds to $x = \frac{k}{y}$ 9. No; does not
correspond to $xy = k$ or $x = \frac{k}{y}$ 11. No; does not correspond to $xy = k$ or $x = \frac{k}{y}$ 13. $xy = 42$ 15. $xy = \frac{1}{2}$
17. $xy = 40$ 19. $x = 4$ 21. $r = 10$ 23. $b = 1\frac{1}{2}$ 25. 12 amps 27. 6 people 29. $2\frac{2}{5}$ hours 31. 36
plants 33. 192 tiles 35. 24; $yx^2 = 24$ 37. 128; $yx^2 = 128$ 39. -80; $yx^2 = -80$ 41. $f\sqrt{w} = k$ or
$f = \frac{k}{\sqrt{w}}$; 254 43. $167\frac{1}{2}$

Page 417 **Classroom Exercises** 1. $a = kbc$ 3. $m = \frac{kn}{p}$ 5. $s = \frac{kt}{r^2}$

Page 417 **Written Exercises** 1. $t = 216$ 3. $x = 70$ 5. $q = 8\frac{1}{6}$ 7. $A = 20$ 9. $m = 10$ 11. 14 in^2
13. 28 cm^3 15. $R = 2.5$ 17. 54 ohms

Page 418 **Review** 1. $\frac{2}{3}, \frac{8}{3}$ 2. 12, 18 3. 700 km 4. 200 km/hr 5. $7\frac{1}{2}$ min 6. 12 hours
7. 20 amps 8. 4 9. 15 square inches 10. $3\frac{3}{4}$ kg

Page 420 **Computer Exercises** See Solution Key.

Page 421 **Chapter Objectives and Review** 1. $n = 18$ 3. $x = 2$ 5. $a = -6$ or $a = 2$ 7. $x = 5$ 9. $a = -1$
or $a = 2$ 11. $y = -7$ or $y = 4$ 13. $y = -3x + 4$ 15. $y = -\frac{1}{2}x - \frac{3}{4}$ 17. $y = 2x + 2$ 19. $y = -x - 8$
21. $y = \frac{3}{2}x - \frac{15}{2}$ 23. $y = 3x + 2$ 25. $y = -5x$ 27. $y = -2x + 1$ 29. $x + y = 8$ 31. $2x + 5y = 3$
33. 6, 8 35. 2 km/hr 37. $2\frac{2}{5}$ hours 39. $xy = 7$ 41. $xy = 4\frac{1}{2}$ 43. $xy = -3$ 45. $4\frac{1}{2}$ units
47. $r = 7\frac{1}{2}$ 49. $h = 800$ 51. $F = 2\frac{1}{4}$

Page 423 **Chapter Test** 1. $x = 18$ 3. $a = 1$ or $a = 4$ 5. $y = \frac{1}{3}x - \frac{7}{3}$ 7. $y = -x + 8$ 9. $y = -\frac{2}{5}x + \frac{3}{5}$
11. 12 min 13. $p = 2$ 15. $c = 3$

Page 424 **Additional Practice** 1. $y = 18$ 3. $n = 3$ 5. $y = -2x - 6$ 7. $y = -\frac{1}{2}x + \frac{9}{2}$ 9. $y = -\frac{3}{4}x$
11. $y = -\frac{3}{2}x$ 13. $y = x - 1$ 15. $y = 3x + 2$ 17. $x + 8y = -12$ 19. $y = 4$ 21. $x = 72$ 23. 16, 17
25. 325 km/hr

Page 425 **Review of Word Problems: Chapters 1-11** 1. 39.1¢ 3. Louise: 4; Alex: 16 5. rectangle with length (a + 5) units and width (a − 3) units; 9 square units greater   7. length: (x + 6) units; width: (x − 2) units   9. 13 m   11. $\frac{5}{6}, \frac{1}{10}$ 13. $1\frac{1}{2}$ hours

Page 426   Cumulative Review: Chapters 8-11   1. a   3. d   5. c   7. d   9. b   11. b   13. a   15. b
17. b   19. b   21. c   23. a   25. b   27. a

Page 428   Preparing for College Entrance Tests   1. a   3. a   5. b   7. d   9. a   11. a

Page 429   Preparing for College Entrance Tests   1. a   3. d   5. a   7. d   9. c   11. c   13. d   15. a

CHAPTER 12: RADICALS

Page 433   Classroom Exercises   1. ±8   3. $\pm\frac{5}{6}$ 5. ±100   7. −6   9. $-\frac{5}{13}$ 11. −18

Page 433   Written Exercises   1. 4   3. 7   5. ±10   7. 100   9. −4   11. ±100   13. $\frac{3}{7}$ 15. $\pm\frac{5}{6}$
17. $-\frac{8}{5}$ 19. $\frac{9}{10}$ 21. 17   23. 25   25. $|b|$ 27. $\pm|t^5|$ 29. $c^2|d^3|$ 31. $-h^4s^6$ 33. $3|c|$ 35. $-8|c^3|$
37. $\pm5d^2$ 39. $2|xy|$ 41. 0.7   43. −1.5   45. $0.8|b|$ 47. $\pm2.5t^2$ 49. $5r^4s^8t^6$ 51. $-9a^6b^4d^8$
53. $\pm\frac{7t^2}{5|b^3|}$ 55. $\frac{7a^2|b|}{3}$ 57. $13|c|^3$ 59. $4a^4$ 61. 3   63. 4   65. a^2b 67. $c^4f^6g^2$ 69. $14b^2$ 71. $16f^6$
Page 434   Review Capsule for Section 12-2   1. Q   2. Q   3. Ir   4. Ir   5. Q   6. Ir   7. Yes; Yes; No;
Yes   8. Yes; Yes; No; Yes   9. Yes; Yes; No; Yes   10. No; Yes; No; Yes   11. No; Yes; No; Yes   12. No;
Yes; No; Yes

Page 435   Classroom Exercises   1. $3 < \sqrt{13} < 4$ 3. $9 < \sqrt{92} < 10$ 5. 2.8   7. 3.6   9. 9.6

Page 436   Written Exercises   1. $\frac{4}{9}$ 3. $\frac{5}{33}$ 5. $\frac{8}{11}$ 7. $\frac{62}{333}$ 9. $\frac{181}{333}$ 11. $\frac{11}{9}$ 13. $\frac{83}{33}$ 15. $\frac{311}{99}$
17. $\frac{91}{66}$ 19. $\frac{1667}{450}$ 21. $8 < \sqrt{67} < 9$ 23. $5 < \sqrt{27} < 6$ 25. $11 < \sqrt{123} < 12$ 27. $11 < \sqrt{136}$
< 12 29. $7 < \sqrt{56} < 8$ 31. $16 < \sqrt{260} < 17$ 33. $100 < \sqrt{10{,}001} < 101$ 35. $90 < \sqrt{8101} < 91$
37. 25.1 cm   39. 3.0 m   41. width: 6.4 in; length: 32 in

Page 437   Classroom Exercises   1. 9   3. 100   5. 4   7. 25×5 9. 100×3 11. 81×3

Page 438   Written Exercises   1. $2\sqrt{2}$ 3. $2\sqrt{5}$ 5. $2\sqrt{3}$ 7. $5\sqrt{3}$ 9. 10   11. $4\sqrt{2}$ 13. $11\sqrt{2}$
15. 14   17. $24\sqrt{2}$ 19. $6\sqrt{7}$ 21. $2\sqrt{14}$ 23. $45\sqrt{2}$ 25. $16\sqrt{3}$ 27. −12   29. $-20\sqrt{2}$
31. $30\sqrt{10}$ 33. 3,000   35. $30{,}000\sqrt{10}$ 37. 10   39. $1000\sqrt{10}$ 41. $6b\sqrt{b}$ 43. $3p^2\sqrt{2p}$
45. $5q^5\sqrt{3q}$ 47. $4a^4b\sqrt{2ab}$ 49. 2.83   51. 4.47   53. 9.90   55. 12.12   57. 13.86   59. 18.97
61. $(x+y)\sqrt{3}$ 63. $2(c^2+d^2)\sqrt{7(c^2+d^2)}$ 65. $x+y$

Page 438   Review Capsule for Section 12-4   1. 100   2. 225   3. 49   4. $a^2 − 2a + 1$ 5. $a^2 + 2a + 1$
6. $4t^2 + 20t + 25$ 7. 2   8. 5   9. 9   10. 16   11. 7   12. 25   13. $a^2 = 119$ 14. $a^2 = 207$
15. $a^2 = 57$ 16. $a^2 = 148$ 17. $a = −9$ or $a = 9$ 18. $a = −6$ or $a = 6$ 19. $a = −12$ or $a = 12$
20. $a = −11$ or $a = 11$

Page 440   Classroom Exercises   1. 5   3. 9   5. 2

Page 441   Written Exercises   1. 10   3. 15.7   5. 15.6   7. 12.0   9. 19.2   11. Yes   13. No   15. Yes
17. No   19. No   21. Yes   23. 7.2 m   25. 9.9 km   27. 36.7 ft   29. 7.1 cm   31. 60.7 ft
33. 192 cm^2 35. A whole is equal to the sum of its parts.   37. substitution principle $[2ab = 4(\frac{1}{2}ab)]$
39. $h = \sqrt{3}(\frac{s}{2})$ 41. Use Theorem 12-3: $(2pq)^2 + (p^2 − q^2)^2 \overset{?}{=} (p^2 + q^2)^2$; $4p^2q^2 + p^4 − 2p^2q^2 + q^4 \overset{?}{=}$
$p^4 + 2p^2q^2 + q^4$; $p^4 + 2p^2q^2 + q^4 = p^4 + 2p^2q^2 + q^4$

Page 442   Review Capsule for Section 12-5   1. 18   2. 3   3. 2   4. 1   5. 10   6. 256   7. 169   8. 4
9. 144   10. 4   11. 17   12. 9   13. 13   14. 53

Page 444   Classroom Exercises   1. 5   3. $\sqrt{97}$ 5. $\sqrt{106}$

Page 444   Written Exercises   1. 5   3. 8   5. 6   7. 10   9. 5   11. $5\sqrt{2}$ 13. $\sqrt{41}$ 15. 14   17. 13

19. 2   21. 25   23. $5 + \sqrt{37} + 3\sqrt{2}$ 25. $4\sqrt{10} + 4\sqrt{5}$ 27. $3\sqrt{2} + \sqrt{5} + \sqrt{29}$

Page 445   Review   1. 8   2. -20 3. $10|x|$ 4. $\pm a^4 b^2$ 5. 2.6 m   6. w: 10.4 units; ℓ: 20.8 units
7. $2\sqrt{7}$ 8. $4\sqrt{5}$ 9. $-2x^2\sqrt{6x}$ 10. $12d\sqrt{d}$ 11. 15   12. 7.5   13. 3   14. $6\sqrt{2}$ 15. $\sqrt{185}$

Page 447   Career Applications   1. $V_o = 5.6 \times 10^3$ m/sec; $V_e = 7.8 \times 10^3$ m/sec   3. $V_o = 5.0 \times 10^3$ m/sec;
$V_e = 7.0 \times 10^3$ m/sec   5. Orbit the earth   7. 25 km   9. 225 km

Page 448   Classroom Exercises   1. $\sqrt{14}$ 3. $3\sqrt{2}$ 5. -6 7. $5\sqrt{15}$ 9. $120\sqrt{3}$ 11. $20\sqrt{10}$

Page 448   Written Exercises   1. $\sqrt{10}$ 3. $\sqrt{14}$ 5. $3\sqrt{2}$ 7. $5\sqrt{2}$ 9. 6   11. 6   13. $5\sqrt{3}$ 15. 7
17. $2\sqrt{6}$ 19. $4\sqrt{10}$ 21. $15\sqrt{10}$ 23. $28\sqrt{3}$ 25. -168 27. $-24\sqrt{15}$ 29. $24\sqrt{42}$
31. $-63\sqrt{30}$ 33. $a\sqrt{b}$ 35. $4bc\sqrt{2}$ 37. $3m^2 n\sqrt{2m}$ 39. $abc\sqrt{ac}$ 41. 2   43. 4   45. 10
47. $2\sqrt[3]{3}$ 49. $-6a^3 b$ 51. $2xy^3\sqrt{x}$ 53. $10k^2 t^3$

Page 449   Calculator Exercises   1. 46.4758   3. 69.7137   5. -43.817805 7. 19.595918

Page 449   Review Capsule for Section 12-7   1. 2   2. 3   3. 5   4. 8   5. 125   6. $\dfrac{\sqrt{2}}{2}$ 7. $\dfrac{\sqrt{5}}{5}$
8. $2\sqrt{3}$ 9. $2\sqrt{7}$ 10. $9\sqrt{2}$

Page 452   Classroom Exercises   1. $\dfrac{4}{5}$ 3. $\dfrac{16\sqrt{2}}{9}$ 5. $\pm\dfrac{3\sqrt{5}}{7}$ 7. $\dfrac{\sqrt{2}}{2}$ 9. $\dfrac{\sqrt{2}}{4}$ 11. $\dfrac{\sqrt{2}}{3}$ 13. $2\sqrt{10}$
15. $\dfrac{\sqrt{x}}{x^2}$

Page 452   Written Exercises   1. $\dfrac{2}{5}$ 3. $\dfrac{\sqrt{7}}{6}$ 5. $\dfrac{\sqrt{6}}{4}$ 7. $\dfrac{15}{14}$ 9. $\dfrac{7\sqrt{11}}{12}$ 11. $\dfrac{4\sqrt{3}}{15}$ 13. $\dfrac{10\sqrt{6}}{11}$
15. $\dfrac{7\sqrt{3}}{5}$ 17. $\dfrac{2\sqrt{3}}{3}$ 19. $\dfrac{\sqrt{6}}{3}$ 21. $\dfrac{\sqrt{14}}{2}$ 23. $\dfrac{\sqrt{35}}{5}$ 25. $\sqrt{6}$ 27. $\dfrac{3\sqrt{6}}{2}$ 29. $\dfrac{9\sqrt{2}}{2}$ 31. $\dfrac{8\sqrt{3}}{3}$
33. $\dfrac{2\sqrt{21}}{15}$ 35. $\dfrac{1}{3}$ 37. $\dfrac{7\sqrt{y}}{y}$ 39. $\dfrac{7\sqrt{c}}{c}$ 41. $\dfrac{\sqrt{3b}}{b^2}$ 43. $\dfrac{\sqrt{x}}{2x^2}$ 45. $\dfrac{\sqrt{7d}}{3d^2}$ 47. $bd\sqrt{d}$ 49. $2m\sqrt{3n}$
51. $\dfrac{\sqrt{2}}{2}$ 53. $\dfrac{7\sqrt{10}}{10}$ 55. $\dfrac{3\sqrt{70}}{35}$ 57. 1   59. $\dfrac{\sqrt{10}}{2}$ 61. $\dfrac{5\sqrt{3}}{2}$ 63. $2.309\overline{3}$ 65. 0.866   67. 0.6708
69. 1.580852   71. $1.649\overline{6}$ 73. $1.0434\overline{6}$

Page 453   Review Capsule for Section 12-8   1. $2\sqrt{6}$ 2. $4\sqrt{5}$ 3. $2\sqrt{10}$ 4. $8\sqrt{2}$ 5. $12\sqrt{2}$
6. 24   7. $10\sqrt{7}$ 8. $-6\sqrt{2}$ 9. $40\sqrt{2}$ 10. $6\sqrt{3}$ 11. $-16\sqrt{6}$ 12. $35\sqrt{3}$ 13. $\sqrt{35}$
14. $2\sqrt{15}$ 15. $\sqrt{6}$ 16. 10   17. 60   18. 7   19. 8   20. 8

Page 455   Classroom Exercises   1. $4\sqrt{3}$ 3. $\sqrt{2}$ 5. $-3\sqrt{3}$ 7. $9\sqrt{2} + \sqrt{10}$ 9. $6\sqrt{5} - 10$

Page 455   Written Exercises   1. $\sqrt{2}$ 3. $5\sqrt{2}$ 5. 0   7. $14\sqrt{5} + 9\sqrt{3}$ 9. $9 - 2\sqrt{2}$ 11. $\sqrt{2}$
13. $-\sqrt{5}$ 15. $-44\sqrt{2}$ 17. $35\sqrt{2}$ 19. $10\sqrt{6}$ 21. $27\sqrt{10}$ 23. $\sqrt{14} + 5\sqrt{7}$ 25. $4\sqrt{2} + 4$
27. $\sqrt{10} - \sqrt{15}$ 29. 1   31. $\sqrt{6}$ 33. $-\dfrac{\sqrt{6}}{6}$ 35. $-\dfrac{7\sqrt{2}}{12}$ 37. $7\sqrt{x}$ 39. $b\sqrt{2b}$ 41. $3a\sqrt{3a}$
43. $3b\sqrt{b}$ 45. $3 + \sqrt{5}$ 47. $1 + \sqrt{x}$ 49. $\dfrac{4\sqrt{7} + 8}{3}$ 51. $\dfrac{2\sqrt{6} + 6}{-3}$ 53. $\dfrac{23 + 7\sqrt{10}}{39}$
55. $\dfrac{3x - 4\sqrt{x} + 1}{x - 1}$ 57. $(a + \sqrt{10})(a - \sqrt{10})$ 59. $5(x + \sqrt{5})(x - \sqrt{5})$ 61. $(1 + x\sqrt{2})(1 - x\sqrt{2})$
63. $(a - \sqrt{5})^2$

Page 456   Puzzle   See Solution Key.

Page 456   Review Capsule for Section 12-9   1. 5   2. 15   3. 11   4. 565   5. x   6. $a - 1$ 7. $2b - 1$
8. 9x   9. 32b   10. $25a - 25$ 11. Yes   12. No   13. No   14. Yes   15. No   16. Yes

Page 458   Classroom Exercises   1. $y = \dfrac{4}{25}$ 3. $x = 25$ 5. Multiply both sides by $\dfrac{1}{3}$.   7. Add -4 to
both sides.

Page 458 Written Exercises 1. $x = 36$ **3.** $n = 20$ **5.** $r = \frac{63}{5}$, or $12\frac{3}{5}$ **7.** $x = 5$ **9.** $x = 14$ **11.** ϕ

13. $x = \frac{4}{25}$ **15.** ϕ **17.** $y = 81$ **19.** ϕ **21.** ϕ **23.** ϕ **25.** $y = 2$ **27.** $x = \frac{3}{4}$ **29.** $x = 4$ **31.** $\frac{4}{25}$

33. 16 **35.** $\frac{39}{2}$, or $19\frac{1}{2}$ **37.** 300 ft **39.** 6 mi **41.** $x = 2$ **43.** $x = -5$ **45.** $y = -5$ or $y = 1$

47. $a = \frac{73}{8}$, or $9\frac{1}{8}$ **49.** $t = \frac{5}{3}$, or $1\frac{2}{3}$ **51.** Yes; squaring both sides of the second equation produces the first.

Page 460 Review Capsule for Section 12-10 1. x^7 **2.** a^7 **3.** c^3 **4.** 5^5 **5.** 10^7 **6.** x^4 **7.** x^6

8. x^6 **9.** x^9 **10.** $16b^6$ **11.** z^{12} **12.** $\frac{1}{4}z^2$ **13.** $64t^3$ **14.** $-64c^6$ **15.** $0.25d^2$ **16.** $\frac{1}{125}$ **17.** $\frac{3}{b^2}$

18. $\frac{1}{9b^2}$ **19.** $-\frac{1}{64}$ **20.** $\frac{1}{100}$ **21.** $\frac{1}{6}$ **22.** $4b^2$ **23.** $\frac{1}{16}$ **24.** 6 **25.** 16

Page 461 Classroom Exercises 1. $7^{\frac{1}{2}}$ **3.** $5^{\frac{3}{2}}$ **5.** $9^{\frac{3}{4}}$ **7.** -4 **9.** 32

Page 461 Written Exercises 1. 3 **3.** 2 **5.** 3 **7.** 11 **9.** -6 **11.** $-\frac{1}{2}$ **13.** $-\frac{1}{3}$ **15.** 3 **17.** $\frac{2}{3}$

19. $-\frac{2}{5}$ **21.** -8 **23.** -3 **25.** 5 **27.** 2 **29.** 2 **31.** 8 **33.** -7 **35.** -5 **37.** $\frac{2}{5}$ **39.** $-\frac{1}{2}$ **41.** 81

43. 8 **45.** 343 **47.** $\sqrt[3]{-8}$ **49.** $\sqrt[4]{93}$ **51.** $\sqrt[3]{y}$ **53.** $\sqrt[3]{x^2}$ **55.** $\sqrt[5]{ab}$ **57.** 3 **59.** -3 **61.** 27

63. 1 **65.** $73^{\frac{1}{2}}$ or $\sqrt{73}$

Page 462 Review 1. 6 **2.** $-12\sqrt{21}$ **3.** $x\sqrt{y}$ **4.** $3a\sqrt{2}$ **5.** $\frac{2}{3}$ **6.** $\frac{\sqrt{6}}{6}$ **7.** $\frac{\sqrt{10}}{5}$ **8.** $\frac{\sqrt{5x}}{x^2}$

9. $\frac{a\sqrt{6}}{b}$ **10.** 0 **11.** $3\sqrt{5} + 2\sqrt{2}$ **12.** $3r\sqrt{6}$ **13.** $x = 99$ **14.** $x = 25$ **15.** $x = 6$ **16.** 10 **17.** -5

18. -2 **19.** 32 **20.** 4

Page 462 Calculator Exercises 1. 4.5 **3.** 6.5 **5.** 8.9

Page 464 Computer Exercises See Solution Key.

Page 465 Chapter Objectives and Review 1. 11 **3.** $3|xy^3|$ **5.** $\frac{5}{9}$ **7.** $\frac{16}{99}$ **9.** 4.5 m **11.** $3\sqrt{2}$

13. $3x\sqrt{6x}$ **15.** 20.0 **17.** 361 m **19.** 5 **21.** $9\sqrt{2}$ **23.** $-60\sqrt{6}$ **25.** $-3n^2\sqrt{2n}$ **27.** $\frac{\sqrt{10}}{10}$

29. $\frac{\sqrt{6y}}{2y^3}$ **31.** $\sqrt{7}$ **33.** $2x\sqrt{6}$ **35.** $\frac{12 + 3\sqrt{3}}{13}$ **37.** $-\frac{\sqrt{2} + 2}{2}$ **39.** ϕ **41.** 25 **43.** 10 **45.** 12

47. -100

Page 467 Chapter Test 1. ±10 **3.** $3\sqrt{7}$ **5.** -2 **7.** 25 **9.** 5 **11.** $2\sqrt{10}$ **13.** $12\sqrt{2}$ **15.** $2n\sqrt{3}$

17. $x = 11$ **19.** 26 m

Page 467 Additional Practice 1. -12 **3.** ±19 **5.** $\frac{8}{9}$ **7.** $\frac{9}{11}$ **9.** $\frac{11}{37}$ **11.** $3\sqrt{6}$ **13.** $-12x\sqrt{5x}$

15. $30a^2b^2\sqrt{5b}$ **17.** 9 **19.** 10 **21.** $6\sqrt{3}$ **23.** $2a\sqrt{7}$ **25.** $\frac{\sqrt{3}}{4}$ **27.** $\frac{\sqrt{3}}{2}$ **29.** $2x$ **31.** $-\sqrt{5}$

33. $x = 27$ **35.** $x = \frac{5}{2}$, or $2\frac{1}{2}$ **37.** -7 **39.** $\frac{1}{4}$ **41.** width: 5.5 m; length: 11 m **43.** 8.5 cm **45.** 81

CHAPTER 13: QUADRATIC FUNCTIONS AND EQUATIONS

Page 471 Classroom Exercises 1. $x = -5$ or $x = 5$ **3.** $x = -1$ or $x = 5$ **5.** $x = 0$ or $x = 1$
7. $a = -2\sqrt{3}$ or $a = 2\sqrt{3}$

Page 471 Written Exercises 1. $x = -4$ or $x = 4$ **3.** $x = -\sqrt{11}$ or $x = \sqrt{11}$ **5.** $m = -1$ or $m = 1$

7. $x = -3$ or $x = 3$ **9.** $r = -10$ or $r = 10$ **11.** $z = -4\sqrt{2}$ or $z = 4\sqrt{2}$ **13.** $x = -\frac{1}{2}$ or $x = \frac{1}{2}$ **15.** $b = -11$

or $b = 11$ **17.** $m = -\sqrt{3}$ or $m = \sqrt{3}$ **19.** $z = -\frac{2}{3}$ or $z = \frac{2}{3}$ **21.** $x = 2$ **23.** $x = -2$ or $x = 8$

25. $x = -14$ <u>or</u> $x = 0$ 27. $x = -1\frac{1}{2}$ <u>or</u> $x = 2\frac{1}{2}$ 29. $a = -9$ <u>or</u> $a = -3$ 31. $z = 2$ <u>or</u> $z = 10$ 33. $b = -4\frac{3}{4}$ <u>or</u> $b = 3\frac{1}{4}$ 35. $x = 0$ <u>or</u> $x = \frac{1}{2}$ 37. $x = -\frac{4}{7}$ <u>or</u> $x = -\frac{2}{7}$ 39. $k = 1$ <u>or</u> $k = 5$ 41. $n = -1$ <u>or</u> $n = 6$ 43. $r = 1$ <u>or</u> $r = 3$ 45. $y = -1\frac{1}{2}$ <u>or</u> $y = 2\frac{1}{2}$ 47. $v = -5$ <u>or</u> $v = -2$ 49. $x = -\sqrt{a+b}$ <u>or</u> $x = \sqrt{a+b}$ 51. $x = -\sqrt{ab}$ <u>or</u> $x = \sqrt{ab}$ 53. $x = -\frac{a}{2}$ <u>or</u> $x = \frac{a}{2}$ 55. $x = -\sqrt{bc}$ <u>or</u> $x = \sqrt{bc}$ 57. $x = -a - \sqrt{b}$ <u>or</u> $x = -a + \sqrt{b}$ 59. $x = \frac{-a - \sqrt{b}}{2}$ <u>or</u> $x = \frac{-a + \sqrt{b}}{2}$ 61. $x = \frac{-b - \sqrt{c}}{a}$ <u>or</u> $x = \frac{-b + \sqrt{c}}{a}$ 63. $x = \frac{-2 + b}{a}$ <u>or</u> $x = \frac{2 + b}{a}$

Page 472   Review Capsule for Section 13-2   1. $(m - 2)^2$ 2. NP   3. NP   4. $(t + 0.1)^2$ 5. $(q - 0.3)^2$ 6. $(p^3 - 6)^2$ 7. $(r + \frac{1}{3})^2$ 8. NP   9. $(b - \frac{7}{4})^2$ 10. $(t - \frac{1}{6})^2$ 11. $(a + \frac{3}{5})^2$ 12. $(c + \frac{3}{8})^2$

Page 474   Classroom Exercises   1. 4   3. 16   5. $\frac{1}{4}$ 7. $\frac{1}{16}$ 9. $\frac{b^2}{4a^2}$

Page 474   Written Exercises   1. 25; $(x + 5)^2$ 3. 4; $(m + 2)^2$ 5. $\frac{1}{4}$; $(r - \frac{1}{2})^2$ 7. 100; $(r - 10)^2$ 9. $\frac{25}{4}$; $(x + \frac{5}{2})^2$ 11. $\frac{1}{25}$; $(x - \frac{1}{5})^2$ 13. $x = -6$ <u>or</u> $x = 2$ 15. $n = 3$ <u>or</u> $n = 5$ 17. $a = 2$ <u>or</u> $a = 4$ 19. $a = -5$ <u>or</u> $a = 1$ 21. $x = 4$ <u>or</u> $x = 10$ 23. $x = 4$ <u>or</u> $x = 6$ 25. $x = 6$ <u>or</u> $x = 10$ 27. $a = 1$ <u>or</u> $a = 2$ 29. $x = 3$ <u>or</u> $x = 6$ 31. $n = -3$ <u>or</u> $n = -2$ 33. $x = -2$ <u>or</u> $x = 3$ 35. $x = -5$ <u>or</u> $x = 6$ 37. $y = -1$ <u>or</u> $y = 2$ 39. $x = 0$ <u>or</u> $x = 3$ 41. $n = -1$ <u>or</u> $n = 1\frac{1}{2}$ 43. $x = -1\frac{1}{3}$ <u>or</u> $x = 2$ 45. $n = \frac{1}{4}$ <u>or</u> $n = 4$ 47. $x = \frac{1}{2}$ <u>or</u> $x = 3$ 49. $a = -1\frac{1}{2}$ <u>or</u> $a = 4$ 51. $p = \frac{1 - \sqrt{3}}{2}$ <u>or</u> $p = \frac{1 + \sqrt{3}}{2}$ 53. $x = \frac{1 - \sqrt{73}}{12}$ <u>or</u> $x = \frac{1 + \sqrt{73}}{12}$ 55. $x = 3 - \sqrt{13}$ <u>or</u> $x = 3 + \sqrt{13}$ 57. $x = \frac{5 - \sqrt{57}}{4}$ <u>or</u> $x = \frac{5 + \sqrt{57}}{4}$ 59. $x = \frac{-b - \sqrt{b^2 - 4c}}{2}$ <u>or</u> $x = \frac{-b + \sqrt{b^2 - 4c}}{2}$ 61. $x = -1$ <u>or</u> $x = 3$ 63. $t = 5\frac{1}{2}$ <u>or</u> $t = 4$ 65. $b = 2$ <u>or</u> $b = 4\frac{7}{8}$

Page 475   Review Capsule for Section 13-3   1. $3\sqrt{6}$ 2. $-2\sqrt{6}$ 3. $36\sqrt{3}$ 4. $15\sqrt{2}$ 5. $-8\sqrt{2}$ 6. $35\sqrt{2}$ 7. $-2\sqrt{2}$ 8. $-6\sqrt{10}$ 9. $-20\sqrt{2}$ 10. $10\sqrt{11}$ 11. 13   12. -23 13. 81   14. 36   15. 40   16. 104

Page 476   Classroom Exercises   1. $a = 1$; $b = -4$; $c = -5$ 3. $a = 4$; $b = 12$; $c = -7$ 5. $a = 1$; $b = 3$; $c = -7$ 7. $a = 3$; $b = 0$; $c = -45$ 9. $a = 5$; $b = -2$; $c = -1$

Page 477   Written Exercises   1. $x = -3$ <u>or</u> $x = 7$ 3. $x = -1$ <u>or</u> $x = 1\frac{1}{2}$ 5. $p = 0$ <u>or</u> $p = 4$ 7. $a = -5$ <u>or</u> $a = 1$ 9. $n = -3$ <u>or</u> $n = -2$ 11. $x = -1\frac{1}{2}$ <u>or</u> $x = 1$ 13. $y = -1$ <u>or</u> $y = 2$ 15. $x = -3$ 17. $x = -1 - \sqrt{2}$ <u>or</u> $-1 + \sqrt{2}$ 19. $x = -3 - \sqrt{6}$ <u>or</u> $x = -3 + \sqrt{6}$ 21. $x = \frac{-3 - \sqrt{5}}{2}$ <u>or</u> $x = \frac{-3 + \sqrt{5}}{2}$ 23. $x = \frac{-1 - \sqrt{41}}{4}$ <u>or</u> $x = \frac{-1 + \sqrt{41}}{4}$ 25. $x = \frac{-7 - \sqrt{33}}{4}$ <u>or</u> $x = \frac{-7 + \sqrt{33}}{4}$ 27. $x = \frac{-5 - \sqrt{10}}{3}$ <u>or</u> $x = \frac{-5 + \sqrt{10}}{3}$ 29. $x = -\frac{1}{2}$ <u>or</u> $x = 1$ 31. $y = \frac{3 - \sqrt{41}}{4}$ <u>or</u> $y = \frac{3 + \sqrt{41}}{4}$ 33. $x = \frac{3 - \sqrt{37}}{14}$ <u>or</u> $x = \frac{3 + \sqrt{37}}{14}$ 35. $n = \frac{-7 - \sqrt{113}}{16}$ <u>or</u> $n = \frac{-7 + \sqrt{113}}{16}$ 37. $b = 1\frac{1}{2}$ 39. $t = \frac{1 - \sqrt{33}}{4}$ <u>or</u> $t = \frac{1 + \sqrt{33}}{4}$ 41. $x = -0.8$ <u>or</u> $x = 1.2$ 43. $n = -0.8$ <u>or</u> $n = 1.3$ 45. $b = -1.4$ <u>or</u> $b = -0.2$ 47. $x = \frac{-cd - c\sqrt{d^2 + 8}}{2}$ <u>or</u> $x = \frac{-cd + c\sqrt{d^2 + 8}}{2}$ 49. $x = 1$ 51. $a = \frac{11 - \sqrt{17}}{2}$ <u>or</u> $a = \frac{11 + \sqrt{17}}{2}$ 53. $\left(\frac{-b + \sqrt{b^2 - 4ac}}{2a}\right)\left(\frac{-b - \sqrt{b^2 - 4ac}}{2a}\right) = \frac{b^2 - (\sqrt{b^2 - 4ac})^2}{4a^2} = \frac{b^2 - b^2 + 4ac}{4a^2} = \frac{4ac}{4a^2} = \frac{c}{a}$ 55. $x^2 - 4x - 1 = 0$

Page 478 Review Capsule for Section 13-4 1. $n, n + 1, n + 2$ 2. $n, n + 2$ 3. Let $n =$ the number, then $\frac{1}{n} =$ the reciprocal. 4. Let $n =$ the number, then $\frac{1}{n} - 5 =$ five less than the reciprocal. 5. Let $n =$ number of rows, then $n - 10 =$ the number of seats. 6. Let $n =$ the numerator, then $2n + 1 =$ the denominator.

Page 479 Classroom Exercises 1. a. Let $w =$ width, then $w + 3 =$ length. b. $w(w + 3) = 40$ 3. a. Let $n =$ first integer, then $n + 2 =$ second integer. b. $n(n + 2) = 35$ 5. a. Let $n =$ number, then $n^2 =$ square of number. b. $n^2 = 3n + 10$

Page 479 Word Problems 1. 27 seats 3. width: 5 cm; length: 8 cm 5. 8, or -7 7. length: 9 m; width: 6 m 9. $\frac{2}{3}$, or $\frac{1}{3}$ 11. 10 cm 13. 13 and 15, or -15 and -13 15. width: 20 m; length: 50 m 17. numerator: 3, denominator: 4; or numerator: $-\frac{8}{5}$, denominator: $-\frac{3}{5}$ 19. 3.39 m 21. 42 mi/hr

Page 481 Review 1. $x = -8$ or $x = 8$ 2. $y = -1$ or $y = 1$ 3. $x = -2\sqrt{3}$ or $x = 2\sqrt{3}$ 4. $n = -2$ or $n = 2$ 5. $x = 4$ 6. $a = 3$ or $a = 7$ 7. $x = -3$ or $x = 5$ 8. $x = -3$ or $x = -2$ 9. $n = -2$ or $n = 4$ 10. $a = -1$ or $a = 2$ 11. $t = -2$ or $t = 1\frac{1}{2}$ 12. $s = \frac{3 - 2\sqrt{3}}{3}$ or $s = \frac{3 + 2\sqrt{3}}{3}$ 13. $a = -3$ or $a = 7$ 14. $c = 0$ or $c = 4$ 15. $y = -2$ or $y = 4$ 16. $b = \frac{-1 - \sqrt{10}}{3}$ or $b = \frac{-1 + \sqrt{10}}{3}$ 17. $x = \frac{-2 - \sqrt{6}}{2}$ or $\frac{-2 + \sqrt{6}}{2}$ 18. $y = \frac{1 - \sqrt{17}}{4}$ or $y = \frac{1 + \sqrt{17}}{4}$ 19. 12 20. 6.4 m

Page 481 Review Capsule for Section 13-5 1. 12, 8, 6, 6, 8, 12 2. 79, 37, 11, 1, 7, 29

Page 483 Career Applications 1. $3°$F 3. $-27°$F 5. $-36°$F 7. $-62°$F 9. $-21.6°$C; $16.4°$C 11. $-29.2°$C; $18.4°$C 13. $-27.6°$C; $21.8°$C

Page 485 Classroom Exercises 1. No 3. Yes 5. Yes 7. No

Page 485 Written Exercises For Exercises 1-12, the coordinates of seven points are given. 1. $(-8, 12)$, $(-7, 5)$, $(-6, 0)$, $(-4, -4)$, $(-2, 0)$, $(-1, 5)$, $(0, 12)$ 3. $(0, 8)$, $(1, 3)$, $(2, 0)$, $(3, -1)$, $(4, 0)$, $(5, 3)$, $(6, 8)$ 5. $(-3, 7)$, $(-2, 0)$, $(0, -8)$, $(1, -9)$, $(2, -8)$, $(4, 0)$, $(5, 7)$ 7. $(-5, 9)$, $(-4, 0)$, $(-2, -12)$, $(0, -16)$, $(2, -12)$, $(4, 0)$, $(5, 9)$ 9. $(-3, 6)$, $(-2, 0)$, $(0, -6)$, $(\frac{1}{2}, -6\frac{1}{4})$, $(1, -6)$, $(3, 0)$, $(4, 6)$ 11. $(0, 8)$, $(-1, 3)$ $(-2, 0)$, $(-3, -1)$, $(-4, 0)$, $(-5, 3)$, $(-6, 8)$ 13. a. -4 b. -4 15. a. none b. none 17. a. $-1\frac{1}{2}$ and 2 b. $-1\frac{1}{2}$ and 2 For Exercises 19-33, the zeros and the coordinates of several points are given. 19. Zeros: -3 and 2; $(-4, 6)$, $(-2, -4)$, $(-\frac{1}{2}, -6\frac{1}{4})$, $(1, -4)$, $(3, 6)$ 21. Zeros: -3 and 3; $(-4, 7)$, $(-1, -8)$, $(0, -9)$, $(1, -8)$, $(4, 7)$ 23. Zero: -1; $(-4, 9)$, $(-2, 1)$, $(-1, 0)$, $(0, 1)$, $(2, 9)$ 25. Zeros: -1 and 13; $(-2, -15)$ $(3, 40)$, $(6, 49)$, $(9, 40)$, $(14, -15)$ 27. Zeros: -5 and 1; $(-6, -7)$, $(-4, 5)$, $(-2, 9)$, $(0, 5)$, $(2, -7)$ 29. Zeros: $-\frac{2}{3}$ and 1; $(-2, 12)$, $(\frac{1}{6}, -2\frac{1}{12})$, $(2, 8)$ 31. Zeros: $-\frac{3}{4}$ and $\frac{1}{2}$; $(-2, 3\frac{3}{8})$, $(-\frac{1}{8}, -\frac{25}{64})$, $(2, 4\frac{1}{8})$ 33. Zeros: $-2\frac{1}{2}$ and $1\frac{1}{2}$; highest point: $(-\frac{1}{2}, 16)$

Page 486 Review Capsule for Section 13-6 1. rational 2. irrational 3. rational 4. rational 5. irrational 6. irrational 7. $a = -11$ or $a = 11$ 8. $x = -\frac{3}{4}$ or $x = \frac{3}{4}$ 9. $y = -\frac{2}{3}$ or $y = -\frac{1}{4}$ 10. $b = \frac{1}{3}$ or $b = 3$ 11. $d = -7$ or $d = -\frac{1}{4}$ 12. $t = 2\frac{1}{2}$ 13. $x = 5$ 14. $b = 3 - 3\sqrt{2}$ or $b = 3 + 3\sqrt{2}$ 15. $r = -\sqrt{5}$ or $r = \sqrt{5}$ 16. $z = \frac{3 - \sqrt{29}}{10}$ or $z = \frac{3 + \sqrt{29}}{10}$ 17. $q = \frac{3 - \sqrt{17}}{4}$ or $q = \frac{3 + \sqrt{17}}{4}$ 18. $d = \frac{-7 - \sqrt{249}}{10}$ or $d = \frac{-7 + \sqrt{249}}{10}$

Page 487 Classroom Exercises 1. 17; two real solutions 3. 0; one real solution 5. -3; no real solutions

Page 488 Written Exercises 1. 61 3. 0 5. -47 7. 36 9. -48 11. -56 13. no real solutions 15. two real solutions 17. two real solutions 19. two real solutions 21. no real solutions 23. two real solutions 25. 10, -10 27. $k < -2\sqrt{3}$ or $k > 2\sqrt{3}$ 29. one real solution 31. two real solutions

Page 488 **Calculator Exercises** 1. 0.72 3. 1.85 5. −1.62

Page 491 **Classroom Exercises** 1. minimum 3. maximum 5. maximum

Page 491 **Written Exercises** 1. a. $x = 0$ b. $(0, 0)$; min. 3. a. $x = 0$ b. $(0, 4)$; min. 5. a. $x = -4$
b. $(-4, -9)$; min. 7. a. $x = 1\frac{1}{2}$ b. $(1\frac{1}{2}, -2\frac{1}{4})$; min. 9. a. $x = 1$ b. $(1, -1)$; min. 11. a. $x = 0$ b. $(0, 1)$;
max. 13. a. $x = -1$ b. $(-1, 9)$; max. 15. a. $x = 1\frac{1}{2}$ b. $(1\frac{1}{2}, \frac{1}{4})$; max. 17. 5 19. −25 21. 625 ft^2
23. second width: x; length: $60 - 2x$ 25. 450 ft^2 27. maximum, or minimum, $= [-\frac{b}{2a}, f(-\frac{b}{2a})]$

Page 493 **Classroom Exercises** 1. a. D b. inside 3. a. S b. outside 5. a. S b. outside 7. a. D
b. outside

Page 493 **Written Exercises** For Exercises 1-16, the coordinates of several points are given. D represents a
dashed curve and S represents a solid curve. The terms inside and outside indicate whether the graph includes
the region inside or outside the curve. 1. $(-2, 4), (-1, 1), (0, 0), (1, 1), (2, 4)$; S; outside 3. $(-2, 8)$,
$(-1, 5), (0, 4), (1, 5), (2, 8)$; S; inside 5. $(-2, -8), (-1, -2), (0, 0), (1, -2), (2, -8)$; D; outside
7. $(-1, 4), (0, 0), (1\frac{1}{2}, -2\frac{1}{4}), (3, 0), (4, 4)$; S; outside 9. $(0, 4), (1, 1), (2, 0), (3, 1), (4, 4)$; S; outside
11. $(-2, -2), (-\sqrt{2}, 0), (0, 2), (\sqrt{2}, 0), (2, -2)$; D; inside 13. $(-4, 0), (-3, -5), (-1, -9), (1, -5)$,
$(2, 0)$; D; inside 15. $(-3, -3), (-\sqrt{6}, 0), (3, -3), (0, 6), (\sqrt{6}, 0)$; S; outside
17. 19. 21. 23.

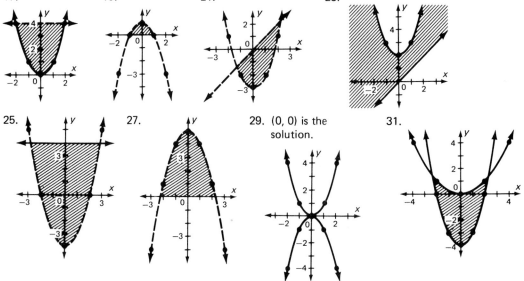

25. 27. 29. $(0, 0)$ is the 31.
solution.

Page 495 **Computer Exercises** See Solution Key.

Page 496 **Review** 1. Parabola opens upward; vertex: $(-2.5, -0.25)$; y intercept: $(0, 6)$; zeros: −3, −2.
2. Parabola opens upward; vertex and y intercept: $(0, -1)$; zeros: −1, 1. 3. Parabola opens downward;
vertex: $(2, 0)$; y intercept: $(0, -4)$; zero: 2. 4. two distinct, real solutions 5. no real solutions 6. no
real solutions 7. a. $x = 0$ b. $(0, 0)$; maximum 8. a. $x = 0$ b. $(0, 6)$; minimum 9. a. $x = 4$
b. $(4, -9)$; minimum c. zeros: 1, 7 10. The graph consists of all points outside the parabola, opening
downward, with vertex at $(0, 0)$. 11. The graph consists of all points outside the parabola, opening upward,
with vertex at $(0, 2)$. 12. The graph consists of all points on and outside the parabola, opening downward,
with vertex at $(1, 1)$.
Page 497 **Chapter Objectives and Review** 1. $x = -11$ or $x = 11$ 3. $y = -3$ or $y = 3$ 5. $t = -5$ or $t = -1$
7. $y = -\frac{2}{3}$ or $y = -\frac{1}{3}$ 9. $x = 2\frac{3}{5}$ or $x = 3\frac{2}{5}$ 11. $a = -1$ or $a = 7$ 13. $x = -5$ or $x = 6$ 15. $b = -2$ or

$b = 5$ 17. $c = -1\frac{2}{3}$ or $c = -1$ 19. $y = -8$ or $y = 2$ 21. $b = -5$ or $b = 1$ 23. $x = -5$ or $x = -\frac{1}{2}$
25. $c = -\frac{2}{3}$ or $c = -\frac{1}{3}$ 27. $d = \frac{1}{3}$ or $d = 5$ 29. 6 and 7   31. width: 2.9 m; length: 3.9 m   33. The
graph is a parabola, opening upward, with vertex at (1.5, −2.25) and y intercept at the origin; zeros: 0, 3.
35. The graph is a parabola, opening upward, with vertex at (2.5, −2.25) and y intercept at (0, 4); zeros:
1, 4.   37. The graph is a parabola, opening downward, with vertex at (3, 0) and y intercept at (0, −9);
zero: 3.   39. two distinct, real solutions   41. two distinct, real solutions   43. no real solutions
45. no real solutions   47. $k = -16$ or $k = 16$

Page 498 Chapter Test   1. $x = -2$ or $x = 2$ 3. $x = -8$ or $x = 0$ 5. $x = 3$ or $x = 6$ 7. $y = -4$ or $y = 1$
9. $c = 2 - \sqrt{2}$ or $c = 2 + \sqrt{2}$ 11. $x = 4$ 13. −3, 1   15. one distinct, real solution   17. two distinct,
real solutions   19. width: 6 ft; height: 4 ft

Page 499 Additional Practice   1. $y = -9$ or $y = 9$ 3. $x = -5\sqrt{3}$ or $x = 5\sqrt{3}$ 5. $x = -4$ or $x = 2$
7. $x = 0$ or $x = 4$ 9. $x = -1 - \sqrt{5}$ or $x = -1 + \sqrt{5}$ 11. $x = 0$ or $x = 5$ 13. $x = -5$ or $x = 8$
15. $a = -1$ or $a = 1\frac{1}{2}$ 17. $p = -\frac{1}{4}$ or $p = 1$ 19. Parabola opens upward; vertex: $(1\frac{1}{2}, -6\frac{1}{4})$; y intercept:
(0, −4); zeros: −1, 4   21. Parabola opens upward; vertex: (0, −36); y intercept: (0, −36); zeros: −6, 6.
23. Parabola opens upward; vertex: (2, 0); y intercept: (0, 4); zero: 2.   25. two distinct, real solutions
27. no real solutions   29. no real solutions   31. 26 seats   33. smaller garden: 4 ft; larger garden: 7 ft

Page 500 Review of Word Problems: Chapters 1-13   1. $230   3. $136   5. 6   7. painter: $736;
assistant: $552   9. Linda: 73 km/hr; Bob: 68 km/hr   11. 15 m   13. $1\frac{1}{2}$ m   15. 25 and 44, or −17
and −40

Page 501 Cumulative Review: Chapters 1-13   1. b   3. c   5. a   7. b   9. b   11. d   13. b   15. b
17. c   19. b   21. c   23. b   25. d   27. c   29. d   31. b   33. a   35. a   37. b   39. a   41. b
43. c   45. a   47. a   49. a   51. b   53. b   55. c   57. d   59. b   61. a

Page 505 Preparing for College Entrance Tests   1. b   3. a   5. a   7. b

Page 506 Preparing for College Entrance Tests   1. a   3. d   5. d

CHAPTER 14: STATISTICS AND PROBABILITY

Page 509 Classroom Exercises   1. mean: 40; median: 41   3. median: 85.5; mode: 85

Page 509 Written Exercises   1. 1:00–6:00   3. The greatest number of customers are in the store at the time.
5. No. It doesn't indicate when the most help is needed.   7. greater than   9. median yearly salary   11. 1 cm
13. 0.5 cm

Page 512 Classroom Exercises

1.

Interval	Frequency
31-41	7
41-51	3
51-61	3
61-71	5
71-81	1
81-91	5

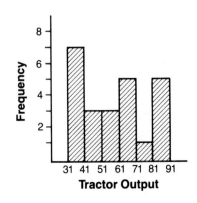

Tractor Output

Page 512   Written Exercises

1. a. mean: 30; median: 30

b.

Interval	Frequency
17-24	2
24-31	11
31-38	5
38-44	2

c.

3. a. mean: 28; median: 30

b.

Interval	Frequency
14-19	2
19-24	2
24-29	5
29-34	7
34-39	4

c.

5. a. mean: 32; median: 21

b.

Interval	Frequency
10-20	22
20-30	9
30-40	2
40-50	9
50-60	0
60-70	2
70-80	3
80-90	2

c.

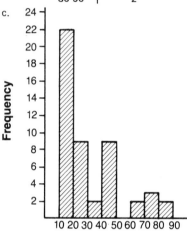

7. a. mean: 53; median: 54

b.

Interval	Frequency
0-15	5
15-30	2
30-45	6
45-60	8
60-75	3
75-90	9
90-105	3

c.

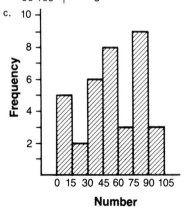

d. Since the mean and median are close, either can be used.

9. a. mean: 166; median: 170

b.

Interval	Frequency
100-120	1
120-140	4
140-160	6
160-180	10
180-200	6
200-220	3

c.

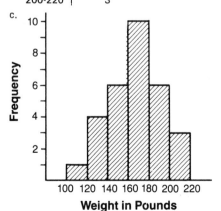

d. The weights are not distributed symmetrically, so the median gives a better description.

Page 515 Classroom Exercises   1. 6.1   3. 5.3

Page 515 Written Exercises   1. 3.0   3. 16%   5. 500 light bulbs   7. 16,300 light bulbs   9. 19,500 light bulbs   11. a. 16% b. 68% c. 95%   13. A: 3.5 students; B: 18.9 students; C: 89.6 students; D: 18.9 students; F: 3.5 students   15. The mean and the standard deviation for Y will be 10 times the mean and standard deviation for X.

Page 517 Review   1. mean: 27; median: 27; mode: 32

3. mean: 70; median: 67; See the histogram at the right.   5. standard deviation: 2.1

Interval	Frequency
51-61	4
61-71	8
71-81	5
81-91	2
91-101	1

Height(cm)

Page 517 More Challenging Problems   For Exercises 1 and 3, answers will vary. Sample answers are given.
1. $\{6, 8, 8, 8, 10\}$ 3. $\{1, 3, 4, 14, 18, 20, 20\}$ 5. mean; The mode would be a whole number and the median would be a whole number or a decimal with a 5 in the tenths place.

Page 518 Career Applications   1. 465   3. 380; 570

5.

Page 520 Classroom Exercises   1. 2   3. $\frac{1}{2}$

Page 520 Written Exercises   1. $\{1, 2, 3, 4, 5, 6\}$ 3. $\frac{1}{6}$ 5. $\frac{1}{2}$ 7. $\frac{1}{3}$ 9. 0   11. $\frac{1}{2}$ 13. $\frac{5}{12}$
15. 0   17. $\frac{3}{4}$ 19. $\frac{5}{12}$ 21. 2 ways   23. $\frac{1}{4}$ 25. $\frac{1}{2}$ 27. $\frac{1}{2}$ 29. 36   31. $\frac{5}{36}$ 33. $\frac{11}{12}$ 35. $\frac{1}{4}$
37. 0   39. $\frac{1}{6}$

Page 523 Classroom Exercises   1. not mutually exclusive   3. mutually exclusive

Page 523 Written Exercises   1. $\frac{1}{2}$ 3. $\frac{1}{2}$ 5. $\frac{3}{25}$ 7. $\frac{1}{5}$ 9. $\frac{1}{5}$ 11. $\{6, 7, 7, 8, 8, 8, 9, 9, 9, 10, 10, 11\}$ 13. $\frac{1}{4}$ 15. $\frac{3}{4}$

Page 524 Classroom Exercises   1. $\frac{2}{5}$, or 0.40   3. 24

Page 525 Written Exercises   1. $\frac{4}{5}$, or 0.80   3. 12   5. 0.30   7. 0.23   9. 0.38   11. 1520 students
13. 1240 students   15. 112.5

Page 526 Review   1. $\frac{1}{3}$ 3. $\frac{1}{2}$ 5. $\{2, 3, 5, 6, 8, 9\}$ 7. $\frac{1}{2}$ 9. $\frac{2}{3}$ 11. $\frac{3}{8}$, or 0.375   13. 9

Page 527 Chapter Objectives and Review   1. 83   3. Since the mean and median are close, either can be used.   5. See below.   7. 3.5   9. 2.0   11. $\{1, 2, 3, 4, 5, 6, 7, 8\}$ 13. $\frac{3}{8}$ 15. 0   17. $\frac{1}{10}$ 19. 1   21. NE; $\frac{2}{3}$ 23. E; $\frac{1}{2}$ 25. $\frac{8}{25}$ 27. $\frac{1}{5}$ 29. 0.40   31. 0.50   33. 9

5. a. mean: 17; median: 17   b.

Interval	Frequency
11-14	3
14-17	4
17-20	4
20-23	1
23-26	3

c.

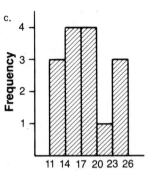

Height(m)

Page 530 Chapter Test   1. \$13,000   3. greater than   5. mean: 75; median: 74   7. 3.2   9. 15   11. $\frac{7}{15}$ 13. $\frac{3}{5}$ 15. $\frac{4}{5}$ 17. $\frac{2}{5}$, or 0.40   19. 10

Page 531 Additional Practice   1. mean: 8; median: 9   3. mean: 5; median: 5   5. 10   7. See below.   9. 1.4   11. 1.0   13. $\frac{4}{9}$ 15. $\frac{2}{3}$ 17. $\frac{1}{6}$ 19. $\frac{2}{3}$ 21. 0.25   23. 300

7.

Interval	Frequency
15-20	1
20-25	2
25-30	1
30-35	6
35-40	5

Miles

CHAPTER 15: OTHER APPLICATIONS OF ALGEBRA

Page 535 Word Problems   1. angle: 60°; complement: 30°   3. 120°   5. 45°   7. 135°   9. angle: 120°; supplement: 60°   11. $180 - x$ 13. x

Page 537 Classroom Exercises   1. 50°   3. 60°   5. $\sqrt{2}$ 7. 4   9. $2\sqrt{3}$

Page 537 Word Problems   1. ∠G: 100°; ∠H: 40°; ∠K: 40°   3. ∠A: 50°; ∠B: 55°; ∠C: 75°   5. ∠A: 74°; ∠B: 90°; ∠C: 16°   7. $4\sqrt{2}$ m   9. 13 ft   11. $15\sqrt{3}$ ft   13. $\frac{4\sqrt{14}}{3}$ dm

Page 540 Classroom Exercises   1. $\frac{8}{4}$ or $\frac{4}{8}$ 3. $\frac{9}{n} = \frac{12}{8}$ or $\frac{n}{9} = \frac{8}{12}$

Page 540 Written Exercises   1. 30 m   3. 6.4 m   5. 3.8 m

Page 541 Review   1. angle: 17.5°; complement: 72.5°; supplement: 162.5°   2. angle: $51\frac{3}{7}$°; complement: $38\frac{4}{7}$°; supplement: $128\frac{4}{7}$°   3. ∠A: 25°; ∠B: 75°; ∠C: 80°   4. $30\sqrt{3}$ cm   5. $6\frac{3}{4}$ 6. $6\frac{2}{3}$

Page 544   Classroom Exercises   1. tan A = .7500; tan B = 1.3333   3. tan A = $\frac{y}{x}$; tan B = $\frac{x}{y}$ 5. .1763

Page 544   Written Exercises   1. .3640   3. .4040   5. 1.4281   7. .0875   9. .7536   11. 11.4301
13. 30°   15. 7°   17. 58°   19. increases; 57.2900   21. 15.4   23. 1; 1; 1.0000   25. 27°   27. 21 cm
29. 72 m   31. 201 m

Page 548   Classroom Exercises   1. .2079   3. .7071   5. sin A = .8660; cos A = .5000

Page 548   Written Exercises   1. sin: .5736; cos: .8192   3. sin: .8090; cos: .5878   5. sin: .9511;
cos: .3090   7. 8°   9. 41°   11. 66°   13. increase   15. 40°   17. 80°   19. 9°   21. 40.146 m
23. 13.6 m   25. 127.0 m   27. 163.5 m   29. 9.5 cm   31. 81.9 m   33. 2.47485 cm ≈ 2.5 cm

Page 551   Classroom Exercises   1. tan   3. sin   5. cos

Page 551   Word Problems   1. about 175 m   3. about 37°   5. about 68°   7. $\overline{BD}$: about 123 cm;
$\overline{BC}$: about 136 cm   9. length of wire: about 87 m; distance: about 71 m

Page 552   Review   1. .6249   2. 1.0724   3. .2679   4. 14.3007   5. 22°   6. 65°   7. 83°   8. 52 m
9. .4226   10. .4540   11. .9945   12. .9744   13. 18°   14. 33°   15. 74°   16. 5747 m

Page 556   Written Exercises   1. 1 + 1 = 2; 1 + 2 = 3; 1 + 3 = 0; 2 + 2 = 0; 2 + 3 = 1; 3 + 1 = 0; 3 + 2 = 1
3. No; each element does not have a multiplicative inverse; there is no number by which to multiply 2 to
get the identity element, 1   5. 1 X 1 = 1; 1 X 3 = 3; 1 X 4 = 4; 1 X 5 = 5; 2 X 1 = 2; 2 X 2 = 4; 2 X 3 = 0;
2 X 4 = 2; 2 X 5 = 4; 3 X 1 = 3; 3 X 2 = 0; 3 X 3 = 3; 3 X 5 = 3; 4 X 2 = 2; 4 X 3 = 0; 4 X 4 = 4; 5 X 1 = 5;
5 X 3 = 3; 5 X 4 = 2   7. Yes; a "two-hour clock" is a field   9. 1 X 1 = 1; 1 X 2 = 2; 2 X 1 = 2; 2 X 2 = 1
11. Yes

Page 558   Classroom Exercises   1. Conditional: If a triangle is a right triangle, then it has one right angle.
Converse: If a triangle has one right angle, then it is a right triangle.   3. Conditional: If a number is an odd
number, then it is not divisible by two. Converse: If a number is not divisible by two, then it is an odd
number.

Page 559   Written Exercises   1. If you have no more than 2 errors, then you do not get an A.   3. If I
drive over the speed limit, then I do not break the law.   5. False   7. True   9. True   11. If 15 is not a
real number, then 15 is not a rational number; If 15 is not a rational number, then 15 is a rational number; If 15
is a real number, then 15 is a rational number.   13. If I get tired, then I work hard.   15. If Q has exactly
3 sides and 3 angles, then Q is a triangle.   17. Conditional: If a number is an irrational number, then it cannot
be expressed as the ratio of an integer and a natural number. Converse: If a number cannot be expressed as the
ratio of an integer and a natural number, then it is an irrational number.   19. Conditional: If an angle is an
obtuse angle, then its measure is greater than 90° and less than 180°. Converse: If the measure of an angle is
greater than 90° and less than 180°, then the angle is an obtuse angle.   21. Conditional: If two equations are
equivalent, then they have the same solution set. Converse: If two equations have the same solution set, then
they are equivalent.   23. Conditional: If a polynomial is a binomial, then it has two terms. Converse: If a
polynomial has two terms, then it is a binomial.

Page 561   Written Exercises   For Exercises 1-27, the Reason appears in parentheses following each Statement.
1. Hypothesis: x is any number. Conclusion: 2x + 3x = 5x   Proof: 1. x is any number. (Given)
2. 2x + 3x = (2 + 3)x (Dist. post.)   3. (2 + 3)x = 5x (Addition)   4. 2x + 3x = 5x (Substitution)
3. Hypothesis: x and y are any numbers. Conclusion: 3x + (5y + 7x) = 10x + 5y   Proof: 1. x and y are any
numbers. (Given)   2. 3x + (5y + 7x) = 3x + (7x + 5y) (Comm. post. for add.)   3. 3x + (7x + 5y) = (3x + 7x)
+ 5y (Assoc. post. for add.)   4. (3x + 7x) + 5y = 10x + 5y (Add. of like terms)   5. 3x + (5y + 7x) =
10x + 5y (Substitution)
5. Hypothesis: a is any number. Conclusion: (−2a)(−3a) = 6a²   Proof: 1. a is any number. (Given)
2. (−2a)(−3a) = (−2 · −3)(a · a) (Assoc. and comm. post. for mult.)   3. (−2 · −3)(a · a) = 6(a · a)
(Pos. prod. theorem)   4. 6(a · a) = 6a² (Def. of exponents)   5. (−2a)(−3a) = 6a² (Substitution)
7. Hypothesis: x is any number. Conclusion: (x + 3)(x + 4) = x² + 7x + 12   Proof: 1. x is any number.

(Given) 2. $(x + 3)(x + 4) = (x + 3)x + (x + 3)4$ (Dist. post.) 3. $(x + 3)x + (x + 3)4 = x(x) + 3(x) + x(4)$ $+ 3(4)$ (Dist. post.) 4. $x(x) + 3(x) + x(4) + 3(4) = x^2 + 3(x) + x(4) + 3(4)$ (Def. of exponents)
5. $x^2 + 3(x) + x(4) + 3(4) = x^2 + (3x + 4x) + 3(4)$ (Comm. and assoc. post. for mult.) 6. $x^2 + (3x + 4x)$ $+ 3(4) = x^2 + 7x + 3(4)$ (Add. of like terms) 7. $x^2 + 7x + 3(4) = x^2 + 7x + 12$ (Multiplication)
8. $(x + 3)(x + 4) = x^2 + 7x + 12$ (Substitution)

9. Hypothesis: x is an even number. Conclusion: x^2 is an even number. Proof: 1. x is an even number.
(Given) 2. Let $x = 2n$. Then $x^2 = (2n)^2$ where n is an integer. (Def. of an even number.) 3. $(2n)^2 = (2n)(2n)$
(Def. of exponents) 4. $(2n)(2n) = 2(n \cdot 2n)$ (Assoc. post. for mult.) 5. $2(n \cdot 2n) = 2(2n^2)$ (Comm. post.
for mult.; Def. of exp.) 6. $2n^2$ is an integer (Closure post. for mult.) 7. $2(2n^2)$ is even (Def. of even
numbers) 8. x^2 is even (Substitution)

11. Hypothesis: a and b are even numbers. Conclusion: $a + b$ is an even number. Proof: 1. a and b are even.
(Given) 2. Let $a = 2n$, $b = 2k$. Then $a + b = 2n + 2k$ (n and k are integers) (Def. of even number) 3. $2n$ $+ 2k = 2(n + k)$ (Dist. post.) 4. $n + k$ is an integer (Closure post. for add.) 5. $2(n + k)$ is an even number
(Def. of even number) 6. $a + b$ is an even number (Substitution)

13. Hypothesis: a and b are any odd numbers. Conclusion: ab is odd Proof: 1. a and b are odd (Given)
2. Let $a = 2k + 1$, $b = 2p + 1$ (k and p are integers.) Then $a \cdot b = (2k + 1)(2p + 1)$ (Def. of odd number)
3. $(2k + 1)(2p + 1) = 4kp + 2k + 2p + 1$ (Mult. of binomials) 4. $4kp + 2k + 2p + 1 = 2(2kp + k + p) + 1$
(Dist. post.) 5. $2kp + k + p$ is an integer (Closure post. for add. and mult.) 6. $2(2kp + k + p) + 1$ is an
odd number (Def. of odd number) 7. ab is odd (Substitution)

15. Hypothesis: a is any odd number. b is any even number. Conclusion: ab is even Proof: 1. a is odd,
b is even (Given) 2. Let $a = 2k + 1$, $b = 2p$. Then $ab = 2p(2k + 1)$. (k and p are integers) (Def. of even and
odd numbers) 3. $2p(2k + 1) = 2[p(2k + 1)]$ (Assoc. post. for mult.) 4. $2[p(2k + 1)] = 2(2kp + p)$
(Dist. post.) 5. $2kp + p$ is an integer (Closure post. for add. and mult.) 6. $2(kp + p)$ is an even number
(Def. of even number) 7. ab is an even number (Substitution)

17. Hypothesis: a and b are multiples of 3. Conclusion: ab is a multiple of 3 Proof: 1. a and b are mult.
of 3 (Given) 2. Let $a = 3n$, $b = 3k$, where n and k are integers. Then $ab = (3n)(3k)$. (Def. of mult. of 3)
3. $(3n)(3k) = 3(n \cdot 3k)$ (Assoc. post. for mult.) 4. $3(n \cdot 3k) = 3(3kn)$ (Comm. post.) 5. 3kn is an integer
(Closure post. for mult.) 6. $3(3kn)$ is a mult. of 3 (Def. of mult. of 3) 7. ab is a mult. of 3 (Substitution)

19. Hypothesis: a is divisible by 6. Conclusion: a is divisible by 2 Proof: 1. a is divisible by 6. (Given)
2. Let $a = 6k$, where k is an integer (If a is divisible by 6, then 6 is a factor of a.) 3. $6k = (2 \cdot 3)k$ (Factors
of 6) 4. $(2 \cdot 3)k = 2(3 \cdot k)$ (Assoc. post. for mult.) 5. 3k is an integer (Closure post. for mult.)
6. $2(3k)$ is divisible by 2 (Even numbers are divisible by 2) 7. a is divisible by 2 (Substitution)

21. Hypothesis: a and b are any multiples of 5. Conclusion: ab is a multiple of 5 Proof: 1. a and b are
mult. of 5 (Given) 2. Let $a = 5n$, $b = 5k$, where n and k are integers. Then $ab = (5n)(5k)$ (Def. of mult. of
5) 3. $(5n)(5k) = 5(n \cdot 5k)$ (Assoc. post. for mult.) 4. $5(n \cdot 5k) = 5(5nk)$ (Comm. post.) 5. 5nk is an
integer (Closure post. for mult.) 6. $5(5nk)$ is a mult. of 5 (Def. of mult. of 5) 7. ab is a mult. of 5
(Substitution)

23. Hypothesis: a and b are any real numbers. Conclusion: $(a - b)$ and $(b - a)$ are opposites Proof:
1. a and b are real numbers. (Given) 2. $(a - b) + (b - a) = [a + (-b)] + [b + (-a)]$ (Def. of subtraction)
3. $[a + (-b)] + [b + (-a)] = a + (-b + b) + (-a)$ (Assoc. post. for add.) 4. $a + (-b + b) + (-a)$ $= [a + (-a)] + (-b + b)$ (Comm. and assoc. post. for add.) 5. $[a + (-a)] + (-b + b) = 0 + 0 = 0$ (Add.
inverse post.) 6. $(a - b) + (b - a) = 0$ (Substitution) 7. $a - b$ and $b - a$ are opposites (Def. of opposites)

25. Hypothesis: a is any even number, b is any odd number. Conclusion: $(a + b)^2$ is an odd number
Proof: 1. a is even, b is odd. (Given) 2. $a + b$ is odd (Ex. 12) 3. $(a + b)^2$ is odd (Ex. 10)

27. Hypothesis: x is not a multiple of 4. Conclusion: x^2 is not a multiple of 8. Proof: 1. x is not a mult.
of 4. (Given) 2. x may be represented as $4n + 1$, $4n + 2$, or $4n + 3$ where n is an integer (4 cannot be a factor
of x, since x is not a mult. of 4) 3. $(4n + 1)^2 = 16n^2 + 8n + 1$; $(4n + 2)^2 = 16n^2 + 16n + 4$; $(4n + 3)^2 = 16n^2$ $+ 24n + 9$ (Mult.; (Ex. 8)) 4. $16n^2 + 8n + 1 = 8(2n^2 + n) + 1$; $16n^2 + 16n + 4 = 8(2n^2 + 2n) + 4$; $16n^2 + 24n$ $+ 9 = 8(2n^2 + 3n) + 9$ (Dist. post.) 5. $(2n^2 + n)$, $(2n^2 + 2n)$ and $(2n^2 + 3n)$ are integers (Closure post. for add.
and mult.) 6. $8(2n^2 + 1) + 1$, $8(2n^2 + 2n) + 4$, $8(2n^2 + 3n) + 9$ are not multiples of 8 (They do not have 8
as a factor.) 7. x^2 is not a multiple of 8. (Substitution)

Page 562 Review   1. No; 2 and 4 do not have multiplicative inverses.   2. No; 2, 3, and 4 do not have
multiplicative inverses.   3. Yes   4. No; 2, 4, and 6 do not have multiplicative inverses.   5. If a number
is an odd number, then the number is a rational number.   6. If the sky is not cloudy, then it is sunny outside.

7. If the electricity is working, then the lights are shining.   8. 5. If a number is a rational number, then it is an odd number; False   6. If it is sunny outside, then the sky is not cloudy; True   7. If the lights are shining, then the electricity is working; True For Exercises 9 and 10, the Reason appears in parentheses following each Statement.

9. Hypothesis: a is any odd number. Conclusion: a^3 is an odd number Proof: 1. a is an odd number. (Given) 2. Let a = 2n + 1, where n is an integer. Then $a^3 = (2n + 1)^3$ (Def. of odd number) 3. $(2n + 1)^3 = (2n + 1)^2$ (2n + 1) (Factoring) 4. $(2n + 1)^2$ is an odd number (The square of an odd number is odd.) (Ex. 10, page 561) 5. $(2n + 1)^2$ (2n + 1) is an odd number. (The product of 2 odd numbers is odd.) (Ex. 13, page 561) 6. a^3 is an odd number. (Substitution)

10. Hypothesis: a, b, c are any odd numbers. Conclusion: a + b + c is an odd number Proof: 1. a, b, c are any odd numbers. (Given) 2. Let a = 2k + 1, b = 2n + 1, c = 2p + 1, where k, n and p are integers. Then a + b + c = 2k + 1 + 2n + 1 + 2p + 1 (Def. of odd number; add prop. of equations) 3. 2k + 1 + 2n + 1 + 2p + 1 = 2k + 2n + 2p + 3 (Comm. and assoc. post. for add.) 4. 2k + 2n + 2p + 3 = 2(k + n + p) + 3 (Dist. post.) 5. k + n + p is an integer (Closure post. for add.) 6. 2(k + n + p) + 3 is odd (Def. of odd number) 7. a + b + c is an odd number (Substitution)

Page 563 Chapter Objectives and Review   1. angle: 50°; complement: 40°; supplement: 130°

3. ∠G: 100°; ∠F: 50°; ∠H: 30°   5. $90\sqrt{2}$ ft   7. $\dfrac{12}{5}$ 9. $\dfrac{12}{13}$ 11. $\dfrac{5}{13}$ 13. x = 14.0; y = 24.4   15. 49°

17. 53°   19. Yes   21. Yes   23. If 6 is a factor of 12, then 6 is a factor of 24.   25. If a number is an odd number, then it is a natural number that is not divisible by 2. If a number is a natural number that is not divisible by 2, then it is an odd number.

27. In the following proof, the Reason appears in parentheses following each Statement.
Hypothesis: a and b are any multiples of 4. Conclusion: a + b is a multiple of 4 Proof: 1. a and b are multiples of 4. (Given) 2. Let a = 4n, b = 4k, where n and k are integers. Then a + b = 4n + 4k. (Def. of mult. of 4) 3. 4n + 4k = 4(n + k) (Dist. post.) 4. n + k is an integer (Closure post. for add.) 5. 4(n + k) is a mult. of 4 (Def. of mult. of 4) 6. a + b is a mult. of 4 (Substitution)

Page 566 Chapter Test   1. angle: 60°; complement: 30°; supplement: 120°   3. 12.7 cm   5. 2.625

7. $\dfrac{3}{4}$ 9. $\dfrac{4}{3}$ 11. $\dfrac{3}{5}$ 13. If 5 is a whole number, then 5 is a rational number.   15. If a figure is a square, then the figure is a rectangle.   17. 13. If 5 is a rational number, then 5 is a whole number; True   14. If Saturday is the last day of the week, then today is Saturday; False   15. If a figure is a rectangle, then the figure is a square; False   16. If his father's name is Joe, then his name is Joe Junior; False   19. No. There is no inverse element $\dfrac{1}{a}$, such that $a \cdot \dfrac{1}{a} = 1$.